# Physics

## Principles and Problems

**James T. Murphy**
Chairman, Science Department
Reading Memorial High School
Reading, Massachusetts

Consultant
**Robert C. Smoot**
Chairman, Science Department
McDonogh School
McDonogh, Maryland

**Charles E. Merrill Publishing Co.**
**A Bell & Howell Company**
**Columbus, Ohio**
London • Toronto • Sidney

## A Merrill Science Program

**Physics:** Principles and Problems
**Physics:** Principles and Problems, Teacher's Annotated Edition
**Physics:** Principles and Problems, Spirit Duplicating Evaluation Program
**Laboratory Physics**
**Laboratory Physics,** Teacher's Annotated Edition

**Project Editor:** Ellen M. Lappa
**Editors:** Eric Smith, Dale L. Neff

**Project Designer:** Lester L. Shumaker
**Project Artist:** Michael T. Henry
**Artists:** Larry W. Collins, David Germon

**Photo Editor:** M. Lisy Boren

**Illustrators:** Bert Dodson, Jim Robison, Jim Shough

**Reviewers:**
**Bill Dempsey,** Arkansas High School, Texarkana, Arkansas
**Dr. Judith Doyle,** Ann Arbor, Michigan
**Robert Guigley,** Reading Sr. High, Reading Pennsylvania
**Dr. Lee Hutton,** McGill University, Montreal, Canada
**Priscilla King,** Miami Sunset Sr. High, Miami, Florida
**Gordon Morphew,** Tucson High School, Tucson, Arizona
**Sister Rosalima,** Marian Catholic High School, Chicago Heights, Illinois

ISBN 0-675-07491-6

Published by
**Charles E. Merrill Publishing Co.**
**A Bell & Howell Company**

**Columbus, Ohio 43216**

Printed in the United States of America

# Preface

*Physics: Principles and Problems* provides a clear and straightforward presentation of the basic concepts of physics. The central theme, the interrelationship between matter and energy, applies to all sciences. The essential concepts of physics are developed in an orderly manner so as to present a unified, logical sequence. Excessive detail has been omitted where it would obscure or confuse the main idea.

The authors have written this text in a manner which bridges the gap between the understanding of a general statement, theory, or law and the application of principles to the solution of problems. Reasoning is based on experience and experiment, and leads students to an awareness of these principles and how they interrelate with physical phenomena. Photographs and artwork are used extensively throughout the text to illustrate physics principles and their applications in research and everyday living.

Mechanics, needed to interpret most phenomena, is the first concept presented. Then, each form of energy—heat, light, electric, nuclear—and the basic structure of matter are intertwined. As these interrelationships are developed, the conservation laws are demonstrated and emphasized.

Mathematics, the language of science, is necessary to understand physics. To make the text self-sustaining, a brief review of algebra and trigonometry is provided in Chapter 1. Thus, use of outside resources has been eliminated.

*Physics: Principles and Problems* helps students understand the application of several principles to arrive at a solution to a problem. More complex problems are developed as combinations of fundamental concepts. Each problem emphasizes the thinking process involved in setting up a logical solution.

*Examples* with step-by-step solutions are provided throughout the text to guide students in mastery of problem-solving. These Examples are immediately reinforced with review *Problems*. Answers to the odd-numbered review Problems are provided as blue annotations within the text. Thus, students can immediately check their understanding of the material just studied.

Each chapter is introduced with a *photograph* and a *thought-provoking paragraph* which relate the theme of the chapter to the student's world.

A *Goal Statement* appears in the margin at the beginning of each chapter. This statement gives students an overall purpose for studying the chapter.

*Margin notes* are carefully positioned throughout the text to highlight important terms and ideas. Students should use these notes in organizing information for study and review. New terms are printed in boldface type and defined within the text when introduced.

Feature pages, *Dimensions in Physics*, provide visual presentations of current topics of interest in physics.

An extensive *Summary*, designed to provide a chapter overview, appears at the end of each chapter. Comprehensive sets of *Questions* and *Problems* are also included at the end of each chapter to provide further opportunity for students to check their knowledge and understanding of concepts. The *Applying Physics* sections contain problems related to topics of current social and economic concern such as the environment, conservation, and the growing interest in the dynamics of the universe.

The *Readings* section at the end of each chapter has been thoroughly revised to include readings from many new and popular scientific journals. These sections provide students with an opportunity to expand their knowledge beyond the limitations necessarily placed upon a textbook.

The *Appendices* consist of an optional teaching feature on relativity, reference tables, and a listing of physics-related careers. The reference tables include trigonometric tables, the elements, physical constants, and important equations. The career appendix includes descriptions and educational requirements for a variety of physics-related careers.

A *Glossary* has been added to this edition providing students with a ready reference to the definitions of new terms.

A study of physics and its practical applications is basic and vital to all students whatever their educational goals. *Physics: Principles and Problems* appeals to students with a wide range of interests and can be used successfully for both classroom and individual study.

*Physics: Principles and Problems* also reflects the consensus of recent recommendations made by curriculum committees and by teachers using this material. Following these guidelines, the authors have designed a physics program which is both manageable and realistic in terms of its expectations of students.

The authors wish to express their gratitude to the many physics students, teachers, and science educators who have made suggestions for changes based on their use of the first and second editions of *Physics: Principles and Problems.*

# Contents

---

### Cover Photo Credits and Description:

The cover photograph was chosen to illustrate the applications of physical laws to natural settings. The laws of physics are clearly a part of the design, construction, and motion of a sailboat. Throughout this book, you will find other applications of these laws in many of the devices you use everyday. A study of the interrelationship of matter and energy is basic to the operation of automobiles, television, radio, computers, and nuclear reactors. Your study of physics will give you greater knowledge and awareness of the world around you. It will help you in making informed and intelligent decisions concerning important issues such as energy and the environment.
Photo by Chris Caswell/Tom Stack and Associates

Science is the result of curiosity about the universe. Through the ages, people have observed phenomena which occur over and over. Using systematic methods of analyzing these observations, people have attempted to gain a better understanding of their world. We now know that there are a few fundamental laws that govern our universe. What are these laws? How do they affect you? Your study of physics will help you answer these questions.

# Fundamental Mathematics 1

One of the most exciting discoveries concerning science is that all of it is tied together by a few simple and fundamental mathematical relationships. The movement of the earth around the sun, the movement of electrons through a TV set, and the flow of blood through your veins can be described by these relationships. Scientists have also found that sunlight, radio waves, sound waves, and the ripples in a puddle of water act similarly and show the same relationships. In short, there are laws that are basic to all the sciences. The science that examines these fundamental laws is called **physics.**

## 1:1   Physics: The Search for Knowledge

The primary goal of physics is the total understanding of how the universe operates. The discovery process moves at an ever increasing pace. Ideas that were sheer speculation a few years ago are common knowledge to today's physicist. For example, are we the only intelligent beings in the universe? We can speculate from the latest scientific evidence that probably we are not.

As you study this course in physics, you should find that the basic laws of the universe are usually quite simple. For example, as our first true spaceship, the Space Shuttle, breaks into orbit, it follows simple equations for acceleration and energy transfer. You will study these same equations in the early chapters of this text. Later, you will learn about concave mirrors, the origin of light, and radio waves. You will understand why scientists have designed a system to listen for evidence of other civilizations. The proposed system, called Cyclops, is a circular cluster of radio telescopes. Cyclops will eventually consist of hundreds of steerable antennas, each larger than a football field.

GOAL: You will review the basic mathematics needed to solve problems associated with this physics course.

Physics is the science that examines the relationships of matter and energy.

**FIGURE 1-1. The photograph shows an artist's concept of the proposed Cyclops radio telescope array. The diameter of the antenna array is about 16 kilometers.**

Today's most fascinating quest may be the search for knowledge concerning the elementary particles that make matter. Fermilab's huge synchrotron is designed to transfer high energy to minute particles so we might learn of these particles. Scientists are sure these particles exist. However, proving their existence has been the difficult part of their research.

**FIGURE 1-2. Professor Stephen Hawking (a), an astrophysicist, is currently studying black holes. At nineteen, Jackie Parker (b), was chosen as part of the space shuttle flight control team.**

a                                                    *NASA/JPL*          b                        *NASA*

Physics is basic to all other sciences. Biologists, chemists, astronomers, geologists, and all engineers must have a thorough
background in physics. Every form of research and development
(R & D) is associated fundamentally with physics. Since almost
every career is now affected by recent scientific findings, an
understanding of basic physics is important to even nonscience
careers. Also, many of the decisions that we, as citizens, will make
call for an understanding of physics.

In studying physics, you will need a basic background in fundamental mathematics. You should develop skill in manipulating
units and solving problems. This skill is only acquired through
practice. The remainder of this chapter concerns reviewing your
knowledge of the mathematics you will use as a base in studying
physical laws.

**FIGURE 1-3. The Voyager
mission to Saturn (a) and
the Space Shuttle project
(b) will provide us with
more knowledge about
interplanetary space. A
knowledge of physics is
vital to the design and function of both spacecrafts.**

## 1:2   Solving Equations Algebraically

The fundamental laws of physics are often stated as equations.
Suppose that you need to solve an equation for an unknown. For
example, you may need to find the value of $a$ in the equation

$$F = ma$$

To do this, the equation must be solved for $a$. You can do this by
remembering that when an operation is performed on one side of
an equation, the same operation must also be done on the other

Practice this method of
solving equations until
you can solve them on
sight.

side of the equation. In the present example, we first divide both sides of the equation by $m$. This operation gives us the equation

$$\frac{F}{m} = \frac{ma}{m} \quad \text{or} \quad \frac{F}{m} = a$$

The unknown is usually placed on the left side of an equation. Thus, this expression should be rewritten

$$a = \frac{F}{m}$$

If an equation contains several factors, the same process is followed until the unknown is isolated on the left side of the equation.

**EXAMPLE:  Solving Equations**

Solve the following equation for $x$.    $\dfrac{ay}{x} = \dfrac{cb}{s}$

*Solution:*

Multiply both sides by $x$.    $ay = \dfrac{cbx}{s}$

Multiply both sides by $s$.    $ays = cbx$

Divide both sides by $cb$.    $\dfrac{ays}{cb} = x$

Rewrite with $x$ on the left side.    $x = \dfrac{ays}{cb}$

**PROBLEMS**

1. a. $8 = 2 \times 4$
   b. $4 = 8/2$

**1.** You know that $2 = \dfrac{8}{4}$. Use the method described above to isolate the following variables on the left side of the equation.
   **a.** 8    **b.** 4

**2.** Solve the following equations for $v$.

   **a.** $s = vt$    **b.** $t = \dfrac{s}{v}$    **c.** $a = \dfrac{v^2}{2s}$    **d.** $\dfrac{v}{a} = \dfrac{b}{c}$

3. $t^2 = 2s/a$
   $a = 2s/t^2$
   $2 = at^2/s$

**3.** Solve the equation $s = \dfrac{at^2}{2}$ for $t^2$, $a$, and 2.

**4.** Solve each of these equations for $E$.

   **a.** $f = \dfrac{E}{s}$    **b.** $m = \dfrac{2E}{v^2}$    **c.** $\dfrac{E}{c^2} = m$

5. $h = P/D$
   $D = P/h$

**5.** Solve the equation $P = hD$ for $h$ and $D$.

**6.** Solve the equation $v^2 = 2as$ for $s$, $a$, and $v$.

7. a. $x = W/f$
   b. $x = f/g$
   c. $x = my$
   d. $x = \sqrt{\dfrac{2s}{a}}$

**7.** Solve each of these equations for $x$.

   **a.** $W = fx$    **b.** $g = \dfrac{f}{x}$    **c.** $m = \dfrac{x}{y}$    **d.** $s = \dfrac{ax^2}{2}$

# 1:3  Scientific Notation

Scientists often work with very large and very small numbers. For example, the mass of the earth is about

  6 000 000 000 000 000 000 000 000 kilograms*

and the mass of an electron is

0.000 000 000 000 000 000 000 000 000 000 911 kilograms.

In this form, numbers take up much space and are difficult to use in calculations. To work with such numbers more easily, you can write them in a shortened form by expressing decimal places as powers of ten. This method of expressing numbers is called **scientific notation.**

To write numbers using scientific notation in proper form, *move the decimal point until only one digit appears to the left of the decimal point.* Count the number of places you moved the decimal point and use that number as the exponent of the power of ten. Thus, the mass of the earth can also be expressed as $6 \times 10^{24}$ kilograms. Note that the exponent is positive when the decimal point is moved to the left.

$$1\ 000\ 000 = 1 \times 10^6$$
$$96\ 000 = 9.6 \times 10^4$$
$$365 = 3.65 \times 10^2$$

To write the mass of the electron in scientific notation, the decimal point is moved 31 places to the right.

  0.000 000 000 000 000 000 000 000 000 000 911

Scientific notation greatly simplifies the handling of large and small numbers.

Place one digit to the left of the decimal point in scientific notation.

A positive exponent shows the number of places the decimal point has been moved to the left.

FIGURE 1-4. The Andromeda Galaxy (a) is thought to have a diameter of about 200 000 light years, or $1.9 \times 10^{18}$ kilometers. The human hair (b) passing through the eye of this needle has a diameter of about 0.1 millimeter or $1.0 \times 10^{-4}$ meter.

a

*Lick Observatory*

b

*Courtesy of Eastman Kodak Company*

*Spaces are used to group digits in long numbers. In some countries, a comma indicates a decimal point. Therefore, commas will not be used.

A negative exponent shows the number of places the decimal point has been moved to the right.

Thus, the mass of the electron can also be written as $9.11 \times 10^{-31}$ kilograms. Note that the exponent is negative when the decimal point is moved to the right.

$$0.000\ 63 = 6.3 \times 10^{-4}$$
$$0.007 = 7 \times 10^{-3}$$
$$0.000\ 000\ 95 = 9.5 \times 10^{-7}$$

## PROBLEMS

*Express the following numbers in scientific notation.*

**8. a.** 5800    **b.** 450 000    **c.** 60 000    **d.** 86 000 000 000

**9. a.** 0.000 58    **b.** 0.000 000 45    **c.** 0.0036    **d.** 0.004

**10. a.** 300 000 000    **b.** 186 000    **c.** 93 000 000

**11. a.** 0.0073    **b.** 0.000 87    **c.** 0.0032

**12. a.** 5 000 000 000 000 000 000 000 000
   **b.** 0.000 000 000 000 000 000 166

**13. a.** 650 000    **b.** 5 000 000    **c.** 226    **d.** 4500

**14. a.** 0.025            **c.** 0.0006
   **b.** 0.000 25        **d.** 0.000 000 000 000 19

9. a. $5.8 \times 10^{-4}$
   b. $4.5 \times 10^{-7}$
   c. $3.6 \times 10^{-3}$
   d. $4 \times 10^{-3}$

11. a. $7.3 \times 10^{-3}$
   b. $8.7 \times 10^{-4}$
   c. $3.2 \times 10^{-3}$

13. a. $6.5 \times 10^{5}$
   b. $5 \times 10^{6}$
   c. $2.26 \times 10^{2}$
   d. $4.5 \times 10^{3}$

## 1:4   Addition and Subtraction in Scientific Notation

Suppose you need to add or subtract numbers expressed in scientific notation. If they have the same exponent, you simply add or subtract the coefficients and keep the same power of ten.

**EXAMPLE: Adding and Subtracting with Like Exponents**

   **a.** $4 \times 10^{8} + 3 \times 10^{8} = 7 \times 10^{8}$
   **b.** $4 \times 10^{-8} + 3 \times 10^{-8} = 7 \times 10^{-8}$
   **c.** $8 \times 10^{6} - 4 \times 10^{6} = 4 \times 10^{6}$
   **d.** $8 \times 10^{-6} - 4 \times 10^{-6} = 4 \times 10^{-6}$

When adding or subtracting in scientific notation, exponents of 10 must be the same.

If the powers of ten are not the same, they must be made the same before the numbers are added or subtracted. Move the decimal points until the exponents are the same.

**EXAMPLE: Adding and Subtracting with Unlike Exponents**

   **a.** $4.0 \times 10^{6} + 3 \times 10^{5}$    $= 4.0 \times 10^{6} + 0.3 \times 10^{6}$    $= 4.3 \times 10$
   **b.** $4.0 \times 10^{6} - 3 \times 10^{5}$    $= 4.0 \times 10^{6} - 0.3 \times 10^{6}$    $= 3.7 \times 10$
   **c.** $4.0 \times 10^{-6} - 3 \times 10^{-7} = 4.0 \times 10^{-6} - 0.3 \times 10^{-6} = 3.7 \times 10$

## PROBLEMS

*Solve the following problems. Express your answers in scientific notation.*

**15.**
  **a.** $5 \times 10^7 + 3 \times 10^7$
  **b.** $6 \times 10^8 + 2 \times 10^8$
  **c.** $4.2 \times 10^4 + 3.6 \times 10^4$
  **d.** $1.8 \times 10^9 + 2.5 \times 10^9$

**16.**
  **a.** $5 \times 10^{-7} + 3 \times 10^{-7}$
  **b.** $4 \times 10^{-3} + 3 \times 10^{-3}$
  **c.** $1.66 \times 10^{-19} + 2.30 \times 10^{-19}$
  **d.** $7.2 \times 10^{-12} + 2.6 \times 10^{-12}$

**17.**
  **a.** $6 \times 10^8 - 4 \times 10^8$
  **b.** $3.8 \times 10^{12} - 1.9 \times 10^{12}$
  **c.** $5.8 \times 10^9 - 2.8 \times 10^9$
  **d.** $6.25 \times 10^4 - 4.50 \times 10^4$

**18.**
  **a.** $6 \times 10^{-8} - 4 \times 10^{-8}$
  **b.** $3.8 \times 10^{-12} - 1.9 \times 10^{12}$
  **c.** $5.8 \times 10^{-9} - 2.8 \times 10^{-9}$
  **d.** $2.26 \times 10^{-18} - 1.80 \times 10^{-18}$

**19.**
  **a.** $6.0 \times 10^8 + 4 \times 10^7$
  **b.** $7.0 \times 10^4 + 2 \times 10^3$
  **c.** $4 \times 10^4 + 3.0 \times 10^5$
  **d.** $6.0 \times 10^{10} + 5.0 \times 10^{11}$

**20.**
  **a.** $5.0 \times 10^{-7} + 4 \times 10^{-8}$
  **b.** $6.0 \times 10^{-3} + 2 \times 10^{-4}$
  **c.** $3.0 \times 10^{-14} + 2 \times 10^{-15}$
  **d.** $4.0 \times 10^{-12} + 6.0 \times 10^{-13}$

**21.**
  **a.** $5.0 \times 10^{-7} - 4 \times 10^{-8}$
  **b.** $6.0 \times 10^{-3} - 2 \times 10^{-4}$
  **c.** $3.0 \times 10^{-14} - 2 \times 10^{-15}$
  **d.** $8.2 \times 10^{-16} - 4.5 \times 10^{-17}$

**22.**
  **a.** $6 \times 10^8 + 3 \times 10^8$
  **b.** $2.2 \times 10^4 + 3.6 \times 10^4$
  **c.** $5.0 \times 10^8 + 6.0 \times 10^7$
  **d.** $9.8 \times 10^5 + 2.0 \times 10^4$

**23.**
  **a.** $8.4 \times 10^{-8} - 3.2 \times 10^{-8}$
  **b.** $5.4 \times 10^7 - 3.4 \times 10^7$
  **c.** $6.0 \times 10^{-8} - 6.0 \times 10^{-9}$
  **d.** $2.2 \times 10^{12} - 8.0 \times 10^{11}$

**15.**
  **a.** $8 \times 10^7$
  **b.** $8 \times 10^8$
  **c.** $7.8 \times 10^4$
  **d.** $4.3 \times 10^9$

**17.**
  **a.** $2 \times 10^8$
  **b.** $1.9 \times 10^{12}$
  **c.** $3.0 \times 10^9$
  **d.** $1.75 \times 10^4$

**19.**
  **a.** $6.4 \times 10^8$
  **b.** $7.2 \times 10^4$
  **c.** $3.4 \times 10^5$
  **d.** $5.6 \times 10^{11}$

**21.**
  **a.** $4.6 \times 10^{-7}$
  **b.** $5.8 \times 10^{-3}$
  **c.** $2.8 \times 10^{-14}$
  **d.** $7.75 \times 10^{-16}$

**23.**
  **a.** $5.2 \times 10^{-8}$
  **b.** $2.0 \times 10^7$
  **c.** $5.4 \times 10^{-8}$
  **d.** $1.4 \times 10^{12}$

# 1:5   Multiplication and Division in Scientific Notation

Numbers expressed in scientific notation can be multiplied when the exponents are not the same. First, multiply the numbers preceding the powers of ten. Then, add the exponents of ten to obtain the correct power of ten for the product.

### EXAMPLE: Multiplication Using Scientific Notation

  **a.** $(3 \times 10^6)(2 \times 10^3) = 6 \times 10^{6+3} \quad = 6 \times 10^9$
  **b.** $(2 \times 10^{-5})(4 \times 10^9) = 8 \times 10^{(-5)+9} = 8 \times 10^4$
  **c.** $(4 \times 10^3)(5 \times 10^{11}) = 20 \times 10^{3+11} = 20 \times 10^{14}$
  $= 2 \times 10^{15}$

When multiplying in scientific notation, the exponents of 10 are added.

Numbers expressed in scientific notation can also be divided when the exponents are not the same. First, divide the numbers preceding the powers of ten. Then, subtract the exponent in the denominator from the exponent in the numerator. The result is the power of ten for the answer.

When dividing in scientific notation, the exponents of 10 are subtracted.

EXAMPLE: Division Using Scientific Notation

**a.** $\dfrac{8 \times 10^6}{2 \times 10^3} = 4 \times 10^{6-3} = 4 \times 10^3$

**b.** $\dfrac{8 \times 10^6}{2 \times 10^{-2}} = 4 \times 10^{6-(-2)} = 4 \times 10^8$

## PROBLEMS

*Find the value of each of the following problems.*

**24. a.** $(2 \times 10^4)(4 \times 10^8)$     **c.** $(6 \times 10^{-4})(5 \times 10^{-8})$
     **b.** $(3 \times 10^4)(2 \times 10^6)$     **d.** $(2.5 \times 10^{-7})(2.5 \times 10^{16})$

25. a. $6 \times 10^8$
     b. $2.4 \times 10^{11}$
     c. $7.9 \times 10^{32}$
     d. $5.7 \times 10^{23}$

**25. a.** $(3 \times 10^4)(2 \times 10^4)$     **c.** $(2.2 \times 10^{12})(3.6 \times 10^{20})$
     **b.** $(4 \times 10^6)(6 \times 10^4)$     **d.** $(9.5 \times 10^{14})(6.0 \times 10^8)$

**26. a.** $\dfrac{6 \times 10^8}{2 \times 10^4}$   **b.** $\dfrac{6 \times 10^8}{2 \times 10^{-4}}$   **c.** $\dfrac{6 \times 10^{-8}}{2 \times 10^4}$   **d.** $\dfrac{6 \times 10^{-8}}{2 \times 10^{-4}}$

27. a. $2 \times 10^4$
     b. $2 \times 10^{12}$
     c. $3 \times 10^8$
     d. $3 \times 10^1$

**27. a.** $\dfrac{(3 \times 10^4)(4 \times 10^4)}{6 \times 10^4}$     **c.** $\dfrac{(2.5 \times 10^6)(6 \times 10^4)}{5 \times 10^2}$

     **b.** $\dfrac{(3 \times 10^4)(4 \times 10^4)}{6 \times 10^{-4}}$     **d.** $\dfrac{(6 \times 10^{12})(6 \times 10^{-6})}{1.2 \times 10^6}$

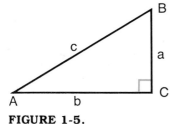

**FIGURE 1-5.**

Trigonometry is the study of the properties of triangles.

## 1:6 Trigonometry of Right Triangles

**Trigonometry** (trig uh NAHM uh tree) deals with the relations between angles and sides of triangles. A right triangle is shown in Figure 1-5. A right triangle is one which contains a 90° angle. In Figure 1-5, the angles are labeled $A$, $B$, and $C$. The side opposite angle $A$ is labeled $a$. The side opposite angle $B$ is labeled $b$. The side opposite angle $C$ is labeled $c$.

Three common functions of an angle are called the sine (sin), cosine (cos), and tangent (tan). For angle $A$, these functions are expressed as

$$\text{sine } A = \frac{\text{opposite side}}{\text{hypotenuse}} \text{ or } \sin A = \frac{a}{c}$$

$$\text{cosine } A = \frac{\text{adjacent side}}{\text{hypotenuse}} \text{ or } \cos A = \frac{b}{c}$$

$$\text{tangent } A = \frac{\text{opposite side}}{\text{adjacent side}} \text{ or } \tan A = \frac{a}{b}$$

Sine, cosine, and tangent are 3 common functions of angles.

A table of numerical values for trigonometric functions is given in Table B-1 of the Appendix.

### EXAMPLE:  Length of Sides on a Triangle

Angle $A$ in Figure 1-5 is 30°. The hypotenuse is 8.0 cm. What is the length of side $a$ and of side $b$? (The sine and cosine of 30° are found in Table B-1 of the Appendix.)

*Solution:*

Side $a$   $\sin A = \dfrac{a}{c}$     Side $b$   $\cos A = \dfrac{b}{c}$

$$a = c \sin A \qquad\qquad b = c \cos A$$
$$= 8.0 \text{ cm} \times 0.500 \qquad = 8.0 \text{ cm} \times 0.866$$
$$= 4.0 \text{ cm} \qquad\qquad = 6.9 \text{ cm}$$

## PROBLEMS

**28. a.** Which side of the triangle is opposite angle $R$?
   **b.** Which side is adjacent to angle $R$?
   **c.** Write the equations for the sine, cosine, and tangent of angle $R$.

**29.** Find the size of the angles associated with each trigonometric function below. The Greek letter *theta*, $\theta$, is used to designate the unknown angle.

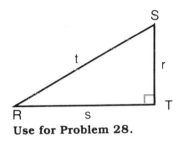

**Use for Problem 28.**

   **a.** $\sin \theta = 0.500$     **d.** $\sin \theta = 0.707$     **g.** $\tan \theta = 2.050$
   **b.** $\sin \theta = 0.985$     **e.** $\tan \theta = 1.00$     **h.** $\cos \theta = 0.866$
   **c.** $\cos \theta = 0.707$     **f.** $\tan \theta = 0.364$

29. a. 30°    e. 45°
    b. 80°    f. 20°
    c. 45°    g. 64°
    d. 45°    h. 30°

**30.** One angle of a right triangle is 20.0°. The length of the hypotenuse is 6.00 cm.
   **a.** Draw the triangle to scale and measure the lengths of the other two sides.
   **b.** Use trigonometry to calculate the lengths of these two sides.

**31.** One angle of a right triangle is 40°. The length of the hypotenuse is 12 cm.
   **a.** Draw the triangle to scale and measure the lengths of the other two sides.
   **b.** Use trigonometry to calculate the lengths of these two sides.

31. a. should agree with b
    b. opp = 7.7 cm
       adj = 9.2 cm

**32.** One angle of a right triangle is 60°. The length of the hypotenuse is 15 cm. Calculate the lengths of the other two sides.

**33.** One angle of a right triangle is 35°. The length of the side opposite the angle is 14 cm. Use the tangent of 35° to calculate the length of the side adjacent to the angle.

33. 20 cm

**34.** One angle of a right triangle is 37°. The length of the side opposite the angle is 12 cm.
   **a.** Calculate the length of the side adjacent to the angle.
   **b.** Calculate the length of the hypotenuse.

William Maddox

FIGURE 1-6. Survey teams make use of trigonometric functions in their measurements.

## 1:7  Law of Cosines

To use the trigonometry of the right triangle, two of the sides of a triangle must be perpendicular. That is, you must have a right triangle. But sometimes you will need to work with a triangle that is not a right triangle. The law of cosines applies to all triangles. Consider the two triangles shown in Figure 1-7. They are not right triangles. When angle $C$ is known, the lengths of the sides obey the following relationship.

The law of cosines applies to all triangles.

$$c^2 = a^2 + b^2 - 2ab \cos C$$

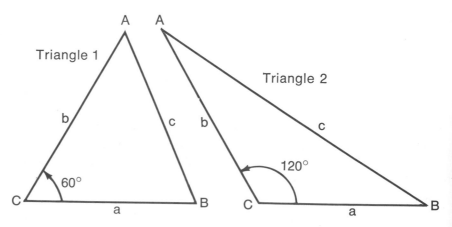

FIGURE 1-7.

When angle $C$ is larger than 90°, its cosine is negative and is numerically equal to the cosine of its supplement. In triangle 2, Figure 1-6, angle $C$ is 120°. Therefore, its cosine is the negative of the cosine of (180° − 120°) or 60°. The cosine of 60° is 0.500. Thus, the cosine of 120° is −0.500.

**EXAMPLE: Law of Cosines**

In triangle 1 of Figure 1-7, assume the length of side $a$ is 4 cm, side $b$ is 5 cm, and angle $C$ is 60°. Use the law of cosines to calculate the length of side $C$.

*Solution:*

The law of cosines is
$$c^2 = a^2 + b^2 - 2ab \cos C$$

The length of side $c$ is
$$c = \sqrt{a^2 + b^2 - 2ab \cos C}$$

Substitute the values given in the problem.

$a = 4$ cm     angle $C = 60°$
$b = 5$ cm     therefore, $\cos C = 0.500$

$$c = \sqrt{(4)^2 + (5)^2 - 2(4)(5)(0.500)}$$
$$= \sqrt{21} = 4.6$$

**PROBLEMS**

**35.** In triangle 1 of Figure 1-7, assume that the length of side $a$ is 7.0 cm, side $b$ is 8.0 cm, and angle $C$ is 60°.
   **a.** Draw this triangle to scale and measure side $c$. Record the value.
   **b.** Use the law of cosines to calculate the length of side $c$. Compare the measured and calculated values.

**36.** In triangle 2 of Figure 1-7, assume that the length of side $a$ is 8.00 cm, side $b$ is 10.0 cm, and angle $C$ is 120°.
   **a.** Draw this triangle to scale and measure the length of side $c$.
   **b.** Use the law of cosines to calculate the length of side $c$. Compare this length with your measured length.

**37.** In triangle 2 of Figure 1-7, assume angle $C$ is 140°. The length of side $a$ is 12 cm, and side $b$ is 5.0 cm. What is the length of side $c$?

35. a. should agree with b
    b. 7.5 cm

37. 16 cm

# 1:8   Law of Sines

Just as the law of cosines applies to all triangles, the law of sines also applies to all triangles. The relationship is

The law of sines applies to all triangles.

$$\frac{a}{\sin A} = \frac{b}{\sin B} = \frac{c}{\sin C}$$

**EXAMPLE:  Law of Sines**

In triangle 1 of Figure 1-7, assume the length of side $a$ is 4 cm, side $c$ is 4.6 cm, and angle $C$ is 60°. Calculate the value of angle $A$.

*Solution:*
According to the law of sines

$$\frac{a}{\sin A} = \frac{c}{\sin C}$$

Substitute the values given in the problem.

$a = 4$ cm        angle $C = 60°$
$c = 4.6$ cm       therefore, $\sin C = 0.866$

$$\frac{4}{\sin A} = \frac{4.6}{0.866}$$

$$\sin A = \frac{(4)(0.866)}{4.6} = 0.753$$

Therefore, angle $A = 49°$.

**PROBLEMS**

**38.** In triangle 1 of Figure 1-7, the length of side $a$ is 7.0 cm, and the length of side $b$ is 4.0 cm. If angle $A$ is 53°, calculate the value of angle $B$.

**39. 33°**

**39.** In triangle 2 of Figure 1-7, the length of side $b$ is 10 cm, and the length of side $a$ is 8.0 cm. Angle $A$ is 26°. Calculate the value of angle $B$. (For the sine of 120°, use the sine of its supplement, 60°.)

**40.** The three angles of a triangle are angle $A = 55.0°$, angle $B = 55.0°$, and angle $C = 70.0°$. If the length of side $c$ is 20.0 cm, what are the lengths of sides $a$ and $b$?

# 1:9   Units and Equations

**Units must be uniform when solving a problem.**

In mathematics, you learned not to mix units if you wanted meaningful answers to problems. To find the area of a rectangle, you cannot multiply length by width if the two sides are measured in different units. You must change one unit to agree with the remaining unit in order to obtain a reasonable answer. To multiply 12 meters by 60 centimeters, you must first change the units so they are all the same. Thus, our example might be written 12 meters × 0.60 meters. A meaningful answer of 7.2 square meters is obtained. Similar quantities must be expressed in the same units in calculations.

Quantities such as length, speed, and area are called **dimensional quantities.** A measured dimensional quantity has a numerical value that depends upon the system of units used. For example, a given area can be stated as either 1 square meter or 10 000 square centimeters. When making a measurement, the most convenient unit is used.

Examples of dimensional quantities are length, speed, and area.

When substituting values into an equation in physics, you must state the units as well as the numerical values. This helps you to keep consistent units in the equation. You also know if the equation is dimensionally correct.

All equations in physics must agree dimensionally.

**EXAMPLE:  Dimensionally Correct Equation**

$$\text{mass} = (\text{density})(\text{volume})$$

$$kg = \left(\frac{kg}{m^3}\right)(m^3)$$

$$kg = kg$$

Note that the units on the right side of the equation divide out. This shows that the dimensions on both sides of the equation are the same. The equation is dimensionally correct.

Units divide out as factors to give the correct label in the solution.

**EXAMPLE:  Dimensionally Incorrect Equation**

$$\text{velocity} = (\text{distance})(\text{time})$$

$$\frac{m}{s} = (m)(s)$$

$$\frac{m}{s} \neq m \cdot s$$

Derive the dimensionally correct form of this equation.
(Distance = velocity × time.)

Notice that the units on the right do not agree with those on the left. By inspecting the dimensions, you should be immediately aware that the equation is not correct. Blue lines will be used throughout this book to show units which divide out of an equation. You should use this practice in working your own problems as an additional check on the correct answer.

**PROBLEM**

**41.** Substitute suitable units into the following equations and state which are dimensionally correct.

**a.** area = (length)(width)(height)

**b.** time = $\dfrac{\text{distance}}{\text{velocity}}$

**c.** distance = (velocity)(time)$^2$

41. a. incorrect
    b. correct
    c. incorrect

**Summary**

1. Physics is the study of the basic scientific laws that apply to all the sciences.   1:1

2. A knowledge of physics is important to all individuals in order that they might better understand the world around them.   1:1

3. A knowledge of physics makes us, as citizens, better able to make decisions about science-related questions.   1:1

4. The physicist must often work with numbers that are unusually large or small. Expressed in scientific notation, these numbers are easily read and handled in calculations.   1:3–1:5

5. Trigonometry is useful in calculations that involve triangles. There are simple relationships among angles and the lengths of sides of right triangles.   1:6

6. The law of sines and the law of cosines are used for calculations with all types of triangles.   1:7 –1:8

7. Units should always be included in physics problems. The units can be used to check for dimensional accuracy.   1:9

**Questions**

1. Define physics.

2. How may an equation be checked to tell whether or not it is written correctly?

**Problems**

1. Consult Table B-1 of the Appendix to find the number of degrees associated with these trigonometric functions.

   **a.** $\sin \theta = 0.0872$     **d.** $\cos \theta = 0.9816$     **g.** $\tan \theta = 0.3640$
   **b.** $\sin \theta = 0.5150$     **e.** $\cos \theta = 0.7771$     **h.** $\tan \theta = 1.000$
   **c.** $\sin \theta = 0.3090$     **f.** $\cos \theta = 0.2588$     **i.** $\tan \theta = 3.0777$

2. One angle of a right triangle is 26°. The hypotenuse is 10 cm. Calculate the lengths of the other two sides.

3. One angle of a right triangle is 50°. The length of the side opposite the 50° angle is 8.5 cm. Calculate the length of the adjacent side and the hypotenuse.

4. The three included angles of a triangle are: angle $A = 39°$, angle $B = 31°$, and angle $C = 110°$. If the length of side $c$ is 14.7 cm, what is the length of side $a$ and side $b$?

5. Substitute any suitable and consistent units into each of the following equations and then state which are correct and which are incorrect equations.

**a.** velocity $= \dfrac{\text{distance}}{\text{time}}$

**b.** area $= \dfrac{\text{height}}{\text{volume}}$

**c.** distance $= \dfrac{\text{velocity}}{\text{time}}$

**d.** time $= \sqrt{\dfrac{\text{length}}{\text{length/time}^2}}$

---

**Applying Physics**

**1.** *Astronomy:* The average distance between the earth and the sun is $1.50 \times 10^8$ km.
  **a.** Calculate the average velocity, in km/h, of the earth along its orbital path.
  **b.** Convert your answer from km/h to m/s. Show all units.

**2.** *Engineering:* During a preliminary survey of a future bridge site, an engineer measures the distance across a river by laying a baseline 30.0 m in length along the shoreline. One end of the baseline, end *A*, is directly across from a tree on the opposite shoreline. Using a sighting instrument, the engineer finds that a line from the tree to the other end of the baseline, end *B*, would form an angle of 76° with the baseline. What is the distance across the river?

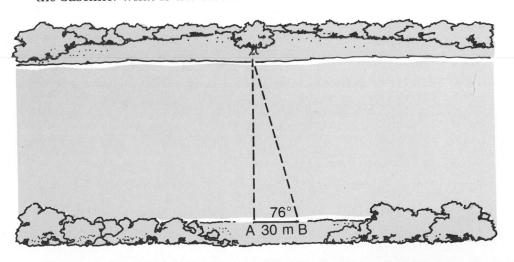

76°

A 30 m B

**FIGURE 1-8.**

---

**Readings**

Gamow, G., *One, Two, Three . . . . . . . Infinity.* New York, Bantam Books, 1971.

Gardner, Martin, *Mathematical Carnival.* Westminister, Maryland, Alfred A. Knopf, Inc., 1975.

Overbye, Dennis, "The Wizard of Space and Time." *Omni,* February, 1979.

Park, David, "But What is a Clock?" *Science Digest,* August, 1980.

White, Robert, "Disk-Storage Technology." *Scientific American,* August, 1980.

The instruments used to make measurements are constantly being improved. Also, measurement standards have been approved for international use. As a result, we are able to learn more about our world and share this knowledge with others. However, exact measurements are not confined to the research laboratory. Think of the number of activities in which you are involved that require exact measurements. How many measurements are associated with the sport of baseball?

# Measurement 2

Our knowledge of science has grown rapidly during the last 300 years. This growth is due to the use of a special method for studying the world around us. This method involves experimentation. In order to do meaningful experiments, early scientists had to develop measuring devices and standards for measurement. This finally led to the development of the metric system of measurement. The SI version of the metric system is now used by scientists all over the world. As improved measuring devices and standards are developed, we will be able to find out much more about our world.

**GOAL: You will gain knowledge and understanding of the basic process of measurement, SI units of measurement, significant digits, and graphing data.**

## 2:1 Measurement and Scientific Method

Physics received great impetus during the sixteenth and seventeenth centuries. At that time, scientists began to realize that all physical events follow understandable laws. One of the first scientists to understand this was Galileo Galilei (1564–1642). While still attending the university, he challenged so-called knowledge that was based on little, if any, observation or experimentation. He questioned the belief that the earth is the center of the universe. He doubted Aristotle's views on physics, especially the idea that objects of large mass fall faster than objects of small mass.

a

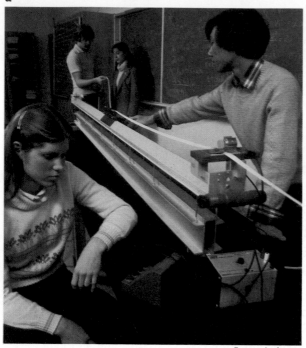

b

*George Anderson*

*Terch*

**FIGURE 2-1.** Much of your knowledge of physics will be gained in the laboratory through experimentation (a). The scientific method of studying natural events was developed by Galileo (b).

Kinematics is the study of motion.

Scientific method requires careful measurement and analysis.

Galileo was dismissed from the university before he could complete his studies. However, he did not change his ideas. He knew that he could answer his critics only by showing them proof that could not be denied. To do this, he developed a systematic method of observation and analysis. He carefully measured the way in which small spheres rolled down smooth ramps and kept a record of his observations. Analysis of this data showed that all objects fall at the same speed regardless of their masses. Galileo also found that all motion follows a simple set of laws. We now call this set of laws the science of kinematics (kin uh MAT iks). **Kinematics** is the study of motion apart from the effects of mass and force. He observed the heavens with a telescope. He confirmed the theory of Copernicus that the earth travels around the sun while spinning on its axis. This discovery did not agree with the religious belief of that day. As a result, Galileo was brought before the Inquisition. He was kept a prisoner in his home for the rest of his life.

The method developed by Galileo to study natural events is known today as the **scientific method.** It is based on systematic experimentation through careful measurement and analysis. From the analyses, conclusions are drawn. These conclusions are then tested to find out if they are valid. Since Galileo's time, scientists all over the world have used this method to gain a better understanding of the universe.

## 2:2   Metric (SI) System

The **metric system** of measurement was created by French scientists in 1790. The metric system is convenient to use because units of different sizes are related by powers of 10. However, in the time since the original metric system was introduced, many versions of it have appeared. In order to have a standardized world system, the **International System (SI)** was established by international agreement. SI is now the standard international language of measurement. The use of SI units will be emphasized throughout this text.

The standard SI unit of length is the **meter** (m). The meter was first defined as one ten-millionth ($10^{-7}$) of the distance from the north pole to the equator as measured along a line passing through Lyons, France. This length was marked on a platinum-iridium bar by making two scratches on the bar. When the bar is at 0° Celsius, the distance between the two scratches is the standard meter. It is necessary to state the temperature because metals expand and contract with changes in temperature.

The standard meter was not exactly one ten-millionth of the distance from the north pole to the equator. The first measurement of this distance was slightly in error. In 1960, the meter was redefined as 1 650 763.73 times the wavelength of orange light emitted by a krypton-86 atom.

*The metric system is a decimal system of measurement.*

*The meter (m) is the standard unit of length.*

305 cm
3.05 m

163 cm
54 kg

14.33 m

4.8 L
270 g

7.4 L
600 g

183 cm
80 kg

*George Anderson*

**FIGURE 2-2. You can use common objects to form concepts of metric measurements.**

**The kilogram (kg) is the standard unit of mass.**

The mass of an object is the quantity of matter it contains. The standard unit of mass is the **kilogram** (kg). One kilogram is the mass of a platinum-iridium cylinder kept near Paris.

**The second (s) is the standard unit of time.**

The standard unit of time is the **second** (s). The second was first defined as 1/86 400 of the mean solar day. A mean solar day is the average length of the day over a period of one year. In 1967, the second was redefined in terms of one type of radiation emitted by a cesium-133 atom.

The other standard SI units will be formally introduced later in this text. The meter, kilogram, and second will be used in your study of mechanics. **Mechanics** deals with the study of forces and energy.

## 2:3  Prefixes Used with SI Units

The advantage of the metric system is that it is a decimal system. Each fraction or multiple of an SI unit is a power of ten. Thus, a tenth of a meter is a *decimeter*, a hundredth of a meter is a *centimeter*, and a thousandth of a meter is a *millimeter*. Each of these divisions can be found on a meter stick. Ten meters is a *dekameter*, a hundred meters is a *hectometer*, and a thousand meters is a *kilometer*. Units for other quantities use the same prefixes. A thousandth of a gram is a *milligram*, and a thousand grams is a *kilogram*. To use SI units effectively, it is important to know the meanings of the prefixes in Table 2-1.

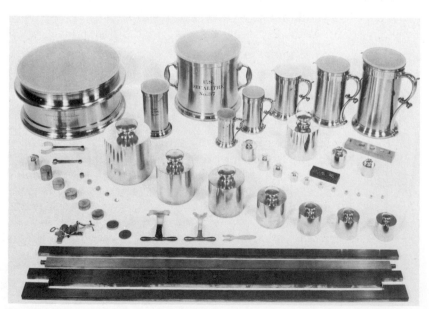

**FIGURE 2-3. The National Bureau of Standards maintains prototype length, mass, and volume standards.**

*National Bureau of Standards*

## TABLE 2-1
### Prefixes Used With SI Units

| Prefix | Symbol | Meaning | Example |
|---|---|---|---|
| | | *Fractions* | |
| deci | d | 1/10 or $10^{-1}$ | decimeter (dm) |
| centi | c | 1/100 or $10^{-2}$ | centimeter (cm) |
| milli | m | 1/1 000 or $10^{-3}$ | milligram (mg) |
| micro | $\mu$ | 1/1 000 000 or $10^{-6}$ | microgram ($\mu$g) |
| nano | n | 1/1 000 000 000 or $10^{-9}$ | nanometer (nm) |
| | | *Multiples* | |
| deka | da | 10 or $10^{1}$ | dekagram (dag) |
| hecto | h | 100 or $10^{2}$ | hectometer (hm) |
| kilo | k | 1 000 or $10^{3}$ | kilometer (km) |
| mega | M | 1 000 000 or $10^{6}$ | megagram (Mg) |
| giga | G | 1 000 000 000 or $10^{9}$ | gigameter (Gm) |

Units in the metric system are related by powers of 10.

*Keith Turpie*

**FIGURE 2-4. Fifty-three centimeters can also be expressed as 530 millimeters.**

**EXAMPLE: Conversion between Units**

What is 500 nanometers equivalent to in meters?
*Solution:* From Table 2-1, we see the conversion factor is

$$1 \text{ nanometer} = 1 \times 10^{-9} \text{ meter}$$

Therefore,

$$(500 \text{ nm})(1 \times 10^{-9} \text{ m/nm}) = 500 \times 10^{-9} \text{ m}$$
$$= 5.0 \times 10^{-7} \text{ m}$$

It is customary to express SI measurements in certain ways. For example, the decimeter is rarely used. A measurement of 53 centimeters would be called 53 centimeters and not 5 decimeters and 3 centimeters. This is similar to the custom of saying 53 cents rather than 5 dimes and 3 cents. In the same way, a distance of 530 meters is not referred to as 5 hectometers and 3 dekameters but is stated as either 0.53 kilometers or 530 meters.

If volume is stated in terms of liters, only the prefix milli- is used. Large volume measurements are more commonly expressed as cubic meters.

*I.M. Whillans, Institute of Polar Studies, Ohio State Univ.*

**FIGURE 2-5. Scientists make observations and measurements in studies conducted in the field as well as in the laboratory.**

## 2:4  Fundamental and Derived Units

In mechanics, three fundamental units are used to measure the quantities mass, length, and time.

Derived units are combinations of fundamental units.

In the study of mechanics, three fundamental quantities are used in measuring forces and their effects. These quantities are mass, length, and time. These fundamental quantities are commonly expressed using the units kilogram, meter, and second. All other quantities can be expressed in terms of the three fundamental quantities. Thus, their units are derived from the units used in expressing mass, length, and time. For example, area is found by multiplying length times length and it has a derived unit. The area of a rectangle which is 10 cm by 5 cm is 50 cm$^2$. Square centimeters is a derived unit. In the same way, volume is length times length times length and is also expressed in derived units. The quantity, density which is mass divided by volume, can be expressed in g/cm$^3$. Grams per cubic centimeter is a derived unit. Velocity, which is distance (length) divided by time, can be expressed in meters per second—a derived unit. Thus, all units used in mechanics are composites of the fundamental units kilogram, meter, and second.

$$\text{density} = \frac{\text{mass}}{\text{volume}} = \frac{\text{mass}}{(\text{length})^3}$$

$$\text{velocity} = \frac{\text{distance}}{\text{time}} = \frac{\text{length}}{\text{time}}$$

## 2:5   Errors in Measurement

Scientists are constantly measuring quantities and comparing the data they obtain. If relationships are found, they must be confirmed through further experimentation. Only then do these findings become accepted scientific theories.

**Data (singular, datum) are recorded observations.**

When measuring, keep in mind that every measurement is subject to error. The length of a ruler can change with changes in temperature. An electric measuring device is affected by any magnetic fields near it. In one way or another, all instruments are subject to external influence. Errors in measurement are to be expected.

**All measurements are in error to some degree.**

In addition to error due to external causes, accuracy of measurement depends on the person taking the reading. Measuring devices must be read by looking at them straight on. In a car, the passenger's reading of the gas gauge and the driver's reading of the same gauge can be quite different. From the passenger's seat, the gauge may read empty. From the driver's seat, the gauge may read one-quarter full. The driver's reading is the more correct one. The difference in the readings is parallax error. **Parallax** (PAR uh laks) is the apparent shift in the position of an object when it is viewed from different angles. An object does not move when it is viewed from various angles. It is the reference points behind the object that differ. Thus, the object looks as if it has moved. When sitting next to the driver, you line up the gauge needle on the empty mark. But if you move to the driver's seat, you will line up the needle on the one-quarter-full mark. Measurement instruments should be read at eye level to avoid parallax errors.

**Parallax is the apparent shift in position of an object as it is viewed from different angles.**

a

b

*John Morgan*                    *John Morgan*

**FIGURE 2-6. A parallax example is shown when a gasoline gauge is viewed from the passenger's seat (a). The same gauge is shown in (b) as seen from the driver's seat. Note the apparent difference in readings.**

## 2:6   Accuracy and Precision

**Accuracy** is the extent to which a measured value agrees with the accepted value for a quantity. For example, the accepted value of $\pi$ to six digits is 3.141 59. Suppose you calculate the value of $\pi$ to six digits as 3.141 76. Only the first four digits of your value agree with the accepted value. Thus, your value is accurate to only four places.

**Precision** is the degree of exactness with which a quantity is measured. Precision need not be an indication of accuracy. Your value for $\pi$ is just as precise as the accepted value because both values contain six digits.

The precision of a measuring device is limited by the finest division on its scale. The smallest division on a meter stick is a millimeter. Thus, a measurement of any smaller length with a meter stick can be only an estimate. There is a limit to the precision of even the best instruments.

The accuracy of a measuring device depends upon how well a value obtained using the instrument agrees with its accepted value. Thus, when a measurement is made, the measuring device should first be checked for accuracy. This can be done by using the instrument to measure quantities whose values are known. The measured values are then compared with the known values.

FIGURE 2-7. The micro-
meter (a) and analytical
balance (b) are used to obtain very precise and accurate measurements of
length and mass. The pre-
cision of each is limited
by the finest division on
the scale.

Errors in measurement affect the accuracy of a measurement. But the precision is not affected since values are still stated in terms of the smallest division on the instrument.

a

*George Anderson*

b

*George Anderson*

# 2:7   Significant Digits

Because the precision of all measuring devices is limited, the number of digits that can be assumed for any measurement is also limited. When making a measurement, read the instrument to its smallest division. Estimate within a part of the division. The figures that you write down for the measurements are called significant digits.

**Significant digits are the figures which best represent the value of a measurement.**

Suppose you want to measure the length of a strip of metal with a meter stick. The metal strip in Figure 2-8 is somewhat longer than 5.6 centimeters. Looking closely at the scale, you can see that the end of the metal strip is about four-tenths of the way between 5.6 centimeters and 5.7 centimeters. Therefore, the length of the strip is best stated as 5.64 centimeters. The last digit is an estimate. Either 5.6 centimeters or 5.7 centimeters would be more in error than 5.64 centimeters. The readings of 5.6 centimeters and 5.7 centimeters are at least 0.03 centimeter and probably 0.04 centimeter in error. It is not likely that a reading of 5.64 centimeters is more than 0.01 centimeter in error.

**One estimated reading in the measurement improves the accuracy.**

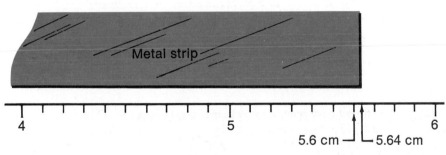

FIGURE 2-8. The accuracy of any measurement depends on both the instrument used and the observer. After a calculation, keep only those digits which truly imply the accuracy of the original measurement.

Suppose that the end of the metal strip is right on the 5.6 centimeter mark. In that case, you can write the measurement as 5.60 centimeters. The zero indicates that the strip is not 0.01 centimeters more or less than 5.6 centimeters. Therefore, the zero is a significant digit for it has meaning. It is the uncertain digit because you are still guessing. The last digit written down for any measurement is the uncertain digit. All nonzero digits in a measurement are significant.

**Nonzero digits are always significant.**

Zeroes are often a problem. The zero mentioned in 5.60 centimeters is significant. However, a zero that only serves to locate the decimal point is not significant. Thus, the value of 0.0026 kilograms contains two significant digits. The measurement of 0.002060 kilograms contains four significant digits, the final zero indicating a probable value.

**Zeroes that serve only to locate decimal points are not significant.**

There is no way to tell how many of the zeroes in the number 186 000 are significant. The 6 may have been the estimated digit and the three zeroes may be needed only to place the decimal point. Or, all three zeroes may be significant. To avoid this problem, such measurements are written in scientific notation. In the number that appears before the power of ten, all the digits are significant. Thus, $1.860 \times 10^5$ has four significant digits. To summarize, the following rules are used to determine the number of significant digits:

(1) Digits other than zero are always significant.

(2) Any *final* zero or zeros used after the decimal point are significant.

(3) Zeros between two other significant digits are always significant.

(4) Zeros used solely for spacing the decimal point are not significant.

### PROBLEMS

**1.** State the number of significant digits in each measurement.

    **a.** 2804 m     **c.** 0.0029 m     **e.** $4.6 \times 10^5$ m

    **b.** 2.84 m     **d.** 0.003 068 m     **f.** $4.06 \times 10^5$ m

**2.** State the number of significant digits in each measurement.

    **a.** 75 m     **c.** 0.007 060 kg     **e.** $1.008 \times 10^8$ m

    **b.** 75.00 cm     **d.** $1.87 \times 10^6$ m     **f.** $1.20 \times 10^{-4}$ m

## 2:8   Operations with Significant Digits

The results of any mathematical operation with measured quantities cannot be more precise than the least precise quantity involved. Assume that you must add the lengths 6.48 meters and 18.2 meters. The length 18.2 meters is precise only to a tenth of a meter. Therefore, the sum of the two lengths can be precise only to a tenth of a meter. To add the two lengths, round off 6.48 meters to 6.5 meters. Then add 6.5 meters to 18.2 meters. The sum is 24.7 meters. Subtraction is handled in the same way. To add or subtract measured quantities, first round off all values to correspond to the least precise value involved.

**EXAMPLE:  Significant Digits—Addition**

    Add 24.686 m + 2.34 m + 3.2 m

*Solution:*     24.7 m     Note that 3.2 is the least precise

              2.3 m     measurement. Round off the other values

              3.2 m     to a tenth of a meter.

           30.2 m

To multiply or divide two measured quantities, perform the operation before rounding. Then, keep in the product or quotient only as many significant digits as are in the factor with the lesser number of significant digits.

*After multiplying or dividing, round off each value to agree in accuracy with the least accurate value.*

### EXAMPLE: Significant Digits—Multiplication

Multiply 3.22 cm × 2.1 cm

Solution:

$$
\begin{array}{r}
3.2\,②\ \text{cm} \\
2.\,①\ \text{cm} \\
\hline
③②② \\
6\ 4\ ④ \\
\hline
6.\,⑦\,⑥\,②\ \text{cm}^2
\end{array}
$$
more correctly stated 6.8 cm²

Note that each circled digit is either doubtful or obtained using a doubtful digit. A doubtful digit becomes more doubtful when it is multiplied. Since the 7 in the product is doubtful, the 6 and 2 which represent even finer divisions are certainly not significant. The answer is best stated as 6.8 cm². Recall also that the least precise factor, 2.1, contains two significant digits.

### EXAMPLE: Significant Digits—Division

Divide 36.5/3.414

Solution:   $\dfrac{36.\,⑤}{3.41\,④} = 10.\,⑥\,⑨$   more correctly stated 10.7

Whenever the measurements made during an experiment are recorded, it is important to write these measurements with the correct number of significant digits. In this way, each stated value can be communicated to other scientists in a way showing the precision of the measurement. This information must be considered when judging the validity of experimental results.

When performing laboratory exercises, you should try to observe the use of significant digits. However, in working the practice problems in this text, you should be primarily concerned with the concepts they illustrate, not the number of digits in your solution. You will be working to first approximations only since using realistic values throughout a text would soon fill the text with numbers. For example, a realistic value might be 5.016 50 kg but we will use 5.0 kg. Therefore, since the values given will only be rough values, you need only supply rough solutions. Since you will probably be using a calculator, give a reasonable answer to each problem and concentrate on understanding the principles used to obtain that solution.

George Anderson

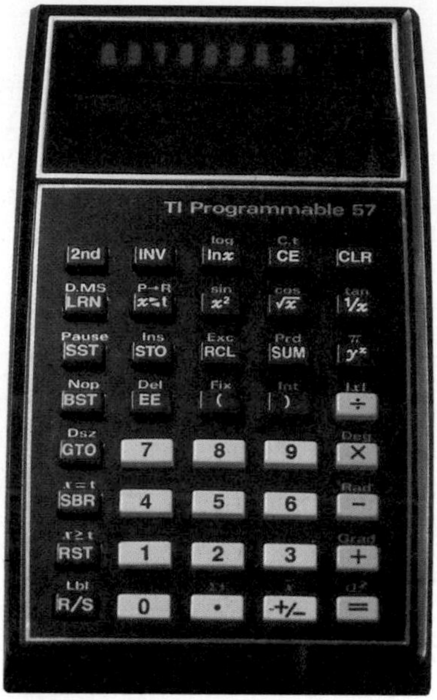

$$\frac{648}{273} = 2.3736263$$
Calculator answer

Each factor in the problem contains 3 significant digits

Therefore, the answer should be 2.37

**FIGURE 2-9. When using a calculator in answering problems, it is important to note that your answers cannot be more precise than the least precise quantity involved.**

**PROBLEMS**

3. 26.3 cm

**3.** Add 6.201 cm + 7.4 cm + 0.68 cm + 12.0 cm

**4.** Add 28.662 m + 32.34 m + 17.5 m

5. 71.7 kg

**5.** Add 26.38 kg + 14.531 kg + 30.8 kg

**6.** The sides of a quadrangular plot of land are measured. Their lengths are found to be 132.68 m, 48.3 m, 132.736 m, and 48.37 m. What is the perimeter of the plot of land as can best be determined with these measurements?

7. 2.5 g

**7.** Subtract 10.8 g − 8.264 g

**8.** Subtract 44.12 mL − 26.82 mL

9. 48.2 kg

**9.** A water tank has a mass of 3.64 kg when empty and a mass of 51.8 kg when filled to a certain level. What is the mass of the water in the tank?

**10.** Multiply
   **a.** 131 cm × 2.3 cm
   **b.** 6.87 cm × 2.2 cm
   **c.** 3.2145 km × 4.23 km

11. a. 2.73
    b. 0.253
    c. 4.73

**11.** Divide
   **a.** 20.2 cm ÷ 7.41 cm
   **b.** 3.1416 cm ÷ 12.4 cm
   **c.** 64.39 m ÷ 13.6 m

**12.** A rectangular floor has a length of 15.72 m and width of 4.40 m. Calculate the area of the floor to the best possible value using these measurements.

## 2:9  Graphs

Quantitative experiments are done to learn what relationships exist between measured quantities. During the experiment, one quantity called the *independent variable* is carefully varied. The value of another quantity called the *dependent variable* is measured for each variation of the independent variable. Both values are recorded in a table. The independent variable is placed in the first column and the dependent variable is placed in the second column. A graph can then be plotted from the table. The values of the **independent variable** are plotted horizontally ($x$ axis). The values of the **dependent variable** are plotted vertically ($y$ axis). The curve that best fits the plotted points is then drawn. Often, the shape of this curve clearly shows the mathematical relationship that exists between the dependent and independent variables. A straight line shows that the dependent variable $y$ varies directly with the independent variable $x$. A hyperbola shows that the dependent variable varies inversely with the independent variable, Table 2-4. A parabola shows that the dependent variable varies with the square of the independent variable.

The independent variable is plotted horizontally. The dependent variable is plotted vertically.

A straight line indicates direct variation.

A hyperbola indicates inverse variation.

A parabola indicates direct variation of a variable with the square of another variable.

## 2:10  Linear and Direct Variation

The most general form for a linear equation is

$$y = mx + b$$

where $m$ and $b$ are constants. The graph of a linear equation is a straight line. For example, the graph of the equation $y = 3x + 2$ is shown in Figure 2-10. The values used to plot this graph are given in Table 2-2.

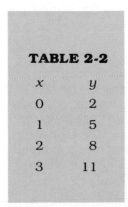

**TABLE 2-2**

| $x$ | $y$ |
|-----|-----|
| 0   | 2   |
| 1   | 5   |
| 2   | 8   |
| 3   | 11  |

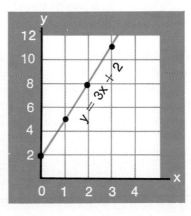

**FIGURE 2-10. The graph of a linear equation.**

Direct variation:
as *x* increases, *y* increases
or
as *x* decreases, *y* decreases

When one quantity varies directly with another, it increases or decreases in proportion to an increase or a decrease in the other quantity. The general equation for direct variation is

$$y = mx$$

where *m* is a constant. The graph of direct variation is always a straight line passing through the origin.

A good example of direct variation is provided by a law discovered by Sir Robert Hooke (1635–1703). Hooke's law states that the stretching of a spring varies directly with the force acting on the spring. Thus, if a force of 1 newton (N)* causes a spring to stretch 1.5 centimeters, a force of 2 newtons will cause it to stretch 3.0 centimeters, and a force of 3 newtons will cause it to stretch 4.5 centimeters.

In a test of this law, the force acting on a spring was varied and the resulting changes in length were measured. The data is shown in Table 2-3.

### TABLE 2-3

| Force (N) | Change in Length (cm) |
| --- | --- |
| 0 | 0.0 |
| 1 | 0.7 |
| 2 | 1.5 |
| 3 | 2.1 |
| 4 | 2.7 |
| 5 | 3.5 |

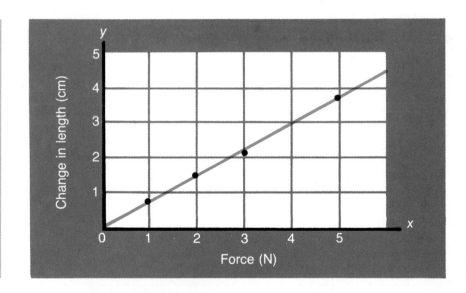

**FIGURE 2-11. A straight-line graph showing direct variation.**

By plotting the independent variable (force) on the *x* axis, and the dependent variable (change in length) on the *y* axis, we obtain the straight-line graph shown in Figure 2-11. This line passes through the origin. The change in length varies directly with the applied force. The equation for the line is

$$y = 0.7x$$

The *b* term is dropped since the line crosses the *y* axis at the origin.

*A newton is a unit of force and will be formally defined in Chapter 6.

# 2:11 Inverse Variation

When one quantity varies inversely with another, the second quantity will either decrease as the first increases or increase as the first decreases. The general equation for inverse variation is

$$y = \frac{k}{x}$$

where $k$ is a constant.

The behavior of a gas under varying pressures shows inverse variation. When the pressure acting on a gas is doubled, the volume of the gas is reduced to one-half its initial volume. In the same way, when the pressure on the gas is reduced to one-half the original pressure, the volume of the gas is doubled. Further reductions in pressure cause corresponding increases in volume. Table 2-4 lists data collected during an experiment with a gas. The resulting graph is a hyperbola.

Inverse variation:
as $x$ increases, $y$ decreases
or
as $x$ decreases, $y$ increases

**FIGURE 2-12. The graph of an inverse relationship.**

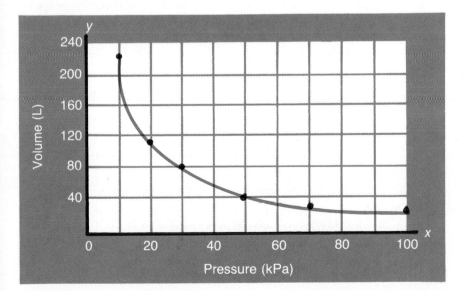

### TABLE 2-4

| Pressure (kPa)* | Volume (L) |
|---|---|
| 10 | 225 |
| 20 | 110 |
| 30 | 74.9 |
| 50 | 44.6 |
| 70 | 32.0 |
| 100 | 22.4 |

\*Kilopascals, kPa, is a pressure unit.

**Summary**

1. Scientific studies show that physical events follow a few fundamental laws.  2:1

2. The scientific method is based upon experimentation. Measurement is basic to experimentation.  2:1

3. The three fundamental units of measurement in mechanics are those for length, mass, and time. Other units are combinations of the fundamental units and are called derived units.  2:2–2:4

4. In the metric system (SI), the basic units of length, mass, and time are the meter, kilogram, and second.   2:2

5. SI units are based upon powers of ten.   2:2–2:3

6. Accuracy is the extent to which a measured value agrees with the accepted value for a quantity.   2:6

7. Precision is the degree of certainty with which a quantity is measured.   2:6

8. When making a measurement, the number of meaningful digits read is limited by the size of the divisions on the scale of the measuring device.   2:7

9. The last digit in a reading is always an estimate. Only one estimated digit is significant.   2:7

10. Graphs are plotted to show relationships between independent and dependent variables. The independent variable is plotted on the $x$ or horizontal axis. The dependent variable is plotted on the $y$ or vertical axis.   2:9

11. A straight line graph indicates that one quantity is directly proportional to the other. A hyperbola indicates that one quantity is inversely proportional to the other. A parabola indicates that one quantity varies with the square of the other.   2:10

## Questions

1. What differences are there between fundamental units and derived units?

2. What are the fundamental units used in a study of mechanics?

3. Express speed in terms of fundamental units.

4. What is the importance of the International System of Units?

5. Give the proper name for each multiple of the meter listed.
   a. 1/100 m       b. 1/1000 m       c. 1000 m

6. a. What is mass?
   b. What is the standard unit of mass in SI?

7. a. Which digit of a measured quantity is the doubtful digit?
   b. Is this digit significant?

8. a. Why is it difficult to tell how many significant digits are in a measured value such as 76 000?
   b. How can the number of significant digits in such a number be made clear?

9. During a laboratory experiment, as one quantity is varied, the change in the value of a second quantity is measured. What are each of these quantities called?

10. When plotting a graph
    a. what quantity is plotted vertically?
    b. what quantity is plotted horizontally?

**11.** Aristotle wrote (without performing any experiments) that the rate at which an object falls varies inversely with the density of the medium in which it is falling. What would this mean in terms of an object falling through a vacuum? Why did Aristotle write that there can be no such thing as a vacuum?

**Problems**

**1.** During a laboratory experiment, a student measured the mass of 10 cm$^3$ of water. The student then measured the mass of 20 cm$^3$ of water. In this way, the data in Table 2-5 were collected.
   **a.** Plot the values given in the table and draw the curve that best fits all points.
   **b.** Describe the resulting curve.
   **c.** According to the graph, what is the relationship between the volume of the water and the mass of the water?
**2.** During a science demonstration, an instructor placed a 1-kg mass on a horizontal table that was nearly frictionless. The instructor then applied various horizontal forces to the mass and measured the rate at which the mass gained speed (was accelerated) for each force applied. The results of the experiment are shown in Table 2-6.
   **a.** Plot the values given in the table and draw the curve that best fits all points.
   **b.** According to the graph, what is the relationship between the force applied to a mass and the rate at which it gains speed?
**3.** The teacher who performed the experiment in Problem 2 then changed the procedure. The mass was varied while the force was kept constant. The rate at which each mass gained speed was then recorded. The results are shown in Table 2-7.
   **a.** Plot the values given in Table 2-7 and draw the curve that best fits all points.
   **b.** Describe the resulting curve.
   **c.** According to the graph, what is the relationship between mass and the acceleration produced by a constant force?

*Use the data in the tables that follow to answer Problems 1, 2, and 3.*

| **TABLE 2-5** | | | **TABLE 2-6** | | | **TABLE 2-7** | |
|---|---|---|---|---|---|---|---|
| Volume (cm$^3$) | Mass (g) | | Force (N) | Acceleration (m/s$^2$) | | Mass (kg) | Acceleration (m/s$^2$) |
| 10 | 10.0 | | 5.0 | 4.9 | | 1.0 | 12.0 |
| 20 | 20.1 | | 10.0 | 9.8 | | 2.0 | 5.9 |
| 30 | 29.8 | | 15.0 | 15.2 | | 3.0 | 4.1 |
| 40 | 40.2 | | 20.0 | 20.1 | | 4.0 | 3.0 |
| 50 | 50.3 | | 25.0 | 25.0 | | 5.0 | 2.5 |
| | | | 30.0 | 29.9 | | 6.0 | 2.0 |

4. State the number of significant digits in each of these measurements:
   **a.** 248 m    **b.** 64.01 m    **c.** 0.000 03 m    **d.** 80.001 m

5. State the number of significant digits in the following measurements:
   **a.** $2.40 \times 10^6$ kg    **b.** $6 \times 10^8$ kg    **c.** $4.07 \times 10^{16}$ m

6. Add or subtract the following as indicated.
   **a.** 16.2 m + 5.008 m + 13.48 m
   **b.** 5.006 m + 12.0077 m + 8.0084 m
   **c.** Subtract: 78.05 cm$^2$ − 32.046 cm$^2$
   **d.** Subtract: 15.07 kg − 12.0 kg

7. Multiply the following.
   **a.** 1.42 cm × 1.2 cm    **e.** 4.3 cm × 8.26 cm
   **b.** 6.8 m × 3.145 m    **f.** $(2.0 \times 10^8$m$)(1.6 \times 10^7$m$)$
   **c.** 74.0 cm × 2.54 cm    **g.** 0.000 50 m/s × 0.0030 s
   **d.** 8.002 cm$^2$ × 1.50 cm

8. The length of a room is 16.40 m, its width is 4.5 m, and its height is 3.26 m. What volume of air does the room contain?

9. Gold has a density of 19.3 g/cm$^3$. A cube of gold measures 4.23 cm on each edge.
   **a.** What is the volume of the cube?
   **b.** What is its mass?

10. One cubic centimeter of silver has a mass of 10.5 g.
    **a.** What is the mass of 65.0 cm$^3$ of silver?
    **b.** When placed on a beam balance, the 65.0 cm$^3$ piece of silver is shown to have a mass of only 616 g. What part of it is hollow?

**Applying Physics**

1. *Economics:* Tony's Pizza Shop ordered new 22.86-cm pizza pans (9-inch pans). By mistake, 25.40-cm (10-inch) pans were delivered. Tony says that the difference is too small to worry about. As Tony's accountant, what would you say knowing materials cost about 0.25 cents per square centimeter?

2. *Astronomy:* Estimates of the volume of neutrons have shown that nuclear matter is unbelievably dense. neutrons have a density of about $2.0 \times 10^{14}$ grams per cubic centimeter (more than 200 000 000 tons per cubic centimeter). Pulsars are thought to be the compact remnants of old stars which have collapsed due to gravity. These stars form rapidly spinning, spherical bodies consisting entirely of neutrons. Let us assume that our sun is sufficiently large to form a pulsar. Calculate the diameter in kilometers of the neutron star formed from our sun if it were to collapse completely and its density equaled that of neutrons. The mass of the sun is about $2.0 \times 10^{30}$ kg.

3. *Energy Conservation:* Make a table in which you list the surface areas and volumes of cubes having sides which measure 1 m, 2 m, 3 m, 4 m, 5 m, and 6 m respectively. Add a third column in which you list the ratio of the surface area to volume for each cube. (For example, the first ratio is six to one.) Suppose that you are a member of a building committee in charge of designing a new high school building for a town which has cold winters. Part of the committee is in favor of a one-floor building consisting of many wings. A second group wants a cube-shaped building of several stories. You know that heating is a major cost in the operation of a school and that heat loss takes place through the walls, ceilings, and floors of buildings. How would you cast your vote on the matter? Explain.

4. *Biophysics:* On the basis of what you have found in regard to the ratios of surface areas to volumes in Applying Physics Problem 3, explain the following facts.
   a. Elephants like to wallow in cool streams.
   b. Elephants have large ears containing many veins.
   c. Hummingbirds (one of the smallest of birds) eat almost constantly from sunrise to sunset.
   d. A shrew (one of the smallest mammals) will attack and kill animals much larger than itself to satisfy its tremendous appetite.

**Readings**

Gwynne, Peter, "They're Close to Deciding the Fate of the Universe." *Popular Science,* December, 1980.

Hawkins, Bill, "Three New Home Computers." *Popular Science,* May, 1980.

Presley, et al, *A Guide to Programming in Basic-Plus.* The Lawrenceville School, Lawrenceville, NJ, 1975. (An excellent introduction to the elements of programming in BASIC. Enables students to program for the solutions to the problems in this text.)

Winson, JoAnn, "Roots: The Route to Learning Vocabulary of Science." *Science Digest,* May, 1980.

Whenever you think of the terms speed and acceleration, a race probably comes to mind. The motion of the bikers, as well as all other moving objects, can be described in terms of speed, acceleration, time, and distance. Consider how you move everyday in traveling from home to school and from class to class. How do speed, acceleration, time, and distance affect your everyday life?

# Motion in a Straight Line 3

Everything in the universe is in a state of motion. The earth itself is filled with moving things. The earth spins on its axis. The planets of our solar system orbit the sun. Our solar system moves through space as part of the Milky Way Galaxy. Stars and galaxies move away from one another. It might seem impossible to find a simple way to describe and understand the motions of all these objects. However, this is just what physicists have done! A few simple equations apply to all motions. They are basic to everything the physicist studies. The amazing thing about physics is that the laws of nature tend to be simple, not complex. An understanding of physics begins with an understanding of motion.

**GOAL: You will gain knowledge and understanding of the fundamentals of motion—speed, acceleration, time, and distance.**

## 3:1 Motion

An object can have only two types of motion. There is no other type of motion. An object can be moving either with a constant velocity or with a changing velocity. A change in velocity is called **acceleration.** In this chapter, you will study these two types of motion. By applying this knowledge you can understand all motion. This chapter deals only with motion in a straight line. Motion along a curved path is discussed in Chapter 8.

An object can move either with constant velocity or with acceleration.

Acceleration is the rate of change of velocity.

**39**

**FIGURE 3-1.** One of the first high-speed photographs was taken in 1878. The vertical lines are 68 cm apart. The time between exposures is 1/25 second. What is the average speed of the horse in m/s?

Instantaneous speed is the speed at a given instant.

Average speed is figured over a time period.

The horizontal bar in $\bar{v}$ means "average."

# 3:2   Average and Instantaneous Speed

*In this chapter the terms speed and velocity are used interchangeably.* A detailed discussion of these quantities appears in Chapter 5.

The **instantaneous speed** of a moving object is the actual speed at which it is moving at any given instant. For a car, this speed is the reading of the speedometer at a given moment. Often an object in motion does not move at a constant speed. During even a short trip, a car speeds up and slows down. Thus, the total distance traveled by an object during a period of time is often the result of an average speed. The average speed of an object during a time period can be calculated with the equation

$$\bar{v} = \frac{s}{t}$$

Here, $\bar{v}$ is the average speed or velocity, $s$* is the distance traveled, and $t$ is the time spent traveling. If the speed is truly constant, the small bar over the $v$ is dropped. Thus, $v$ shows uniform speed.

**EXAMPLE: Average Speed**

A car travels 450 kilometers during a 10-hour period. What is its average speed?

*Solution:*

$$\bar{v} = \frac{s}{t}$$

$$= \frac{450 \text{ km}}{10 \text{ h}} = 45 \text{ km/h}$$

*The symbol s is the symbol for displacement, the vector form of distance.

French National Railroad

FIGURE 3-2. This high speed French train will be running commercially at speeds close to 305 km/h. The train moves as a single unit giving it an extremely smooth ride. Japanese and German railroads are working on magnetically-suspended trains which can reach speeds of 480 km/h.

During some calculations, you may need to change kilometers per hour to meters per second. Recall that a given quantity divided by its equivalent is equal to one. Also keep in mind that the value of any quantity when multiplied by one does not change. We have seen that 1 kilometer = 1000 meters, and 1 hour = 3600 seconds. It follows that

$$\frac{1000 \text{ meters}}{1 \text{ kilometer}} = 1 \qquad \frac{1 \text{ hour}}{3600 \text{ seconds}} = 1$$

Therefore, to change 45 km/h to m/s, first multiply by a distance factor equal to one. Then multiply by a time factor equal to one.

$$\frac{45 \text{ km}}{h} \times \frac{1000 \text{ m}}{1 \text{ km}} \times \frac{1 \text{ h}}{3600 \text{ s}} = 12.5 \text{ m/s}$$

This method of converting one unit to an equivalent unit is called the factor-label method of unit conversion. Note that unit labels are also treated as factors and can be divided out. If the final units do not make sense, check your factors. You will find that a factor has either been inverted or stated incorrectly.

In factor-label method, units are divided out as factors.

## PROBLEMS

1. A motorist travels 406 km during a 7.0-h period. What was the average speed in km/h and m/s?

2. During a canoe race, a camper paddles 406 m in 70.0 s. What is the average speed in m/s and km/h?

1. 58 km/h, 16 m/s

3. a. 4.500 s
   b. 2592 km/h

5. $1.3 \times 10^3$ m/s, $1.3 \times 10^5$ cm/s

7. 0.481 s

**3.** A bullet is shot from a rifle with a speed of 720.0 m/s.
   **a.** What time is required for the bullet to strike a target 3240.0 m away?
   **b.** What is the velocity of the bullet in km/h?

**4.** A rocket launched into outer space travels 240 000 km during the first 6.0 h after the launching. What is the average speed of the rocket in km/h and m/s?

**5.** An electron travels through a vacuum tube 2.0 m long in $1.6 \times 10^{-3}$ s. What is the average speed of the electron while in the tube in m/s and cm/s?

**6.** Light from the sun reaches the earth in 8.3 min. The speed of light is $3.0 \times 10^8$ m/s. In kilometers, how far is the earth from the sun?

**7.** The distance from home plate to the pitcher's mound is 18.5 m. If a pitcher is capable of throwing a ball at 38.5 m/s, how much time does it take a thrown ball to reach home plate?

**8.** An experimental rocket car moves along a straight track at a constant speed of 900.0 m/s. The car passes a group of officials, travels a distance of 270.0 m and then explodes. If the officials hear the sound of the explosion 1.1 s after the car passes their position, what is the speed of sound?

**FIGURE 3-3.** This experimental rocket car has reached speeds of 900 m/s. It is used to test the effects of gravity on astronauts.

USAF/Holloman AFB, New Mexico

## 3:3   Uniform Acceleration

Acceleration is the change in velocity per unit time.

Acceleration is the rate at which velocity (or speed) is changing with time. If the speed of a body is increasing, the acceleration is positive. If the speed is decreasing, the acceleration is negative.

As you study physics it is important to distinguish between acceleration and velocity. Never confuse the two! They are NOT the same. Velocity is the rate of change of position and is usually expressed as m/s or km/h. Acceleration, however, is the rate of change of velocity—an entirely different concept.

Acceleration is usually expressed as a distance per second per second. An acceleration expressed as m/s$^2$ is the number of meters per second an object's speed increases or decreases during each second of the acceleration period. Acceleration could also be expressed as kilometers per hour second (km/h·s). This expression would mean the number of kilometers per hour the object's velocity changes per second.

The unit for acceleration is m/s$^2$.

In most cases it is good practice to think through equations used in physics rather than memorize them. Acceleration is the rate of change of velocity. Clearly then, you should divide the change in velocity ($\Delta v$) by the time needed to make that change in order to calculate acceleration.

The symbol $\Delta$ denotes "change in."

$$a = \frac{\Delta v}{t}$$

Here, $a$ represents the acceleration, $\Delta v$ (read "delta vee") is the change in velocity, and $t$ is the time required to bring about that change.

In the strictest sense, the change in velocity of an object, and therefore its acceleration, can occur in spurts. That is, acceleration need not always be constant. However, in this chapter, we will think of all accelerations as being uniform. Thus $a$ will denote constant acceleration.

The change in speed of an object is the difference between its final speed, $v_f$, and its original speed, $v_o$. Thus $\Delta v = v_f - v_o$. By substitution,

$$a = \frac{v_f - v_o}{t}$$

**EXAMPLE: Positive Acceleration**

During an 11-s period, the speed of a racing car is increased uniformly from 44 m/s to 88 m/s. What is the acceleration of the car?

*Solution:*

$$a = \frac{v_f - v_o}{t}$$

$$= \frac{88 \text{ m/s} - 44 \text{ m/s}}{11 \text{ s}}$$

$$= \frac{44 \text{ m/s}}{11 \text{ s}} = 4.0 \text{ m/s}^2$$

Consider what happens should the racing car slow uniformly from 88 m/s to 44 m/s in 11 seconds. The same equation is used. Subtracting the original speed from the final speed will, in this case, give a negative value for $\Delta v$. A negative value means the acceleration is negative since the car is losing speed.

Negative acceleration is deceleration.

### EXAMPLE: Negative Acceleration

During an 11-s period, the speed of a racing car is decreased uniformly from 88 m/s to 44 m/s. What is the acceleration?
*Solution:*

$$a = \frac{v_f - v_o}{t}$$

$$= \frac{44 \text{ m/s} - 88 \text{ m/s}}{11 \text{ s}}$$

$$= \frac{-44 \text{ m/s}}{11 \text{ s}}$$

$$= -4.0 \text{m/s}^2$$

### PROBLEMS

9. 2.0 m/s$^2$

**9.** What is the acceleration of a racing car if its speed is increased uniformly from 44 m/s to 66 m/s over an 11-s period?

**10.** What is the acceleration of a racing car if its speed is decreased uniformly from 66 m/s to 44 m/s over an 11-s period?

11. 2.5 m/s$^2$

**11.** A train moving at a speed of 15 m/s is accelerated uniformly to 45 m/s over a 12-s period. What is its acceleration?

**12.** A plane starting from rest ($v_o = 0$) is accelerated uniformly to its takeoff speed of 72 m/s during a 5.0-s period. What is the plane's acceleration?

13. 9.8 m/s$^2$

**13.** A bullet leaves the muzzle of a rifle in a direction straight up with a speed of 700 m/s. Ten seconds later its speed straight up is only 602 m/s. At what rate does the earth's gravitational field decelerate the bullet?

**14.** An arrow is shot straight up with an initial speed of 98 m/s. Nine seconds later its speed straight up is only 9.8 m/s. At what rate is the arrow decelerated by the pull of the earth's gravitational field?

15. 4.0 × 10$^6$ m/s$^2$

**15.** In a vacuum tube, an electron is accelerated uniformly from rest to a speed of $2.6 \times 10^5$ m/s during a time period of $6.5 \times 10^{-2}$ s. Calculate the acceleration of the electron.

## 3:4 Final Velocity after Uniform Acceleration

In some cases where the uniform acceleration is known, it may be desirable to calculate the final speed of an object at the end of an acceleration period. The equation for acceleration is

$$a = \frac{v_f - v_o}{t}$$

Solving for $v_f$
$$v_f - v_o = at$$

$$\boxed{v_f = v_o + at}$$

EXAMPLE: **Final Velocity after Uniform Acceleration**

A ball rolling down an incline for 5 s undergoes a uniform acceleration of 4.2 m/s². If the ball has an initial speed of 2.2 m/s when it starts down the incline, what is its final speed?
*Solution:*

$$v_f = v_o + at$$
$$= 2.2 \text{ m/s} + (4.2 \text{ m/s}^2 \times 5.0 \text{ s})$$
$$= 2.2 \text{ m/s} + 21.0 \text{ m/s} = 23.2 \text{ m/s}$$

### PROBLEMS

**16.** A car is uniformly accelerated at the rate of 2.5 m/s² for 12 s. If the original speed of the car is 8.0 m/s, what is its final speed?

**17.** An airplane flying at 90 m/s is accelerated uniformly at the rate of 0.5 m/s² for 10 seconds. What is its final speed?   17. 95 m/s

**18.** A race car traveling at 45 m/s is slowed uniformly at the rate of −1.5 m/s² for 10 seconds. What is its final speed in m/s and km/h?

**19.** A spacecraft traveling at 1200 m/s is uniformly accelerated at the rate of 150 m/s² by burning its second-stage rocket. If the rocket burns for 18 seconds, what is the final speed of the craft?   19. $3.9 \times 10^3$ m/s

## 3:5 Distance Traveled during Uniform Acceleration

The distance traveled by an object during any given time period can be calculated from the average speed of the object during that time period. Solving for s, we obtain

$$s = \bar{v}t$$

Distance is the product of average speed and time.

If an object is being uniformly accelerated, its average speed is easy to find. Consider a plane that is accelerated uniformly from 40 m/s to 60 m/s during a 10-s period. The plane passes smoothly through the whole set of speeds between 40 m/s and 60 m/s. Half of these speeds are less than 50 m/s. Half are more than 50 m/s. The average speed is the middle speed, 50 m/s. The average speed of a uniformly accelerating object is always the middle speed.

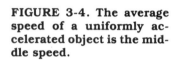

The average speed of an object which is accelerating uniformly is its middle speed.

Speed (m/s)

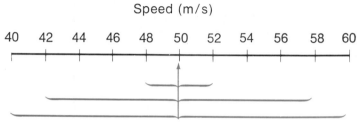

40   42   44   46   48   50   52   54   56   58   60

Average speed

**FIGURE 3-4. The average speed of a uniformly accelerated object is the middle speed.**

The middle speed of the plane can be found by adding the final speed and the initial speed and dividing the sum by two. This expression can be written

$$\bar{v} = \frac{v_o + v_f}{2}$$

Thus, the average speed of the plane in our example is

$$\bar{v} = \frac{40 \text{ m/s} + 60 \text{ m/s}}{2} = 50 \text{ m/s}$$

To find the distance traveled by an object during an acceleration period, substitute the expression for average velocity into the equation $s = \bar{v}t$. This expression becomes

$$s = \left( \frac{v_o + v_f}{2} \right) t$$

**EXAMPLE: Distance Traveled during Uniform Acceleration**

What distance is traveled by a train as it is accelerated uniformly from 22 m/s to 44 m/s in a 20-s period?
*Solution:*

$$s = \left( \frac{v_o + v_f}{2} \right) t$$

$$= \frac{22 \text{ m/s} + 44 \text{ m/s}}{2} \times 20 \text{ s} = 660 \text{ m}$$

## PROBLEMS

**20.** A car traveling at 44 m/s is uniformly decelerated to a speed of 22 m/s over an 11-s period. What distance does it travel during this time?

**21.** A racing car starts from rest ($v_o = 0$) and is accelerated uniformly to 40 m/s in 8 s. What distance does the car travel?

**21.** 160 m

**22.** A plane flying at the speed of 150 m/s is accelerated uniformly at a rate of 5 m/s$^2$.
   **a.** What is the plane's speed at the end of 10 s?
   **b.** What distance has it traveled?

**23.** A rocket traveling at 88 m/s is accelerated uniformly to 132 m/s over a 15-s period. What distance in meters does the rocket travel during this time?

**23.** 1700 m

**24.** An engineer is to design a runway to accommodate airplanes that must gain a ground speed of 60 m/s before they can take off. These planes are capable of being accelerated uniformly at the rate of 1.5 m/s$^2$.
   **a.** How long will it take them to achieve take-off speed?
   **b.** What must be the minimum length of the runway?

## 3:6  Uniform Acceleration—Starting and Stopping

Consider the special case of an object that is accelerated from rest. In this case, $v_o = 0$ and the general equation

$$v_f = v_o + at$$

becomes

$$v_f = at$$

The general equation for the distance traveled by an object with uniform acceleration is

$$s = \left(\frac{v_o + v_f}{2}\right)t$$

However, when an object starts from rest, $v_o = 0$ and $v_f = at$. So we can rewrite the above expression to read

$$s = \left(\frac{at}{2}\right)t$$

This expression can also be written

$$\boxed{s = \tfrac{1}{2}\,at^2}$$

Thus, for an object starting from rest, the distance traveled in any given time can be calculated if the acceleration is known.

An important characteristic of physical laws is what scientists refer to as symmetry. Often we find that exactly opposite situations operate in the same manner. That is, the situations are opposite but symmetrical. In simpler terms we might say that what works one way should work the opposite way.

Symmetry tells us that the same distance will be traveled whether an object starts from rest and is accelerated to 40 m/s in 10 seconds or is moving at 40 m/s and is decelerated to rest in 10 seconds. The two situations are opposite but symmetrical.

Strictly speaking, when an object is slowed the acceleration can be considered negative and $v_o$ is not equal to zero. In this case, a more general equation is appropriate.

$$s = v_o t + \left( \frac{-at^2}{2} \right)$$

The equation, $s = \frac{1}{2} at^2$ is used for an object starting from rest or going to rest.

In recognizing that the result would be the same, a scientist could let $a$ be positive and simply use $s = \frac{1}{2} at^2$ for an object going to rest.

### EXAMPLE: Calculating Distance from Acceleration and Time

A car starting from rest is accelerated at a constant rate of 6.2 m/s². What distance does the car travel during the first 7.0 s of acceleration?
*Solution:*

$$s = \frac{1}{2} at^2$$
$$= \frac{(6.2 \text{ m/s}^2)(7.0 \text{ s})^2}{2} = 152 \text{ m}$$

The same car is then decelerated to rest at a constant rate of 6.2 m/s². If the car is brought to a stop in 7.0 s, what distance does it travel?
*Solution:*

$$s = \frac{1}{2} at^2$$
$$= \frac{(6.2 \text{ m/s}^2)(7.0 \text{ s})^2}{2} = 152 \text{ m}$$

Note that the car covers the same distance regardless of whether it is accelerating or decelerating.

### PROBLEMS

25. 1400 m

**25.** An airplane starts from rest and undergoes a uniform acceleration of 3.0 m/s² for 30 s before leaving the ground. What distance does it travel during the 30 s?

**26.** A jet plane lands on a runway traveling at 88 m/s and is decelerated uniformly to rest in 11 s.
   **a.** Calculate its deceleration in m/s².
   **b.** Calculate the distance it travels.

**27.** The Tokyo express is accelerated from rest at a constant rate of 1.0 m/s² for 1.0 min. How far does it travel during this time?

**28.** Starting from rest, a racing car travels a distance of 200 m in the first 5.0 s of uniform acceleration. At what rate is it being accelerated?

**29.** In an emergency, a driver brings a car to a full stop in 5.0 s. The car is traveling at a rate of 38 m/s when braking begins.
**a.** At what rate is the car decelerated?
**b.** How far does it travel before stopping?

**30.** A stone is dropped from an airplane at a height of 490 m. It required 10 s to reach the ground. At what rate does gravity accelerate the stone?

27. 1800 m

29. a. 7.6 m/s²
    b. 95 m

The general equations for final velocity, $v_f$, and total distance, $s$, can be combined to form an equation for finding the final velocity of an object that starts from rest. Recall that

$$v_f = v_o + at \quad \text{and} \quad s = \frac{v_f + v_o}{2}t$$

When $v_o$ is zero, the equations for $v_f$ and $s$ may be written

$$v_f = at \quad \text{and} \quad s = \frac{v_f}{2}t$$

Solving for $t$, $\quad t = \frac{v_f}{a} \quad \text{and} \quad t = \frac{2s}{v_f}$

Therefore

$$\frac{v_f}{a} = \frac{2s}{v_f}$$

$$\boxed{v_f^2 = 2as} \quad \text{or} \quad v_f = \sqrt{2as}$$

Symmetry tells us that the same expression can be used when a moving object is brought to rest. That is, if we assume $a$ to be positive rather than negative when an object is decelerated to rest, we can write its initial velocity in terms of the distance traveled and the deceleration.

$$v_o^2 = 2as \quad \text{or} \quad v_o = \sqrt{2as}$$

**EXAMPLE: Acceleration When Distance and Initial Velocity Are Known**

An airplane flying at 63 m/s lands on a runway and travels 1000 m before stopping. At what rate is the plane decelerated? (Note: Let $a$ represent deceleration.)

*Solution:*   Since  $v_o^2 = 2as$

$$a = \frac{v_o^2}{2s} = \frac{(63 \text{ m/s})^2}{2 \times 1000 \text{ m}} = -2.0 \text{ m/s}^2$$

31. 55 m/s

## PROBLEMS

**31.** A plane is accelerated from rest at the constant rate of 3.0 m/s$^2$ over a distance of 500 m. What is its speed after traveling this distance?

**32.** Decelerating a plane at the uniform rate of 8.0 m/s$^2$, a pilot stops the plane in 484 m. How fast was the plane going before braking began?

33. 25 m/s

**33.** A box falls off the tailgate of a truck and slides along the street for a distance of 62.5 m. Friction decelerates the box at 5.0 m/s$^2$. At what speed was the truck moving when the box fell?

**34.** A light plane flying at 40 m/s touches down on a runway and travels 100 m before stopping. At what rate is the plane decelerated?

35. 225 m

**35.** Suppose you are driving along a highway at 45 m/s and your brakes decelerate at 4.5 m/s$^2$. What minimum distance will you travel during an emergency stop?

## 3:7  Acceleration Due to Gravity

The rate of acceleration is common to all free-falling objects.

The acceleration of a free-falling body due to gravity is 9.8 m/s$^2$.

All freely falling objects that are close to the surface of the earth gain speed toward the earth at the same rate (neglecting any frictional effects of air.) Hence, it is worthwhile for you to memorize the value of gravitational acceleration. Acceleration due to gravity is 9.8 m/s$^2$. All equations discussed in this chapter apply to gravitational acceleration. It is usual to replace the $a$ used in acceleration equations with $g$ when working with the acceleration of gravity. Hence $v_f = v_o + gt$ and $v_f^2 = 2gs$.

### EXAMPLE:  Acceleration Due to Gravity

A brick falls freely from a high scaffold. **a.** What is its speed in m/s after 4.0 s? **b.** How far does the brick fall during the first 4.0 s?
*Solution:*

**a.** $v_f = v_o + gt$

$= 0$ m/s $+ (9.8$ m/s$^2 \times 4.0$ s$)$

$= 39$ m/s

**b.** $s = \dfrac{gt^2}{2}$

$= \dfrac{9.8 \text{ m/s}^2 (4 \text{ s})^2}{2} = 78$ m

The acceleration of gravity is always 9.8 m/s$^2$ toward the earth. It does not depend on the direction an object is moving —up or down. An object shot straight up slows at the rate of 9.8 m/s$^2$ until it comes to rest. It then is accelerated down at the same rate, 9.8 m/s$^2$. Suppose an arrow is shot from an archer's bow with a speed of 49 m/s straight up. Each second, gravity removes 9.8 m/s from its speed. After 5 seconds, the arrow will have a speed of 0 m/s. For an instant it is at rest. Then the arrow is accelerated downward, the same as any falling object starting from rest. It will fall for just 5 seconds before reaching the point from which it left the bow. At that point it has a speed of 49 m/s (5 s × 9.8 m/s$^2$). The arrow spends 10 seconds in the air. It rises to the same height during the 5 seconds of rise that an object falls from rest in 5 seconds. To find out how high an object will rise when shot straight up, find the time it takes gravity to bring the object to rest. Then calculate the distance the object, starting from rest, will fall during this same time.

**EXAMPLE: Deceleration Due to Gravity**

A mortar shell is shot straight up with an initial speed of 98 m/s. **a.** How long does the shell remain in the air? **b.** How high does the shell rise?

*Solution:*

**a.** Divide the initial vertical speed of the shell by the rate at which gravity causes it to decelerate.

$$t = \frac{v}{g} = \frac{98 \text{ m/s}}{9.8 \text{ m/s}^2} = 10 \text{ s}$$

The 10 s is just the time needed for gravity to bring the shell to a halt vertically. The shell will then spend another 10 s falling back to earth. The time the shell remains in the air is 20 s.

**b.** Since the shell rises for 10 s, the height it reaches equals the distance an object, starting from rest, falls in 10 s. Hence,

$$s = \frac{gt^2}{2} = \frac{9.8 \text{ m/s}^2 (10 \text{ s})^2}{2} = 4.9 \text{ m} \times 100 = 490 \text{ m}$$

# 3:8 Free Fall

All of the examples of falling objects we have used in this chapter assume that the objects involved are undergoing equal accelerations, namely 9.8 m/s$^2$. A few questions should have crossed your mind as you solved the practice problems and read the brief introduction to gravitational acceleration. For one thing, why do all objects fall with equal acceleration?

It might seem to you, as it did to Aristotle, that heavy objects should fall faster than light objects. For example, the earth pulls on a two-kilogram mass with twice the force that it pulls on a one-kilogram mass. We say that the two-kilogram mass is twice as heavy as the one-kilogram mass. Why then doesn't the two-kilogram mass fall twice as fast as the one-kilogram mass? The

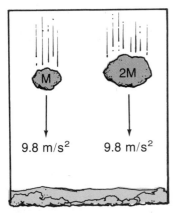

**FIGURE 3-5. The earth pulls on the 2M object with twice as much force as it pulls on M. However, the 2M object has twice the mass to be accelerated. Thus, both masses are accelerated equally.**

Air resistance is the result of an object's collision with air molecules as it falls.

An object reaches terminal velocity when the upward force of air resistance offsets the object's weight thus stopping acceleration.

**FIGURE 3-6. In a vacuum, a coin and feather fall at equal rates at all times.**

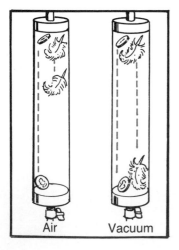

answer is that a two-kilogram mass has twice as much mass to be accelerated by the earth's pull as a one-kilogram mass. It takes twice the force to accelerate twice the mass.

A truck has a larger engine than does a small car. The truck's engine can produce a larger force than the car's engine but it must accelerate a truck, not a car. The result is that the car and truck may very well have equal accelerations. It is the same with falling objects. Heavy objects have more force acting on them but they also have more mass for that force to accelerate than is the case of a light object. Thus, it turns out that all objects are accelerated equally by gravity.

Another consideration that, in practice, cannot be avoided is air resistance. You have noticed that a leaf, a feather, or a piece of paper does not fall quite as fast as a heavier object such as a brick. Aristotle probably noticed the same thing and came to the mistaken notion that heavy objects fall faster than light objects.

As objects fall, air resistance produces an upward force on them. **Air resistance** is the result of the object colliding with the air molecules below it as it falls. This upward force depends upon the number of air molecules the object strikes per second and how fast it strikes them. When the object strikes a large number of air molecules fast enough, the upward force can offset the object's weight and stop it from accelerating. The body will then fall at a steady rate called **terminal velocity.**

A feather has a large surface area and a small weight. As it falls, air resistance rapidly offsets its weight. Terminal velocity for a feather or a leaf is only a few centimeters per second. Tiny droplets of water, such as those found in a dense fog, have large surface areas and low weights. You can watch them fall slowly and steadily in the beam of an automobile's headlamp. Likewise, small insects have large surface areas and low weights. Thus, an ant can fall from the 50th floor of a tall building and upon reaching the sidewalk walk off unharmed. Birds can fly easily because their weights are low compared to their surface areas. On the other hand, a skydiver has a fairly high weight compared to surface area. A falling skydiver must collide at high speed with a large number of air molecules per second to reach terminal velocity which is usually more than 200 km per hour. When the parachute opens, the surface area greatly increases. The terminal velocity is reduced to a point where the skydiver can land safely.

You should recognize that the value used for gravitational acceleration is a general value. As you do calculations in this physics course and use this value, ignore other effects such as air resistance. You are interested in basic concepts. However, if you become an engineer some day, you will be concerned more directly with all factors involved in gravitational acceleration.

**Summary**

1. All motion can be described by a few universal equations.   3:1
2. Motion equations deal with either constant velocity or acceleration (changing velocity). There is no other type of motion.   3:2
3. Instantaneous speed is the actual speed of an object at any given instant.   3:2
4. Average speed is the effective speed over a period of time.   3:2
5. Acceleration is the rate at which velocity changes with time ($\Delta v/t$).   3:3
6. When an object is increasing its speed, its acceleration is positive. When it is slowing down, its acceleration is negative.   3:3
7. Constant acceleration is called uniform acceleration.   3:4–3:6
8. The average speed of an object undergoing uniform acceleration is always its middle speed. The middle speed is found by adding the initial and final speeds and dividing by two.   3:5
9. The acceleration of gravity is 9.8 m/s². The acceleration of gravity is treated in the same way as any other acceleration.   3:7
10. The earth attracts larger masses with greater force but all masses are accelerated by gravity at the same rate because a larger force is required to accelerate a larger mass.   3:7
11. Air resistance often affects the gravitational acceleration of objects whose surface area is large with respect to their mass.   3:8

**Questions**

1. What do you think is the most important aspect of the few simple equations presented in this chapter?
2. Write the equations for
   a. acceleration
   b. the final velocity of a uniformly accelerating object, and
   c. the distance traveled by a moving object during an acceleration period. You should be able to reason these out.

3. Four cars are started from rest. Car A is accelerated at 6 m/s². Car B is accelerated at 5.4 m/s². Car C is accelerated at 8.0 m/s², and Car D speeds up at 12 m/s². In the first column of a table, show the speed of each car at the end of 2 s. In the second column, show the distance each car travels during the same two seconds. What conclusion do you reach about the speed attained and the distance traveled by a body starting from rest at the end of the first two seconds of acceleration?
4. An object shot straight up rises for 7 s before gravity brings it to a halt. A second object falling from rest takes 7 s to reach the ground. What do the two objects have in common?

5. A two-kilogram mass is twice as heavy as a one-kilogram mass. Both masses, however, will be accelerated by the pull of the earth at the same rate, 9.8 m/s$^2$. Explain why.

6. What conditions are necessary for a falling object to reach its terminal velocity? How does the terminal velocity of a feather compare with the terminal velocity of a brick?

## Problems

1. The speed of a car is increased at a constant rate. If the speed is increased by 42 m/s over a 7.0-s period, what is the acceleration?

2. Find the uniform acceleration that will cause an object's speed to change from 32 m/s to 96 m/s in an 8.0-s period.

3. An electron, initially at rest, leaves a cathode and is uniformly accelerated in a straight line toward an anode. It reaches the anode in 0.01 s traveling with a speed of 2000 m/s. What was its acceleration?

4. A car traveling at a speed of 20 m/s is accelerated uniformly at the rate of 1.6 m/s$^2$ for 6.8 s. What is its final speed?

5. Determine the final speed of a proton that has an initial speed of 264 m/s and then is decelerated uniformly in an electric field at the rate of 16 m/s$^2$ for 15 s.

6. A supersonic jet flying at 200 m/s is accelerated uniformly at the rate of 23.1 m/s$^2$ for 20 s.
   a. What is its final speed?
   b. The speed of sound is 331 m/s in air. How many times the speed of sound is the plane's final speed?

7. Determine the distance traveled during constant acceleration by a plane that is accelerated from 66 m/s to 88 m/s in 12 s.

8. How far does a plane fly while being decelerated uniformly from 140 m/s to 70 m/s in 15 s?

9. Starting from rest, a rocket is accelerated at the uniform rate of 18 m/s$^2$ for 5.0 s. What distance does it travel during this time?

10. A plane flying at 110 m/s touches down and travels 302 m before coming to rest. At what rate was the plane decelerated?

11. If a bullet leaves the muzzle of a rifle with a speed of 600 m/s, and the barrel of the rifle is 0.9 m long, at what rate is the bullet accelerated while in the barrel?

12. A car comes to rest after uniform deceleration at the rate of 9 m/s$^2$ for 8.0 s. What distance does it travel during this time?

13. A plane travels a distance of 500 m while being accelerated uniformly from rest at the rate of 5.0 m/s$^2$. What final speed does it attain?

14. A stone falls freely from rest for 8.0 s.
   a. Calculate its final speed.
   b. What distance does the stone fall during this time?

**15.** A weather balloon is floating at a constant height above the earth when it releases a pack of instruments.
  **a.** If the pack hits the ground with a speed of 73.5 m/s, how high is the balloon?
  **b.** How long does the pack fall?
**16.** During a baseball game a batter hits a long fly ball. If the ball remains in the air for 6.0 s, how high does it rise?
**17.** A student drops a rock from a bridge 120 m high. With what speed does the rock strike the water below?
**18.** Just as a traffic light turns green, a waiting car starts off with a constant acceleration of 6.0 m/s$^2$. At the instant the car begins to accelerate, a truck with a constant velocity of 21 m/s passes in the next lane.
  **a.** How far will the car travel before it overtakes the truck?
  **b.** How fast will the car be traveling when it overtakes the truck?

**Applying Physics**

**1.** *A Complex Set of Motions:* A wrench falls from a helicopter which is rising steadily at 6.0 m/s. After 2.0 s,
  **a.** What is the velocity of the wrench?
  **b.** How far below the helicopter is the wrench?
**2.** *Biophysics:* Now that you know about acceleration, test your reaction time. Ask a friend to hold a ruler just even with the top of your fingers. Then have your friend drop the ruler. Taking the number of centimeters that the ruler falls before you can catch it, calculate your reaction time. An average of several trials will give more accurate results. The reaction time for most people is more than 0.15 seconds.

**Readings**

Asimov, Issac, "Point in Time of No Return." *Science Digest,* July, 1980.
Drake, Stillman, "Newton's Apple and Galileo's Dialogue." *Scientific American*, August, 1980.
Fermi, Laura, and Bernardini, Gilberto, *Galileo and the Scientific Revolution*, New York, Basic Books, Inc., 1961.
Overhauser, Albert W., "The Role of Gravity in Quantum Theory." *Scientific American*, May, 1980.

Graphs are used to analyze relationships between quantities. By graphing data relative to the design and performance of a racing car, designers and mechanics can build faster, more efficient machines. In this chapter, you will use graphs to study the basic relationships among speed, acceleration, time, and distance. Of what value are these relationships to the members of a racing team? How might graphs be used to project fuel and tire requirements for a race? How might graphs be useful to you?

Rick Kocks

# Graphical Analysis of Motion 4

Graphs are one of our most useful tools. They are often used to determine if relationships exist between quantities. For instance, a straight line always tells us that one quantity is directly proportional to another. A hyperbola indicates that one quantity is inversely proportional to another. That is, as one increases the other decreases proportionately. The parabola always means that one quantity varies as the square of the other. The straight line, the hyperbola, and the parabola are the curves you will see time and time again as you study physics. This is because nature tends to follow a few simple relationships.

In your working with graphs, you should keep in mind what each axis represents. Then, you will often be able to see at a glance how the graphed quantities are related.

GOAL: You will gain knowledge and understanding of the uses of graphs and will learn to recognize the type of relationship between variables from the shape of a graph.

## 4:1 Distance-Time Graph for Constant Speed

An object moving at a **constant speed** travels the same distance during each second of motion. Therefore, the total distance traveled varies directly with the elapsed time. A graph of distance as a function of time is a straight line that could pass through the origin.

Consider a plane flying at a constant speed of 60 m/s. Table 4-1 lists the time of travel and the total distance traveled during a 5-second interval. Figure 4-1 is a plot of this data. The curve is a straight line passing through the origin.

When speed is constant, distance varies directly with time.

| TABLE 4-1 | |
|---|---|
| *Time* (s) | *Distance* (m) |
| 0 | 0 |
| 1 | 60 |
| 2 | 120 |
| 3 | 180 |
| 4 | 240 |
| 5 | 300 |

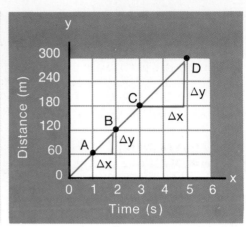

**FIGURE 4-1. A distance-time graph for an object traveling at constant speed.**

## 4:2   Slope of a Graph

The slope of a graph is $\Delta y/\Delta x$.

The steepness of a graph is called the slope of the graph. **Slope** is the vertical change or rise, $\Delta y$, divided by the corresponding horizontal change or run, $\Delta x$, between any two points on the graph. For example, the slope between points $A$ and $B$ in Figure 4-1, is

$$\text{slope} = \frac{\text{rise}}{\text{run}} = \frac{\Delta y}{\Delta x} = \frac{\Delta s}{\Delta t} = \frac{120 \text{ m} - 60 \text{ m}}{2 \text{ s} - 1 \text{ s}} = \frac{60 \text{ m}}{1 \text{ s}} = 60 \text{ m/s}$$

Between points $C$ and $D$,

$$\text{slope} = \frac{\text{rise}}{\text{run}} = \frac{\Delta s}{\Delta t} = \frac{300 \text{ m} - 180 \text{ m}}{5 \text{ s} - 3 \text{ s}} = \frac{120 \text{ m}}{2 \text{ s}} = 60 \text{ m/s}$$

The slope of a distance-time graph represents speed.

Thus, the slope of a distance-time graph gives the speed of the object. A straight line has a constant slope all along its length. therefore, the speed of the object is constant.

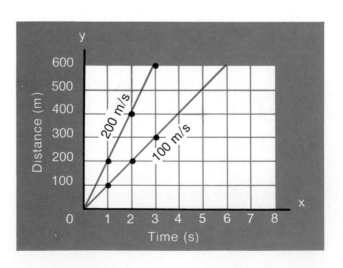

**FIGURE 4-2. As the slope of a distance-time graph increases, so does the speed.**

Figure 4-2 shows the distance-time graph for two airplanes. One is traveling at 100 m/s while the other is traveling at 200 m/s. The slope of the line representing the faster plane is steeper than the slope of the line representing the slower plane. A steeper slope indicates that an object is traveling a greater distance per unit time. For any distance-time graph, the steepest slope corresponds to the fastest speed.

*A steep slope for a distance-time graph indicates a high speed.*

## 4:3   Distance-Time Graph for a Complete Trip

The distance-time graph in Figure 4-3 represents a short car trip. During the first 10 seconds, a car travels a distance of 200 meters from its point of origin. Thus, the speed of the car for the entire 10 seconds is

$$\text{slope} = \frac{\Delta s}{\Delta t} = \frac{200 \text{ m}}{10 \text{ s}} = 20 \text{ m/s}$$

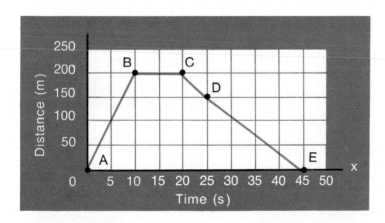

FIGURE 4-3. A distance-time graph for an object traveling at changing speed.

Between points $B$ and $C$, the car is at rest. Its distance from its point of origin does not change. Since $\Delta s = 0$, the slope $\Delta s/\Delta t$ must also be zero. Thus, the speed of the car between the tenth and twentieth seconds of the trip is zero.

*When the slope of a distance-time graph is zero, the object is at rest.*

Between points $C$ and $D$, the distance of the car from the point of origin decreases. Thus, $\Delta s$ is negative. Therefore, the slope $\Delta s/\Delta t$, is also negative. A negative slope indicates the car is traveling in a direction opposite to its original direction. Between points $C$ and $D$, the actual slope is

$$\text{slope} = \frac{\Delta s}{\Delta t} = \frac{-50 \text{ m}}{5 \text{ s}} = -10 \text{ m/s}$$

*A negative slope for a distance-time graph shows that an object is moving in a direction opposite to its original direction.*

At point *D*, the speed of the car decreases and the slope of the line is less steep thereafter. Between points *D* and *E* the actual slope is

$$\text{slope} = \frac{\Delta s}{\Delta t} = \frac{-150 \text{ m}}{20 \text{ s}} = -7.5 \text{ m/s}$$

Note that at point *E* the car is back at its origin.

Suppose the line of the graph extended below the *x* axis. This would indicate that the car had passed its point of origin and was moving in a direction opposite to that of its motion during the first 10 seconds of the trip.

## 4:4  Speed-Time Graph for Constant Speed

Consider a plane flying at a constant speed of 60 m/s. Figure 4-4 plots its speed against the time of travel. Since the speed is constant, every point on the line has the same vertical position. Therefore, the line through these points is parallel to the *x* axis. The slope of the line in this case is equal to zero. Speed is not changing with time which means there is no acceleration.

> The speed-time graph for constant speed is a line parallel to the *x* axis.

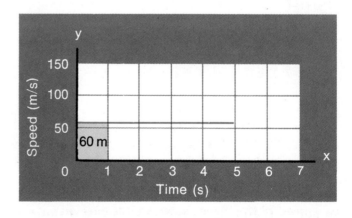

**FIGURE 4-4. The speed-time graph for an object moving with constant speed.**

A speed-time graph is useful because the area between the curve and the *x* axis represents the distance, *s*, traveled by the object. For example, notice the shaded area under the line in Figure 4-4. The vertical side of this area is the speed, $v = 60$ m/s. The horizontal side is the time, $t = 1$ second. The area of this box is $vt$, or 60 meters. This distance, 60 meters, is the distance the plane travels in 1 second.

> The area under a speed-time graph represents distance.

At the end of 3 seconds, the area under the line would be $vt = 60$ m/s $\times$ 3 s $= 180$ m. The area under the curve of a speed-time graph represents distance.

## PROBLEMS

**1.** A plane flies in a straight line with a constant speed of 50 m/s.

**a.** Construct a table showing the total distance the plane travels at the end of each second for a 20-s period.

**b.** Use the data from the table to plot a distance-time graph.

**c.** Show that the slope of the line gives the speed of the plane. Use at least two different sets of points along the graph.

**d.** Plot a speed-time graph of the plane's motion for the first 12 s of the 20-s interval.

**e.** Find the distance the plane travels between the eighth and eleventh seconds.

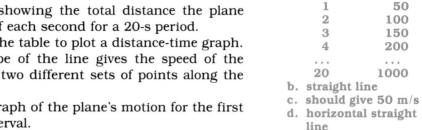

1. a.
| $t$ (s) | $s$ (m) |
|---|---|
| 0 | 0 |
| 1 | 50 |
| 2 | 100 |
| 3 | 150 |
| 4 | 200 |
| ... | ... |
| 20 | 1000 |

b. straight line
c. should give 50 m/s
d. horizontal straight line
e. 150 m

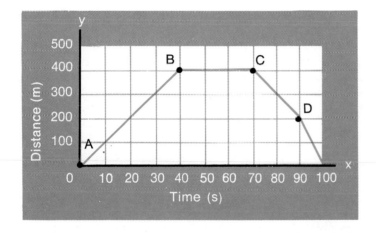

**2.** Use the distance-time graph in Figure 4-5 to find

**a.** how far the object travels between $t = 0$ s and $t = 40$ s.

**b.** how far it travels between $t = 40$ s and $t = 70$ s.

**c.** how far it travels between $t = 90$ s and $t = 100$ s.

**3.** Use Figure 4-5 to find

**a.** the speed of the object during the first 40 s.

**b.** the speed of the object between $t = 40$ s and $t = 70$ s.

**c.** the speed of the object between $t = 70$ s and $t = 90$ s.

**d.** the speed of the object between $t = 90$ s and $t = 100$ s.

**4.** If the slope of the line between points $A$ and $B$ in Figure 4-5 is positive, what is true of the slope of the line between points $C$ and $D$?

**5.** Use the distance-time graph, Figure 4-5, to construct a table showing the speed of the plane during each 10-s interval over the entire 100 s.

**6.** As a solution to Problem 5, plot a speed-time graph using the table you constructed.

FIGURE 4-5. Use this graph for Problems 2, 3, 4, and 5.

3. a. 10 m/s
b. 0 m/s
c. 10 m/s
d. 20 m/s

5.
| $t$ (s) | $v$ (m/s) |
|---|---|
| 0 | 0 |
| 10 | 10 |
| 20 | 10 |
| 30 | 10 |
| 40 | 10 |
| 50 | 0 |
| 60 | 0 |
| 70 | 0 |
| 80 | −10 |
| 90 | −10 |
| 100 | −20 |

7. a. straight line

   b. $\dfrac{\Delta y}{\Delta x}$ = 40 m/s

   c. horizontal straight line—The area under the line is $vt$ and thus represents total distance traveled during a given time interval.

   d. 40 m, the distance traveled during one second.

**7.** A car moves along a straight road at a constant speed of 40 m/s.

   **a.** Plot its distance-time graph for a 10-s interval.

   **b.** Find the slope of the graph using two different points along the line.

   **c.** Plot a speed-time graph for the car. What does the area under the line of the graph represent?

   **d.** Calculate the area under the line of the graph between the fifth and sixth seconds. What does this area represent?

## 4:5  Speed-Time Graph for Uniform Acceleration

The speed-time graph of constant acceleration is a straight line which passes through the origin.

Consider a jet plane that starts from rest on a runway. It is accelerated uniformly at the rate of 20 m/s². Table 4-2 shows the speeds of the plane over 5 seconds. Figure 4-6 is a plot of these speeds against time. This speed-time graph for uniformly accelerated motion is a straight line passing through the origin. During uniform acceleration, the speed varies directly with time.

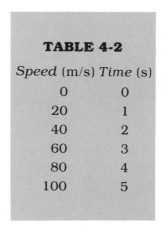

| TABLE 4-2 | |
| --- | --- |
| *Speed* (m/s) | *Time* (s) |
| 0 | 0 |
| 20 | 1 |
| 40 | 2 |
| 60 | 3 |
| 80 | 4 |
| 100 | 5 |

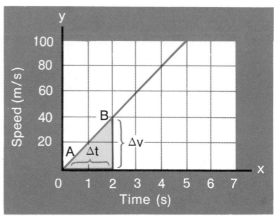

**FIGURE 4-6. A speed-time graph for uniformly accelerated motion.**

The slope of a speed-time graph represents acceleration.

For uniform acceleration, the slope of a speed-time graph is constant along its entire length. Note that the slope gives the acceleration of the object. Between points $A$ and $B$

$$\text{slope} = \frac{\text{rise}}{\text{run}} = \frac{\Delta v}{\Delta t} = \frac{40 \text{ m/s}}{2 \text{ s}} = 20 \text{ m/s}^2$$

The acceleration of any object is the slope of its speed-time graph.

In Section 4:4 you found that, for an object moving with constant speed, the area under the curve gives the distance the object travels. This is also true of an object undergoing uniform acceleration. In fact, the area under any speed-time curve gives distance regardless of the type of motion.

Look at the shaded area under the line between points A and B. Consider the entire rectangle of which the shaded area is half. The vertical limit of the rectangle is the speed of 40 m/s. This limit is the speed attained by the jet plane when it is accelerated at the rate of 20 m/s$^2$ for 2 seconds. So $v$ can be expressed in terms of acceleration and time, or $v = at$. Thus, the vertical side of the rectangle equals $at$. The horizontal limit of the rectangle is the time, 2 seconds. The area of the rectangle is its vertical side multiplied by its horizontal side, or $at \times t = at^2$. However, the area under the line is half this, or $at^2/2$. This triangular area is the distance an accelerating object covers when starting from rest (Section 3:5).

## 4:6    Distance-Time Graph for Uniform Acceleration

Now let us plot a distance-time graph for the jet plane discussed in Section 4:5. The total distance the plane has traveled at the end of each section can be found in two ways. It can be calculated with the equation

$$s = at^2/2$$

It can also be found by determining the area under the speed-time curve of Figure 4-6. The results are given in Table 4-3. The data from Table 4-3 is used to plot a distance-time graph, Figure 4-7.

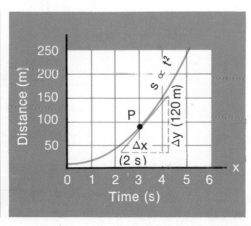

**TABLE 4-3**

| Time (s) | Distance (m) |
|----------|--------------|
| 0 | 0 |
| 1 | 10 |
| 2 | 40 |
| 3 | 90 |
| 4 | 160 |
| 5 | 250 |

**FIGURE 4-7.** A distance-time graph for uniformly accelerated motion.

The distance-time graph for uniform acceleration is a half-parabola (*s* varies directly with $t^2$).

The curve in the distance-time graph is half a parabola. A parabola always shows that one quantity varies directly with the square of the other. In this case, the distance traveled by the accelerating object varies directly with the square of time.

The slope of any distance-time graph yields the speed. When the speed is constant, the distance-time graph is a straight line. Figure 4-1 shows how to find the slope of the line. However, when an object is accelerating, it travels a greater distance each second than it did the second before. The steepness of the curve constantly increases. The resulting smooth curve is a parabola. The slope of this curve is more difficult to find than the slope of a straight line. Often it is found by drawing a tangent to the curve at the point where the slope is wanted. The slope of the tangent gives the instantaneous speed at the point on the curve that the tangent touches. In Figure 4-7, a tangent is drawn at point *P*. The slope of the tangent at this point is

The slope of a parabola can be found by drawing a tangent to the curve at the point where the speed is desired.

$$\frac{\Delta s}{\Delta t} = \frac{150 \text{ m} - 30 \text{ m}}{4 \text{ s} - 2 \text{ s}} = \frac{120 \text{ m}}{2 \text{ s}} = 60 \text{ m/s}$$

Point *P* coincides with the end of 3 seconds of travel. The speed to expect at the end of 3 seconds for an object which accelerates at the rate of 20 m/s$^2$ from rest is 60 m/s. Note also that it is the speed shown on the speed-time graph for the same object after 3 seconds.

## 4:7  Acceleration-Time Graph for Uniform Acceleration

The acceleration-time graph for uniform acceleration is a line parallel to the *x* axis.

Acceleration that does not change with time is called uniform acceleration. If the acceleration is constant, an acceleration-time graph is a line parallel to the *x* axis.

In Figure 4-8, the acceleration of the jet plane of Section 4:5 is plotted against time. As expected, the acceleration-time line is a straight line parallel to the *x* axis.

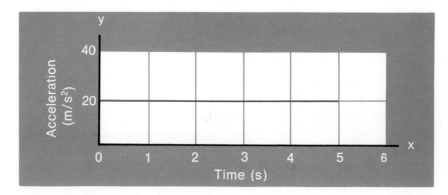

FIGURE 4-8. An acceleration-time graph for uniformly accelerated motion.

Notice that the area under the line of the acceleration-time graph represents the speed of the plane. At any point along the $x$ axis, the area under the line is a rectangle with sides $a$ and $t$. Therefore, the area of the rectangle is $at$. Since $v = at$, the area gives the speed. For example, at the end of 3 seconds the speed of the car is $3 \text{ s} \times 20 \text{ m/s}^2$, or 60 m/s.

The area under an acceleration-time graph represents velocity.

**Summary**

1. Many graphs have characteristic shapes. From these shapes certain relationships can often be recognized. **Intro.**

2. The distance-time graph for an object moving with constant speed is a straight line that may pass through the origin. **4:1**

3. The slope of a distance-time graph is equal to the speed of the object. **4:2**

4. If the distance-time graph is parallel to the $x$ axis, the slope is zero. A zero slope indicates zero speed. **4:3**

5. For an object moving at a constant speed, the speed-time graph is a line parallel with the $x$ axis. The area under the line represents distance. **4:4**

6. The speed-time graph for uniformly accelerated motion is a straight line passing through the origin. This straight line indicates that speed varies directly with time. The slope of the line, $\Delta v/\Delta t$, is equal to the acceleration. The area under the line represents distance and corresponds to $at^2/2$. **4:5**

7. In a distance-time graph for uniformly accelerated motion, the curve is a half parabola. This curve indicates that distance varies with the square of time. The slope of a tangent to the curve at any point yields instantaneous speed. **4:6**

8. When uniform acceleration is plotted against time, the acceleration-time line is a straight line parallel with the $x$ axis. The area under the line represents the speed of the accelerating object. **4:7**

**Questions**

1. Define the slope of a graph.
2. What does the slope of a distance-time graph indicate?
3. What quantity is represented by the area under a speed-time graph?
4. What does the slope of a speed-time graph indicate?
5. If a speed-time curve is a straight line parallel to the $x$ axis, what can be said about the acceleration?
6. What quantity can be found by determining the area under an acceleration-time curve?

**Problems**

1. The speed of an automobile changes over an 8-s time period as shown in Table 4-4 below.
   **a.** Plot the speed-time graph of the motion.
   **b.** Determine the distance the car travels during the first 2 s.
   **c.** What distance does the car travel during the first 4 s?
   **d.** What distance does the car travel during the entire 8 s?
   **e.** Find the slope of the line between $t = 0$ s and $t = 4$ s. What does this slope represent?
   **f.** Find the slope of the line between $t = 5$ s and $t = 7$ s. What does this slope represent?

| TABLE 4-4 | | | |
|---|---|---|---|
| *Time* (s) | *Speed* (m/s) | *Time* (s) | *Speed* (m/s) |
| 0 | 0 | 5 | 20 |
| 1 | 4 | 6 | 20 |
| 2 | 8 | 7 | 20 |
| 3 | 12 | 8 | 20 |
| 4 | 16 | | |

| TABLE 4-5 | |
|---|---|
| *Time* (s) | *Distance* (m) |
| 0 | 0 |
| 1 | 2 |
| 2 | 8 |
| 3 | 18 |
| 4 | 32 |
| 5 | 50 |

2. The total distance a steel ball rolls down an incline at the end of each second of travel is given in Table 4-5 above.
   **a.** Make a distance-time graph of the motion of the ball. When setting up the axes use five divisions for each 10 m of travel on the *y* axis. Use five divisions for each second of time on the *x* axis.
   **b.** What type of curve is the line of the graph?
   **c.** What distance has the ball rolled at the end of 2.2 s?
   **d.** Find the slope of the line at $t = 3$ s. What does this slope show?

3. Use Figure 4-9 to find the acceleration of the moving object
   **a.** during the first 5 s of travel.
   **b.** during the second 5 s of travel.
   **c.** between the tenth and the fifteenth s of travel.
   **d.** between the twentieth and twenty-fifth s of travel.

**FIGURE 4-9. Use with Problems 3 and 4.**    **FIGURE 4-10. Use with Problem 5**

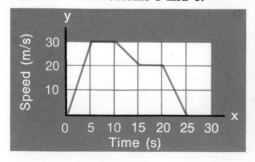

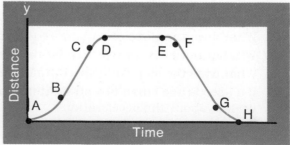

4. Refer to Figure 4-9 to find the distance the moving object travels
   a. between $t = 0$ and $t = 5$ s.
   b. between $t = 5$ s and $t = 10$ s.
   c. between $t = 10$ s and $t = 15$ s.
   d. between $t = 0$ and $t = 25$ s.

5. Use the intervals marked on the graph in Figure 4-10 to describe the entire trip of the moving object.

6. Make a table of the speeds of an object, m/s, at the end of each sec-/ ond for the first 5 s of free-fall from rest.
   a. Use the data in your table to plot a speed-time graph.
   b. What does the total area under the graph represent?

7. a. Compute the total distance the object in Problem 6 travels at the end of each second for the first 5 s of the free-fall.
   b. Use the distances calculated in Part $a$ to plot a distance-time graph.
   c. Find the slope of the curve at the end of 2 and 4 s. What are the approximate slopes? Do these values agree with the table of speeds in Problem 6?

8. Use the data prepared in Problem 7 to plot the distance versus time squared.
   a. What kind of curve is obtained?
   b. Does this agree with the equation $s = at^2/2$?
   c. Find the slope of the curve at any point. Explain the significance of the value you obtain.

**FIGURE 4-11.**   **FIGURE 4-12.**   **FIGURE 4-13.**   **FIGURE 4-14.**   **FIGURE 4-15.**

9. Look at Figure 4-11.
   a. What kind of motion does this graph represent?
   b. What does the slope of the graph represent?

10. Look at Figure 4-12.
    a. What kind of motion does this graph represent?
    b. What does the area under the line of the graph represent?

11. Look at Figure 4-13.
    a. What kind of motion does this graph represent?
    b. What does the slope of the line represent?
    c. What does the area under the line represent?

12. Look at Figure 4-14. What does the area under the line of this graph represent?

13. Look at Figure 4-15.
    a. What type of curve does this graph represent?

**b.** What does the slope of the line taken at any point represent?

**c.** How would slopes taken at higher points on the line differ from those taken at lower points?

| Applying Physics |
|---|

**1.** *Graphs Based on Graphs:* To accompany each of the graphs shown below draw

**a.** a speed-time graph.

**b.** an acceleration-time graph.

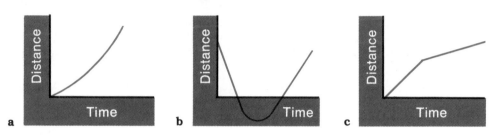

**FIGURE 4-16. Use with Applying Physics 1.**

**2.** *The Amtrak Express vs the Local:* Somehow the Amtrak Express, traveling at 36 m/s, is accidentally sidetracked onto a local train track. The Amtrak engineer spots a local train 100 m ahead on the same track and traveling in the same direction. He jams on the brakes and slows the express at a rate of 3.0 m/s². The engineer of the local is unaware of the situation. If the speed of the local is 11 m/s will the express be able to stop in time or will there be a collision? To solve this problem take the position of the express when it first sights the local as a point of origin. Next, keeping in mind that the local has a 100 m lead, calculate how far each train is from this point at the end of the twelve seconds it would take the express to stop.

**a.** On the basis of your calculations would you conclude that there is or is not a collision?

**b.** The calculations you made in Part *a* do not allow for the possibility that a collision might take place before the end of the twelve seconds required for the express to come to a halt. To check on this take the position of the express when it first sights the local as the point of origin and calculate the position of each train at the end of each second after sighting. The local will always be $100 + (11\ t)$ meters from the origin while the express will be

$$\frac{v_f + v_o}{2} \times t \text{ meters from the origin.}$$

Make a table showing the distance of each train from the origin at the end of each second. Plot these positions on the same graph and draw two lines. If they intersect a collision must occur.

**FIGURE 4-17.**

Chester, Michael, *Relativity, an Introduction for Young Readers.* New York, W. W. Norton Co., Inc., 1967.

Drake, Stillman, "Galileo's Discovery of the Law of Free Fall." *Scientific American,* May, 1973.

Engel, Kenneth, "Shadows of the 4th Dimension." *Science 80,* July/August, 1979.

**Readings**

The motion associated with a tennis serve is quite complex. However, it is possible to break this complex motion into a few simple parts through the use of computers. The movement of each body segment is a component of the total serve. An analysis of these simple movements can show whether or not the server is moving properly to direct the maximum amount of force on the ball. Force is considered a vector quantity. How are vectors related to the motion of the tennis player? How are vectors related to your activities?

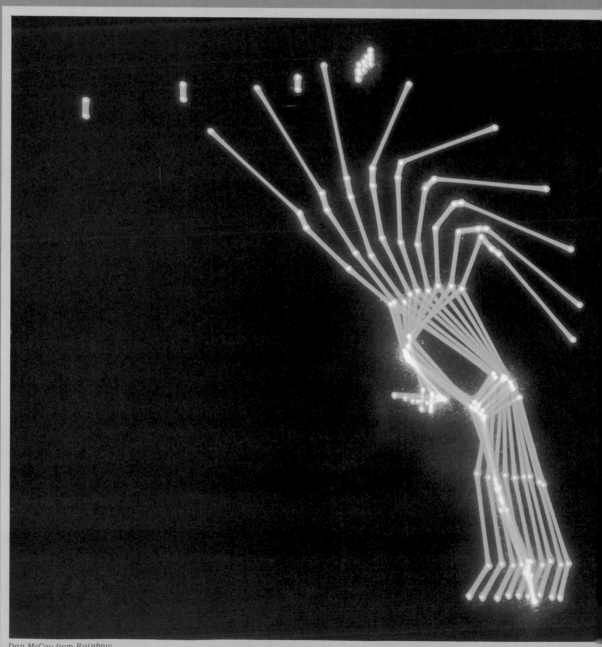

# Vectors 5

You already deal with scalar quantities. For example, you know that twelve dollars plus twelve dollars is twenty-four dollars. Scalar quantities are not affected by anything other than their magnitudes or sizes.

Vector quantities are entirely different from scalar quantities. A vector quantity has both size and direction. The sum of two vector quantities depends as much on their directions as their sizes. The sum of a twelve-newton force plus a twelve-newton force can equal values from zero to twenty-four newtons.

In physics we often deal with vector quantities as well as scalar quantities. An understanding of both is fundamental to an understanding of the basic principles of physics.

**GOAL: You will gain knowledge and understanding of the meaning and use of vector algebra needed to solve vector physics problems.**

## 5:1 Vector Quantities

A **scalar** quantity is completely described by its magnitude. The **magnitude** is made of a number and an appropriate unit. Mass, volume, and distance are scalar quantities. Examples of these scalar quantities are 10 grams, 12 liters, and 15 kilometers. A **vector** quantity is characterized by both magnitude and direction. Force is a vector quantity because a force must always act in some direction. A force is described completely only when both its magnitude and direction are stated. Other vector quantities are velocity and momentum.

Scalar quantities have magnitude only.

Vector quantities have both magnitude and direction.

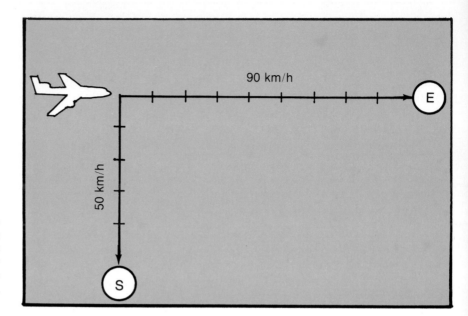

**FIGURE 5-1. The magnitudes and directions of the two velocities shown can be added to produce a vector sum. The vector sum shows the resulting velocity and direction.**

Scalars are added algebraically.

Scalar quantities are added according to the rules of ordinary arithmetic. Thus, 2 liters plus 2 liters is 4 liters. However, the sum of two vector quantities depends on their directions as well as their magnitudes. Consider a plane that is flying due east at 90 km/h and at the same time is being blown south by the wind at 50 km/h. The plane has two velocities but they cannot be added algebraically. The plane is not flying with a velocity of 140 km/h. Nor is its direction east or south. The magnitudes and directions of the two velocities produce a vector sum that must be determined by a process called vector addition.

Vectors are added graphically by vector addition.

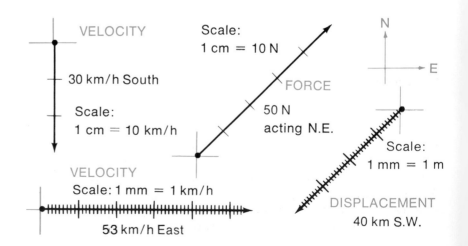

**FIGURE 5-2. A vector is an arrow-tipped line segment showing magnitude and direction.**

# 5:2  Vector Addition—Graphical Method

A vector quantity can be represented by an arrow-tipped line segment. A vector may be represented using a symbol such as $\vec{a}$. The length of the arrow drawn to scale represents the magnitude of the quantity. The direction of the arrow represents the direction of the quantity. This arrow-tipped line segment is a vector. Figure 5-2 shows some typical vectors.

A vector quantity can be shown as an arrow tipped line (length indicates magnitude; arrow indicates vector direction).

The sum of any two vectors can be found graphically. In Figure 5-3, $\vec{a}$ and $\vec{b}$ represent the two velocities of the plane flying east at 90 km/h and being blown south at 50 km/h. The vectors are added by placing the tail of one vector at the head of the other vector. Neither the direction nor the length of either vector is changed. A third vector is drawn connecting the tail of the first vector to the head of the second vector. This vector represents the sum of the two vectors. This third vector is called the **resultant** of $\vec{a}$ and $\vec{b}$. The resultant is always drawn from the tail of the first vector to the head of the second vector. To find the magnitude of the resultant, measure its length and evaluate it according to the same scale used to draw $\vec{a}$ and $\vec{b}$. Its direction is found by using a protractor. In Figure 5-3, the resultant velocity is 103 km/h in the direction 29° south of east.

In adding two vectors, place the tail of one vector at the head of the other vector.

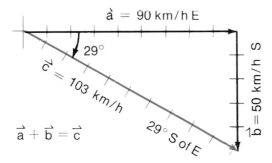

$$\vec{a} = 90 \text{ km/h E}$$

29°

$$\vec{c} = 103 \text{ km/h}$$

$$\vec{b} = 50 \text{ km/h S}$$

$$\vec{a} + \vec{b} = \vec{c}$$

29° S of E

Scale: 1 division = 10 km/h

In adding two vectors, a third vector is drawn from tail of the first to the head of the second. This vector, the resultant, gives the sum of the two vectors.

**FIGURE       5-3.       Vector addition.**

In both algebraic addition and vector addition, the order of addition is of no consequence. The tail of $\vec{a}$ could have been placed at the head of $\vec{b}$. Figure 5-4 shows that the same sum would result. Note that in both cases the vectors are added head to tail and their directions are not changed.

When two vector quantities act in the same or in opposite directions, their numerical sum is the same as their algebraic sum. That is, if a plane flies at 90 km/h due east and the wind blows it along at 50 km/h due east, its velocity is

Regardless of the order in which vectors are added, the sum will be the same.

$$90 \text{ km/h} + 50 \text{ km/h} = 140 \text{ km/h due east}$$

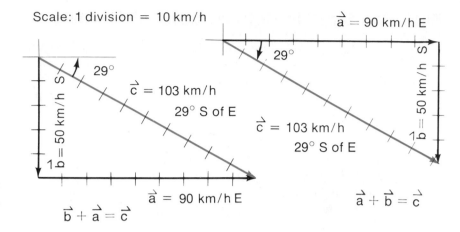

Scale: 1 division = 10 km/h

**FIGURE 5-4.** The vector sum of $\vec{b}$ + $\vec{a}$ is the same as the vector sum of $\vec{a}$ + $\vec{b}$.

**FIGURE 5-5.** When two vectors act in the same or opposite directions, their resultant is numerically just the algebraic sum of the two.

If the wind is blowing due west and the plane must fly directly into it, the plane's velocity is

90 km/h + (−50 km/h) = 40 km/h east

A negative sign is placed in front of 50 km/h to show that this velocity is opposite in direction to the 90 km/h velocity.

Scale: 1 division = 10 km/h

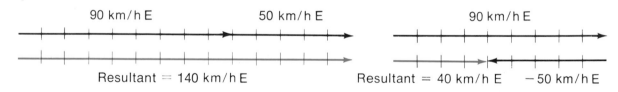

## 5:3  Distance and Displacement

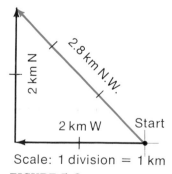

Scale: 1 division = 1 km

**FIGURE 5-6.**

Distance is a scalar quantity; displacement is a vector quantity.

Distance and displacement are not the same. **Distance** is a scalar quantity. **Displacement** is a vector quantity. Suppose you leave your home one morning to take a walk. If you walk 2 kilometers due west and then turn and walk 2 kilometers due north, you will have walked a total distance of 4 kilometers. Looking at Figure 5-6 you will not be 4 kilometers from your home. Instead, you will be a little over 2.8 kilometers northwest of your home. The distance is the scalar sum of the actual paths traveled. In this case, the distance is 4 kilometers. Displacement is a vector quantity and so is quite different from distance. Figure 5-6 treats the walk as two displacements, one of 2 kilometers west and one of 2 kilometers north. These are vectors. The resultant displacement is their vector sum which is 2.8 kilometers north of west. Note that by keeping track of a moving body's displacements it is possible to know its position in relation to the origin at all times.

*John Morgan*

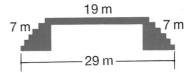

**FIGURE 5-7.** The total distance a person walks in crossing this freeway by way of the foot bridge is 33 meters. The displacement of the person from stairway to stairway is 29 meters directly across the freeway.

## 5:4   Speed and Velocity

The **speed** of a moving object is the distance it travels per unit time. Speed is stated in kilometers per hour or meters per second. The direction is not stated. Speed is a scalar quantity.

The **velocity** of a moving object is the distance it travels per unit time in a given direction. Note that in stating the velocity, both magnitude and direction are given. Velocity is a vector quantity. Speed is merely the magnitude of a velocity vector.

Speed is a scalar quantity; velocity is a vector quantity.

## 5:5   Independence of Vector Quantities

Vectors act independently. Consider a motorboat that heads due east at 8 m/s across a river flowing due south at 5 m/s. The boat will travel 8 meters due east in one second. It will also travel 5 meters due south in the same second. The southerly velocity cannot change the easterly velocity. Neither can the easterly velocity change the southerly velocity. Each velocity is independent of the other and acts as if it were the only velocity. This concept is known as the independence of velocities. All vector quantities behave in this way.

Vectors act independently.

**FIGURE 5-8. A boat traveling 9.4 m/s in the direction 32° south of east can also be described as traveling both east at 8 m/s and south at 5 m/s at the same time.**

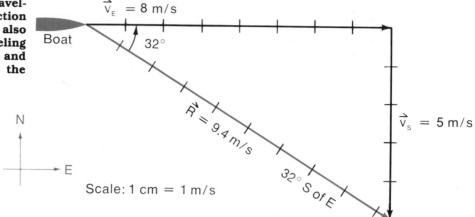

In Figure 5-8, the two velocities of the boat are represented by vectors. When these vectors are added, the resultant velocity is 9.4 m/s in the direction 32° south of east. In one second, this resultant velocity will carry the motorboat 8 meters due east and 5 meters due south. You can think of the boat as traveling east at 8 m/s and south at 5 m/s at the same time. You can also think of it as traveling 9.4 m/s in the direction 32° south of east. Both statements have the same meaning.

Suppose that the river being crossed by the boat is 80 meters wide. Since the boat's velocity is 8 m/s at all times, it will take the boat 10 seconds to cross the river. The boat will also be carried 50 meters downstream during this 10 seconds. However, in no way does the downstream velocity change the river-crossing velocity.

## 5:6  Vector Addition of Forces

**Concurrent forces act on the same point at the same time.**

Force vectors are added in the same ways as velocity vectors. Forces which act on the same point at the same time are called **concurrent forces.** The unit of force is the newton (N).

### EXAMPLE:  Vector Addition of Forces

In Figure 5-9, a force of 40 N and a force of 60 N act concurrently on point P. The 60-N force acts in the direction due east. The 40-N force acts in the direction of 60° north of east. What is the magnitude and direction of their resultant?
*Solution:*
The sum of two forces is $\vec{c}$ found by moving $\vec{a}$ parallel to itself until the tail of $\vec{a}$ is located at the head of $\vec{b}$. The resultant is then drawn and interpreted in terms of the scale used. Note that the resultant is drawn from the tail of the first vector to the head of the second vector.

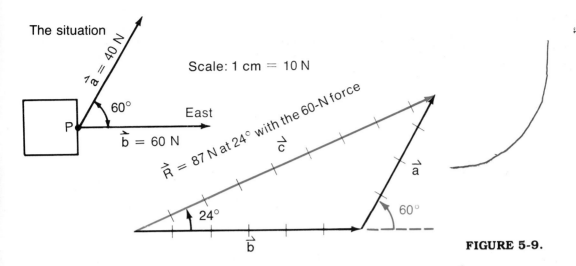

The situation

Scale: 1 cm = 10 N

FIGURE 5-9.

## PROBLEMS

*Draw vector diagrams to solve each problem.*

1. A plane flying due north at 100 m/s is blown due west at 50 m/s by a strong wind. Find the plane's resultant velocity.

2. A hiker leaves camp and walks 10 km due north. The hiker then walks 10 km due east.
   a. What is the total distance walked by the hiker?
   b. Determine the total displacement from the starting point.

3. A motorboat heads due east at 16 m/s across a river that flows due south at 9 m/s.
   a. What is the resultant velocity (speed and direction) of the boat?
   b. If the river is 136 m wide, how long does it take the motorboat to reach the other side?
   c. How far downstream is the boat when it reaches the other side of the river?

4. An airplane flies due west at 120 km/h. At the same time, the wind blows it due north at 40 km/h. What is the plane's resultant velocity?

5. A salesperson leaves the office and drives 26 km due north along a straight highway. A turn is made onto a highway that leads in a direction 30° north of east. The driver continues on the highway for a distance of 62 km and then stops. What is the total displacement of the salesperson from the office?

6. Two soccer players kick the ball at exactly the same time. One player's foot exerts a force of 60 N north. The other's foot exerts a force of 80 N east. What is the magnitude and direction of the resultant force on the ball?

1. 110 m/s, 27° west of north

3. a. 18 m/s, 29° south of east
   b. 8.5 s
   c. 77 m

5. 78 km, 43° east of north

**7. a.** 120 N
   **b.** 115 N
   **c.** 104 N
   **d.** 85 N
   **e.** 0 N

**9.** 16 m/s², 67°

**11.** 210 km/h, 14° east
of north

**7.** Two forces of 60 N each act concurrently on a point *P*. Determine the magnitude of the resultant force acting on point P when the angle between the forces is as follows:
   **a.** 0°    **b.** 30°    **c.** 60°    **d.** 90°    **e.** 180°

**8.** In Problem 7, what happens to the resultant of two forces as the angle between them increases?

**9.** A weather team releases a weather balloon. The balloon's buoyancy accelerates it straight up at 15 m/s². A wind accelerates it horizontally at 6.5 m/s². What is the magnitude and direction (with reference to the horizontal) of the resultant acceleration?

**10.** What is the vector sum of a 65-N force acting due east and a 30-N force acting due west?

**11.** A plane flies due north at 200 km/h. A wind blows it due east at 50 km/h. What is the magnitude and direction of the plane's resultant velocity?

**12.** A meteoroid passes between the moon and the earth. A gravitational force of 600 N pulls the meteoroid toward the moon. At the same time, a gravitational force of 480 N pulls it toward the earth. The angle between the two forces is 130°. The moon's force acts perpendicularly to the meteoroid's original path. What is the resultant magnitude and direction of the force acting on the meteoroid? State the direction in reference to the meteoroid's original path. (The diagram below is not a vector diagram. It is intended to show direction only.)

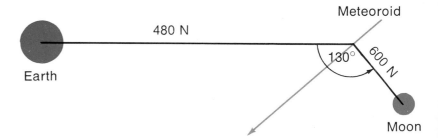

**FIGURE 5-10. Use with Problem 12.**

## 5:7   Vector Addition—Mathematical Methods

The vector sum of any two vectors can be determined mathematically as well as graphically. If two vectors are perpendicular, a right triangle is formed when the tail of one vector is placed at the head of the second vector. The magnitude of their resultant is found using the Pythagorean (puh thag uh REE uhn) theorem.

The Pythagorean theorem can be used to find the length of the third side of a right triangle.

$$c^2 = a^2 + b^2$$

The direction of the resultant is found using the definition of tangent.

$$\tan \theta = \frac{\text{opposite side}}{\text{adjacent side}}$$

### EXAMPLE: Using Pythagorean Theorem and Tangent to Find a Resultant Vector

Again, consider the airplane that is flying due east at 90 km/h and is being blown due south at 50 km/h, Figure 5-11. In what direction and at what speed is the airplane actually flying?

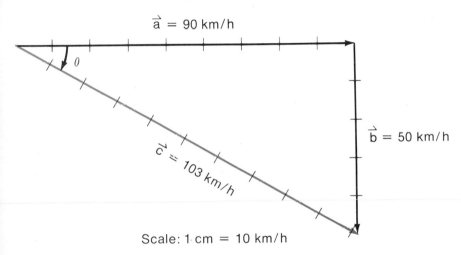

$\vec{a}$ = 90 km/h

$\theta$

$\vec{c} \approx 103$ km/h

$\vec{b}$ = 50 km/h

Scale: 1 cm = 10 km/h

**FIGURE 5-11.**

*Solution:*

$$c^2 = a^2 + b^2$$
$$c = \sqrt{(90 \text{ km/h})^2 + (50 \text{ km/h})^2}$$
$$= \sqrt{10\,600} \text{ km/h}$$
$$= 103 \text{ km/h}$$

To find the direction of the resultant, find the tangent of the angle $\theta$.

$$\tan \theta = \frac{\text{opposite side}}{\text{adjacent side}}$$
$$= \frac{50 \text{ km/h}}{90 \text{ km/h}}$$
$$= 0.556$$

Table B-1 in the Appendix shows that 0.556 is the tangent of 29°. Therefore, the angle $\theta$ is 29°. The resultant is described as 103 km/h at 29° south of east.

When two vectors do not act at a right angle, the magnitude and direction of the resultant is determined by use of the law of cosines or the law of sines (Sections 1:7 and 1:8).

The law of cosines and the law of sines can be used to find the third side of any triangle.

**EXAMPLE: Vector Addition of Nonperpendicular Forces**

A force of 40 N and a force of 60 N act concurrently on a point P. The 60-N force acts in the direction of due east. The 40-N force acts in the direction 60° north of east. What is the magnitude and direction of their resultant?

The situation

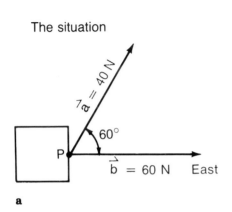

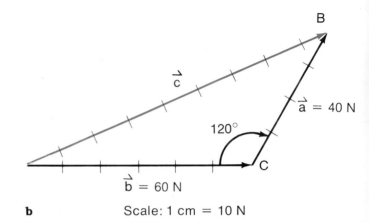

**a**

**b**        Scale: 1 cm = 10 N

**FIGURE 5-12.**

*Solution:*

To determine the magnitude of $\vec{c}$, use the law of cosines.

$$c^2 = a^2 + b^2 - 2ab \cos C$$
$$= (40 \text{ N})^2 + (60 \text{ N})^2 - 2(40 \text{ N})(60 \text{ N})(-0.50)$$

**Remember when C > 90°, the cosine is negative and numerically equal to its supplement**

$$c = \sqrt{1600 \text{ N} + 3600 \text{ N} + 2400 \text{ N}}$$
$$= \sqrt{7600} \text{ N}$$
$$= 87 \text{ N}$$

To determine the direction of $\vec{c}$, use the law of sines to find the angle A.

$$\frac{a}{\sin A} = \frac{c}{\sin C}$$

$$\sin A = \frac{(a)(\sin C)}{c}$$
$$= \frac{(40 \text{ N})(0.866)}{87 \text{ N}}$$
$$= 0.398$$

Using Table B-1 in the Appendix, Angle $A = 23°$. Thus, the direction of $\vec{c}$ is 23° north of east.

## PROBLEMS

*Solve each problem graphically or mathematically depending upon your instructor's directions.*

**13.** A 100-N force and a 50-N force act on point *P*. The 100-N force acts due north. The 50-N force acts due east. What is the magnitude and direction of the resultant force?

**14.** A motorboat travels at 40 m/s. It heads straight across a river 320 m wide.
   **a.** If the water flows at the rate of 8.0 m/s, what is the boat's velocity with respect to the shore?
   **b.** How long does it take the boat to reach the opposite shore?

**15.** A boat heads directly across a river 40 m wide at 8.0 m/s. The current is flowing at 3.8 m/s.
   **a.** What is the resultant velocity of the boat?
   **b.** How long does it take the boat to cross the river?
   **c.** How far downstream is the boat when it reaches the other side?

**16.** An airplane flies at 150 km/h and heads 30° south of east. A 50 km/h wind blows in the direction 25° west of south. What is the resultant velocity of the plane with respect to the compass points of the earth?

**17.** Two 10-N forces act concurrently on point *P*. Find the magnitude of their resultant when the angle between them is
   **a.** 0°    **b.** 30°    **c.** 90°    **d.** 120°    **e.** 180°

**18.** A boat travels at 8.0 m/s and heads straight across a river 240 m wide. The river flows at 4.0 m/s.
   **a.** What is the boat's resultant speed with respect to the riverbank?
   **b.** How long does it take the boat to cross the river?
   **c.** How far downstream is the boat when it reaches the other side?

**19.** Determine the magnitude of the resultant of a 40-N force and a 70-N force acting concurrently when the angle between them is
   **a.** 0°    **b.** 30°    **c.** 60°    **d.** 90°    **e.** 180°

13. 110 N, 27° east of north

15. a. 8.9 m/s, 25° downstream
    b. 5 s
    c. 19 m

17. a. 20 N
    b. 19 N
    c. 14 N
    d. 10 N
    e. 0 N

19. a. 110 N
    b. 110 N
    c. 96 N
    d. 81 N
    e. 30 N

# 5:8  Addition of Several Vectors

Often three or more forces act concurrently on the same point. To determine the resultant of three or more vectors, follow the same procedure you use to add two vectors. Place the vectors head-to-tail. The order of addition is not important. In Figure 5-13a, the three forces $\vec{a}$, $\vec{b}$, and $\vec{c}$, act concurrently on point *P*. In Figure 5-13b and c, the vectors are added graphically. Note

The same procedure is always used regardless of the number of vectors to be added.

The order of vector addition is unimportant.

**a**

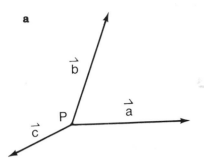

**b**

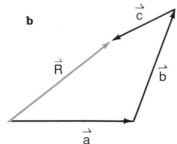

**c**

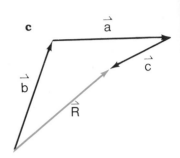

**FIGURE 5-13.** In (a) the three forces act concurrently on point P. In (b) and (c) the vectors are added graphically. The resultant is the same in both diagrams.

that the resultant is the same in both parts although two different orders of addition are used. In placing the vectors head-to-tail, their directions must be maintained.

## 5:9  Equilibrium

When two or more forces act concurrently on an object and their vector sum is zero, the object is in **equilibrium** (ee kwuh LIB ree uhm). An example of equilibrium is the case in which two equal forces act in opposite directions on point *P*, Figure 5-14.

Equilibrium is a zero resultant of forces.

Scale: 1 cm = 10 N

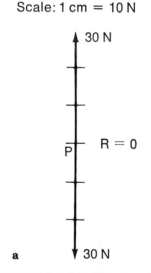

**a**

**b**

*Young/Hoffhines*

**FIGURE 5-14.** In this tug of war, the dog pulls with a force of 30 N. A 30-N force is exerted by a student in the opposite direction. The resultant force is zero.

For a second example, consider three forces acting on Point *P* as in Figure 5-15a. The 3-N force and the 4-N force are at right angles to each other. Their resultant is a 5-N force to the right. Vector *c* is a 5-N force to the left. The resultant of these two 5-N forces is zero. Therefore, the three forces produce no net force on point *P*. Thus, point *P* is in equilibrium. When the three vectors are added head-to-tail, they form a closed triangle, Figure 5-15b. A resultant cannot be drawn when the vector sum is zero.

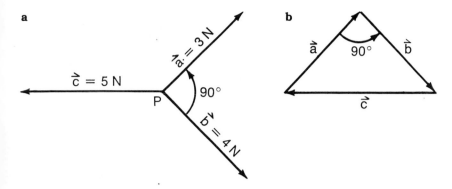

a

b

$\vec{c} = 5\ N$

$\vec{a} = 3\ N$

$90°$

P

$\vec{b} = 4\ N$

$\vec{a}$

$90°$

$\vec{b}$

$\vec{c}$

**FIGURE 5-15. Vectors in equilibrium give a resultant of zero.**

## 5:10   The Equilibrant

Engineers are frequently concerned with the stability of structures and the forces that supporting girders must offset. To have stability, the forces acting on an object must be arranged in such a way as to produce no net force. The vector sum of the forces must be zero. A resultant force of zero is known as the **condition for equilibrium.**

$$\Sigma F = 0$$

**FIGURE 5-16. To keep the bridge motionless, the forces acting concurrently on the bridge must be in equilibrium.**

An equilibrant force offsets forces acting on a given point to produce equilibrium.

The equilibrant is numerically equal to the resultant, but opposite in direction.

When two or more forces act on a point and their vector sum is not zero, an **equilibrant** (ee KWIL uh bruhnt) force can be found. The equilibrant force is the single additional force which, when applied at the same point as the other forces, will produce equilibrium. In Figure 5-17, the equilibrant is a 5-N force whose direction is opposite to the direction of the resultant.

To find the equilibrant of two or more concurrent forces, first find the resultant of the forces. The equilibrant is a force equal in magnitude to the resultant, but opposite in direction.

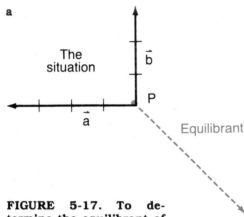

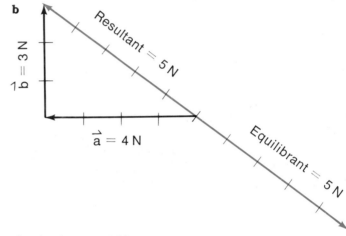

Scale: 1 cm = 1 N

**FIGURE 5-17.** To determine the equilibrant of two forces acting at an angle of 90° with each other, first find the resultant of the two forces.

## PROBLEMS

**20.** A force of 50-N acts due west. What single force places this force in equilibrium?

**21.** Two forces act concurrently on a point *P*. One force is 60 N due east. The second force is 80 N due north.
   **a.** Find the magnitude and direction of their resultant.
   **b.** What is the magnitude and direction of their equilibrant?

21.  a. 100 N, 37° east of north
     b. 100 N, 37° west of south

**22.** A 60-N force acting at 30° east of north and a second 60-N force acting in the direction 60° east of north are concurrent forces.
   **a.** Determine the resultant force.
   **b.** What is the magnitude and direction of their equilibrant?

23.  100 N, 8° south of east

**23.** A 60-N force acts 45° west of south. An 80-N force acts 45° north of west. The two forces act on the same point. What is the magnitude and direction of their equilibrant?

**24.** A 30-N force acting due north and a 40-N force acting 30° east of north act concurrently on point *P*. What is the magnitude and direction of a third force that places these two forces in equilibrium?

# 5:11  Perpendicular Components of Vectors

Up to this point we have dealt with two or more vectors acting in different directions from the same point. We have seen that these vectors may be replaced by a single vector, the resultant, which has the same effect as the two vectors.

It is also possible to regard a single vector quantity as the resultant of two vectors each acting in directions other than the original vector. These two vectors are called the **components** of the given vector. Most of the time we are concerned with the vertical and horizontal components of a given vector.

Component forces, when added, give the resultant force.

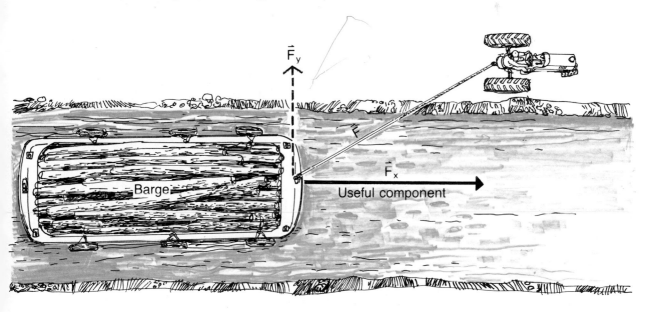

For example, the barge in Figure 5-18 is being pulled along the canal by means of a rope attached to a tractor. The current in the canal is of sufficient speed to keep the barge on course. The force in the rope is clearly not the force that serves to move the barge along the canal. Instead, the effective force is the component $\vec{F}_x$, acting in the same direction as the canal. Therefore, it is $\vec{F}_x$ that is of interest.

The force $\vec{F}_y$ serves no useful purpose although it is a real force. It must be offset by the rudder of the barge. Note that if the vector sum of the two components, $\vec{F}_x$ and $\vec{F}_y$, were obtained, the resultant vector would be $\vec{F}$.

The process of finding the effective value of a vector in a given direction is called **vector resolution.** Consider the sled being pulled in Figure 5-19a. A 50-N force is being exerted on a rope held at an angle of 30° with the horizontal. The 50-N force serves

**FIGURE 5-18. A boat is pulled through a canal by a tractor moving along the bank ahead of the boat. The tension in the rope between the boat and the tractor can be thought of as the sum of two component forces. One force operates in the direction of the canal and the other force operates in the direction of the bank.**

A single force may be resolved into perpendicular components.

As the direction of a force changes, the magnitude of each of the component forces changes.

to pull the sled forward. However, not all of the 50-N force does this. The only force that pulls the sled forward is the horizontal component ($\vec{F}_h$) of the 50-N force.

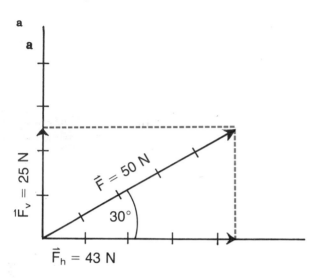

a

b

*PHOTRI*

**FIGURE 5-19. The force used to pull a sled can be resolved into its vertical and horizontal components.**

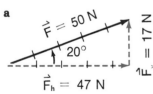

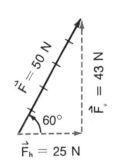

Scale: 1 division = 10 N

**FIGURE 5-20. The horizontal and vertical components of a force depend upon its direction.**

The values of the horizontal and vertical components of $\vec{F}$ can be found by first drawing a set of perpendicular axes, Figure 5-19b. One axis represents the horizontal direction. The other axis represents the vertical direction. The vector to represent the force ($\vec{F}$) in the rope is then drawn to scale at the proper angle with the horizontal axis. To resolve that force into the components $\vec{F}_v$ and $\vec{F}_h$, draw lines perpendicularly from each axis to the tip of the force vector. The magnitudes of the two components are then found in terms of the scale used for $\vec{F}$. (Note that the resultant of $\vec{F}_v$ and $\vec{F}_h$ is the original force, $\vec{F}$.)

The size of the horizontal component is increased when the person pulling the sled lowers the rope. But if the angle between the rope and the horizontal is increased to 60°, the horizontal component is decreased to 25 N. Thus, the magnitudes of the components change as the direction of the force changes.

In resolving velocity and displacement vectors, let one axis represent a north-south direction. Let the second axis represent an east-west direction.

**EXAMPLE: Resolving a Velocity Vector into Its Components**

A wind with a velocity of 40 km/h blows 30° north of east. What is the north component of the wind's velocity? What is the east component of the wind's velocity?

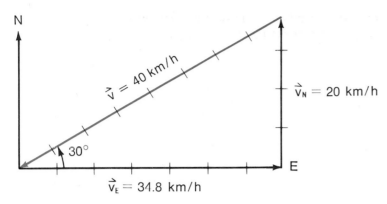

$\vec{V}_E = 34.8$ km/h

Scale: 1 cm = 5 km/h

**FIGURE 5-21. Resolving $\vec{v}$ into north and east components.**

*Solution:*
To find the north component, $v_n$, use the relation

$$\sin 30° = \frac{v_n}{v} \quad \text{Then,} \quad v_n = (v)(\sin 30°)$$
$$= (40 \text{ km/h})(0.50) = 20 \text{ km/h north}$$

To find the east component, $v_e$, use the relation

$$\cos 30° = \frac{v_e}{v} \quad \text{Then,} \quad v_e = (v)(\cos 30°)$$
$$= (40 \text{ km/h})(0.87) = 34.8 \text{ km/h east}$$

## PROBLEMS

**25.** A heavy box is pulled across a wooden floor with a rope. The rope forms an angle of 60° with the floor. A tension of 80 N is maintained on the rope. What force actually is pulling the box across the floor?

25. 40 N

**26.** The rope in Problem 25 is lowered until it forms an angle of 30° with the floor. A force of 80 N is maintained on the rope. What force pulls the box across the floor?

**27.** An airplane flies 30° north of west at 500 km/h. At what rate is the plane moving
   **a.** north    **b.** west

27. **a.** 250 km/h
    **b.** 433 km/h

**28.** A ship sails from Norfolk harbor. It maintains a direction of 45° north of east for a distance of 100 km. How many kilometers north and east has the ship progressed from Norfolk?

**29.** A lawnmower is pushed with a force of 70 N applied to the handle. Find the horizontal component of this force when the handle is held at an angle with the lawn of
   **a.** 60°    **b.** 40°    **c.** 30°

29. **a.** 35 N
    **b.** 54 N
    **c.** 61 N

**30.** A guy wire helps to hold a television tower in place. The wire forms an angle of 40° with the tower. It is under a tension of 4000 N.

**a.** What force tends to support the tower?
**b.** What force tends to pull the tower over?

31. 200 N

**31.** A water skier is towed by a speedboat. The skier moves to one side of the boat in such a way that the towrope forms an angle of 55° with the wake of the boat. The tension on the rope is 350 N. What would be the tension on the rope if the skier were directly behind the boat?

## 5:12   Gravitational Force and Inclined Planes

When an object is on an inclined plane, the gravitational attraction of the earth acting on that object, its weight, is directed toward the center of the earth. This means that its weight, $\vec{W}$, must act perpendicular to the surface of the earth or, as we say, perpendicular to the horizontal.

In Figure 5-22 a trunk resting on an inclined plane is shown. The plane prevents the weight of the trunk, $\vec{W}$, from accelerating it in the vertical direction. Instead, the plane causes $\vec{W}$ to be resolved into two components. One component $\vec{F}_N$ is called the normal force and acts perpendicular to the incline. The second component $\vec{F}_x$ acts parallel to and down the incline.

The right triangle formed by the incline and the right triangle formed by $\vec{W}$, $\vec{F}_N$ and $\vec{F}_x$ are similar triangles (corresponding sides are mutually perpendicular). If $\Theta$ and $\vec{W}$ are both known, a vector diagram similar to Figure 5-22 may be drawn and the force $\vec{W}$ resolved into the components $\vec{F}_x$ and $\vec{F}_n$ by the graphical method. An easier method is to calculate the values of $\vec{F}_x$ and

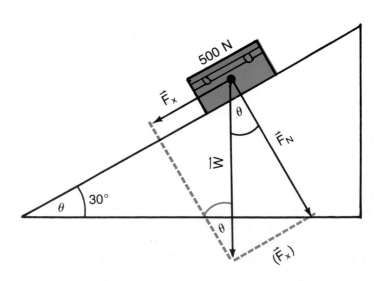

**FIGURE 5-22. The gravitational force vector *W* is resolved into two components. One component acts parallel to the plane. The other acts perpendicular to the plane.**

$\vec{F}_N$ using the trigonometric functions of right triangles. (Note that the trunk weighs 500 newtons and that the angle of the incline is 30°.)

$$\sin 30° = \frac{F_x}{W} \qquad\qquad\qquad \cos 30° = \frac{F_N}{W}$$

$$F_x = (W)(\sin 30°) \qquad \text{Also:} \qquad F_N = (W)(\cos 30°)$$
$$F_x = (500 \text{ N})(0.5) \qquad\qquad\qquad F_N = (500 \text{ N})(0.87)$$
$$F_x = 250 \text{ N} \qquad\qquad\qquad\qquad F_N = 430 \text{ N}$$

As the incline becomes steeper, the component of the weight acting down the incline becomes greater. The component of the weight acting perpendicular to the incline, $\vec{F}_N$, becomes less. As a result, you find smooth inclines treacherous while walking, particularly if they are steep. The normal force holding you against the incline is low and you become more likely to slip. If the incline is steep enough, you may find yourself forced to run down its length when you had no intention of running. The force acting down the incline, $\vec{F}_x$, accelerates you against your will.

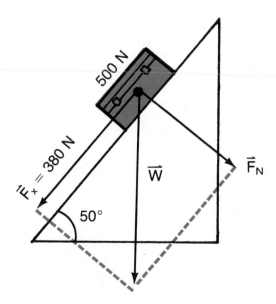

**FIGURE 5-23. As the angle of the incline increases, the component of the weight acting parallel with the plane increases. The component that acts perpendicular to the plane decreases.**

## PROBLEMS

**32.** A 500 N trunk is placed on an incline plane that forms a 66° angle with the horizontal.
    **a.** Calculate the values of $\vec{F}_N$ and $\vec{F}_x$.
    **b.** Compare your results with those given above for the same trunk on a 30° incline.
    **c.** When the angle of an incline increases how do the force components acting on the trunk change?

33. a. 7100 N
    b. 9700 N

**33.** An automobile weighing 12 000 N is parked on a 36° slope.
  **a.** What force tends to cause the auto to roll down the hill?
  **b.** What is the normal force between the auto and the hill?

## 5:13 Nonperpendicular Components of Vectors

In Section 5:11, a single vector was resolved into two components at right angles to each other. However, a vector can be resolved into components that lie in any direction as long as their vector sum is equal to the original vector. In some cases, it may be necessary for you to resolve a vector into components that are not at right angles to each other.

**Components of a vector are not always at right angles.**

a

The situation

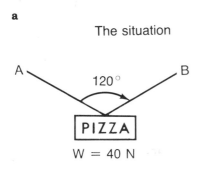

Scale: 1 division = 10 N

b

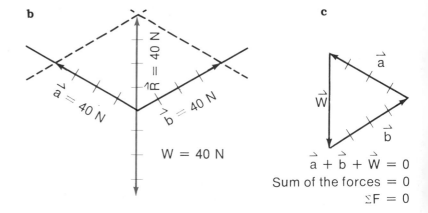

**FIGURE 5-24. Resolving the force $\vec{R}$ into the nonperpendicular components $\vec{a}$ and $\vec{b}$.**

A sign that weighs 40 N is supported by ropes $A$ and $B$, Figure 5-24a. Three forces act on the sign. These are the force in rope $A$, the force in rope $B$, and the force due to gravity (the weight of the sign). The weight of the sign, 40 N, acts in the direction straight down. Because the sign is in equilibrium, the forces in the two ropes must produce a resultant, $\vec{R}$, of 40 N straight up to balance the weight of the sign. Thus, the magnitude and direction of the resultant of the forces in the two ropes is known, although the actual force in each rope is not known.

Figure 5-24b shows how $\vec{R}$ can be resolved into two components to find the force in each rope. Three lines are drawn. These are the known, $\vec{R}$, and two lines which represent the directions of ropes $A$ and $B$.

The vector $R$ is then resolved into two components—one in the direction of rope $A$ and one in the direction of rope $B$. You can resolve $\vec{R}$ by constructing a parallelogram. The broken lines in this diagram represent the parallel sides that are drawn to complete the parallelogram. These broken lines intersect the lines in the direction of ropes $A$ and $B$. In so doing, they define the components of $\vec{R}$. The two components $\vec{a}$ and $\vec{b}$ are then interpreted in terms of the scale of the diagram to find the force in each rope.

In this case, the force turns out to be 40 N in each rope. The fact that the component forces in each rope are equal to the weight is due to the choice of angles. At other angles, the forces in the ropes will vary. Note that when $\vec{a}$, $\vec{b}$, and $\vec{W}$ are added as in Figure 5-24c, they form a closed triangle. This triangle indicates a vector sum of zero. Thus, the sign hangs in equilibrium. No net force implies no acceleration. The sign does not move.

**Summary**

1. Any measurable quantity can be classified as a vector quantity or a scalar quantity. Scalar quantities have magnitude only. Vector quantities have both magnitude and direction.   **5:1**

2. Scalar quantities are added algebraically. Vector quantities are added by a method called vector addition.   **5:1**

3. A vector quantity is represented by an arrow-tipped line segment which is called a vector.   **5:2**

4. Vectors are added by placing them head to tail. The vector sum, or resultant, is drawn from the tail of the first vector to the head of the last vector.   **5:2**

5. Vectors can be added in any order. The order in which they are added does not affect the vector sum.   **5:2**

6. Vectors, when added, produce a resultant. However, each vector remains completely independent of all other vectors. The resultant merely indicates the combined effect of the vectors.   **5:5**

7. When two or more forces act concurrently on an object and their vector sum is zero, the object is in equilibrium.   **5:9**

8. If the vector sum is not zero, the vectors are not in equilibrium. The single force that will place the vectors in equilibrium is equal and opposite to the resultant of the vectors. This single force is called the equilibrant.   **5:10**

9. A vector can be resolved into component vectors. Components, if added, yield the original vector as a resultant. Components are most often drawn at right angles to each other. However, components can be drawn in any direction as long as their vector sum is equal to the original vector.   **5:11**

**Questions**

1. Distinguish between vector quantities and scalar quantities.
2. How are vectors added?
3. When two vectors are added, what is the rule for drawing the resultant vector?

4. A boat travels at 10 m/s. It heads straight across a river which flows at 3.0 m/s. What is the resultant velocity of the boat across the river?

5. What is meant by the term concurrent forces?

6. How does the resultant of two vectors change as the angle between the two vectors increases?

7. A lawnmower is pushed across a lawn. Can the horizontal component of the force be increased without changing the total force applied to the handle of the mower? How?

8. What is the sum of three vectors that form a closed triangle? Assume that the vectors are force vectors. What does this imply about the object upon which the forces act?

9. How can the equilibrant of two or more concurrent forces be found?

10. A gardener may find that it is easier to pull a lawnroller across the lawn than it is to push the same roller across the lawn. Explain.

## Problems

*273*

1. Three people attempt to haul a heavy sign to the roof of a building by means of three ropes attached to the sign. Person *A* stands directly above the sign and pulls straight up on a rope. Person *B* and person *C* stand on either side of person *A*. Their ropes form 30° angles with person *A*'s rope. A force of 100 N is applied on each rope. What is the net upward force acting on the sign?

*$4.0 \times 10^{-24}$*

2. An electron in the picture tube of a television set is subjected to a magnetic force of $2.6 \times 10^{-24}$ N acting horizontally and an electric force of $3.0 \times 10^{-24}$ N acting vertically. What is the magnitude of the resultant force acting on the electron?

*190 N*
*230 E*

3. A plane travels 40° north of east for a distance of 300 km. How far north and how far east does the plane travel?

4. A descent vehicle landing on the moon has a vertical velocity toward the surface of the moon of 30 m/s. At the same time it has a horizontal velocity of 55 m/s.

*63*
  a. At what speed does the vehicle move along its descent path?
*61°*
  b. At what angle with the vertical is this path?

5. A lawnmower is pushed across a lawn by applying a force of 90 N to the handle of the mower. The handle makes an angle of 60° with the horizontal.

*45, 78*
  a. What are the horizontal and vertical components of the force?
*78, 45*
  b. The handle is lowered so that it makes an angle of 30° with the horizontal. What are the horizontal and vertical components of the force?

*64*
6. A force of 90 N is exerted on a heavy box by means of a rope. The rope is held at an angle of 45° with the horizontal. What are the vertical and horizontal components of the 90-N force?

7. A river flows due south. A riverboat pilot heads the boat 27° north of
*3.1, 6.8* west and is able to go straight across the river at 6.0 m/s.

a. What is the speed of the current?

b. What is the speed of the boat?

8. A street lamp weighs 150 N. It is supported by two wires which form an angle of 120° with each other. What is the tension of each of these wires? *150*

9. If the angle between the wires in Problem 8 is changed to 60°, what is the tension of each of the wires? *87*

10. Three forces act concurrently on point *P*. Force *a* has a magnitude of 80 N and is directed 30° east of north. Force *b* has a magnitude of 70 N and is directed due east. Force *c* has a magnitude of 40 N and is directed 45° south of east.

a. Graphically add these three forces in the order *a* + *b* + *c*. *144*

b. Graphically add these three forces in the order *c* + *b* + *a*. *144*

c. What is noted about the solutions in each case.

---

**Applying Physics**

1. *Engineering:* A construction company keeps a wooden crate filled with cement partway up a steel ramp (60° incline). The crate and its contents weigh 1200 N and are held in place by a rope attached to a post. The tension in the rope is 750 N.

a. Compute the normal force between the incline and the crate. *600*

b. Compute the amount of frictional force which helps to keep the crate from sliding down the ramp. *290*

2. *Vector Resolution:* A mass, *M*, starts from rest and slides down the frictionless incline as shown. As it leaves the incline its speed is 24 m/s.

a. What is the acceleration of the mass while on the incline? *4.9*

b. What is the length of the incline? *5.9*

c. How long does it take the mass to reach the floor after it leaves the incline? *|3*

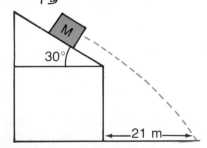

**FIGURE 5-25.**

---

**Readings**

Daich, C. B., *Learn Science Through Ball Games*. New York, Sterling Publishing Co., 1972.

Hewitt, Paul G., *Conceptual Physics*. (Chapter 5). Boston, Little Brown and Company, 1980. (See also, Appendix III.)

Sheffield, Charles, "Earth Scans." *Omni*, June, 1980.

The motion of any object can be described in terms of the forces acting on it. Dynamics deals with the causes of motion. A thorough understanding of forces and motion was necessary in designing this amusement ride. What forces pull the coaster toward the earth? What forces keep it on the track? What forces hold the individual particles of the coaster together? How does the weight of the coaster and its passengers affect these forces?

# Dynamics 6

This chapter introduces the most basic of all scientific concepts, the interaction between forces and matter. You should understand from the outset that any time two or more objects interact forces are the cause of the interaction. There are no exceptions. A baseball leaves a bat after impact due to forces. Blood flows through your veins due to forces. The planets orbit the sun due to forces. Chemical reactions occur due to forces. All interactions are the result of forces.

Sir Isaac Newton (1642–1727) was born in the same year that Galileo died. By the age of eighteen, he had discovered the binomial theorem. He then went on to discover the law of universal gravitation and to explain the motions of the planets, comets, and the moon. Newton also explained the nature of light and invented a system of calculus. Few scientists have contributed as much to science as has Sir Isaac Newton.

About the year 1665, Sir Isaac Newton stated three laws which are now known as Newton's laws of motion. The three laws are basic to the science of physics because they are universal laws. Anytime an interaction takes place it will follow these laws. In this chapter, we will study Newton's first two laws of motion. In Chapter 7, we will study his third law of motion.

**GOAL: You will gain knowledge and understanding of Newton's first two laws of motion and of the distinction between mass and weight.**

Dynamics is the study of forces which cause motion.

# 6:1   Forces

A change in the motion of any object is caused by the action of a force. An object at rest will not move unless the forces acting on it are no longer in equilibrium. An object in motion will not slow down, speed up, or change its direction unless a force acts upon it. All changes in the motions of objects are due to forces.

Most people observe thousands of forces every day. However, there are not a large number of different forces. Forces may be organized into five classes. Three of these—gravitational, electric, and magnetic—cause most observable interactions. The other two forces are the nuclear and weak interaction forces. They are rarely observed because they exist only inside the nuclei of atoms.

The force that appears when you push on an object with your hand is an **electric force.** This electric force develops as the negative electrons in the atoms of your hand get very close to the negative electrons in the atoms of the object. The force between an automobile's tires and the road is also an electric force. Most forces that we notice are electric forces.

Frequently, electric forces are referred to as "mechanical" or "frictional" forces. These terms are general and should be considered as electric forces.

**Gravitational force** is a force of attraction that exists between all masses. It is an extremely weak force in comparison to the other forces. If two tennis balls are held one meter apart, the gravitational force between them is only $1 \times 10^{-11}$ newton. Electric forces, on the other hand, can be very large. If one extra electron could be added to each atom in the two tennis balls, the resulting electric force between them would be $5 \times 10^{20}$ newtons. We could never put such a charge on the tennis balls. They would be forced apart long before the charging was completed.

**Magnetic forces,** like electric forces, are very large in comparison to gravitational forces. Magnetic forces are produced by moving electric charges. In fact, electric and magnetic forces are closely related. At the present time, this relationship is not completely understood.

**Nuclear forces** are much stronger than any of the other forces. The nuclear force holds the nucleus of an atom together in spite of the strong electric force of repulsion between its protons. Sometimes nuclei of atoms change by gaining or losing particles. When this change occurs, a huge amount of nuclear energy is released. One-half gram of nuclear fuel can supply approximately the same energy as eight tons of coal. Today, nuclear power plants use this energy to provide electricity for some cities.

Scientists believe that a second force exists inside the nucleus. This force is called the **weak interaction force.** It is believed to be the force that causes some atoms to break apart. Little is

The five forces known to scientists are the gravitational, electric, magnetic, nuclear, and weak interaction forces.

An electric force results from the electron repulsion of two objects.

Gravitational force is the weakest of the five forces.

Magnetic and electric forces are closely related.

A nuclear force is the strongest of the five forces. It holds the nucleus of an atom together.

known about the process involved. It is difficult to find out what happens inside the extremely small nucleus of an atom.

One unusual thing about forces is their ability to act through distances. The gravitational force between the earth and the moon keeps the moon in its orbital path over a distance of roughly 400 000 kilometers. Likewise, one magnet can affect a second magnet some distance away. This ability of forces to act through a space is one of nature's most puzzling phenomena.

**Forces act through a distance.**

## 6:2 Newton's First Law

Galileo first introduced the idea of acceleration. He guessed that the speed of falling objects increases uniformly with time. Since precise clocks had not yet been invented, Galileo had no way to measure the speeds of falling objects. He got around this difficulty by rolling metal balls down smooth ramps. When the ramps formed small angles with the horizontal, the speeds of the rolling balls were slow enough to measure by using a water clock. For different time intervals, he measured the distances traveled. He used this data to calculate the speed for each trial. In this way, Galileo was able to prove that the balls gained speed uniformly with time. Gradually he developed the equations related to motion that we studied in Chapter 3. These relationships are basic to **kinematics** (kin uh MAT iks), the study of motion.

**Kinematics is the study of motion.**

*Musco Zooliogicó de "La Specolo" Tribunadi. Galileo. France Scala New York/Florence*

**FIGURE 6-1. Galileo studied acceleration due to gravity by rolling metal balls down smooth ramps and timing them with a water clock.**

Silvio A. Bedini/Courtesy of National
Maritime Museum

**FIGURE 6-2. Water clocks
were used to measure time
in the 17th century.**

Inertia is an object's
resistance to change in
motion.

An object at rest is in
equilibrium.

Galileo noticed that when a ball left one of the ramps, it rolled for a long distance. The ball lost very little speed as it rolled across the stone floor. Galileo reasoned that if the floor were frictionless and endless, the ball would never stop moving. This observation required a remarkable amount of insight because nothing on the earth behaves in this way. Friction, an electric force, is ever-present. Friction always causes a moving object to come to rest unless a propelling force is constantly applied to the object. Friction thus creates the false idea that it is a "natural tendency" for an object in motion to come to rest. Galileo used this reasoning to introduce the idea of inertia (in UHR shuh). **Inertia** is the tendency of an object to resist a change in its motion. According to Galileo's reasoning, an object set in motion on a frictionless surface could continue moving indefinitely.

Newton's first law of motion states: *An object continues in its state of rest, or of uniform motion in a straight line, unless it is acted upon by a net external force.* This law means that it is the natural tendency of an object to maintain its motion. An object will resist any change in its state of motion. The first law also makes the function of forces clear. A force is capable of changing the state of motion of an object.

## 6:3  Newton's Second Law

Newton's first law of motion implies that there is no fundamental difference between an object at rest and one that is moving with uniform velocity. Consider the two cars in Figure 6-3. One car is at rest while the other one moves in a straight line at a constant velocity of 60 km/h. The car at rest is acted upon by two forces. The force of gravity pulls it downward. The force of the road pushes it upward. The two forces are equal and opposite. Therefore, their vector sum is zero and the car is in equilibrium.

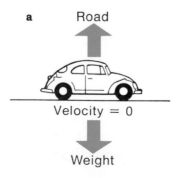

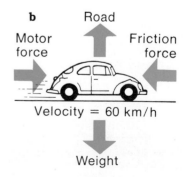

**FIGURE 6-3. When forces
are in equilibrium, there is
no acceleration.**

Four forces act on the car that moves in a straight line at a constant 60 km/h. In the vertical direction, the same two forces are present that act on the car at rest. They are equal and opposite. In the horizontal direction, the force of the motor drives the car forward while the force of friction opposes the forward motion. These two forces must be equal and opposite because the velocity of the car is constant. By Newton's laws, a net force would accelerate the car. Thus, the motor force and the friction force are equal and opposite. The vector sum of all of the forces is zero. The moving car and the car at rest are both in equilibrium. If the driver changes the motor force, the car will accelerate or decelerate. Just as Newton's first law of motion states, any unbalanced force causes acceleration.

**An object moving at a constant velocity is in equilibrium.**

Newton was the first to recognize that a net force always causes acceleration and not just motion. Newton then formulated his second law of motion: *When an unbalanced force acts on an object, the object will be accelerated. The acceleration will vary directly with the applied force and will be in the same direction as the applied force. It will vary inversely with the mass of the object.* The mathematical expression of Newton's second law is

**Newton's second law of motion tells us that an unbalanced force causes acceleration.**

$$a = \frac{F}{m}$$

More often, Newton's second law of motion is written

$$\boxed{F = ma}$$

**The most familiar form of the second law is *F = ma*.**

## 6:4   Units of Force

A force is measured in terms of the acceleration it gives a standard mass. Suppose a 1-kilogram mass is located on a frictionless, horizontal surface. The force that will cause this 1-kilogram mass to accelerate at the rate of 1 meter per second each second ($1 \text{ m/s}^2$) is defined as

**A force of one newton will accelerate a 1-kg mass at the rate of $1 \text{ m/s}^2$.**

$$F = ma$$
$$= (1 \text{ kg})(1 \text{ m/s}^2)$$
$$= 1 \text{ kg} \cdot \text{m/s}^2$$
$$= 1 \text{ newton}$$

The newton (N) is the SI unit of force.

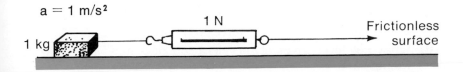

a = 1 m/s²

1 N

1 kg

Frictionless surface

**FIGURE 6-4. Units of force are defined in terms of the acceleration they give to standard masses.**

**EXAMPLE: Using Newton's Second Law to Find Force**

A force gives a 2.0-kg mass an acceleration of 5.0 m/s$^2$. What is the magnitude of the force?

*Solution:*

$$F = ma$$
$$= (2.0 \text{ kg})(5.0 \text{ m/s}^2)$$
$$= 10 \text{ kg} \cdot \text{m/s}^2 \ = 10 \text{ N}$$

**EXAMPLE: Using Newton's Second Law to Find Mass**

A force of 20 N gives a stone an acceleration of 4.0 m/s$^2$. What is the mass of the stone?

*Solution:*  $F = ma \qquad m = \dfrac{F}{a}$

$$= \frac{20 \text{ N}}{4.0 \text{ m/s}^2}$$
$$= \frac{20 \text{ kg} \cdot \cancel{\text{m/s}^2}}{4.0 \ \cancel{\text{m/s}^2}} \ = 5.0 \text{ kg}$$

**PROBLEMS**

1. 2.5 m/s$^2$

3. 7.5 kg

5. a. 4 m/s$^2$
   b. 2 m/s$^2$
   c. 1 m/s$^2$
   d. 0.5 m/s$^2$
   e. 0.2 m/s$^2$

7. 5.6 × 10$^5$ N

9. 5.0 m/s$^2$

1. A net force of 25 N is applied to a 10-kg mass. What is the acceleration given to the mass?

2. A 16-N force is applied to a 2-kg mass. What is the acceleration of the mass?

3. An athlete exerts a force of 150 N on a shot put giving it an acceleration of 20 m/s$^2$. What is the mass of the shot put?

4. A 1.5-kg mass accelerates across a smooth table at 15 m/s$^2$. What is the net force applied to it?

5. What acceleration does a net force of 20 N impart to a mass of
   **a.** 5 kg     **b.** 10 kg     **c.** 20 kg     **d.** 40 kg     **e.** 100 kg

6. What force gives a 1.0-kg mass an acceleration of 9.8 m/s$^2$?

7. An artillery shell has a mass of 8.0 kg. The shell is fired from the muzzle of a gun with a speed of 700 m/s. The gun barrel is 3.5 m long. What is the average force on the shell while it is in the gun barrel? (Hint: use $v^2 = 2as$)

8. A racing car has a mass of 700 kg. It starts from rest and travels 120 m in 2.0 s. The car undergoes uniform acceleration during the entire 2.0 s. What force is applied to it? (Ignore friction; use $s = at^2/2$.)

9. Determine the acceleration that a force of 25 N gives to a 4.0-kg mass. The friction force to be overcome is 5.0 N.

10. What net force gives an acceleration of 8 m/s$^2$ to a 750 kg racing car?

# 6:5   Weight and Mass

It is important to clearly understand the distinction between weight and mass. **Mass** depends upon the amount of matter in an object. It is related to the actual number of protons, neutrons, and electrons that make up the object. **Weight** refers to the gravitational force exerted on the object by the earth. Weight is another name for gravitational force. Like other forces, weight is measured in newtons. Mass, however, is measured in kilograms.

Consider the force that must act on a 1-kg mass allowed to fall freely from some point near the earth's surface. The mass accelerates at the rate of 9.8 m/s². By Newton's second law of motion, the force needed to accelerate a 1-kg mass at the rate of 9.8 m/s² is

$$F = ma$$
$$= (1 \text{ kg})(9.8 \text{ m/s}^2)$$
$$= 9.8 \text{ kg} \cdot \text{m/s}^2$$
$$= 9.8 \text{ N}$$

Thus, the earth must exert a force of 9.8 newtons on the 1-kilogram mass. The mass weighs 9.8 newtons. If you hang a 1-kg mass on a spring scale, you will find that it does indeed weigh 9.8 newtons. If you hang a 2-kilogram mass on the spring scale, you will find that it weighs 19.6 newtons. A force of 19.6 newtons is the force needed to give a 2-kilogram mass an acceleration of 9.8 m/s². In the same way, a 3-kg mass weighs 29.4 N. Mass and weight are proportional.

Note that all masses accelerate at the same rate, even though the earth pulls with a greater force on large masses. This happens because a greater force is needed to accelerate a large mass than a small mass.

To determine the weight of a mass, Newton's second law may be written in the form $W = mg$. Here, $W$ represents the weight, $m$ represents the mass, and $g$ represents the acceleration of gravity. The weight of a 5-kilogram mass is

$$W = mg$$
$$= (5 \text{ kg})(9.8 \text{ m/s}^2)$$
$$= 49 \text{ kg} \cdot \text{m/s}^2$$
$$= 49 \text{ N}$$

The weight of an object varies with its location. An object weighs slightly less in an airplane in flight than it does at sea level. An object on the moon weighs one-sixth as much as it does on the earth. But, the mass of an object is always the same. Moving an object from one place to another never changes the mass of the object.

Mass is the quantity of matter in an object.

Weight is the earth's gravitational force on an object.

The unit for mass is the kilogram.

The acceleration of gravity is 9.8 m/s².

A 1-kg mass has a weight of 9.8 N on the earth's surface.

When dealing with gravity, $F = ma$ can be written $W = mg$.

Weight varies with location. Mass does not.

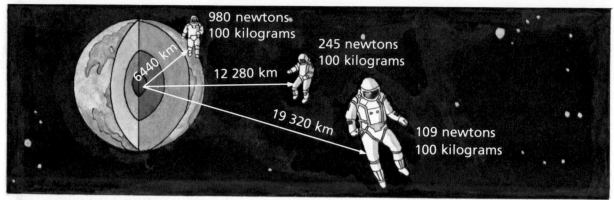

**FIGURE 6-5. The weight of this astronaut varies with the location of the astronaut. The mass of this astronaut does not change with location.**

11. a. 140 N
    b. 4.2 N
    c. 6.9 N

13. 20 N

15. 9800 N

17. 9.8 m/s²

## PROBLEMS

*Use Newton's second law, expressed as W = mg, to solve these problems.*

**11.** Determine the weights of these masses:
    **a.** 14 kg    **b.** 0.43 kg    **c.** 0.7 kg

**12.** Determine the mass of these weights:
    **a.** 98 N    **b.** 80 N    **c.** 0.98 N

**13.** How much force is needed to keep a 20-N stone from falling?

**14.** An economy car has a mass of 800 kg. What is the weight of the car?

**15.** A car has a mass of 1000 kg. What is its weight in newtons?

**16.** A small yacht weighs 14 700 N. What is its mass in kilograms?

**17.** An 8.0-kg mass weighs 78.4 N. At what rate does the weight of the mass accelerate the mass?

**18. a.** A car has a mass of 1200 kg. What is the weight of the car?
    **b.** Disregarding friction, what force must the car motor apply to accelerate the car along a level highway at the rate of 4.0 m/s²?

## 6:6    Net Forces and Acceleration

In Newton's second law of motion, $F = ma$, the force $F$ which causes the mass to accelerate is the net force acting on the mass. Consider a 10-kg mass, resting on a smooth, horizontal surface. If a 100-N force is applied to the mass, then the acceleration is

A net force acting on a mass causes the acceleration of the mass.

$$a = \frac{F}{m} = \frac{100 \text{ N}}{10 \text{ kg}} = \frac{100 \text{ kg·m/s}^2}{10 \text{ kg}} = 10 \text{ m/s}^2$$

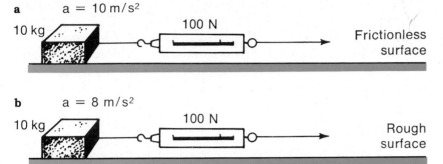

**a**   $a = 10 \text{ m/s}^2$

10 kg       100 N

Frictionless surface

**b**   $a = 8 \text{ m/s}^2$

10 kg       100 N

Rough surface

**FIGURE 6-6. When acted upon by a 100-N force, the acceleration of a 10-kg mass resting on a friction-less surface (a) is greater than the acceleration of a 10-kg mass resting on a rough surface (b).**

Suppose the 10-kg mass rests on a rough surface. Then when the 100-N force is applied, a friction force will also be present. The resulting acceleration will be caused by the net force, which is the difference between the applied force and the friction force. If the friction force is 20 N, then

$$F_{net} = 100 \text{ N} - 20 \text{ N} = 80 \text{ N}$$

and

$$a = \frac{F}{m} = \frac{80 \text{ N}}{10 \text{ kg}}$$
$$= \frac{80 \text{ kg} \cdot \text{m/s}^2}{10 \text{ kg}} = 8 \text{ m/s}^2$$

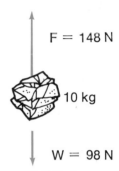

F = 148 N

10 kg

W = 98 N

**FIGURE 6-7. A mass is accelerated upward if the total force exerted upward is greater than the weight.**

Friction is not the only force preventing the total force applied to an object from being the net force acting on it. The stone in Figure 6-7 weighs 98 newtons. This statement means that the earth pulls down on the stone with a force of 98 newtons. If someone lifts the stone with a force of 148 newtons, the net force acting on it is 50 newtons upward. The acceleration given to the 10-kilogram mass by the net force of 50 newtons will be in accord with the second law of motion, $F = ma$.

$$a = \frac{F}{m} = \frac{50 \text{ N}}{10 \text{ kg}} = \frac{50 \text{ kg} \cdot \text{m/s}^2}{10 \text{ kg}} = 5.0 \text{ m/s}^2$$

## PROBLEMS

**19.** A rubber ball weighs 4.9 N.
   **a.** What is its mass?
   **b.** At what rate is the ball accelerated straight up if a 69-N force is applied to it in that direction?
**20.** What applied force accelerates a 20-kg stone straight up at 10 m/s²?
**21.** A rocket weighs 9800 N.
   **a.** What is its mass?
   **b.** What force gives it a vertical acceleration of 4.0 m/s².

19. a.  0.50 kg
    b.  130 m/s²

21. a.  1000 kg
    b.  13 800 N

23. 3.75 m/s$^2$

**22.** A car weighing 9800 N travels at 30 m/s. What braking force brings it to rest in 100 m? in 10 m?

**23.** A car located on a level highway has a mass of 400 kg. The friction force opposing the motion of the car is 750 N. What acceleration will a force of 2250 N produce on the car?

**24.** A small rocket weighs 14.7 N.
  **a.** What is its mass?
  **b.** The rocket is fired from a high platform but its engine fails to burn properly. The rocket gains a total upward force of only 10.2 N. At what rate and in what direction is the rocket accelerated?

25. a. 0.75 kg
    b. 82.7 N
    c. 110 m/s$^2$

**25.** A force of 90 N is exerted straight up on a stone that weighs 7.35 N. Calculate
  **a.** the mass of the stone.
  **b.** the net force acting on the stone.
  **c.** the acceleration of the stone.

**26.** The instruments attached to a weather balloon have a mass of 5.0 kg.
  **a.** What do the instruments weigh?
  **b.** The balloon is released on a calm day and exerts an upward force of 98 N on the instruments. At what rate does the balloon with instruments accelerate straight up?
  **c.** After accelerating for 10 seconds the weather instruments are released automatically. What is the magnitude and direction of their velocity at that instant?
  **d.** What net force acts on the instruments after their release?
  **e.** What time elapses before the instruments begin to fall.

27. a. 800 kg
    b. 3.25 m/s$^2$
    c. 32.5 m/s

**27.** A rocket which weighs 7840 N on the earth is fired. The force of propulsion is 10 440 N. Determine
  **a.** the mass of the rocket.
  **b.** the upward acceleration of the rocket.
  **c.** the velocity of the rocket at the end of 10 s.

## 6:7   Two Ways to Measure Mass

There are two fundamentally different ways to measure the mass of an object. One method is to use a beam balance. An unknown mass is placed on a pan at the end of a beam. Known masses are placed on the pan at the other end of the beam. When the pans balance, the force of gravity is the same on each pan. Then the masses on either side of the balance must also be the same. The beam-balance method is a method of comparison. The variations of gravitational force from place to place do not affect measurements made in this way. The same result for a measurement by the beam-balance method is obtained anywhere.

Mass can be determined by comparing the unknown mass with a known mass.

a

b

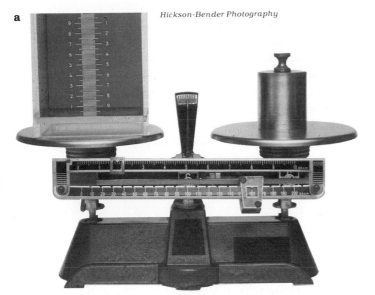

The second method to determine the mass of an object is quite different. It uses the property of inertia. An unknown is placed on a frictionless, horizontal surface. A known force is applied to the object and the acceleration of the object is measured. The mass of the object can then be calculated using the equation $m = F/a$. This second method is seldom used because it involves both a frictionless surface and a difficult measurement of acceleration. The gravitational method of measuring mass is easier and more widely used.

Gravitational mass and inertial mass are two essentially different concepts. But for a given object, they are always numerically equal. Thus, an important relationship exists between gravitational mass and inertial mass. For a long time, this equivalence was thought to be one of nature's most remarkable coincidences. However, Albert Einstein (1879–1955) recognized that this was more than a coincidence. Einstein used this phenomenon as the foundation for his general theory of relativity.

**FIGURE 6-8. A beam balance (a) allows you to compare an unknown mass to a known mass. Using an inertial balance (b), you can calculate the mass using Newton's second law.**

Inertial mass is calculated with the equation $F = ma$. In this case, $F$ is known and $a$ is measured.

**Summary**

1. A force must always be present to bring about a change in the motion of any object. Intro.
2. There are five fundamental forces in nature. These are the gravitational, electric, magnetic, nuclear, and weak interaction forces. 6:1
3. Gravitational forces are the weakest and nuclear forces are the strongest. 6:1
4. Our understanding of all motion is based upon three laws stated by Newton. Intro.

5. Newton's first law of motion states that an object will retain its state of motion unless acted upon by a net external force. The tendency of all objects to resist changes in motion is called inertia.  **6:2**

6. Newton's second law of motion states that when a net external force acts on an object, that object is accelerated in accordance with the equation $F = ma$.  **6:3,   6:5**

7. Mass is the amount of matter an object contains. Weight is gravitational force acting on an object. Mass is measured in kilograms. Weight is measured in newtons.  **6:5**

8. Gravitational mass and inertial mass are two essentially different concepts. However, for a given mass they are always numerically equal.  **6:7**

## Questions

1. A ball is rolled across the top of a table and slowly comes to a stop. Considering Newton's first law of motion, explain why the ball stops. How could the ball have remained in motion?

2. Generally speaking, how do gravitational forces compare with electric and magnetic forces?

3. If gravitational forces are so weak, why don't we fall off the earth?

4. An object on Earth has a mass of 3 kg. What would be the mass of the object if it were taken to Jupiter where the pull of gravity is 10 times that of Earth?

5. What is the difference between uniform velocity and uniform acceleration?

6. Why do you fall backward on a bus when it accelerates from rest? Why do you fall forward when the driver decelerates to rest?

7. Why does a car burn more gasoline traveling in a city than it does traveling on an interstate highway?

8. What is the difference between mass and weight?

9. A person weighing 490 N stands on a scale in an elevator.
   a. What does the scale read when the elevator is at rest?
   b. The elevator starts to ascend and accelerates the person upward at 2 m/s². What does the scale read now?
   c. When the elevator reaches a desirable speed it no longer accelerates. What is the reading on the scale as the elevator rises uniformly?
   d. The elevator begins to slow down as it reaches the proper floor. Do the scale readings increase or decrease?
   e. The elevator starts to descend. Does the scale reading increase or decrease?
   f. What does the scale read if the elevator descends at a constant speed?
   g. If the cable snapped and the elevator fell freely, what would the scale read?

**10.** A spacecraft is accelerated away from the earth by its rockets. Once the ship reaches a high speed and is far from the earth must it continue to fire its rockets to keep moving? Explain.

**Problems**

**1.** A 20-kg sled is pulled along level ground. The sled's rope makes an angle of 60° with the snow-covered ground and pulls on the sled with a force of 180 N. Find the acceleration of the sled if the friction force to be overcome is 15 N.

**2.** The mass of an elevator plus occupants is 750 kg. The tension in the cable is 8950 N. At what rate does the elevator accelerate upward?

**3.** Determine the acceleration of the system in Figure 6-9.

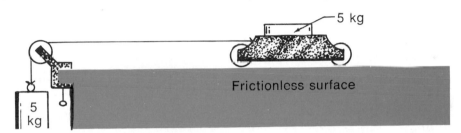

**FIGURE 6-9.**

**4.** An astronaut 100 m from the spaceship observes a 200-kg meteoroid that drifts toward the ship at 10 m/s. If the astronaut can grab the meteoroid and the astronaut's rocket gun is capable of delivering a force of 100 N, can the meteoroid be stopped before it hits the spaceship? (Neglect the mass of the astronaut.)

**Applying Physics**

**1.** *Rocketry:* A spaceship on its launching pad has a mass of 50 000 kg. Its rockets produce an upward thrust of 980 000 N during blastoff. If the ship is 30 m in height, what time will elapse after ignition before the craft rises a distance equal to its own height?

**2.** *Safety Engineering:* Safety engineers estimate that an elevator can hold 20 persons of 75-kg average mass. The elevator itself has a mass of 500 kg. Tensile strength tests show that the cable supporting the elevator can tolerate a maximum force of 29 600 N. What is the greatest upward acceleration that the elevator's motor can produce without breaking the cable?

**Readings**

Bixby, William, *The Universe of Galileo and Newton.* (Horizon Caravel Books). New York, Harper and Row, Inc., 1964.
Cohen, I., "Newton." *Scientific American*, December, 1955.
Sciama, Dennis, "Inertia." *Scientific American*, February, 1957.
Yang, C., "Einstein's Impact on Theoretical Physics." *Physics Today*, June, 1980.

All objects in motion have momentum. Momentum is actually a calculated quantity. It is the product of the mass and the velocity of an object. The sum of the momenta of the racket and ball before impact is equal to the sum of the momenta after impact. This relationship is known as the law of conservation of momentum. Would the momentum of a tennis ball hit by a child equal that of a ball hit by an adult? How might the momentum of a tennis ball be increased?

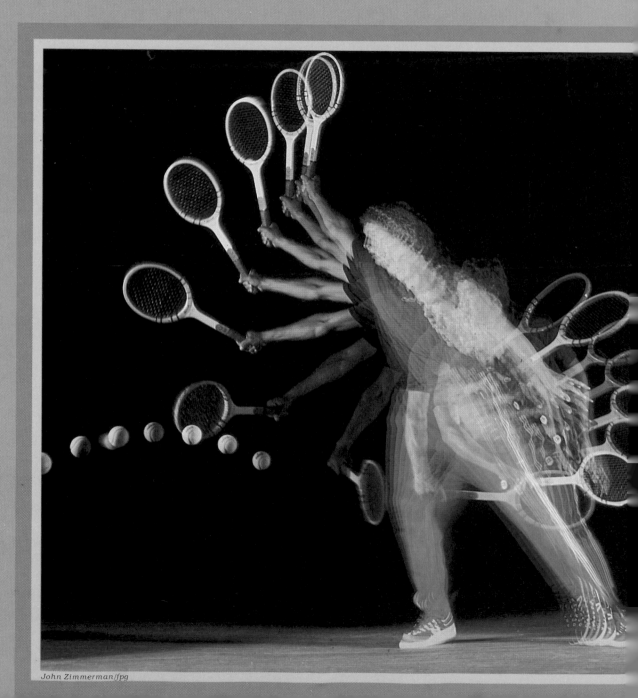

John Zimmerman/fpg

# Momentum and Its Conservation 7

The quantity known as momentum is one of the cornerstones of physics. It is a concept that explains much of the behavior of matter. The idea of momentum was first introduced by Newton in his studies of motion. Further studies of motion led to the law of conservation of momentum. The law of conservation of momentum is equal in importance to the law of conservation of energy, which you will study in a later chapter.

**GOAL:** You will gain knowledge and understanding of momentum, Newton's third law of motion, and the law of conservation of momentum.

## 7:1 Momentum

It is more difficult to stop a heavy truck than it is to stop a car moving at the same speed as the truck. A high-speed bullet has a much stronger interaction with a tree than does a small stone thrown at a tree. This aspect of moving objects is what we mean when we speak of momentum (moh MENT uhm). In physics, momentum has a very precise definition. **Momentum** is the product of the mass of an object and its velocity.

$$Momentum = (Mass)(Velocity)$$
$$= mv$$

A moving object has a large momentum if its mass is large, its velocity is large, or both its mass and velocity are large. If a heavy truck and a car are both moving at the same speed, the truck has more momentum than the car because of its larger mass. On the other hand, if the car moves fast and the truck moves slowly, they could both have the same momentum. A high-speed bullet and a slow-moving train can both have large momenta.

Momentum is the product of a body's mass and its velocity.

**a**                                          *Eric Hoffhines*    **b**                                          *Eric Hoffhines*

**FIGURE 7-1. A light bowling ball (a) generally has less momentum when it reaches the pins than a heavier ball (b). Notice the difference in pin action between the two photographs.**

Since velocity is a vector quantity, momentum is also a vector quantity. The momentum of an object has the same direction as its velocity.

Momentum changes whenever velocity changes. If the velocity of an object is changing, the object is being accelerated. Since acceleration is caused by a net force, a momentum change must be caused by a net force. Substituting the expression $a = \Delta v/t$ into Newton's second law of motion yields

$$F = ma = \frac{m\,\Delta v}{t}$$

$$Ft = m\,\Delta v$$

An unbalanced force causes a change in momentum.

This equation is the momentum form of Newton's second law of motion. It says that an unbalanced force acting on an object causes a change in the momentum of the object. The direction of the momentum change will be the same as the direction of the applied force. The magnitude of the momentum change will be proportional to the force and the length of time that the force acts.

Impulse is the product of force and time.

An impulse produces a change in momentum.

The quantity, $Ft$, is called impulse. An **impulse** produces a change in momentum, $m\,\Delta v$. The statement above is read:

*impulse = change in momentum*

This relationship is useful. If we know what change in velocity must be given to a mass, we can calculate the impulse needed. Or, if we measure a change in momentum, we can calculate the force involved.

John Zimmerman/fpg

**FIGURE 7-2.** A change in the momentum of a baseball occurs when a pitcher exerts a force on the baseball over a period of time. For this reason, a pitcher follows through in throwing the ball.

**EXAMPLE: Impulse and Change in Momentum**

A force of 20 N acts on a 2.0-kg mass for 10 s. Compute **a.** the impulse and **b.** the change in speed of the mass.
*Solution:*

**a.** $Ft = (20\ N)(10\ s) = 200\ N \cdot s$

**b.** $Ft = m\Delta v$

$$\Delta v = \frac{Ft}{m}$$

$$= \frac{200\ N \cdot s}{2\ kg}$$

$$= \frac{(200\ kg \cdot m/s^2)(s)}{2\ kg} = 100\ m/s$$

**EXAMPLE: Impulse and Change in Momentum**

A car that weighs 7840 N is accelerated from rest to a velocity of 25.0 m/s eastward by a force of 1000 N. **a.** What is the car's mass? **b.** What was the car's change in momentum? **c.** How long did the force act to give the car its velocity?
*Solution:*

**a.**
$$W = mg$$

$$m = \frac{W}{g}$$

$$= \frac{7840\ N}{9.8\ m/s^2}$$

$$= \frac{7840\ kg \cdot m/s^2}{9.8\ m/s^2} = 800\ kg$$

**b.**     $\Delta mv = mv_f - mv_o$
$$= (800 \text{ kg})(25.0 \text{ m/s}) - 0$$
$$= 2.0 \times 10^4 \text{ kg} \cdot \text{m/s}$$

**c.**     $Ft = m \Delta v$
$$t = \frac{m \Delta v}{F}$$
$$= \frac{2.0 \times 10^4 \text{ kg} \cdot \text{m/s}}{1000 \text{ N}}$$
$$= \frac{2.0 \times 10^4 \text{ kg} \cdot \text{m/s}}{1000 \text{ kg} \cdot \text{m/s}^2}$$
$$= 20 \text{ s}$$

## PROBLEMS

1. a. 60 N·s
   b. 20 m/s

**1.** A force of 6.0 N acts on an object for 10 s. The mass of the object is 3 kg.
  **a.** What is the object's change in momentum?
  **b.** What is its change in velocity?

**2.** A car of mass 1100 kg moves at 22 m/s. What braking force is needed to bring the car to a halt in 20 s? (Neglect friction.)

3. 100 s

**3.** A net force of 2000 N acts on a rocket of mass 1000 kg. How long does it take this force to increase the rocket's velocity from 0 m/s to 200 m/s?

**4.** A snow-scooter has a mass of 250 kg. A constant force acts upon it for 60 s. The scooter's initial velocity is 6.0 m/s and its final velocity is 28 m/s.
  **a.** What change in momentum does it undergo?
  **b.** What is the magnitude of the force which acts upon it?

5. a. 1600 kg
   b. $3.2 \times 10^4$ N·s
   c. $3.2 \times 10^4$ N·s
   d. 50 s

**5.** A car weighing 15 680 N and moving at 20 m/s is acted upon by a 640-N force until it is brought to a halt.
  **a.** What is the car's mass?
  **b.** What is its initial momentum?
  **c.** What change in the car's momentum does the force bring about?
  **d.** How long does the braking force act on the car to bring it to a halt?

**6.** A constant force acts on a 600-kg mass for 68 s. The velocity of the mass is 10 m/s before the force is applied. Its final velocity is 44 m/s.
  **a.** What change in momentum does the force produce?
  **b.** What is the magnitude of the force?

7. $1.1 \times 10^2$ m/s

**7.** A rocket of mass $2.0 \times 10^4$ kg, starting from rest, is acted upon by a net force of $1.5 \times 10^5$ N for 15.0 s. What is the final velocity of the rocket?

## 7:2   Newton's Third Law of Motion

Newton's first two laws of motion were introduced in Chapter 6. Newton's third law of motion is called the **law of action and reaction.** It states that *every force is accompanied by an equal and opposite force.* According to this law, there is no such thing as a single force. An object can produce a force only if there is some other object upon which it can exert its force. Your hand pushes a ball. A magnet repels a second magnet. A charged object repels another charged object. Every interaction involves at least two objects.

Newton's second law of motion states that when one object exerts a force on another, the second object accelerates. But, a fact often overlooked is that the object causing the force also accelerates. For example, a golf ball is hit with a golf club. The ball is accelerated. But so is the club. The club is accelerated, but in a direction opposite to the ball. While striking the ball, the club slows down. The force exerted on the club by the ball gives the club a negative acceleration. If *A* produces a force on *B*, then *B* exerts an equal and opposite force on *A*. Walking is a good example of Newton's third law of motion. As you walk, you attempt to push the earth away from you. The reaction force of the earth on your feet propels you forward.

Newton's third law of motion is also known as the law of action and reaction.

A single force can never exist. Every force is accompanied by an equal and opposite force.

**FIGURE 7-3. During a golf swing (a), the golf club exerts a force on the golf ball while the golf ball also exerts a force on the golf club (b).**

a

b

Courtesy of Harold E. Edgerton, Massachusetts Institute of Technology

The third law of motion leads to the law of conservation of momentum.

Newton's third law of motion is a way of stating the law of conservation of momentum. According to the third law, exactly equal and opposite forces appear whenever two objects interact. The equal and opposite forces act for the same time. One never exists without the other. Thus the impulse, *Ft*, given to one object must be exactly the same as the impulse given to the second object, but in the opposite direction.

$$\begin{array}{ccc} \textit{for Object A} & & \textit{for Object B} \\ Ft & = & -Ft \end{array}$$

and therefore:    $m\,\Delta v \quad = \quad -m\,\Delta v$

It follows from this that a gain in momentum by one object occurs only through the loss of the same amount of momentum by a second object.

## 7:3  Law of Conservation of Momentum

The law of conservation of momentum always holds for any closed system. For this reason, scientists consider this law to be of great importance. It helps them to understand what happens during all collisions. Since all interactions are collisions in one form or another, the law of conservation of momentum is a powerful tool.

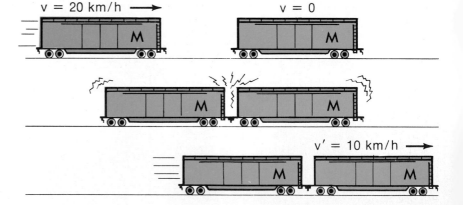

FIGURE 7-4. The total momentum of the freight car system after collision is the same as the total momentum of the system before collision.

Consider the two freight cars of equal mass shown in Figure 7-4. At first, one car moves at 20 km/h while the other car is at rest on the track. Then, the two cars collide and are coupled together. How does the velocity of the coupled cars, *v′*, compare with the velocity of the single freight car, *v*, before the collision? This question can be answered by using the law of conservation of momentum.

The **law of conservation of momentum** *states that the total momentum of an isolated system cannot change.* The freight cars, if they are considered together, form an isolated system. The total momentum of the freight car system cannot be any greater or any less after the cars collide than it was before they collided.

$$Total\ momentum_{before\ collision} = Total\ momentum_{after\ collision}$$

Let $M$ represent the mass of each freight car and let $v'$ represent the velocity of the coupled cars. Substituting the known quantities into the equation, we obtain

$$M \times 20\ km/h = 2M \times v'$$

Solving for $v'$, we find that the coupled freight cars have a velocity of 10 km/h after collision. Note carefully that there are two important aspects of this collision. First, the momentum given up by the first freight car was gained by the second freight car. Second, the total momentum of the two cars is the same after the collision as it was prior to the collision.

To better understand the law of conservation of momentum, consider a system consisting of many particles, such as the molecules in a small container of gas. The gas particles are constantly colliding and changing one another's momentum. However, each particle can gain only the momentum lost by another particle during a collision. Therefore, the total momentum of the system does not change. The total momentum of an isolated system is constant. An isolated system is a system upon which no outside force is acting.

According to the law of conservation of momentum, the total momentum of an isolated system always remains the same.

An isolated system has no outside forces acting on it.

**FIGURE 7-5. Momentum is transferred when billiard balls collide. However, some momentum is lost due to friction between the balls and the table. If we consider the billiard balls and table together as a system, momentum is conserved.**

*Hickson-Bender Photography*

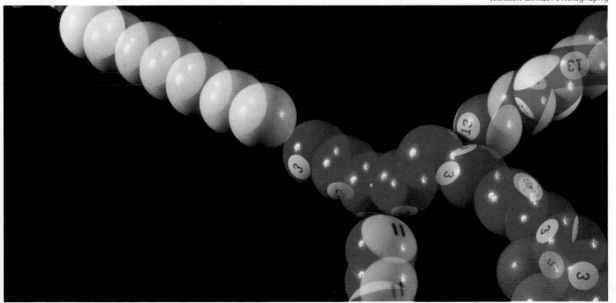

**In a collision, one object gains the momentum lost by the other.**

When two particles collide, one particle can gain only the momentum lost by the other. Therefore, the momentum of the first particle plus the momentum of the second particle must be the same after the collision as it was before the collision. This relationship can be expressed as

$$m_1 v_1 + m_2 v_2 = m_1 v_1' + m_2 v_2'$$

Where $m_1$ and $m_2$ are the masses of the two particles, $v_1$ and $v_2$ are their initial velocities, and $v_1'$ and $v_2'$ are their velocities after collision.

### EXAMPLE:  Conservation of Momentum in a Collision

A glass ball of mass 5.0 g moves with a velocity of 20 cm/s. This ball collides with a second glass ball of mass 10 g which is moving along the same line with a velocity of 10 cm/s. After the collision, the 5.0 g mass is still moving along the same line, but with a velocity of 8.0 cm/s. What is the velocity (speed and direction) of the 10 g mass?

*Solution:*

$$m_1 v_1 + m_2 v_2 = m_1 v_1' + m_2 v_2'$$

$$(5.0 \text{ g})(20 \text{ cm/s}) + (10 \text{ g})(10 \text{ cm/s}) = (5.0 \text{ g})(8 \text{ cm/s}) + (10 \text{ g})(v_2')$$

$$200 \frac{\text{g} \cdot \text{cm}}{\text{s}} = 40 \frac{\text{g} \cdot \text{cm}}{\text{s}} + (10 \text{ g})(v_2')$$

$$160 \frac{\text{g} \cdot \text{cm}}{\text{s}} = (10 \text{ g})(v_2')$$

$$v_2' = 16 \text{ cm/s in its original direction}$$

### PROBLEMS

**8.** A plastic ball of mass 200 g moves with a velocity of 30 cm/s. This plastic ball collides with a second plastic ball of mass 100 g which is moving along the same line with a velocity of 10 cm/s. After the collision, the velocity of the 100-g mass is 26 cm/s along the same line. What is the velocity of the 200-g mass?

**9.** 16 cm/s in its original direction

**9.** An ivory ball of mass 10 g moving with a velocity of 20 cm/s collides with a second ivory ball of mass 20 g moving along the same line with a velocity of 10 cm/s. After the collision, the first ball is still moving in its original direction, but it has a velocity of only 8 cm/s. Determine the velocity of the second ball after the collision.

**10.** A steel glider of mass 5.0 kg moves along an air-track with a velocity of 15 m/s. It overtakes and collides with a second steel glider of mass 10 kg moving in the same direction along the track with a velocity of 7.5 m/s. After the collision, the first glider continues along the same line at 7.0 m/s.

a. With what velocity did the second steel glider leave the collision?

b. What is the change in momentum of the first glider?

c. What is the change in momentum of the second glider?

11. A car of mass 700 kg travels at 20 m/s. The car collides with a stationary truck of mass 1400 kg. The two vehicles interlock as a result of the collision. What is the velocity of the car-truck system?

12. A bullet of mass 50 g strikes a wooden block of mass 5.0 kg. The bullet becomes embedded in the block. The block with the bullet in it then flies off at 10 m/s. What was the original velocity of the bullet?

13. A billiard ball of unknown mass travels at 40 cm/s. This ball overtakes a second billiard ball of mass 150 g which is traveling along the same line at 15 cm/s. After the collision, the first ball moves along the same line at 20 cm/s. The second ball is moving at 42 cm/s. What is the mass of the first ball?

11. 6.7 m/s in the original direction

13. 200 g

# 7:4    Internal Forces—External Forces

The law of conservation of momentum tells us that an outside force is needed to change the total momentum of a system. An internal force can never change the total momentum of a system. Consider the two skaters of Figure 7-6a. One skater has a mass of 30 kg and the second has a mass of 60 kg. They are standing still on smooth ice. The 60-kg skater pushes the 30-kg skater and moves backward as the 30-kg skater moves forward. The larger skater applied an internal force to the system. The total momentum of the system was zero before the internal force was applied. Thus, it must be zero after the internal force is applied. The forward momentum of the smaller skater is

An internal force cannot change the total momentum of a system.

$$30 \text{ kg} \times 0.40 \text{ m/s}$$

It must equal the backward momentum of the larger skater which is

$$60 \text{ kg} \times 0.20 \text{ m/s}$$

If forward is a positive direction, then backward is a negative direction. Thus, the sum of the momenta of the two skaters is zero in Figure 7-6b.

0.20 m/s     0.40 m/s

**FIGURE 7-6. The internal forces exerted by these skaters cannot change the total momentum of the system.**

A force can be internal or external depending on the definition of the system.

The momentum of the universe remains unchanged. This is the meaning of the law of conservation of momentum in its broadest sense.

Note that the momentum of each skater is changed. But, the total momentum of the system does not change. The force between the two skaters was an internal force in the two-skater system. If we consider the system to be only one of the skaters, the force would be an external force. Classifying a force as internal or external depends on how we define the system.

Suppose we consider all the particles in the universe as one large system. Then all forces would be internal forces and there could never be a change in the total momentum of the universe. This reasoning follows the law of conservation of momentum in its broadest sense—the total momentum of the universe is constant.

**EXAMPLE: Conservation of Momentum—Objects Initially at Rest**

A 20-kg projectile leaves a 1200-kg launcher with a velocity of 600 m/s forward. What is the recoil velocity of the launcher?
*Solution:*

$$Momentum_{before\ firing} = Momentum_{after\ firing}$$

$$m_1v_1 + m_2v_2 = m_1v_1' + m_2v_2'$$
$$(1200\ kg \times 0) + (20\ kg \times 0) = (1200\ kg \times v_1') + (20\ kg \times 600\ m/s)$$
$$0 = (1200\ kg \times v_1') + 12\ 000\ kg \cdot m/s$$

$$\text{Then,}\ v_1' = -10\ m/s$$

The negative sign means that the direction of the launcher is in a direction opposite to that of the projectile.

## PROBLEMS

**14.** A 40-kg projectile leaves a 2000-kg launcher with a velocity of 800 m/s forward. What is the recoil velocity (speed and direction) of the launcher?

**15.** A cesium nucleus emits a beta particle of mass $9.1 \times 10^{-31}$ kg with a velocity of $1.5 \times 10^7$ m/s. The resulting barium nucleus has a mass of $2.2 \times 10^{-25}$ kg. What is the recoil velocity of the barium nucleus?

15. 62 m/s

**16.** Upon launching, a model rocket expels 50 g of oxidized fuel from its exhaust at an average velocity of 600 m/s. If the mass of the rocket is 4.0 kg, what is the vertical velocity after the launch? (Disregard gravitational effects.)

**17.** A neutron of mass $1.67 \times 10^{-27}$ kg is ejected from a boron nucleus of remaining mass $17.0 \times 10^{-27}$ kg. If the neutron leaves the nucleus with a velocity of $2.0 \times 10^4$ m/s, what is the recoil velocity of the nucleus?

17. $2.0 \times 10^3$ m/s

**18.** Two campers dock a canoe. One camper steps onto the dock. This camper has a mass of 80 kg and moves forward at 4.0 m/s. With what velocity will the canoe and the other camper with a combined mass of 110 kg move away from the dock?

**19.** A locomotive with a rocket engine is being tested on a smooth horizontal track. The mass of the locomotive is unknown. Starting from rest, the engines are fired for 20 s. During this time they expel 500 kg of oxidized kerosene. The kerosene particles are expelled at an average velocity of 1200 m/s. At the end of the 20-s period the speed of the locomotive is 50 m/s. What is its mass?

19. 12 000 kg

**20.** A thread holds two carts together on a frictionless surface as in Figure 7-7. A compressed spring acts upon the carts. The thread is burned. The 1.5-kg cart moves with a velocity of 27 cm/s to the left. What is the velocity of the 4.5-kg cart?

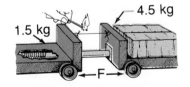

**FIGURE 7-7.**

# 7:5    Conservation of Momentum in General

Thus far, our treatment of the law of conservation of momentum has covered only interactions that take place along the same line. But the law of conservation of momentum holds for all interactions. Momentum is conserved regardless of the directions of the particles before and after they collide.

Figure 7-8a shows a spray can exploding after being thrown from a spacecraft into the near-vacuum conditions of space. We will assume that the can breaks into only two pieces. Before the explosion, the momentum of the can is represented by the vector

Momentum is conserved in all interactions, regardless of the directions of the bodies involved.

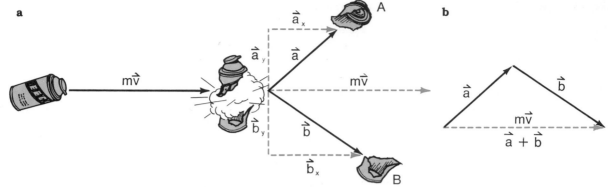

a

b

**FIGURE 7-8. The momen-
tum of the can before it explodes is the same as the
sum of the momenta of the
pieces of the can after it
explodes.**

$m\vec{v}$. After the explosion, the momenta of the two pieces are represented by $\vec{a}$ and $\vec{b}$. Notice that the $y$ components of $\vec{a}$ and $\vec{b}$ are
equal and opposite and have a vector sum of zero. The vector
sum of the $x$ components of $\vec{a}$ and $\vec{b}$ is equal to the original momentum of the can.

As shown in Figure 7-8b, the vectors representing the momenta
of the two pieces can be added. The resultant is the original momentum of the can. Even if the can breaks into many pieces, the
vector sum of the momenta of all the pieces will still be equal to
the initial momentum of the can.

Figure 7-9 shows how the vector sum of the momenta of a system remains constant when collisions are at an angle rather than
head-on. A 2-kg steel ball moves at 5 m/s across a smooth surface toward a second stationary steel ball of mass 2 kg. The balls
collide and move off in the directions shown. Since the mass of
each ball is 2 kg and the velocity of each can be measured, it is
possible to calculate the momentum of each after the collision
takes place. Vectors $a$ and $b$ of the diagram represent the momenta after the collision. In Part b, these vectors are added. Their
vector sum is equal to the momentum of the original ball. If the
collision had taken place between more than two steel balls at the
same time, the result would be the same. The vector sum of the
momenta before the collision would be the same as the vector
sum of the momenta after the collision.

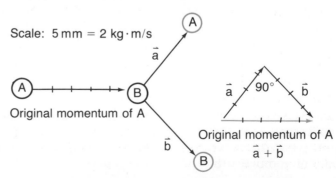

**FIGURE 7-9. The vector
sum of the momenta is
constant.**

### EXAMPLE:  Conservation of Momentum—Collisions at an Angle

Ball *A* of mass 2.0 kg is moving at a velocity of 5.0 m/s. Ball *A* collides with stationary ball *B*, also of mass 2.0 kg, Figure 7-10. After the collision, ball *A* moves off in a direction 30° to the left of its original direction. Ball *B* moves off in a direction 60° to the right of ball *A*'s original direction. **a.** Draw a vector diagram to find the momentum of ball *A* and of ball *B* after the collision. **b.** What is the velocity of each ball after collision?

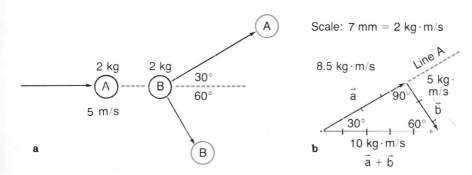

FIGURE 7-10.

*Solution:*

**a.** The vector sum of ball *A*'s momentum and ball *B*'s momentum after the collision must equal the vector sum of the momenta of both balls before the collision took place. Ball *B* was at rest prior to the collision and so had no momentum. Thus, the total momentum of the two balls before the collision was just the momentum of ball *A*.

$$mv = (2.0 \text{ kg})(5.0 \text{ m/s}) = 10 \text{ kg} \cdot \text{m/s}$$

To solve the problem by the graphical method:

1. Draw a vector to represent the original momentum of the system ($\vec{a} + \vec{b}$).

2. Draw a long line at 30° with this vector to represent the path of *A*. (We can call this "line *A*.")

3. We know that *B* moved off at 90° with *A*. Find the point along line *A* where a line from the tip of $\vec{a} + \vec{b}$ would strike at 90°. (Place the corner of a piece of paper on line *A* and adjust it until one edge runs from line *A* to the tip of $\vec{a} + \vec{b}$ and the other edge runs right along line *A*. Draw a line from line *A* to the tip of $\vec{a} + \vec{b}$.)

4. Notice that because you know the directions of $\vec{a}$, $\vec{b}$ and what their resultant must be, the two vectors can be made to delineate each other as you have just done. You have found the only two vectors in the directions of *A* and *B* that would give you $\vec{a} + \vec{b}$.

When the vectors are drawn, measurements to scale yield the magnitudes of the momenta of balls A and B.

$$\vec{a} = 8.5 \text{ kg} \cdot \text{m/s}$$
$$\vec{b} = 5.0 \text{ kg} \cdot \text{m/s}$$

**b.** The masses of balls A and B are 2 kg each. We can calculate the velocity of each.

$$\text{Momentum of } A = (2.0 \text{ kg})(v) = 8.5 \text{ kg} \cdot \text{m/s}$$
$$v = 4.25 \text{ m/s}$$
$$\text{Momentum of } B = (2.0 \text{ kg})(v) = 5.0 \text{ kg} \cdot \text{m/s}$$
$$v = 2.5 \text{ m/s}$$

## PROBLEMS

21. a. 14.1 kg·m/s,
       14.1 kg·m/s
    b. 2.8 m/s, 2.8 m/s

**21.** Ball A of mass 5.0 kg moves at a speed of 4 m/s. It collides with a second stationary ball B, also of mass 5.0 kg. After the collision, ball A moves off in the direction 45° to the left of its original direction. Ball B moves off in the direction 45° to the right of ball A's original direction.

   **a.** Draw a vector diagram to determine the momentum of ball A and of ball B after the collision.

   **b.** What is the speed of each ball after the collision?

**22.** Object A of mass 6.0 kg moves at a speed of 3.0 m/s. It collides with a second stationary object B, also of mass 6.0 kg. After the collision, object A moves off in the direction 50° to the left of its original direction. Object B moves off in the direction 40° to the right of object A's original direction.

   **a.** Draw a vector diagram to determine the momentum of object A and of object B.

   **b.** What is the speed of each object after the collision?

**FIGURE 7-11. Use with Problem 22.**

*From PSSC Physics, D.C. Heath & Co., Lexington, 1965*

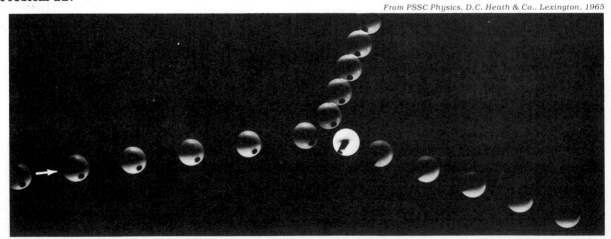

**23.** A billiard ball of mass 0.50 kg moves at a speed of 10 m/s. It collides with a second stationary billiard ball, also of mass 0.50 kg. After the collision, the first ball moves off in a direction 60° to the left of its original direction. The second ball moves off in a direction 30° to the right of the first ball's original direction.

**a.** Draw a vector diagram to determine the momentum of each billiard ball.

**b.** What is the speed of each ball after the collision?

23. a. 4.3 kg·m/s to the right and 2.5 kg·m/s to the left

b. $v_r = 8.6$ m/s, $v_l = 5.0$ m/s

---

**Summary**

**1.** Momentum is the product of the mass of an object and its velocity. 7:1

**2.** When one object collides with another, its change in momentum, $m\Delta v$ is equal to the impulse, $Ft$, that acts on the object. 7:1

**3.** Newton's third law of motion states that every force is accompanied by an equal and opposite force. Forces always exist in pairs. 7:2

**4.** Paired forces are equal in magnitude but opposite in direction. They also exist for equal periods of time. 7:2

**5.** The law of conservation of momentum states that whenever two objects interact the total momentum is the same both before and after the interaction. 7:3

**6.** Only an outside force can change the total momentum of a system. 7:4

**7.** If the universe is considered a closed system, then all the particles in the universe can only exchange momentum. Thus, as for any closed system according to the law of conservation of momentum, the total momentum of the universe is constant. 7:4

**8.** The vector sum of the momenta of any closed system cannot change. 7:5

---

**Questions**

**1.** A spacecraft in outer space accelerates by firing rockets. How can the hot gases escaping from the rocket propel the craft if there is nothing in space for these gases to push against?

**2.** If only an external force can change the momentum of an object, how can the internal force of a car's brakes bring the car to a stop?

**3.** A student stands on a turntable and holds a mass in each hand. The masses are held to the side at arm's length and at shoulder height. Another student slowly turns the turntable. As the student draws the masses in to each side, the table begins to rotate much faster. Explain the increase in speed of rotation.

**FIGURE 7-12.**

**4.** An astronaut on a "space walk" finds that the rope connecting him to the space capsule has broken. Using a pistol, the astronaut manages to get back to the capsule. Explain.

**5.** Explain why the cannoneers in Figure 7-12 have found that their giant cannon is useless.

6. Billiard ball *A* travels across a pool table and collides with a stationary billiard ball *B*. The mass of ball *B* is equal to the mass of ball *A*. After the collision, ball *A* is at rest. What must be true of ball *B*?

7. Is it possible for a bullet to have the same momentum as a truck? Explain.

8. Newton's third law of motion states that for every action force there is an equal and opposite reaction force. The gravitational force acting on a falling object as its weight. If we recognize the pull of the earth on the object as one force what is the reaction force?

## Problems

1. A force of 50 N is applied to a hockey puck for 2.0 s. Calculate the magnitude of the impulse. $100 \ N$

2. Assume the puck in Problem 1 has a mass of 0.50 kg and is at rest before the impulse acts upon it. With what speed does it move across the ice after the 2.0-s period? $200 \ m/s$

3. A 1500-kg car leaves a parking lot. Thirty seconds later it is moving along a highway at 72 km/h.
   a. What is the car's change in momentum? $30,029$
   b. What average force does the motor produce to bring about this change in momentum?

4. A force of 8.0 N acts on a 2.0-kg mass for 5.0 s.
   a. What is the change in momentum of the mass? $40$
   b. What is the change in the speed of the mass? $20$

5. The mass of a car is 1600 kg. The car's velocity is 20 m/s.
   a. What is its momentum? $32000$
   b. How long must a force of 800 N act on the car to give it this momentum? (Assume the direction of the force and the direction of the motion are the same.)

6. A plastic ball of mass 100 g moves with a speed of 20 cm/s. A second plastic ball of mass 40 g is moving along the same path at 10 cm/s. The two balls collide. After the collision, the 100-g mass has a velocity of 15 cm/s in its original direction. What is the velocity (speed and direction) of the 40-g ball after the collision? $22.5$

## Applying Physics

1. *Control of Space Probes:* A space probe of mass 7600 kg is traveling through space at 120 m/s. Houston Control determines that a change in course of 30° is necessary and by electronic communication instructs the probe to fire rockets perpendicular to its direction of motion. If the escaping gas leaves the craft's rockets at an average speed of 3200 m/s, what is the mass of the gas Houston Control should allow to be expelled?

2. *Frictional Effects:* A brick that weighs 24.5 N is released on a long frictionless incline at a point 10 m above a horizontal wooden table. (The angle or length of the incline is of no interest to us here. The brick will reach the bottom of the incline with the same speed it would have if it fell 10 m straight down.) The brick slides down the incline and strikes a second brick that weighs 36.75 N.

   **a.** If the two bricks stick together, with what initial speed will they move along the table?

   **b.** If the force of friction acting on the two bricks is 5.0 N what time will elapse before the bricks come to rest? (Do not compute acceleration.)

   **c.** How far will the two bricks slide before coming to rest?

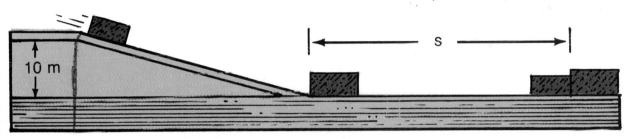

**FIGURE 7-13. Use with Applying Physics 2.**

Forward, Robert L., "Comet Catcher," *Omni*, February, 1980.

Gore, Rick, "What Voyager Saw: Jupiter's Dazzling Realm." *National Geographic*, January, 1980.

Hewitt, Paul, *Conceptual Physics.* (Chapter 5). Boston, Little, Brown and Company, 1980.

Lerner and Gosselin, "Giordano Bruno." *Scientific American*, April, 1973.

**Readings**

The motion of the person on the skateboard is certainly not as simple as that of a car moving along a straight highway. However, straight line motion is similar to curved motion in that it is the result of forces acting on an object. You can understand curved motion more easily if you think of it as motion in two directions at the same time. How can the motion of the skateboard be described? What are some other examples of curved motion?

# Motion in Two Dimensions 8

All curved motion is the result of a force that causes an object to deviate from its straight-line motion. This principle is in accord with Newton's laws of motion. The first law says that an object in motion will travel in a straight line unless acted upon by an unbalanced force. From this we can conclude that an object moving in a curved path must be acted upon by a net force. Thus, the curved path followed by an object depends only upon the direction and size of the unbalanced force that causes the object to change directions.

GOAL: You will gain knowledge and understanding of motion in two dimensions and will apply this knowledge to the study of projectile motion, uniform circular motion, and simple harmonic motion.

## 8:1  Projectile Motion

**Projectile** (proh JEK tyl) **motion** includes all cases of objects thrown or otherwise projected into the air. Examples of projectiles are baseballs and artificial satellites. To begin the study of projectile motion, consider a baseball thrown in a horizontal direction. The baseball will not remain at the same height from which it was thrown. It will begin at once to fall toward the earth. The path followed by the baseball is called its **trajectory.** The vertical and horizontal motions are independent of one another.

Projectile motion is the curved motion of an object that is projected into the air.

A trajectory is the path of a projectile.

Vertical motion and horizontal motion are independent.

*Sports Illustrated/Photo by Jerry Cooke © Time, Inc.*

**FIGURE 8-1. A ski jumper has a horizontal velocity and a vertical velocity. These velocities are independent of one another.**

Consider the two golf balls shown in Figure 8-2. The two balls are released at the same time. One ball is projected horizontally. The other ball is dropped. Strobe photography shows the path followed by each ball. Even though the projected ball moves to the right, its vertical position is, at all times, the same as the vertical position of the dropped ball. Vertically, the projected ball acts as if it has no horizontal velocity and is simply falling. Note also that the projected ball moves the same distance to the right during each time interval. The falling motion does not change the rate at which the ball moves to the right. Both the horizontal and vertical velocities of the ball act as if the other velocity did not exist.

**Vertical velocity is constantly changing because of gravity.**

**Horizontal velocity remains constant.**

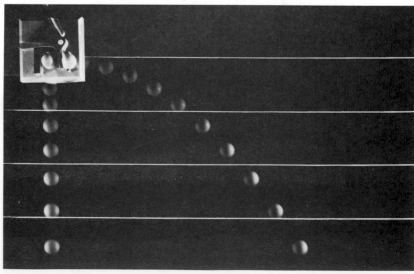

**FIGURE 8-2. A flash photograph of two golf balls released simultaneously. Both balls were allowed to fall freely, but one was projected horizontally with an initial velocity of 2.00 m/s. The light flashes are 1/30 s apart.**

*From PSSC Physics, D.C. Heath & Co., Lexington, 1965*

The horizontal displacement, $s_h$, a projectile moves while it is falling, depends on the horizontal velocity, $v_h$, and the time the projectile is in the air. Then the horizontal distance is the horizontal velocity times the time of fall.

$$s_h = v_h t$$

**EXAMPLE:  Projectile Thrown Horizontally**

A stone is thrown horizontally at 15 m/s. It is thrown from the top of a cliff 44 m high. **a.** How long does it take the stone to reach the bottom of the cliff? **b.** How far from the base of the cliff does the stone strike the ground?

*Solution:*

**a.** Find the time it takes for an object starting from rest to fall 44 m.

$$s_v = \frac{gt^2}{2}$$

$$t = \sqrt{\frac{2s_v}{g}}$$

$$= \sqrt{\frac{2 \times 44 \text{ m}}{9.8 \text{ m/s}^2}}$$

$$= \sqrt{9 \text{ s}^2} = 3.0 \text{ s}$$

When solving problems, the component velocities are treated separately.

**b.** The stone moves horizontally at 15 m/s all the time that it is falling.

$$s_h = v_h t$$

$$= (15 \text{ m/s})(3.0 \text{ s}) = 45 \text{ m}$$

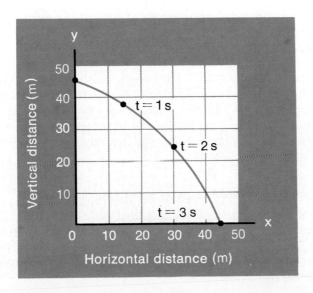

FIGURE 8-3. The path of the projectile for the above Example.

## PROBLEMS

1. 64 m

1. A steel projectile is shot horizontally at 20 m/s from the top of a 49-m high tower. How far from the base of the tower does it hit the ground?

2. A stone is thrown horizontally at a speed of 10 m/s from the top of a cliff 78.4 m high.
   a. How long does it take the stone to reach the bottom of the cliff?
   b. How far from the base of the cliff does the stone strike the ground?

3. 380 m

3. At a height of 784 m, sky divers fall from an airplane flying horizontally at 30 m/s. What horizontal distance do the divers travel before striking the ground? (Neglect air resistance.)

4. A car traveling at 20 m/s rolls off the edge of a cliff. The cliff is 44.1 m above the ocean. How far from the base of the cliff does the car strike the water?

5. 47 m

5. A person standing on a cliff throws a stone with a horizontal speed of 15 m/s. The stone hits the ground 47 m from the base of the cliff. How high is the cliff?

6. A plane drops a rubber raft to the survivors of a shipwreck. The plane is flying at a height of 1960 m and at a speed of 90 m/s. The raft lands next to the survivors. How far away from the shipwreck was the plane when the raft was dropped?

7. 20 m

7. An arrow is fired directly at the bull's-eye of a target 60 m away. The arrow has a speed of 89 m/s. When it is fired, the arrow is 1.0 m above the ground. How far short of the target does it strike the ground?

**FIGURE 8-4. The path of this diver can be analyzed by treating the diver as a projectile fired at an angle with the horizontal.**

## 8:2  Projectiles Fired at an Angle

When a projectile is fired at an angle with the horizontal, the principle of independence of velocities still holds. The initial velocity of the projectile can be resolved into two components. One component is directed vertically. The second is directed horizontally. These component velocities are treated separately when solving problems.

**EXAMPLE: Projectile Fired at an Angle**

A famous motorcyclist plans to jump across a canyon, 3.5 km wide. To do this, the cyclist plans to leave a 30° ramp on one side of the canyon at a speed of 196 m/s. If the motorcycle, equipped with rockets, can attain this speed, will it reach the other side of the canyon on the jump?

United Press International

United Press International

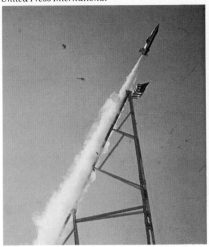

**FIGURE 8-5. Evil Knieval's attempt to jump the Snake River.**

*Solution:*

First, find the horizontal and vertical components of the velocity. This can be done by the graphical method or by the use of mathematics.

$v_v = (v)(\sin 30°)$

$= (196\text{ m/s})(0.5) = 98\text{ m/s}$

$v_h = (v)(\cos 30°)$

$= (196\text{ m/s})(0.866) = 170\text{ m/s}$

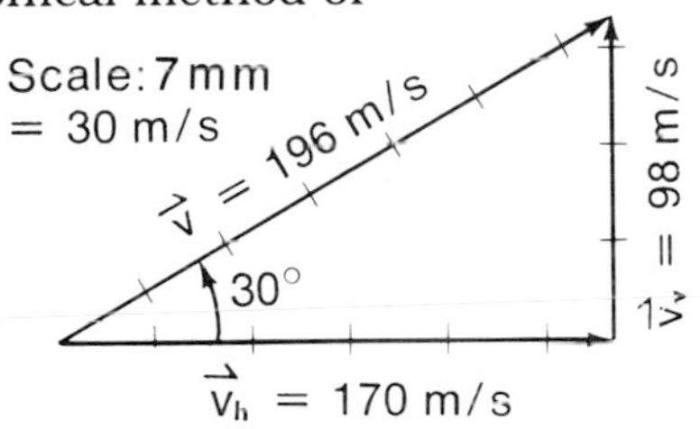
Scale: 7 mm
= 30 m/s
v = 196 m/s
30°
v = 98 m/s
v_h = 170 m/s

**FIGURE 8-6.**

Second, find the total time the bike is in the air. Since, $a = \Delta v/t$, the time needed for the bike to reach its greatest height is

$$t_{up} = \frac{\Delta v_v}{a}$$

$$= \frac{\Delta v_v}{g}$$

$$= \frac{98\text{ m/s}}{9.8\text{ m/s}^2} = 10\text{ s}$$

It will take another 10 s for the bike to return to the earth. Thus, the total time in the air is 20 s. Third, find the horizontal distance the bike travels. The horizontal velocity of 170 m/s is constant. Since the bike spends 20 seconds in the air, the horizontal distance it travels is

**The velocity of a projectile can be resolved into horizontal and vertical components.**

$$s_h = v_h t$$

$$= (170\text{ m/s})(20\text{ s})$$

$$= 3400\text{ m} = 3.4\text{ km}$$

The distance across the canyon is 3.5 km. Therefore, the bike will miss the rim of the canyon by 0.1 km.

**PROBLEMS**

*Assume no frictional effects.*

8. A projectile is fired at such an angle that the vertical component of its velocity is 49 m/s. The horizontal component of its velocity is 60 m/s.
   a. How long does the projectile remain in the air?
   b. What horizontal distance does it travel?

9. a. vertical velocity
   = 170 m/s
   horizontal velocity
   = 98 m/s
   b. 35 s
   c. 3400 m

9. A projectile is fired with a speed of 196 m/s at an angle of 60° with the horizontal. Calculate
   a. the vertical velocity and the horizontal velocity of the projectile.
   b. the time the projectile is in the air.
   c. the horizontal distance the projectile travels.

10. A projectile is fired at an angle of 53° with the horizontal. The speed of the projectile is 200 m/s. Calculate
    a. the time the shell remains in the air.
    b. the horizontal distance it travels.

11. a. 20 s
    b. It hits the archer.
    c. 700 m

11. While standing on an open bed of a truck moving at 35 m/s an archer sees a duck flying directly overhead. The archer shoots an arrow at the duck and misses. The arrow leaves the bow with a vertical velocity of 98 m/s. The truck maintains a constant speed of 35 m/s and does not change its direction.
    a. How long does the arrow remain in the air?
    b. Where does the arrow finally land?
    c. What horizontal distance does the arrow travel while it is in the air?

12. A golf ball is hit at an angle of 45° with the horizontal. If the initial velocity of the ball is 50 m/s, how far will it travel horizontally before striking the ground?

# 8:3   Uniform Circular Motion

Uniform circular motion results when a net force, acting on an object moving with a constant speed, changes direction in such a way that it is always acting at a right angle to the direction in which the mass is moving.

Consider Figure 8-7. A stone is tied to the end of a string. Then the stone is swung in a horizontal circle. The force which keeps the stone in its circular path is called **centripetal** (sen TRIP uht uhl) **force,** $F_c$. Centripetal means center-seeking. This force is exerted on the stone through the string. If this force is removed, the stone travels off in a straight line at its point of release. This behavior is in accord with the first law of motion. The straight line path is tangent to the circle at the point of release. This line is shown as $v_i$ on Figure 8-7.

Centripetal force is a force directed toward the center.

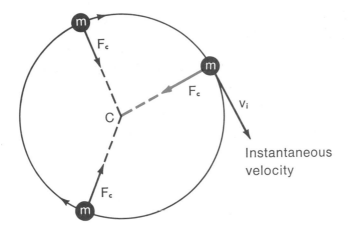

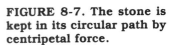

FIGURE 8-7. The stone is kept in its circular path by centripetal force.

Note that the centripetal force always acts at right angles to the instantaneous velocity of the stone. Therefore, the centripetal force cannot change the magnitude of the velocity. However, the force does change the direction of the velocity. Since velocity is a vector quantity, a change in direction is a change in velocity, $\Delta v$. A change in the velocity of the stone means that the stone is being accelerated. According to the second law of motion, acceleration is always in the same direction as the applied force. The force, $F_c$, acting on the stone is always directed toward the center of the circle. Thus, the acceleration is always directed toward the center of the circle. This acceleration is called **centripetal acceleration.**

By drawing a vector diagram, we can analyze uniform circular motion. That is, we can derive equations for the magnitude of both the centripetal acceleration and the centripetal force.

In circular motion, the centripetal force must be perpendicular to the object's instantaneous velocity.

Circular motion, like all motion, is governed by Newton's laws of motion.

Centripetal acceleration, like centripetal force, is always directed toward the center of the circle.

*Hickson Bender Photography*

FIGURE 8-8. In flying a hand-controlled airplane, the force on the plane is always directed toward the center of the circle.

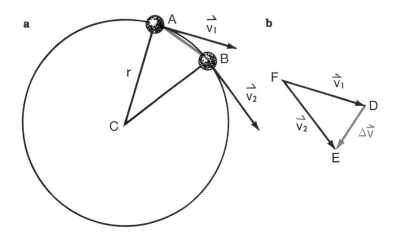

**FIGURE 8-9. A mass moving with uniform circular motion.**

The equations for centripetal acceleration and centripetal force can be derived by drawing a vector diagram.

In Figure 8-9a, $A$ and $B$ are two successive positions of a mass that is moving with uniform circular motion. The radius of the circle is $r$. The vector $v_1$ represents the instantaneous velocity of the mass at $A$. The vector $v_2$ represents the velocity of the mass at $B$. Note that $\vec{v}_1$ and $\vec{v}_2$ are identical in magnitude, but their directions are different. The magnitude will be denoted by the symbol $v$.

Vectors are subtracted by placing them tail to tail.

In Figure 8-9b, $\vec{v}_1$ and $\vec{v}_2$ have been placed tail to tail. We learned in Chapter 5 that by placing vectors head to tail, we could find their vector sum. By placing two vectors tail to tail, we can find their vector difference. Subtracting vectors can be used to find the change in velocity, $\Delta\vec{v}$. By drawing the vector $\Delta\vec{v}$, you can see that the vector $\vec{v}_2$ is the resultant of $\vec{v}_1$ and $\Delta\vec{v}$. Because $\vec{v}_1 + \Delta\vec{v} = \vec{v}_2$, it is apparent that $\Delta\vec{v} = \vec{v}_2 - \vec{v}_1$. Therefore, $\Delta\vec{v}$ is the vector difference between $\vec{v}_1$ and $\vec{v}_2$.

The triangles $ABC$ and $DEF$ are similar triangles because the corresponding sides of angles $C$ and $F$ are perpendicular. Thus,

$$\frac{\Delta v}{v} = \frac{chord\ AB}{r}$$

The arc $AB$ is the displacement, $s$, the mass moves during the time interval $\Delta t$. The distance, $s$, may be expressed as $v\Delta t$. If we choose $A$ and $B$ such that they are very close together, the chord $AB$ and the arc $AB$ become the same length within a small margin of error. Thus, we may express the chord $AB$ as $v\Delta t$.

$$\text{Since} \quad \frac{\Delta v}{v} = \frac{v\Delta t}{r} \qquad \text{Then} \quad \frac{\Delta v}{\Delta t} = a$$

$$\frac{\Delta v}{\Delta t} = \frac{v^2}{r} \qquad\qquad a = \frac{v^2}{r}$$

This equation allows us to find the magnitude of the centripetal acceleration of any object moving in a circle when the radius of the circle and the instantaneous velocity of the object are known.

The velocity of a moving object is

$$v = s/t$$

The time it takes for the object to traverse the circumference of its circular path once is called its period, $T$. The distance the object travels in a single revolution is the circumference of the circle, $2\pi r$. Thus, its speed is

The period, $T$, is the time it takes an object to travel once around a circular path.

$$v = \frac{2\pi r}{T}$$

This expression for $v$ can be substituted into the equation for centripetal acceleration to yield

$$a = \frac{v^2}{r}$$
$$= \frac{(2\pi r/T)^2}{r}$$
$$= \frac{4\pi^2 r}{T^2}$$

Since magnitude of any force is equal to $ma$, the centripetal force, $F_c$, producing the circular motion must be

$$F_c = ma$$
$$= \frac{mv^2}{r}$$
$$= \frac{m4\pi^2 r}{T^2}$$

FIGURE 8-10. Centripetal force holds these people in position. The force on each swing is directed toward the center of the circle.

*Nancy Butler/fpg*

**EXAMPLE: Centripetal Force**

In a laboratory, metals are tested for tensile strength. Tensile strength is a measure of the force needed to break a metal. In doing this, a 1.5-kg mass is attached to the end of a metal wire. Then the mass is swung in a horizontal circle. If the wires tested are 2.0 m long, to what force is each wire subjected when the mass is swung at a rate of 2.0 rev/s?

*Solution:*

Find the period, $T$, the time needed for the mass to complete one revolution. Since the mass completes 2.0 rev/s, its period is 0.50 s. Then calculate the value of $F_c$.

$$F_c = \frac{m4\pi^2 r}{T^2}$$

$$= \frac{(1.5 \text{ kg})(4)(9.9)(2.0 \text{ m})}{(0.5 \text{ s})^2}$$

$$= \frac{119 \text{ kg} \cdot \text{m}}{0.25 \text{ s}^2}$$

$$= 476 \text{ N}$$

**PROBLEMS**

13. a. 630 m/s²
    b. 634 N

**13.** A 1-kg mass is attached to a string of 1.0 m long and moves in a horizontal circle at a rate of 4.0 rev/s.
    **a.** Find the centripetal acceleration of the mass.
    **b.** Calculate the centripetal force (the tension in the string).

**14.** What is the centripetal acceleration of an object moving in a circular path of 20-m radius with a speed of 20 m/s?

15. a. 62 m/s²
    b. 120 N

**15.** A 2.0-kg mass is attached to a string 1.0 m long and swings in a circle parallel to the horizontal. The mass goes around its path once each 0.80 s.
    **a.** What is its centripetal acceleration?
    **b.** What tension is in the string?

**16.** It takes a 600-kg racing car 10 s to travel at a uniform speed around a circular racetrack of 50-m radius.
    **a.** What average force must the car's tires exert against the track to maintain its circular motion?
    **b.** What is the acceleration of the car?

17. a. 6.3 N
    b. 25 N
    c. The ratio is 4:1.

**17.** A child twirls a yo-yo about his head. The yo-yo has a mass of 0.20 kg and is attached to a string 0.80 m long.
    **a.** If the yo-yo makes one complete revolution each second, what tension must exist in the string?
    **b.** If the child increases the speed of the yo-yo to 2 rev/s, what tension must be in the string?
    **c.** What is the ratio of the answer in (b) to (a)? Why?

18. The radius of the moon's orbit about the earth is about $3.6 \times 10^8$ m. The moon's period is $2.3 \times 10^6$ seconds (27.3 days). Find the centripetal acceleration of the moon.

19. An early major objection to the idea that the earth is spinning on its axis was that the earth would turn so fast (1600 km/h) at the equator that people would be thrown off into space. Show the error in this logic by calculating
    a. the weight of a 100-kg person.
    b. the centripetal force needed to hold the same person in place at the equator. The radius of the earth is about 6400 km.

19. a. 980 N
    b. 3.1 N

## 8:4   Placing a Satellite in Orbit

The earth is nearly a sphere. Looking at Figure 8-11, you can see that the earth curves away from a line tangent to its surface at a rate of 4.9 meters for every 8 kilometers. An object falling from rest will fall a distance of 4.9 meters in one second. It becomes clear that if a cannon ball could be fired from a mountain top at a speed of 8 km/s, the ball would fall toward the earth. However, it would be no closer to the surface of the earth at the end of the second than it was to begin with.

If there were no air surrounding the earth to cause friction, the cannon ball would continue to travel forward at 8 km each second as it falls 4.9 m each second. The cannon ball would literally fall around the earth. The ball would continue to go around the earth and become an artificial satellite. The orbital speed of the satellite would be

$$8 \text{ km/s} \times 3600 \text{ s/h} = 28\,800 \text{ km/h}$$

**FIGURE 8-11. If the cannonball travels 8 km horizontally in 1 s, it will fall the same distance toward the earth as the earth falls from the cannonball.**

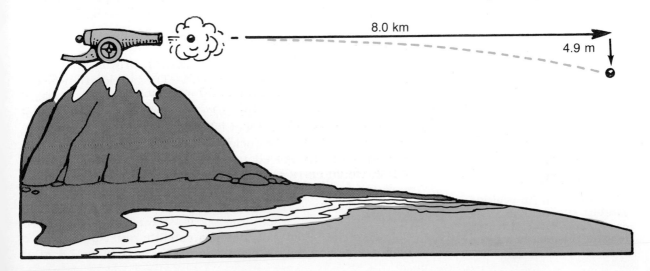

8.0 km

4.9 m

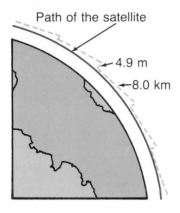

Path of the satellite

4.9 m

8.0 km

**FIGURE 8-12. An Earth satellite keeps falling 4.9 m toward the earth for each 8 km it travels horizontally.**

A satellite's weight provides the centripetal force to maintain its circular motion.

A satellite's mass does not affect its orbital velocity.

Most satellites are placed in orbit at a height of more than 320 km above the earth's surface. At such heights, there is very little atmosphere to cause friction and reduce the speed of the satellite. Thus, a launched satellite will orbit the earth for long periods of time. Further power input will not be needed.

Notice that the motion of the satellite above the earth would be circular motion. The conditions for placing a satellite in orbit are the same as those for any other circular motion. Since the satellite circles the earth, it is acted upon by a centripetal force ($F_c$) that is always directed toward the center of the earth. The gravitational force (or weight) that acts on the satellite provides just such a force. Thus, the weight of a space capsule is what keeps it in its orbital path.

The equation for circular motion is $F_c = mv^2/r$. Because it is the weight ($mg$) of a satellite that must provide the necessary centripetal force to keep it in its orbital path, we may write

$$mg = \frac{mv^2}{r}$$

This equation reduces to

$$g = \frac{v^2}{r}$$

Thus, the velocity a satellite must have to orbit the earth is

$$v = \sqrt{gr}$$

where $g$ is the acceleration of gravity and $r$ is roughly the radius of the earth. You can verify that this "orbital velocity" is about $2.9 \times 10^4$ km per hour, in Problem 20.

Note that the mass of the satellite does not affect its orbital velocity. Even though a more massive satellite weighs more, the centripetal force increases in exact accord with the increased mass. As shown above, the mass of the satellite drops out of the equation.

Satellites are accelerated to reach an orbital velocity by large rockets such as the Saturn V. The acceleration of any mass follows Newton's second law ($F = ma$). A massive satellite requires a large force to accelerate it to orbital velocity. Thus, the mass of launched satellites is limited by the capabilities of the rocket that is used. Large space platforms could be placed in orbit by using several rockets. Each would carry parts of the platform to be assembled in orbit.

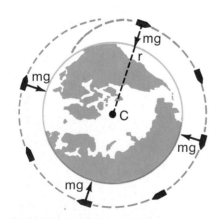

mg
r
mg
C
mg
mg

**FIGURE 8-13. An orbiting satellite is acted upon by a centripetal force directed toward the center of the earth.**

## PROBLEMS

**20.** Calculate the velocity at which a satellite must be launched in order to achieve an orbit about the earth. Use 9.8 m/s² as the acceleration of gravity and 6500 km as the earth's radius.

**21.** During the lunar landings, the command module orbited the moon while waiting for the lunar module to return from the moon's surface. If the diameter of the moon is 3570 km and the acceleration of gravity on the moon is 1.6 m/s$^2$, at what velocity did the command module orbit the moon?

**22.** Calculate the velocity at which Viking I orbited Jupiter. The acceleration of gravity on Jupiter is 5800 m/s$^2$. The diameter of the planet is 142 200 km.

21. 1.7 km/s

# 8:5 Simple Harmonic Motion

A swinging pendulum and vibrating guitar string are both examples of vibrational motion. In this type of motion, an object moves back and forth over the same path.

**Simple harmonic motion** (SHM) is a special kind of vibrational motion. In SHM, the acceleration of the object is directly proportional to its displacement, $x$, from its rest position. In this way, SHM differs from other vibrational motions. For example, when the mass hanging from the spring in Figure 8-14 is pulled down, the force tries to restore the mass to its rest position. This force increases in direct proportion to the distance the mass is pulled from its rest position. Since the force increases directly, the acceleration of the mass must do likewise because $F = ma$. Thus, the acceleration varies directly with the displacement and this is an example of SHM. The acceleration of the mass is greatest at $C$, zero at $B$, and in full magnitude again at $A$. Note that at all times, the acceleration is directed toward the rest position which is another characteristic of SHM.

Vibrational motion is the to and fro movement of an object over the same path.

In SHM, the acceleration varies directly with the displacement.

**FIGURE 8-14.** Vibrating objects undergo simple harmonic motion.

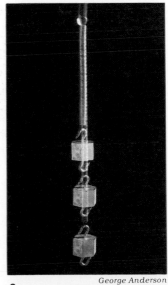

*George Anderson*

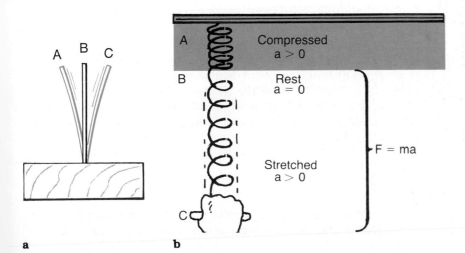

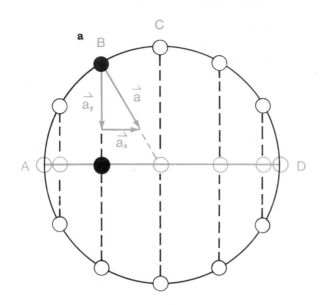

**FIGURE 8-15. A diagram of uniform circular motion (a). The uniform circular motion of a mass as viewed from above (b) and from the side (c).**

SHM can be explained as the projection of circular motion.

Period is the time needed for one vibration.

A relationship exists between SHM and circular motion. Look at Figure 8-15a. A ball is shown moving in a circle with uniform speed. The acceleration of the ball is directed toward the center of the circle at all times. However, at point *B*, we can consider the acceleration to consist of the *x* and *y* components shown. The *x* component $a_x$, is always directed parallel to the diameter *AD*. Notice that $a_x$ is zero at *C* and greatest at its maximum displacement from *C*. In between, $a_x$ fluctuates smoothly between zero and maximum.

Consider a ball moving back and forth along the axis *AD*. The ball moves in such a way as to always align with the mass going around the circle at any given point in time. At any position, its acceleration would be the same as $a_x$, and it would be undergoing SHM. Simple harmonic motion can be described as the projection of circular motion on one axis.

The time required for one complete back and forth motion is called the **period** of vibration. The period of an object undergoing uniform circular motion and an object undergoing SHM would be the same. For example, it would take the ball in Figure 8-15 as long to go back and forth along its axis as it would take it to go around the circle. We have found that, for uniform circular motion,

$$a = 4\pi^2 r/T^2$$

Thus, the period of both circular motion and SHM must be given as

$$T^2 = \frac{4\pi^2 r}{a}$$

To show the usefulness of the relationship between circular motion and SHM, we will use the pendulum of Figure 8-16. In this figure, the gravitational acceleration $\vec{g}$ is resolved into two components. The component $\vec{g}_x$ is at a right angle to the direction of the string. Since the motion of the pendulum is always at a right angle to the direction of the string, $\vec{g}_x$ represents the acceleration of the pendulum. The two triangles of Figure 8-16 are similar triangles. Therefore,

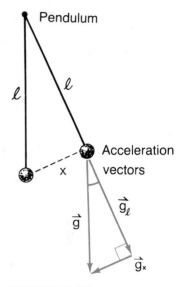

Pendulum

Acceleration vectors

**FIGURE 8-16.**

$$\frac{g_x}{x} = \frac{g}{l} \quad \text{and} \quad g_x = \frac{gx}{l}$$

The equation for the period of a pendulum can be derived.

$$T^2 = \frac{4\pi^2 r}{a} = \frac{4\pi^2 x}{(g/l)x} = \frac{4\pi^2 l}{g}$$

$$T = 2\pi \sqrt{\frac{l}{g}}$$

Notice that the period of a pendulum does not depend on the mass of the object nor on the amplitude of the swing. **Amplitude** is the distance from the pendulum's rest position to the point of greatest displacement. In any one location, the period depends only on the length of the pendulum ($g$ being constant for a given location). Note also that a simple pendulum can be used to measure the acceleration of gravity.

Amplitude is the greatest displacement from the rest position.

**EXAMPLE: The Period of a Pendulum**

Determine the period of a pendulum 6.0 m in length.
*Solution:*

$$T = 2\pi \sqrt{\frac{l}{g}}$$

$$= 6.28 \sqrt{\frac{6.0 \text{ m}}{9.8 \text{ m/s}^2}}$$

$$= 6.28 \sqrt{0.61 \text{ s}^2}$$

$$= 4.9 \text{ s}$$

**PROBLEMS**

**23.** Determine the period of a pendulum 1.0 m long.          23. 2.0 s

**24.** What is the period of a pendulum 0.50 m long?

**25.** The period of a pendulum is 1.0 s. Find its length in meters.          25. 0.25 m

**26.** The period of a pendulum is 4.0 seconds. If the pendulum is 4.0 m in length, determine the acceleration of gravity.

**27.** After landing on Planet Zither, you carefully measure the period of a pendulum 2.0 m long. You find it to be 2.8 seconds. What is the value of $g$ on Planet Zither?          27. 10 m/s²

**Summary**

1. An object thrown horizontally falls in accordance with the acceleration of gravity. Its horizontal velocity is constant.   **8:1**

2. When an object is projected at an angle with the horizontal, the vertical component is used to find the time the object will spend in the air. The horizontal component is constant and is used to find the horizontal distance traveled.   **8:2**

3. Uniform circular motion results when a net force, called the centripetal force, constantly acts at a right angle to the direction in which the mass is moving.   **8:3**

4. Both the centripetal force and the centripetal acceleration are always directed toward the center of the circle.   **8:3**

5. The weight of a satellite provides the centripetal force needed to keep it in its orbital path. To put a satellite in orbit it must be given a velocity that agrees with the expression $g = v^2/r$.   **8:4**

6. If an object moves back and forth over the same path in a regular manner its motion is called simple harmonic motion. This type of motion is related to circular motion.   **8:5**

**Questions**

1. A hunter standing on a high platform aims a rifle straight at a monkey who is hanging on a distant tree branch by one hand. The barrel of the rifle is parallel to the horizontal. Just as the hunter pulls the trigger, the monkey lets go of the branch and begins to fall. Will the bullet hit the monkey?

2. An airplane is flying at a constant speed in a straight line parallel to the horizontal, and the pilot drops a flare. Where will the plane be relative to the flare when the flare hits the ground?

3. What relationship must exist between an applied force and a moving mass if uniform circular motion is to result?

4. Distinguish between the period and the amplitude of a pendulum.

5. How is simple harmonic motion distinguished from other types of vibrational motion?

**FIGURE 8-17. Use with Question 6.**

6. Consider the path of the ball in Figure 8-17.
   a. At which point is the vertical velocity the greatest? (You may find two points.)
   b. At which point is the horizontal velocity the greatest?
   c. Where is the vertical velocity least?
   d. Name the curve traveled by the ball.

1. A stone is thrown horizontally at 8.0 m/s from a cliff 78.4 m high. How far from the base of the cliff will the stone strike the ground?

2. A bridge is 176.4 m above a river. If a lead-weighted fishing line is thrown from the bridge with a horizontal speed of 22 m/s, what horizontal distance will it travel before striking the water?

3. **a.** If an object falls from a resting height of 490 m, how long will it remain in the air?
   **b.** If the object had a horizontal velocity of 200 m/s when it began to fall what horizontal distance will it travel?

4. A toy car moves off the edge of a table that is 1.225 m high. If the car lands 0.40 m from the base of the table,
   **a.** how long did it take for the car to fall to the floor?
   **b.** with what horizontal velocity was the car moving?

5. Divers at Acapulco dive from a cliff that is 61 m high. If the rocks below the cliff extend outward for 23 m, what is the minimum horizontal velocity a diver must have to clear them?

6. A projectile is fired at an angle of 37° with the horizontal. If the initial velocity of the projectile is 1000 m/s, what horizontal distance will it travel?

7. A baseball is hit at 30 m/s at an angle of 53° with the horizontal. An outfielder runs at 4 m/s toward the infield and catches the ball. What was the original distance between the batter and the outfielder?

8. An athlete twirls a 7-kg hammer tied to the end of a 1.3-m rope in a horizontal circle. The hammer moves at the rate of 1 rev/s.
   **a.** What is the centripetal acceleration of the hammer?
   **b.** What is the tension in the rope?

1. *Particle Accelerators:* In a cyclotron an electromagnet exerts a force of $7.50 \times 10^{-13}$ N on a beam of protons. Each proton has a mass of $1.67 \times 10^{-27}$ kg. The electromagnet causes the protons to travel in a circular path of radius 1.20 m. What is the velocity of the proton beam?

2. *Aeronautics:* A 75-kg pilot flies her plane in a loop and notices that at the top of the loop, where the plane is completely upside-down for an instant, she hangs freely in her seat. The airspeed indicator reads 120 m/s. What is the radius of the plane's loop?

Drake, Stillman, "Galileo's Discovery of the Parabolic Trajectory." *Scientific American*, March, 1975.
Overbye, Dennis, "The Ears of Socorro." *Discovery*, October, 1980.
Wesson, Paul S., "Does Gravity Change With Time?" *Physics Today*, July, 1980.

At one time, gravity was thought to be a special force which pulls everything to the earth. However, in the 17th century, Sir Isaac Newton began to think that all objects might exert gravitational forces on all other objects. He found evidence to support this idea in the motions of heavenly bodies. From experience, we know that this parachutist is being pulled to the ground by the earth's gravitational force. However, does the parachutist also exert a gravitational pull on the earth?

*Kim Massie from Rainbow*

# Universal Gravitation 9

Until Newton's time, gravitational force was thought to be a unique property of the earth. However, Newton suspected that the earth was not unique among the heavenly bodies. He had already found that all motion follows three universal laws. Perhaps the gravitational force of the earth was only one example of a universal force which acts between any two bodies.

GOAL: You will gain knowledge and understanding of the law of universal gravitation and of some of the methods which scientists use to solve complex problems.

## 9:1 Kepler's Laws of Planetary Motion

As a boy of fourteen, Tycho Brahe (1546–1601) heard that astronomers had predicted an eclipse of the sun on August 21, 1560. Tycho watched for the eclipse and on that date it did indeed occur. However, Tycho noticed that the astronomers' prediction of the exact time of the eclipse was 20 minutes in error. He was disturbed by the error in their predictions and thereupon decided to become an astronomer and set matters straight.

Tycho studied at many universities as he prepared for his career. Once out of the classroom he lost no time in beginning his life's work. In 1576, King Frederick II of Denmark gave Tycho an observatory on the island of Hveen. Here, for most of his life, he observed the heavens. Night after night, for more than 20 years, he recorded the positions of the planets and stars. Near the end of his life, Brahe hired an assistant named Johannes Kepler (1571–1630). Although Kepler did not have Brahe's patience for observation, he was an excellent mathematician. Using Brahe's vast amount of data, Kepler formulated three laws of planetary motion.

*The Bettman Archive Inc.*

**FIGURE 9-1. An artist's rendition of Tycho Brahe's laboratory.**

1. The paths of the planets are ellipses.
2. An imaginary line from a planet to the sun sweeps out equal areas each second whether the planet is close or far from the sun.
3. If the radius of a planet's orbit about the sun is cubed and then divided by the planet's period (the time for it to travel about the sun once) squared, the same number or constant ($k$) is always obtained. This constant is expressed as

$$\frac{r^3}{T^2} = k$$

**FIGURE 9-2. An imaginary line from the earth to the sun sweeps out equal areas each second whether the earth is close or far from the sun.**

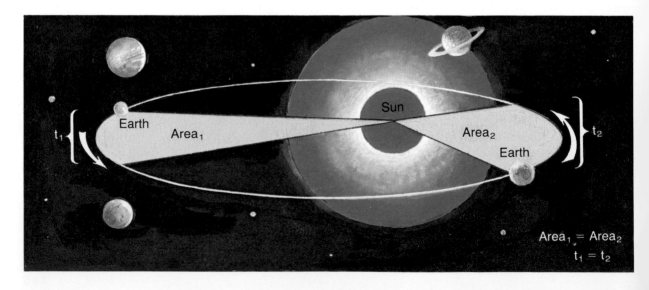

## 9:2  Universal Gravitation

The observations of Tycho Brahe and the calculations of Johannes Kepler provided the basis for Newton's theory of universal gravitation. Legend has it that while watching an apple fall from a tree, Newton recognized that the apple fell because an unbalanced force acted on it. (Newton's second law of motion.) This force was gravity. Newton wondered if this special force was peculiar to the earth. Did other bodies also have it? Perhaps every body exerts a gravitational force on every other body. Newton looked for a way to describe this force and to determine its magnitude. He reasoned that if gravitational force is found throughout the universe, it might also be the force that keeps the planets in their orbits about the sun. Kepler's studies revealed two important facts about the planets. First, their elliptical orbits are nearly circular. Thus, the force that causes the planets to move around the sun must conform to the equations for circular motion,

$$F_c = mv^2/r \quad \text{or} \quad F_c = \frac{m4\pi^2 r}{T^2}$$

Secondly, Kepler found that for all of the planets, $r^3/T^2$ is the same number, $k$. Newton knew that this relationship was no accident. It had to be the result of the force keeping the planets in their orbits. He rearranged $r^3/T^2 = k$ to read $T^2 = r^3/k$. The $T$ in this equation represents the period of any planet as it orbits the sun. He then substituted $r^3/k$ for $T^2$ in the equation for the centripetal force acting on the planet.

$$F_c = \frac{m4\pi^2 r}{T^2}$$

$$= \frac{m4\pi^2 r}{r^3/k}$$

$$= \frac{m4\pi^2 k}{r^2}$$

In this expression, $4\pi^2 k$ is considered to be a single factor or constant. The value of each of its components is always the same. Thus $4\pi^2 k$ is called $K$. The equation becomes

$$F_c = \frac{mK}{r^2}$$

This result told Newton that the force between any planet and the sun varies inversely with the square of its distance (radius) from the sun. It also told him that the force varies directly with the mass of a planet.

Newton reasoned that if the force between the sun and a planet depends on the mass of the planet, the force must also depend on the mass of the sun. After all, the planet is one mass and the

Newton wondered if every body exerts a gravitational force on every other body.

Newton then reasoned that this universal gravitational force keeps the planets in their orbits.

Newton substituted Kepler's third law into the expression for centripetal force.

Gravitational force varies inversely with the square of the distance between two bodies.

Gravitational force varies directly with the product of the masses.

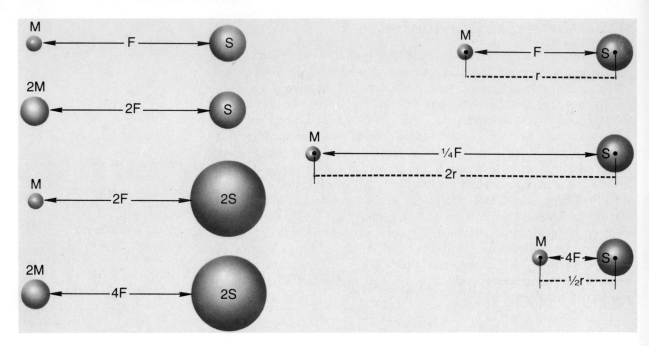

**FIGURE 9-3. The gravitational force between any two bodies increases as the product of their masses and decreases as one over the square of their distances.**

sun is another. Since the sun exerts a force on the planet, then, by the third law of motion, the planet must exert an equal but opposite force on the sun. If the mass of a planet were suddenly doubled, the gravitational force between the planet and the sun would be doubled. If instead the mass of the sun were doubled, then the gravitational force between the sun and the planet would still be doubled. If the mass of both the planet and the sun were doubled, the gravitational force between the two would increase by a factor of four. Thus, the gravitational force between any two bodies must increase as the product of their masses $m_1 m_2$.

Newton assumed that the gravitational force between any two bodies acts in the same way as the force between a planet and the sun. From this assumption, he wrote the **law of universal gravitation.** This law states that *every body in the universe attracts every other body in the universe with a force that varies directly with the product of the masses and inversely with the square of the distance between the centers of the two masses.* This law is written

The law of universal gravitation gives the equation for the gravitational force between two bodies.

$$F = G \frac{m_1 m_2}{r^2}$$

The universal gravitational constant, $G$, is equal to $6.67 \times 10^{-11}$ N·m²/kg².

In the equation, $m_1$ and $m_2$ are the masses of the two bodies, $r$ is the distance between the centers of the masses, and $G$ is a universal constant. The value of $G$ is $6.67 \times 10^{-11}$ N·m²/kg².

Ward's Natural Science Establishment, Inc.

**FIGURE 9-4. Gravitational forces hold the stars in their relative positions in this spiral galaxy.**

## EXAMPLE: Law of Universal Gravitation

Two freight cars, each of mass $3.0 \times 10^5$ kg, are located on adjacent tracks. Their centers are 9.0 m apart. What gravitational force exists between them?

*Solution:*

$$F = G \frac{m_1 m_2}{r^2}$$
$$= \left(6.67 \times 10^{-11} \frac{\text{N} \cdot \text{m}^2}{\text{kg}^2}\right) \frac{(3.0 \times 10^5 \text{ kg})(3.0 \times 10^5 \text{ kg})}{(9.0 \text{ m})^2}$$
$$= \left(6.67 \times 10^{-11} \frac{\text{N} \cdot \text{m}^2}{\text{kg}^2}\right) \frac{(9.0 \times 10^{10} \text{ kg}^2)}{81 \text{ m}^2}$$
$$= 0.074 \text{ N}$$

## PROBLEMS

*Assume the distance, r, is between the centers of the two masses.*

1. Two people are standing 2.0 m apart. One has a mass of 80 kg. The other has a mass of 60 kg. What is the gravitational force between them?

   1. $8.0 \times 10^{-8}$ N

2. **a.** What is the gravitational force between two 800-kg cars that are 5.0 m apart?

   **b.** What is the gravitational force between them when they are 50 m apart?

3. Two ships are docked next to each other. Their centers of gravity are 40 m apart. One ship weighs $9.8 \times 10^7$ N. The other ship weighs $1.96 \times 10^8$ N. What gravitational force exists between them?

   3. 8.3 N

4. Two space capsules, of equal mass, are put into orbit 30 m apart. The gravitational force between them is $2.0 \times 10^{-7}$ N.
   **a.** What is the mass of each space capsule?
   **b.** What is the initial acceleration given to each capsule by this force?

5. $7.2 \times 10^{22}$ kg

5. The mass of the earth is $6.0 \times 10^{24}$ kg. If the centers of the earth and moon are $3.9 \times 10^8$ m apart, the gravitational force between them is about $1.9 \times 10^{20}$ N. What is the approximate mass of the moon?

6. Use Newton's second law of motion to find the acceleration given to the moon by the force calculated in Problem 5.

7. $1.0 \times 10^{-47}$ N

7. The mass of an electron is $9.1 \times 10^{-31}$ kg. The mass of a proton is $1.7 \times 10^{-27}$ kg. They are about $1.0 \times 10^{-10}$ m apart in a hydrogen atom. What force of gravitation exists between the proton and the electron of a hydrogen atom?

Newton tested the law of universal gravitation indirectly by calculating to see if the earth's gravitational force could keep the moon in orbit.

FIGURE 9-5. The moon is held in its orbit around the earth by the earth's gravitational field.

## 9:3 Newton's Test of the Inverse Square Law

Newton lacked the necessary equipment to make a direct test of the law of universal gravitation. That is, he could not measure the gravitational force between two small masses. However, Newton did know something about the moon and its orbit. Therefore, he applied his new law to the moon to determine whether or not it could be gravitational force that keeps it in its orbital path about the earth.

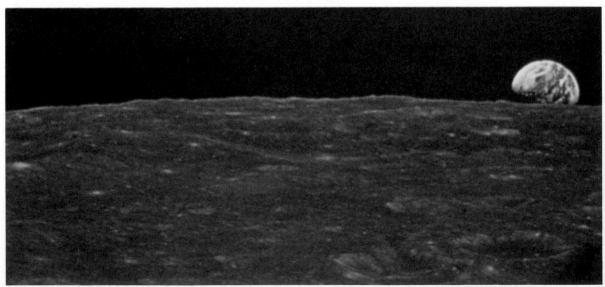

*NASA*

The moon is about 60 earth radii from the earth. Gravitational force varies inversely with the square of the distance between two masses. Newton reasoned that the acceleration of the moon should vary in the same way if it is gravitational force that causes its centripetal acceleration. Thus, the gravitational acceleration given to the moon by the earth should be only $1/(60)^2$ or $1/3600$ of the gravitational acceleration found at the earth's surface. This would be

$$(9.8 \text{ m/s}^2)\left(\frac{1}{3600}\right) = 0.0027 \text{ m/s}^2$$

Because Newton knew the distance to the moon and its period, he could calculate its centripetal acceleration. He could compare the moon's centripetal acceleration with the acceleration predicted by the inverse square law. The calculation is

$$a = \frac{v^2}{r}$$
$$= \frac{4\pi^2 r}{T^2}$$
$$= \frac{4(3.14)^2(3.9 \times 10^8 \text{ m})}{(2.3 \times 10^6 \text{ s})^2} = 0.0029 \text{ m/s}^2$$

The actual centripetal acceleration of the moon is in close agreement with the acceleration predicted by the law of universal gravitation. This agreement was strong evidence that the law of universal gravitation, as stated, was correct.

## 9:4  Cavendish Experiment

In 1798 the law of universal gravitation was confirmed by Henry Cavendish (1731–1810). The experimental arrangement he used is shown in Figure 9-6. Cavendish attached a lead ball on each end of a long rod. He carefully suspended the rod from a wire. Then he placed two large lead balls close to the small ones as shown. The two small balls were attracted by the two large balls. This caused the wire to twist. Earlier, Cavendish had measured the force needed to twist the wire through given angles. Therefore, from the twisting of the wire, Cavendish was able to find the force between the lead masses. He found that the force exactly followed the law of gravitation.

Cavendish measured the masses of the balls and the distances between their centers. Substituting these values for force, mass, and distance into the law of gravitation, he solved for $G$. The value of $G$ was found to be $6.67 \times 10^{-11} \text{ N} \cdot \text{m}^2/\text{kg}^2$.

**FIGURE 9-6. Cavendish verified the existence of gravitational forces between masses by using apparatus similar to the type shown.**

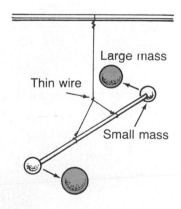

Large mass

Thin wire

Small mass

## 9:5 Law of Universal Gravitation and Weight

Because of the earth's large mass, the effect of its gravitational pull is noticeable.

The force that causes an object to fall toward the earth is the gravitational force between that object and the earth. This force is called weight. The weight of any object follows the law of universal gravitation. The weight of any mass is

$$W = G \frac{m_o m_e}{r^2}$$

where $m_o$ is the mass of the object, $m_e$ is the mass of the earth, and $r$ is the radius of the earth. (Gravitational force is always calculated by using the distances between the centers of two attracting objects.)

Since $W$ also equals $mg$, we can rewrite the equation above as

$$m_o g = G \frac{m_o m_e}{r^2}$$

which reduces to

$$g = G \frac{m_e}{r^2}$$

Because gravity causes weight, all bodies close to the earth are accelerated at the same rate.

$G$ is a constant. Therefore only two factors affect the acceleration of gravity, $g$. The first factor is the mass of the earth. The second factor is the position of the mass in relation to the center of the earth. Thus, the acceleration of gravity is the same for all bodies near the earth's surface.

The weight of the rocket varies inversely with the square of its distance from the earth's center. Figure 9-7 shows the change in a rocket's weight as the distance between the rocket and the earth increases.

**FIGURE 9-7. The change in gravitational force with distance follows the inverse square law.**

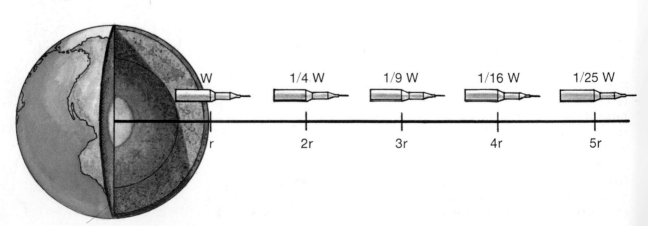

| W | 1/4 W | 1/9 W | 1/16 W | 1/25 W |

| r | 2r | 3r | 4r | 5r |

# 9:6   Gravitational Fields

One of the outstanding aspects of all forces, including gravitational force, is their ability to act for long distances through seemingly empty space. The earth and the sun are millions of kilometers apart, yet it is the gravitational force between the two that keeps the earth in its orbital path.

In order to describe and predict the effects of forces acting through a distance, the field concept is highly useful. In the case of gravity, the **field concept** considers that a mass distorts the space around it, setting up a gravitational field. In this sense a **gravitational field** is not some mysterious force of attraction between masses, but rather it is a peculiarity of space itself. All objects somehow curve and warp the space around them. Therefore, the path of any body in space is determined by the curvature of the space in which it finds itself.

When gravitational force is treated as a characteristic of the space around a mass rather than the mass itself, astronomers have found that they are better able to explain astronomical events. This statement has the reverse effect of supporting the idea that space is changed due to the presence of a mass. At the moment our understanding of space is far from complete so it is not possible to explain how this change takes place.

One way to picture curved space is to compare it to a two dimensional rubber sheet. Each object on the sheet will form an indentation. Rolling marbles across the sheet simulates the motion of matter in space. If a marble is moving near a sagging region in the sheet its path will curve. In the same way, the earth orbits the sun due to the space distortion which is caused by the masses of the two bodies.

Newton's law of universal gravitation allows us to calculate the magnitude of the force that exists between two masses due to their masses. The law describes how gravitational force varies with mass and distance but does not attempt to explain the nature of gravitational force as such. The concept of gravity as a peculiarity of space itself was proposed by professor Albert Einstein during the early twentieth century. Many tests of Einstein's theory have consistently verified his concept of gravity as a property of space.

The gravitational field concept is used to describe the gravitational force at various locations.

**FIGURE 9-8. Matter causes space to curve just as a mass on a rubber sheet curves the sheet around it. Moving bodies, near the mass, follow the curvature of space.**

*Photo by Arthur Selby*

**Summary**

1. Johannes Kepler used Brahe's data to formulate three laws of planetary motion. His third law states that the cube of any planet's radius is proportional to the square of its period.   9:1
2. Gravitational force was once thought to be a unique property of the earth. However, Newton showed that gravity is a property of all matter.   9:2
3. The law of universal gravitation states that every body in the universe attracts every other body with a force that varies directly with the product of the masses and inversely with the square of the distance between the centers of the masses.   9:2
4. Newton tested his inverse square law by calculating the acceleration of the moon and comparing the result with the acceleration predicted by his new law. He found excellent agreement.   9:3
5. Using the law of universal gravitation, it can be shown that only two factors affect the acceleration of gravity ($g$). These are the mass of the earth and the distance from its center.   9:5
6. A gravitational field is the result of the distortion of space by masses. The path of any body in space is determined by the curvature of the space through which it moves.   9:6

**Questions**

1. The radius of the earth is about 6400 km. A 7200 N spacecraft travels away from the earth. What would be the weight of the spacecraft at these distances from the earth's surface?
   - **a.** 6400 km
   - **b.** 12 800 km
   - **c.** 19 200 km
   - **d.** 25 600 km
   - **e.** 32 000 km
2. The force of gravity acting on an object near the earth's surface is proportional to the mass of the object. Why doesn't a heavy object fall faster than a light object?
3. Two 1-kg masses are 1 m apart. What is the force of attraction between them?
4. The earth and the moon are attracted to each other by gravitational force. Does the more massive earth attract the moon with a greater force than the moon attracts the earth?
5. Astronomers have noticed that some stars wobble slightly as they move through space. They claim that this is evidence that these stars have a planet or system of planets orbiting them. Explain this reasoning.
6. How did Cavendish demonstrate that a gravitational force of attraction exists between two small bodies?
7. During space flight astronauts often refer to forces as multiples of the force of gravity on the earth's surface. What would a force of 5 $G$ mean to an astronaut?

**8.** Newton assumed that gravitational force acts directly between the earth and the moon. How would Einstein's view of the attraction between the two bodies differ from Newton's view?

**9.** An imaginary line from a planet to the sun sweeps out equal areas in equal times. Does the planet move faster along its orbital path when it is close to or far away from the sun?

**1.** Two bowling balls each have a mass of 6.8 kg. The spheres are located next to one another with their centers 21.8 cm apart. What gravitational force do they exert on each other?

**Problems**

**2.** Two locomotives stand so that their centers are 10 m apart. Each weighs $1.96 \times 10^5$ N. What gravitational force exists between them?

**3.** Use the following data to compute the gravitational force the sun exerts on Jupiter.

  Mass of Earth = $6.0 \times 10^{24}$ kg
  Mass of the Sun = $3.3 \times 10^5$ times the mass of the earth
  Mass of Jupiter = $3.0 \times 10^2$ times the mass of the earth
  Distance between Jupiter and the Sun = $7.8 \times 10^{11}$ m

**4.** If a small planet were located 8 times as far from the sun as the earth's distance from the sun ($1.5 \times 10^{11}$ m), how many years would it take the planet to orbit the sun? ($r^3/T^2 = 3.35 \times 10^{18}$ m$^3$/s$^2$; a year is $3.15 \times 10^7$ s)

**1.** *Space Physics:* The astronauts in a space laboratory orbiting the earth cause a small scientific instrument to fall straight down, from rest, toward the earth. Assume the instrument was located one earth radius above the earth at the time of release and has a mass of 100 kg.

**Applying Physics**

  **a.** What is its weight when released?
  **b.** What is its acceleration upon release?

**2.** *Astronomy:* Section 9:4 explains how Cavendish determined the universal gravitational constant of proportionality, $G$. Use the value for $G$ ($6.67 \times 10^{-11}$ N·m$^2$/kg$^2$) and the fact that a kilogram mass weighs 9.8 N on the surface of the earth.

  **a.** Calculate the mass of the earth. The radius of the earth is roughly $6.4 \times 10^6$ m.
  **b.** Calculate the average density of the earth.

Drake, Stillman, "Newton's Apple and Galileo's Dialogue." *Scientific American,* August, 1980.

Forward, Robert L., "How to Build a Time Machine." *Omni,* May, 1980.

Gingerich, Owen, "Copernicus and Tycho." *Scientific American.* December, 1973.

**Readings**

Sawing a board is work. In physics, work is not merely an activity where one exerts strength. Work is a physical quantity. The amount of work done in sawing the board can be calculated. Power is also a physical quantity. It is not merely a measure of one's strength, but the rate at which work is done. What factors affect the amount of work required to saw the board? Is there ever a time when the act of sawing would not be considered work?

# Work and Power 10

In everyday conversation the words work and power are used in a general sense. However, in physics these terms have specific meanings. They each represent definite quantities that can be measured. In this chapter we will take a close look at the scientific meanings of work and power.

GOAL: You will gain knowledge and understanding of the concepts of work and power.

## 10:1 Work

When a person lifts a weight of some kind or pushes a lawnmower or shovels snow we say that work is done. When the force generated by exploding gasoline in your automobile's engine pushes the auto along the road, work is done. All examples of work have one thing in common—a force acts through a distance. **Work** is done only when an object moves some distance due to an applied force. Work is the product of the net force and the distance through which an object moves in the direction of the net force. As an equation, work is expressed as

$$Work = Force \times Distance$$
$$\boxed{W = F \times d}$$

Work is a scalar quantity even though force and displacement are vectors. Note that this definition includes a force and a distance. If you push against a car for hours and do not move it, you may become very tired. However, you have done no work on the car. A force must cause motion if work is to be done.

To calculate the work done by a force, use the equation $W = Fs$. Thus, if a person lifts a box that weighs 80 N to a height of 1.5 m, 80 N × 1.5 m or 120 N·m of work is done on the box. The unit of work is the joule (jool). A **joule** is equal to a newton-meter. Therefore, 120 N·m of work is called 120 joules of work or 120 J.

Work is the product of force and the distance through which the force acts.

A joule is the SI unit of work.

**157**

*Young/Hoffhines*

*Young/Hoffhines*

**FIGURE 10-1. In order to do work on the car, the car must move. Work is done only when an object moves some distance due to an applied force.**

**EXAMPLE: Work**

A person applies a force of 60 N for a distance of 20 m to push a desk across a floor. How much work is done?
*Solution:* $W = Fs = (60\ N)(20\ m) = 1200\ J$

**PROBLEMS**

1. 3.2 × 10⁴ J

**1.** A force of 800 N is needed to push a car across a lot. Two students push the car 40 m. How much work is done?

**2.** How much work is done in lifting a 60-kg crate a vertical distance of 10 m? (Note: The force needed to lift a 60-kg crate is its weight. You are given the mass of the crate here, not its weight.)

3. 48 N

**3.** Using a pulley system a worker does 1920 J of work to lift a crate from one floor to the next in a warehouse. The force is exerted through a distance of 40 m on the rope of the pulley system. How much force was used to lift the crate?

**4.** A package weighs 35 N. A person carries the package from the ground floor to the fifth floor of an office building, or 15 m upward.
  **a.** How much work does the person do on the package?
  **b.** The person weighs 750 N. How much total work is done?

5. 7500 J

**5.** In order to change a tire, a force of 80 N is exerted on the handle of a screw type bumper jack. The handle to which the steel shaft is attached has a radius of 0.50 m. The handle is turned through 30 revolutions. How much work is done?

**6. a.** What is the weight of a 49-kg crate?
  **b.** What work is done to lift the crate a distance of 10 m?

7. A worker carries cement blocks, weighing 150 N each, up a ladder onto a scaffold 8.0 m high. The worker carries them at a rate of 2 blocks per minute. How much work is done by the worker in **a.** 10 min? **b.** 1 h?

7. a. 24 000 J
   b. $1.4 \times 10^5$ J

8. The hammer of a pile-driver has a mass of 100 kg. The machine's engine lifts it to a height of 5.0 m every 10 s.
   **a.** How much does the hammer weigh?
   **b.** How much work must the machine do to lift the hammer?
   **c.** How much work does the machine do in 1 min?

9. Gasoline has a fuel value of about $4.80 \times 10^7$ J/kg. This value equals 48.0 MJ/kg (megajoules per kilogram).
   **a.** If the force of friction that a truck on a level highway must overcome at 60 km/h is 1500 N, what distance in kilometers should a liter of gasoline of mass 700 g propel the truck? Assume the engine to be 25% efficient.
   **b.** At 75 km/h the force of friction increases to 2500 N. What distance will a liter of gasoline propel the truck at this higher speed?

9. a. $5.6 \times 10^3$ m
   b. $3.4 \times 10^3$ m

10. A force of 60 N is needed to push a crate weighing 300 N across a waxed floor. How much work is required to push the crate 15 m?

11. A force of 25.0 N is needed to move automobile wheels up a smooth incline 10.0 m long in an automotive plant.
    **a.** If the wheels weigh 125 N what work is done on each?
    **b.** How high above the floor is the top of the incline?

11. a. 250 J
    b. 2.0 m

12. Workers use a force of 1760 N to push a piano weighing 8800 N up a 20.0 m ramp.
    **a.** How much work is done?
    **b.** The piano is being moved from street level to the second floor of a building. The second floor is 4.0 m above street level. If the workers decide to lift the piano straight up by using ropes, how much work would they do?

# 10:2　Work and the Direction of Force

When work is done, the force that does the work is the net force. If a force is applied to an object at an angle with the direction of motion, the **net force** is the component of the force that acts in the direction of motion. For example, if you pull a bobsled across the snow, the force that is doing the work is the horizontal component ($F_h$) of the force in the rope. The vertical component ($F_v$) of the force in the rope is balanced by gravity. In Figure 10-2, a 100-N force ($F$) is applied to the handle of a lawnmower. The vertical component of the force is balanced by the upward push of the ground. The force doing the work is $F_h$.

In calculating work, use only the component of force that acts in the direction of motion.

**FIGURE 10-2. If a force is applied to the mower at an angle, the net force doing the work is the component that acts in the direction of the force.**

b

*Edwin L. Shay*

a

1 division = 20 N

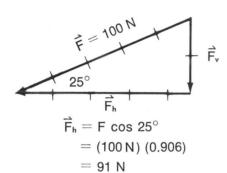

$$\vec{F}_h = F \cos 25°$$
$$= (100 \text{ N}) (0.906)$$
$$= 91 \text{ N}$$

The value of the horizontal component of a force $F_h$ is found by multiplying the force $F$ by the cosine of the angle between $F$ and the horizontal. Thus,

$$W = F_h s$$
$$= (F)(\cos \theta)(s)$$

### EXAMPLE:  Work—Force at an Angle to the Direction of Motion

A sailor pulls a boat along a dock with a force of 250 N. The rope is held at an angle of 60° with the horizontal. **a.** What horizontal force acts on the boat? **b.** How much work is done if the sailor pulls the boat 30 m?
*Solution:*

**a.**
$$F_h = (F)(\cos \theta)$$
$$= (250 \text{ N})(0.50)  = 125 \text{ N}$$

**b.**
$$W = F_h s$$
$$= (125 \text{ N})(30 \text{ m}) = 3750 \text{ J}$$

### PROBLEMS

13.  6300 J

**13.** A force of 600 N is applied to a metal box to pull it 15 m across a floor. The rope used to pull the box is held at an angle of 46° with the floor. How much work is done?

**14.** A person uses a rope to pull a 1000-kg boat 50 m along a wharf. The rope makes an angle of 45° with the horizontal. If a force of 40 N is used to move the boat, how much work is done?

**15.** It takes 12 000 J of work to pull a loaded sled weighing 800 N a distance of 200 m. To do this, a force of 120 N is exerted on a rope which makes an angle with the horizontal. At what angle is the rope held?

**16.** A cable attached to a small tractor pulls a barge through a canal lock. The tension in the cable is 2500 N. It makes an angle of 30° with the direction in which the barge is moving.
**a.** What force moves the barge along the lock?
**b.** If the lock is 200 m long, how much work is done to get the barge through the lock?

**17.** Due to friction, a force of 400 N is needed to drag a wooden crate across a floor. The rope tied to the crate is held at an angle of 56° with the horizontal.
**a.** How much tension is needed in the rope to move the the crate?
**b.** What work is done if the crate is dragged 25 m?

15. 60°

17. **a.** 720 N
    **b.** 10 000 J

## 10:3  Power

**Power** is the rate of doing work. The concept of power is important in physics in that it allows us to measure the rate at which work is done.

Power is work per unit time.

$$Power = \frac{Work}{Time}$$

Power is measured in watts. A **watt** is one joule per second. A machine that does work at a rate of one joule per second has a power of one watt. Since a joule is a newton-meter, a watt is a newton-meter per second. A watt is a relatively small unit of power. The power needed to lift a glass of water is about one watt. Thus, power is often measured in kilowatts (kW). A kilowatt is 1000 watts.

A watt is the SI unit of power.

A kilowatt is 1000 watts.

**EXAMPLE: Power**

A machine produces a force of 40 N through a distance of 100 m in 5.0 s. **a.** How much work is done? **b.** What is the power of the machine in watts and in kilowatts?

*Solution:*

**a.**  $W = Fs$
$= (40 \text{ N})(100 \text{ m})$
$= 4000 \text{ J}$

**b.**  $P = \dfrac{W}{t}$
$= \dfrac{4000 \text{ J}}{5.0 \text{ s}}$
$= 800 \text{ W}$

or, $P = \dfrac{800 \text{ W}}{1000 \text{ W/kW}} = 0.80 \text{ kW}$

Robert Nulieb

ERDA

FIGURE 10-3. The power needed to lift this cup of milk (a) is about one watt. Windmills (b) are now being used to produce electric power.

**PROBLEMS**

18. A box that weighs 1000 N is lifted a distance of 20 m straight up by a rope and pulley system. The work is done in 10 s. What amount of power is used in watts and in kilowatts?

19. a. 44 000 J
    b. 8800 W   8.8 kW

19. A diesel engine lifts a 225-kg hammer of a pile driver 20 m in 5 s.
    **a.** How much work is done in lifting the hammer?
    **b.** What is the power of the engine in watts and in kilowatts?

20. A hiker carries a 20-kg knapsack up a trail. After 30 minutes, the hiker is 300 m higher than the starting point.
    **a.** What is the weight of the knapsack?
    **b.** How much work in joules is done on the knapsack?
    **c.** If the hiker weighs 600 N, how much total work is done?
    **d.** During the 30 min, what is the hiker's average power in watts and in kilowatts?

21. a. 350 000 J
    b. 8800 W   8.8 kW

21. An electric motor lifts a 2000-kg elevator 18 m in 40 s.
    **a.** How much work is done?
    **b.** What is the power of the motor in watts and in kilowatts?

22. A gardener applies a force of 150 N to push a wheelbarrow 60 m with a constant speed in 20 s.
    **a.** How much work is done?
    **b.** What is the gardener's power in watts?

23. a. $1.08 \times 10^5$ J
    b. 7200 W   7.2 kW

23. A loaded elevator weighs $1.2 \times 10^4$ N. An electric motor hoists the elevator 9.0 m in 15 s.
    **a.** How much work is done?
    **b.** What is the power in watts and in kilowatts?

# 10:4   A More Meaningful View of Work

Up to this point we have treated work as a mathematical quantity only. You have used an equation to calculate work in given practice problems. However, you should know what work means.

Work is an artificial quantity which was created to enable the scientist to measure energy. Work has about the same relationship to energy as a meter stick has to length. It is a measuring tool and nothing more.

For example, if you push a wooden block across the surface of a table, you do work. What this statement really means is that your body loses energy while the surface of the table and the wooden block gain energy. The act of pushing the block causes your body to use a small amount of the energy you obtain from the food you eat. On the other hand, the rubbing of the block on the table causes the particles that compose the table and the block to move faster. The block-table system becomes a bit warmer. Thus, energy has been transferred from you to the system.

It would be impossible to measure the energy obtained by the particles in the table and the block. The particles are too small, there are too many of them, and they quickly pass along some of the energy to other particles. Still, we know how much energy, in joules, the block-table system gained. All we need to do is measure the work done on the block. That is, the force applied to block times the distance it is moved. This quantity is the energy transferred. All measurements of work are actually measurements of energy transfer.

It is not an easy matter to measure the total energy of any object. A lump of coal or a liter of gasoline has energy. However, we are not able to measure that energy by inspecting the molecules of coal or gasoline. Instead we burn the fuel and measure the work it does. This work is the measure of its energy.

As you study other areas in this text, you will encounter other equations for measuring energy. You should notice the final units used to express these measurements will be joules. These equations can be considered equivalent to each other.

> Work is an artificial quantity created as a measure of energy transfer.

> All measurements of work are measurements of energy transfer.

> Energy measurements are expressed in joules.

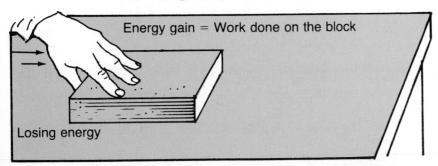

Energy gain = Work done on the block

Losing energy

**FIGURE 10-4. Energy is transferred from you to the block and table.**

**Summary**

1. In physics, work is defined as the product of force and distance.    **10:1**
2. Regardless of the magnitude of the force that acts on an object, if it does not move through a distance, no work is done.    **10:1**
3. If the force acts at some angle with the direction of motion, the work done is equal to $(F)(\cos \theta)(s)$.    **10:2**
4. When force is measured in newtons and the distance in meters, work has the unit newton-meters (N·m). A newton-meter is called a joule (J).    **10:1**
5. Power is the time rate of doing work. The unit of power is the watt (W). A watt is a joule per second.    **10:3**
6. Measurements of work are actually measurements of energy transfer.    **10:4**

**Questions**

1. Define work, the joule, and power.
2. A student takes a 30-kg box from a table which is 1 m high and carries it down a long corridor 20 m in length. The student then places the box on another table which is the same height as the first. How much work was done on the box?
3. In a factory, motor $X$ lifts a 250-N engine a vertical distance of 20 m while motor $Y$ lifts a 500-N engine a vertical distance of 10 m. Which motor performed the most work?
4. If both motors in the preceding question were able to lift their loads in the same time how does the power of each motor compare?
5. Which requires more work—the lifting of a 50-N crate 10 m or the lifting of a 50-kg crate 5 m? Why?
6. In a factory, a large worker lifts three 500-N crates from the floor to a dock one meter above the floor. The lifting of the three crates takes a total of one minute. Another worker, who is much smaller lifts six 300-N crates from the floor to the same dock in one minute. Which worker is the more powerful?
7. How many kilojoules (kJ) of work must be done on an electric generator to operate a 100-watt light bulb for one hour?

**Problems**

1. The third floor of a house is 8.0 m above street level. How much work is required to move a 100-kg refrigerator up to the third floor?
2. A 50-kg mass is raised by a machine to a height of 20 m. Calculate the work done in
   a. newton-meters    b. joules

**3.** How much work does a 400-watt motor do in 5.0 min?

**4.** Calculate the wattage of a motor that does 11 250 J of work in 25 s.

**5.** A pump raises 30 liters of water per minute from a depth of 100 m. What is the wattage expended? (A liter of water has a mass of 1 kg.)

**6.** A horizontal force of 800 N is needed to drag a crate across a horizontal floor. A worker drags the crate by means of a rope held at an angle of 60°.
**a.** What force is applied to the rope?
**b.** How much work is performed in dragging the crate 22 m?
**c.** If the worker completes the job in 8.0 s, what is the power in watts?

**7.** A boat's engine propels it through water at a steady rate of 15 m/s. The force of friction that the boat must overcome to maintain this speed is 6000 N. What is the power of the engine in kilowatts?

**8. a.** Neglecting frictional effects, how much work is done to accelerate a 1000-kg car from an initial speed of 20 m/s to 30 m/s, if the acceleration given to it by its engine is 1.25 m/s$^2$?
**b.** What is the power of the car's engine in kilowatts?

---

**Applying Physics**

**1.** *Biophysics:* An overweight painter has a mass of 105 kg. On a typical workday the painter climbs a ladder to a vertical height of 7.0 m twenty-five times. If body fat has an energy value of 38 J/g what mass, in kg, could the overweight painter "work off" if the painter refrained from eating all day?

**2.** *Work and Hydroelectric Power:* Water falls at a rate of 8000 kg/s from the top of a large dam and strikes the blades of a turbine 50 m below. If 80% of the falling water effectively does work on the turbine, what electric power in megawatts (1 MW = 1 × 10$^6$ J/s) can the turbine develop? (Consider the work per second that would have to be done to raise the same amount of water to the top of the dam. Round off your solution to show two significant digits.)

---

**Readings**

Bascom, Willard, "Wave-Tide-Current Power." *Science Digest,* July, 1980.
Fisher, John C., "Energy Crises in Perspective." *Physics Today,* December, 1973.
Kantrowitz, Arthur, "MHD Power Generator." *The Physics Teacher,* November, 1975.
National Geographic Society, *Powers of Nature,* Washington, D.C., Special Publications Division, 1978.

All forms of energy are interchangeable. When energy changes form, the total energy of a system remains the same. The potential energy of the water above the waterwheel is converted to kinetic energy as the water falls. This kinetic energy turns the waterwheel. This kinetic energy could be converted to electricity. What is energy? What are other examples of energy changing form? How do energy changes help you?

# Energy and Its Conservation 11

Energy is a term that most of us take for granted and use quite freely. We assume we know what we are talking about when speaking of energy. In truth, energy is probably the most complex and least understood of all physical quantities. Thus, in this chapter, energy will be defined as the capacity to do work. However, this definition states what energy does, not what it is. Still, as you learn the basic concepts related to energy, we will refer to it this way.

**GOAL: You will gain knowledge and understanding of energy and its conservation and of the relationship between energy and work.**

Energy is the capacity to do work.

## 11:1 Energy

While an in-depth discussion of energy is beyond the scope of this course, one or two aspects of energy are worth noting. Earlier (Section 6:1) you read that there are five forces: gravitational, electric, magnetic, weak interaction, and nuclear. Recent studies strongly indicate that electric, magnetic, and weak interaction forces are actually different components of the same force. In the strictest sense, there may be only three forces: gravitational, electromagnetic, and nuclear.

Since only a few basic forces exist, there are ultimately only a few forms of energy. These are gravitational, electromagnetic, and nuclear energy. Yet, in science books, you read of other different forms of energy. Terms such as thermal energy, mechanical energy, and light energy often appear. These are general terms used by scientists to avoid lengthy discussions of the true nature of energy. For example, thermal energy (heat energy) concerns the motions of particles.* The faster particles move, the more thermal energy we say they have. This energy is noticeable when the particles strike each other. When two particles collide, it is the electric force between the electrons that transfers the energy. Thermal energy is basically electric in nature. Perhaps you can understand why the scientist prefers to call this transfer, thermal energy, rather than make a lengthy statement about the electromagnetic transfer of energy that occurs when particles collide.

In future chapters you will find that light is an electromagnetic wave. Thus, it transfers energy by electromagnetic forces. All forms of energy are dependent upon forces and there are only a few forces. For this reason, work (*Force × Distance*) is a convenient method of measuring energy. As you study the remainder of this chapter, keep the following points in mind.

**The unit of energy is the same as the unit of work.**

1. Energy is measured in terms of the work it does or can do.
   a. Energy has the same units as work.
   b. Like work, energy is a scalar quantity.

**Energy always exists as either potential or kinetic energy.**

2. Regardless of its form, energy is always either potential or kinetic.
   a. Potential energy is energy of position.
   b. Kinetic energy is the energy an object possesses by virtue of its motion.

## 11:2   Potential Energy

**Potential energy is energy of position.**

**Potential energy** is the energy an object has because of its position or state. A hammer resting on the ground has no potential energy. As the hammer is lifted, it gains gravitational potential energy. If the hammer then falls toward the earth, it can do work. It might, for example, drive a stake into the ground by exerting a force on the stake through a distance.

**Electric potential energy depends on the positions of charged particles in relation to one another.**

There are other forms of potential energy. A stretched spring has electric potential energy due to the electric interactions between the atoms that make the spring. A charged battery also has electric potential energy. If the negative plate has an excess of electrons and the positive plate lacks electrons, the electrons have electric potential energy with respect to the positive plate. If

*The general term particles can mean atoms, ions, or molecules.

a

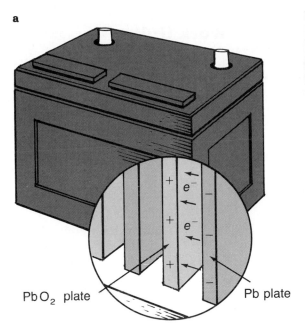

J. Wilson/fpg

PbO$_2$ plate                    Pb plate

b

the electrons are allowed to flow from the negative plate to the positive plate, they can do work. For example, they can operate a flashlight.

Chemical bonds have electric energy. In a chemical reaction this energy can be released as bonding changes (potential energy changes) take place. Thus, the energy in coal or oil is actually electric potential energy.

It is also possible to produce magnetic potential energy by placing magnets close to one another. Electric motors run on this basis.

Matter itself can be considered a form of potential energy since matter can be converted to energy during nuclear reactions.

**FIGURE 11-1. In a battery (a), the electrons have electric potential energy with respect to the positive plate. Electrons can do work in moving to the positive plate. This drill bit (b) has potential energy with respect to the earth. In drilling the bit does work.**

Magnetic potential energy can be produced by placing magnets close together.

## 11:3   Base Levels

The potential energy an object has due to its position above the surface of the earth is called its **gravitational potential energy.** A falling object can release energy to do work as it falls from a higher to a lower level. This energy is equal to its change in potential energy. A change in potential energy is measured with a reference to some arbitrary base which is not necessarily the surface of the earth. Suppose a person on the third floor of a building drops a weight on a nail also located on the third floor. The potential energy of the weight is measured with respect to the nail, not with respect to the surface of the earth. A **base level** is an arbitrary reference position and depends upon the situation.

Gravitational potential energy depends on the position of a body above the earth's surface.

A base level is a position defined for a specific case.

## 11:4   Energy Units—Work Units

Energy, the capacity to do work, is measured in the same units as work (joules). Under ideal conditions, energy and work are completely interchangeable. For example, 200 joules of work are needed to lift a 20-newton building block to the top of a 10-meter wall. If the same block falls back to the ground, it should be able to do 200 joules of work. The increase in the potential energy of a system is equal to the amount of work needed to place the system in its final position. That is

**The increase in the potential energy of any system is equal to the work done on the system.**

*Change in Potential Energy = Force × Distance*

$$\Delta PE = Fs$$

The force needed to lift an object is equal to its weight $(mg)$. Thus, when an object is lifted to a height $h$, the increase in gravitational potential energy is $mgh$.

**Gravitational potential energy depends on mass and height.**

$$\Delta PE = Fs$$
$$= (mg)h$$
$$= mgh$$

We have shown that work is needed to increase the gravitational potential energy of an object. Work is related to all energy exchanges. When energy changes form or location, the change is always brought about by work.

**EXAMPLE:  Potential Energy**

A 5.0-kg bowling ball is lifted from the floor to a height of 1.5 m. What is its increase in potential energy?

*Solution:*    $\Delta PE = Fs$
$$= mgh$$
$$= (5.0 \text{ kg})(9.8 \text{ m/s}^2)(1.5 \text{ m}) = 73.5 \text{ J}$$

**PROBLEMS**

1. 20 000 J

**1.** The 200-kg hammer of a pile driver is lifted 10 m. Find the potential energy of the system when the hammer is at this height.

**2.** A 60-kg shell is shot from a cannon to a height of 400 m.
   **a.** What is the potential energy of the earth-shell system when the shell is at this height?
   **b.** What is the change in potential energy of the system when the shell falls to a height of 200 m?

3. a. 3200 J
   b. 3200 J

**3.** A person weighing 630 N climbs up a ladder to a height of 5.0 m.
   **a.** What work does the person do?
   **b.** What is the increase in the potential energy of the earth-person system when the person is at this height?

4. In order to charge the plates of a small storage battery, a hand generator is cranked through a total distance of 250 m. An average force of 120 N is applied to the crank as it is turned.

   **a.** What is the total work done to charge the plates?

   **b.** If the work is done in one minute, what power is developed?

   **c.** The storage battery is then used to power a 10-watt light bulb. How many minutes can the bulb be used before the battery must be recharged?

5. A hydroelectric power company finds that during the hours between midnight and 7:00 a.m. the demand for its power output is only 50% of capacity. However, during other hours the company's output cannot keep up with peak demand. In order to fully utilize its hydroelectric resources, the company constructs a reservoir above its dam having an average height of 50 m. During the hours of low demand, it uses four generators to operate pumps that fill the reservoir with water from the river at a rate of $4.0 \times 10^8$ kg/h.

   **a.** What is the total potential energy stored each night by this means?

   **b.** If the generators are 100% efficient, what is the power of each in kilowatts? In megawatts ($1 \times 10^6$ watts)?

5. **a.** $1.4 \times 10^{12}$ J
   **b.** 14 MW

*Consumer Power Co.*

**FIGURE 11-2. The pumped water storage reservoir in Problem 5.**

## 11:5  Kinetic Energy

**Kinetic energy is energy of motion.**

**Kinetic energy** is the energy an object possesses by virtue of its motion. In deriving an equation for kinetic energy, let us consider as an example an object of mass $m$ resting on a frictionless surface. A constant force $F$ acts on it through a displacement $s$. The force will accelerate the object in accordance with Newton's second law of motion,

$$F = ma$$

If we multiply both sides of this equation by $s$, the left side of the equation represents work done on the mass.

$$Fs = mas$$

The speed of an object starting from rest is $v^2 = 2as$. This expression can be rearranged to read, $as = v^2/2$. Substituting into the equation $Fs = mas$, we obtain

$$Fs = \frac{mv^2}{2}$$

This expression relates the work done on the mass to its resulting speed. The right-hand side of the equation states the amount of work mass $m$ moving with velocity $v$ can do as it is brought to rest. The energy the object has because of its velocity equals the work that was done to give the mass its velocity. Thus, the quantity $mv^2/2$ is called the kinetic energy, KE, of the object.

**Kinetic energy depends on mass and velocity.**

$$\boxed{KE = \tfrac{1}{2}\,mv^2}$$

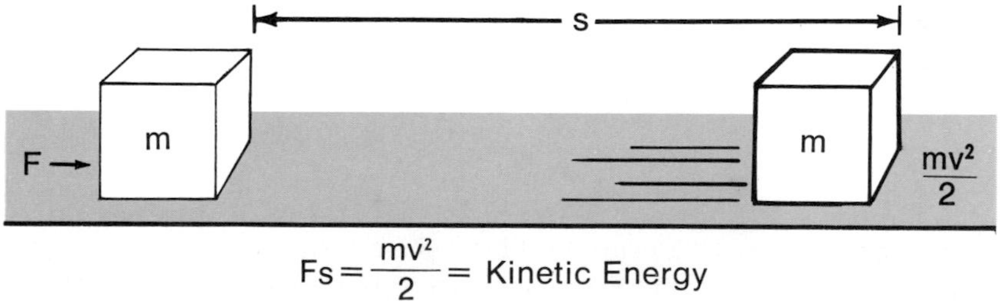

**FIGURE 11-3. The kinetic energy of a mass is equal to the work done on the mass to give it that kinetic energy. Therefore, the speed of an object is dependent upon the amount of work done on it.**

$$Fs = \frac{mv^2}{2} = \text{Kinetic Energy}$$

**EXAMPLE:  Kinetic Energy**

An 8.0-kg mass moves at 30 m/s. What is its kinetic energy?

*Solution:*

$$
\begin{aligned}
KE &= \tfrac{1}{2}\,mv^2 \\
&= \frac{(8.0 \text{ kg})(30 \text{ m/s})^2}{2} \\
&= 3600 \text{ J}
\end{aligned}
$$

## PROBLEMS

**6. a.** A 10-kg mass moves with a speed of 20 m/s. Find its kinetic energy.

   **b.** If the 10-kg mass moves with a speed of 10 m/s, what is its kinetic energy?

   **c.** What is the ratio of the answer of (a) to that of (b)? Why?

**7.** What is the kinetic energy of a 1600-kg car which moves at
   **a.** 30 km/h?   **b.** 60 km/h?
   **c.** What is the ratio of (b) to (a)?

7. a. $5.5 \times 10^4$ J
   b. $2.2 \times 10^5$ J
   c. $\approx 4:1$

**8.** A baseball that weighs 1.6 N leaves a bat with a speed of 40 m/s. Calculate the kinetic energy of the ball.

**9.** An alpha particle travels at $1.6 \times 10^7$ m/s. The kinetic energy of the particle is $6.0 \times 10^{-13}$ J. What is the mass of the alpha particle?

9. $4.7 \times 10^{-27}$ kg

**10.** An electron with a mass of $9.0 \times 10^{-31}$ kg moves through a vacuum with a speed of $2.5 \times 10^8$ m/s. Find the electron's kinetic energy.

**11.** Consider a 5.0-kg mass located 10 m from the earth's surface.

   **a.** What potential energy does the mass have?

   **b.** How much potential energy does the mass lose if it falls 5.0 m?

   **c.** What kinetic energy does the mass have after it falls 5.0 m?

   **d.** What speed does the mass have after it falls the 5 m? (Assume that it starts from rest.)

11. a. 490 J
    b. 245 J
    c. 245 J
    d. 9.9 m/s

# 11:6   Conservation of Energy

As energy does work, or as work is done on a system, energy changes form or position. You can store energy in a bow by doing work on it. That energy appears again as the kinetic energy of the arrow. If the arrow strikes a tree, it pushes the particles of the tree. This compression makes the particles move faster and thus raises the temperature. The work done on the particles of the tree appears as heat energy. The heat energy in the tree is gradually lost to the atmosphere as the particles of the tree do work and emit radiation. Energy never disappears. It simply moves from place to place, often changing form as it does.

The **law of conservation of energy** states that *the total energy of a system cannot change, unless work is done on the system.* Within an isolated system, energy can change from one form to another, but the total amount of energy always remains the same. Energy can never be "lost" by a system.

The law of conservation of energy states that energy can neither be created nor destroyed.

As an example of the law of conservation of energy, consider a mass weighing 100 newtons located 20 meters above the earth.

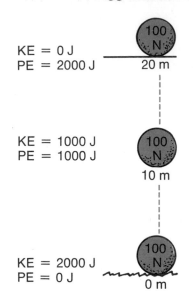

KE = 0 J
PE = 2000 J

20 m

KE = 1000 J
PE = 1000 J

10 m

KE = 2000 J
PE = 0 J

0 m

**FIGURE 11-4. The loss of potential energy is equal to the gain of kinetic energy.**

A decrease in potential energy causes an equal increase in kinetic energy.

At this height above the earth's surface the potential energy of the mass is

$$Fs = (100 \text{ N})(20 \text{ m}) = 2000 \text{ J}$$

If the mass is allowed to fall freely for a distance of 10 meters, its potential energy will be

$$Fs = (100 \text{ N})(10 \text{ m}) = 1000 \text{ J}$$

The mass loses half of its potential energy in falling 10 meters.

When the mass has fallen 10 meters, its vertical velocity will be 14 m/s. Its kinetic energy will be

$$KE = \frac{mv^2}{2}$$

$$= \left(\frac{W}{g}\right)\left(\frac{v^2}{2}\right)$$

$$= \frac{(100 \text{ N})(14 \text{ m/s})^2}{(9.8 \text{ m/s}^2)(2)} = 1000 \text{ J}$$

The loss of potential energy by the mass is always equal to its gain in kinetic energy. The transition of potential energy to kinetic energy occurs as the mass falls. By the time the mass reaches the earth's surface, all of its potential energy has been changed to kinetic energy. Upon impact with the earth, the kinetic energy is changed to heat, and sometimes, to sound energy.

The path an object follows as it is raised does not affect the potential energy of the object. A 200-newton barrel positioned 8 meters above the ground has 1600 joules of potential energy whether it is raised straight up to that height or pushed up an incline. This same point also applies to kinetic energy. The barrel's kinetic energy, neglecting friction, is 1600 joules when it reaches ground level, whether it falls straight down or rolls down the incline.

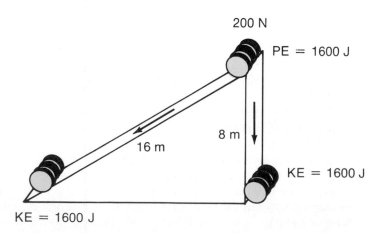

200 N

PE = 1600 J

8 m

16 m

KE = 1600 J

**FIGURE 11-5. The path followed in raising the barrel does not affect its potential energy.**

KE = 1600 J

**EXAMPLE:  Conservation of Energy**

A large chunk of ice with a mass of 15 kg falls from a roof 8.0 m above the ground. **a.** What is the kinetic energy of the ice as it reaches the ground? **b.** What is its speed just as it reaches the ground?

*Solution:*

**a.** The kinetic energy of the ice as it reaches the ground equals the potential energy the ice possessed while attached to the roof.

$$KE = PE$$
$$= mgh$$
$$= (15 \text{ kg})(9.8 \text{ m/s}^2)(8.0) = 1180 \text{ J}$$

**b.** The speed can be found by using the equation for kinetic energy.

$$KE = \frac{mv^2}{2} \qquad\qquad 1180 \text{ J} = \frac{mv^2}{2}$$

$$v^2 = \frac{(2)(1180 \text{ J})}{m}$$

$$v = \sqrt{\frac{(2)(1180 \text{ J})}{15 \text{ kg}}}$$

$$= \sqrt{\frac{157 \text{ m}^2}{\text{s}^2}} = 12.5 \text{ m/s}$$

**PROBLEMS**

**12.** An 8.0-kg flower pot falls from a window ledge 12.0 m above a sidewalk.
  **a.** What is the kinetic energy of the pot just as it reaches the sidewalk?
  **b.** Using energy considerations only, determine the speed of the pot just before it strikes the walk.

**13.** A 15.0-kg model plane flies horizontally at 12.5 m/s.
  **a.** Calculate its kinetic energy.
  **b.** The plane goes into a power dive and levels off 20.4 m closer to the earth. How much potential energy did it lose during the dive?
  **c.** How much kinetic energy did the plane gain during the dive?
  **d.** What is its new kinetic energy?
  **e.** Neglecting frictional effects, what is its new horizontal velocity?

13. **a.** 1170 J
    **b.** 3000 J
    **c.** 3000 J
    **d.** 4170 J
    **e.** 23.6 m/s

**14.** A partially-filled bag of cement having a mass of 16.0 kg falls 40.0 m into a river from a bridge.
  **a.** What is the kinetic energy of the bag as it hits the water?
  **b.** Using energy considerations only, what vertical speed does it have?

15. a. 6300 J
    b. 6300 J
    c. 35 m/s

**15.** A block weighing 98.0 N falls 64.0 m.
   **a.** What is the potential energy of the block at 64.0 m?
   **b.** What is the kinetic energy of the block just as it strikes the ground?
   **c.** What speed does the block have as it strikes the ground?

**16.** During the hammer throw at a track meet an 8.0-kg hammer is accidentally thrown straight up. If 784.0 J of work were done on the hammer to give it its vertical velocity, how high will it rise?

17. 20 m

**17.** A 10.0-kg test rocket is fired from Kennedy Space Center. Its fuel gives it a kinetic energy of 1960 J before it leaves its ramp. How high will the rocket rise?

**18.** A skater on a lake pushes on a 5.0-kg log to clear a skating area. If the skater does 600 J of work on the log and the ice is nearly frictionless, what speed is given to the log?

19. a. 12.5 m/s
    b. 780 J

**19.** In an electronics factory, small cabinets slide down a 30° incline for a distance of 16.0 m to reach the next assembly stage. The cabinets have a mass of 10.0 kg each.
   **a.** Calculate the speed each cabinet would acquire if the incline were frictionless.
   **b.** What kinetic energy would a cabinet have under such circumstances?

**20.** A 5.0-kg mass is projected straight up with a speed of 15 m/s.
   **a.** What is the kinetic energy of the mass at the outset?
   **b.** To what height does the mass rise?

## 11:7 Conservation of Matter and Energy

Energy is always conserved when it changes form. A given amount of potential energy always changes to an equal amount of another form of energy. For example, the electrons on a charged plate have potential energy that can be changed to heat energy as the electrons flow through a heater. Energy never disappears. It just changes form or position.

The law of conservation of matter states that matter can neither be created nor destroyed.

The **law of conservation of matter** parallels the law of conservation of energy. This law states that *matter can neither be created nor destroyed.* However, matter can change form. For example, when a piece of paper is burned, it is not destroyed. Instead, it is all transformed to ashes and gas.

The law of conservation of energy and the law of conservation of matter were once thought to be completely true. However, research in nuclear physics has shown that matter can be changed into energy. The amount of energy obtained from a certain amount of mass is

Matter and energy are interchangeable.

$$E = mc^2$$

In this equation, E represents the energy released, m is the quantity of mass converted into energy, and c is the speed of light. This equation was derived by Dr. Albert Einstein (1879–1955). Experiments have shown that it is correct. The law of conservation of energy and the law of conservation of matter are now combined into the law of conservation of mass-energy. This law states that the total amount of matter plus energy in the universe is a constant.

**The law of conservation of mass-energy was stated to account for this interchange of matter and energy. The sum of matter and energy is constant.**

## 11:8  Elastic Collisions

An **elastic collision** is a collision in which the total kinetic energy of the objects involved is exactly the same before and after the collision. Strictly speaking, all collisions between objects larger than individual particles of matter are inelastic. In an **inelastic collision,** the total kinetic energy decreases during the collision. Therefore, the velocity of the objects involved in the collision also decreases. The loss in energy is accounted for by an increase in the heat energy content of the colliding objects, by the generation of sound during the collision, or by both. The amount of kinetic energy lost in an inelastic collision varies. Remember that energy is not really lost. It merely changes form.

The collision between some large objects is nearly elastic. A collision between two billiard balls or two glass marbles moving across a smooth surface is nearly elastic. Such a collision may be considered elastic.

**In an elastic collision, the KE is constant.**

**In an inelastic collision, some KE changes to other forms of energy.**

**FIGURE 11-6. A golf ball (a) collides with a hard surface. How can you tell if the collision is nearly elastic? The collisions of the pucks on this nearly frictionless air table (b) are examples of nearly perfect elastic collisions.**

a

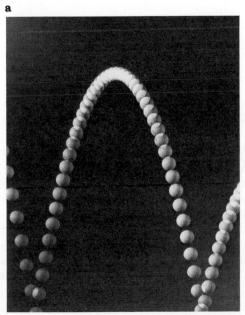

b

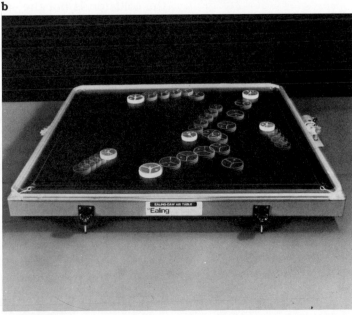

*Frederic Lewis*

*The Ealing Corp.*

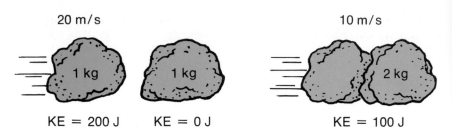

**FIGURE 11-7. Kinetic energy is not conserved in an inelastic collision.**

**Momentum is conserved in all collisions.**

The law of conservation of momentum holds for all collisions. Although kinetic energy decreases during an inelastic collision, there is no change in momentum. For example, consider a 1-kg block of putty sliding across a frictionless surface at 20 m/s. This block of putty collides head-on with a 1-kg block of putty which is at rest. The two blocks of putty stick together and move off as one mass. According to the law of conservation of momentum, the total momentum of the two blocks stuck together is equal to the momentum of the original block of putty. The momentum of the original block is

$$mv = (1\ \text{kg})(20\ \text{m/s}) = 20\ \text{kg} \cdot \text{m/s}$$

In order for the momentum to be conserved, the two blocks stuck together must also have a momentum of 20 kg·m/s. Thus, after the collision, the two blocks move with a velocity of 10 m/s in the direction of the original velocity. If the velocity had been different, the law of conservation of momentum would have been violated. However, the kinetic energy of the blocks of putty before and after the collision is not the same.

*Original KE*             *Final KE*

$$\left(\tfrac{1}{2}\,mv^2 = \frac{1\ \text{kg}\,(20\ \text{m/s})^2}{2}\right) \neq \left(\tfrac{1}{2}\,mv^2 = \frac{2\ \text{kg}\,(10\ \text{m/s})^2}{2}\right)$$

$$200\ \text{J} \qquad \neq \qquad 100\ \text{J}$$

While the momentum is conserved, half the kinetic energy is converted to another form of energy (such as heat). This collision is inelastic.

**In an elastic collision, the behavior of objects is predictable.**

The behavior of objects involved in an elastic collision often can be predicted. This is done by considering the laws of conservation of energy and conservation of momentum together. For example, suppose a billiard ball of mass $m$ moves with a speed $v$. This ball collides head-on with a billiard ball of equal mass that is at rest. After the collision, if the two balls rolled off together at half the speed of the original billiard ball, the law of conservation of momentum would be satisfied. However, like the blocks of putty, the total kinetic energy of the billiard balls would be half the kinetic energy before the collision. What actually happens in a collision of this type is that the first ball comes to a complete stop. The second ball (of equal mass) moves off at exactly the speed of the first ball before the collision took place. Thus, momentum and kinetic energy are both conserved. The interesting thing about this is that we know what must happen in advance. The conservation laws tell us what will happen.

Many collisions are neither elastic nor completely inelastic. In such cases, it becomes difficult to predict what will happen during a collision.

*Alpha/Zimmerman*

FIGURE 11-8. Momentum is conserved in the collision between the bowling ball and pins. However, the total kinetic energy of the system decreases.

## PROBLEMS

**21.** Two bowling balls, each with a mass of 8.0 kg, roll together along a smooth ramp at 10 m/s. They collide with a row of 8.0-kg bowling balls at rest. Collisions between bowling balls are nearly elastic.

    **a.** After the collision, can one bowling ball leave the opposite end of the row with a speed of 20 m/s and satisfy the law of conservation of momentum?

21. a. yes

b. 1600 J, 800 J, no
c. yes, yes

**b.** If one bowling ball did leave the opposite end of the row at 20 m/s, what kinetic energy would it possess? What was the total kinetic energy of the two balls before the collision? Would energy be conserved under these circumstances?

**c.** Two bowling balls leave the opposite ends of the row at 10 m/s. Is the law of conservation of momentum obeyed? Is the law of conservation of energy observed?

**22.** What happens if a single bowling ball with a mass of 8.0 kg moving at 10 m/s collides with a row of stationary bowling balls? That is, will one bowling ball move away from the opposite end of the row at 10 m/s? Or will two balls move away from the opposite end of the row at 5 m/s each?

**FIGURE 11-9. Use with Problems 21 and 22.**

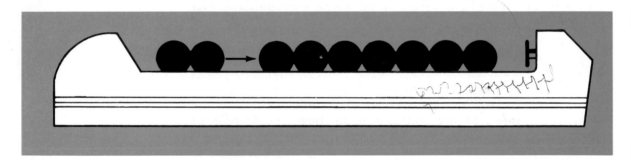

**Summary**

1. All energy is dependent upon forces. There are only a few forces and so only a few forms of energy. **11:1**
2. Energy is loosely defined as the capacity to do work. **11:1**
3. Energy always exists as either potential energy or kinetic energy. **11:1**
4. Potential energy is the energy an object has because of its position or state. The potential energy of a system is equal to the work done to place the system in its energy state. **11:2**
5. Kinetic energy is the energy an object has due to its motion. Kinetic energy and potential energy are interchangeable. **11:5**
6. The units of energy and work are joules. As work is done energy changes form and/or position. **11:4**
7. The law of conservation of energy states that energy can only change form or position. It cannot be destroyed except to create mass. The law of conservation of mass-energy states that the total amount of matter plus energy in the universe is constant. **11:6–11:7**
8. An elastic collision is a collision in which the total kinetic energy of the objects involved in the collision is the same both before and after the collision. **11:8**

**9.** In an elastic collision, both momentum and kinetic energy are conserved. Using these laws the behavior of objects involved in an elastic collision can often be predicted.   11:8

**1.** Explain how energy and forces are related.

**2.** What type of energy does a wound watch spring possess? What form of energy does a running watch use? When the watch runs down, what has happened to the energy?

**3.** Describe the types of energy the earth-sun system possesses.

**4.** The Northern hemisphere of the earth is approximately $6.7 \times 10^6$ km closer to the sun in winter than in summer. The earth moves along its orbit faster in winter than in summer. Explain these two statements in terms of the earth's potential and kinetic energy.

**5.** A rubber ball is dropped from a height of 8 m. After striking the floor, it bounces to a height of 5 m.
  **a.** If the ball had bounced to a height of 8 m, how would you describe the collision between the ball and the floor?
  **b.** If the ball had not bounced at all, how would you describe the collision between the ball and the floor?
  **c.** What happened to the energy lost by the ball during the collision?

**6.** A film was produced that centered around the discovery of a substance called "flubber." This substance could bounce higher than the height from which it was dropped. Explain why "flubber" is not likely to exist.

**7.** If "flubber" did exist, what changes would have to take place in the surface from which "flubber" bounced?

**1. a.** How much work is needed to hoist a 98-N sack of grain to a storage room 50 m above the ground floor of a grain elevator?
  **b.** What is the potential energy of the sack of grain at this height?
  **c.** The rope being used to lift the sack of grain breaks just as the sack reaches the storage room. What kinetic energy does the sack have just before it strikes the ground floor?

**2.** A 1600-kg car travels at a speed of 12.5 m/s. What is its kinetic energy?

**3.** A racing car has a mass of 1500 kg. What is its kinetic energy if it has a speed of 108 km/h? (Convert km/h to m/s.)

4. An archer puts a 0.30 kg arrow to the bowstring. An average force of 200 N is exerted to draw the string back 1.3 m.
   a. Assuming no frictional loss, with what speed does the arrow leave the bow?
   b. If the arrow is shot straight up, how high does it rise?

5. A 1200-kg car starts from rest and accelerates to 72 km/h in 20 s. The average force needed to overcome friction during this period is 450 N.
   a. What distance does the car move during its period of acceleration?
   b. What force does the engine produce on the car during this time?
   c. How much work does the engine do to accelerate the car?

6. A force of 400 N is applied in a direction straight up to a stone that weighs 32 N. If the force is applied through a distance of 2.0 m, to what height, from the point of release, will the stone rise?

7. a. A 20-kg mass is on the edge of a 100-m high cliff. What potential energy does it possess?
   b. The mass falls from the cliff. What is its kinetic energy just before it strikes the ground?
   c. What speed does it have as it strikes the ground?

8. A steel ball has a mass of 4.0 kg and rolls along a smooth, level surface at 60 m/s.
   a. Find its kinetic energy.
   b. At first, the ball was at rest on the surface. A force acted on it through a distance of 20 m to give it the speed of 60 m/s. What was the magnitude of the force?

9. Calculate the amount of energy that is released if a kilogram of mass is destroyed completely. (The speed of light is $3.0 \times 10^8$ m/s.)

10. A submarine's engines use energy at the rate of 3000 J/s. How long can a kilogram of mass propel the sub before the sub will stop? (Assume that one year is equivalent to $3.0 \times 10^7$ s.)

11. Calculate the amount of matter that is destroyed to produce 30.0 J of energy.

12. A railroad car with a mass of $5.0 \times 10^5$ kg collides with a stationary railroad car of equal mass. After the collision, the two cars lock together and move off at 4.0 m/s.
    a. Before the collision, the first railroad car moved at 8.0 m/s. What was its momentum?
    b. What is the total momentum of the two cars after the collision?
    c. Find the kinetic energies of the two cars before and after the collision.
    d. Account for the loss of kinetic energy.

13. A railroad car with a mass of 1500 kg rolls along a level track at a speed of 12 m/s. It collides with a stationary car of equal mass.
    a. The two cars lock and then move off. What is the new velocity?
    b. How much energy is lost during the collision?

**14.** As shown, a bowling ball rolls down an incline. The surface of the incline is frictionless.

    **a.** To what point does the ball rise on the opposite incline?

    **b.** At what point in the diagram is the speed maximum?

    **c.** At what point is the speed zero?

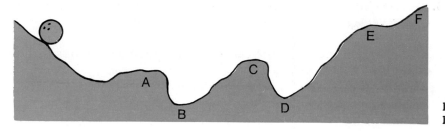

**FIGURE 11-10. Use with Problem 14.**

**Applying Physics**

**1.** *Energy from the Tides:* The Bay of Fundy which separates New Brunswick from Nova Scotia is approximately 240 km long and 80 km wide. For geographic reasons, this bay experiences one of the most rapidly rising and highest tides in the world (20 m). Studies have been made and it has been proposed that gates be constructed to trap the water in the bay at high tide and then release it through generator systems to provide electric energy. If this should be done and the tidal water in the bay falls an average distance of 5.0 m during a period of 6 hours, what power in megawatts (1 MW = $10^6$ watts) could be realized by this venture?

**2.** *Electrical Engineering:* A kilowatt hour (kWh) is an energy unit—not a power unit. It is the total energy that results when 1000 watts is delivered for an entire hour.

    **a.** Show that this energy is 3 600 000 joules.

    **b.** State this result in kilojoules and megajoules.

    **c.** How many joules of energy are consumed by a 100-watt driveway lamp that you leave on all night (10 hours)?

    **d.** If electricity costs 7 cents per kWh, how much does it cost to leave a 100-watt driveway light on all night for an entire year?

**Readings**

Fountain, Kevin, "China Updates Ancient Energy—With Emphasis on Solar." *Science Digest*, April, 1980.

Kraft, B., *Careers in the Energy Industry*. New York, Franklin Watts, 1977.

Post, Jonathan V., "Star Power for Supersocieties." *Omni*, April, 1980.

Socolow, Robert H., et al, "Efficient Use of Energy." *Physics Today*, August, 1975.

Heat always flows from a warmer object or area to a cooler object or area. Heat loss is a significant problem in these times of energy consciousness. New building materials and advanced housing design are helping to minimize heat loss in homes and conserve energy. Analytical techniques such as the one shown are used in pinpointing areas of heat loss in an effort to conserve energy. How can heat losses be prevented? How can waste heat be put to good use?

VANSCAN™ Thermogram by Daedalus Enterprises, Inc., courtesy National Geographic Society

# Measurement of Heat 12

Prior to the nineteenth century, heat was thought to be an invisible fluid called "caloric." It was assumed that a warm object was warm because it contained more caloric than a cool object. "Caloric" could supposedly flow only from a warmer object, where it would be highly concentrated, to a cooler object, where it would be in lower concentration. For this reason, a cool object became warmer when placed close to a warm object. We know today that no mysterious fluid such as caloric exists.

GOAL: You will gain knowledge and understanding of heat and its measurement, temperature, heat exchange, and the law of conservation of energy through a study of the mechanical equivalent of heat.

## 12:1 What Is Heat?

By the middle of the nineteenth century, the caloric theory of heat was replaced by the kinetic theory of heat. The **kinetic theory** states that *all matter consists of minute particles which are in constant motion. Due to their motion, these particles have kinetic energy.* The kinetic theory also states that *these particles must attract one another.* Otherwise, how would any object retain its shape? Because the particles attract one another, they have potential energy.

Heat is explained by the kinetic theory of heat.

The total kinetic and potential energy of all the particles that compose an object is called the **internal energy** of the object. Internal energy is quite distinct from any external kinetic or potential energy an object may have. For example, the external energy of a baseball in flight is due to its motion and position above the earth. The internal energy of the baseball is a result of the kinetic and potential energies of its particles.

Internal energy is the sum of the kinetic and potential energies of the particles of a substance.

External energy concerns the object as a whole.

**185**

**FIGURE 12-1. A baseball in flight has both internal and external energy. The internal energy is the result of the kinetic and potential energies of its particles. The external energy is the result of the position and motion of the baseball in flight.**

Heat energy is the measure of the internal kinetic energy transferred from objects of higher internal energy to objects of lower internal energy.

Temperature refers to the average kinetic energy of an object's molecules.

Heat energy can be used to change potential energy instead of kinetic energy. Then, there is no change in temperature.

It is both impossible and impractical to concern ourselves with the total energy of any given object. It is more important to know the change in internal energy when energy is added or removed from an object. This transferred energy is called heat energy. **Heat energy** is the measure of the internal kinetic energy transferred from objects of higher internal energy (temperature) to objects of lower internal energy. In the strictest sense, heat is a quantity that differs only slightly from work.

## 12:2   Temperature and Heat

Temperature and heat are two different quantities. While temperature is related to heat, it is not the same as heat. The **temperature** of a substance is a measure of the average kinetic energy of the particles* of the substance. Heat, on the other hand, is the total kinetic energy of the particles. Suppose you have two pans filled with boiling water. One pan is very large and the other is quite small. If the temperature of the water in both pans is the same, the water in the large pan would have much more heat energy than the water in the small pan. This difference exists because the water in the large pan has a greater number of molecules. Placed in a cold room, the water in the large pan would transfer much more heat to the room than would the water in the small pan.

Internal energy consists of both the kinetic and potential energy of the particles of a substance. A substance can absorb heat and retain it as potential energy rather than as kinetic energy. Then, there is no increase in temperature. However, there is a large increase in its internal energy.

*The term particles represents atoms, ions, or molecules.

a

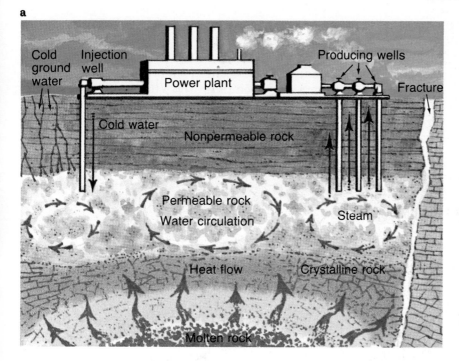

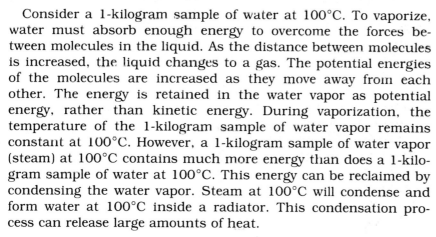

b

Consider a 1-kilogram sample of water at 100°C. To vaporize, water must absorb enough energy to overcome the forces between molecules in the liquid. As the distance between molecules is increased, the liquid changes to a gas. The potential energies of the molecules are increased as they move away from each other. The energy is retained in the water vapor as potential energy, rather than kinetic energy. During vaporization, the temperature of the 1-kilogram sample of water vapor remains constant at 100°C. However, a 1-kilogram sample of water vapor (steam) at 100°C contains much more energy than does a 1-kilogram sample of water at 100°C. This energy can be reclaimed by condensing the water vapor. Steam at 100°C will condense and form water at 100°C inside a radiator. This condensation process can release large amounts of heat.

**FIGURE 12-2. Geothermal wells are designed to tap the energy trapped in heated layers of rock. Steam from the wells can be used to generate electricity.**

# 12:3 Thermometry

In your scientific work, you will measure temperature with a mercury thermometer. Mercury is sealed in a long glass tube. Changes in temperature cause the mercury in the column to expand or contract. Mercury expands at a much greater rate per degree of temperature change than glass. An appropriate scale is placed on the tube. The level of the mercury in the tube varies with the temperature.

Temperature is often measured with a mercury thermometer.

The use of mercury is limited to a short range of temperatures.

To measure very low or very high temperatures, devices other than a mercury thermometer are used.

Mercury and alcohol thermometers are common. However, their use is limited to a short range of temperatures. Mercury is limited by its freezing point ($-39°C$) and its boiling point ($357°C$). For low temperatures, either hydrogen or helium gas can be used. For very high temperatures, devices that measure a property other than expansion are used. For example, the temperature of incandescent substances can be estimated by analyzing the color of light the substance emits. Another means of measuring high temperatures makes use of the fact that the electric conductivity of wire depends on its temperature. Platinum wire shows precise variation in electric conductivity with temperature. Thus, it is often used to measure temperature.

## 12:4  Celsius Temperature Scale

The Celsius temperature scale was devised by Anders Celsius (1701-1744). Two fixed temperatures were selected and marked on a scale. These were the freezing and boiling points of water. At fixed atmospheric pressure, these points are reproduced easily. On the Celsius scale, the freezing point of water is defined as 0°, and the boiling point of water is defined as 100°. There are 100 gradations between these two points.

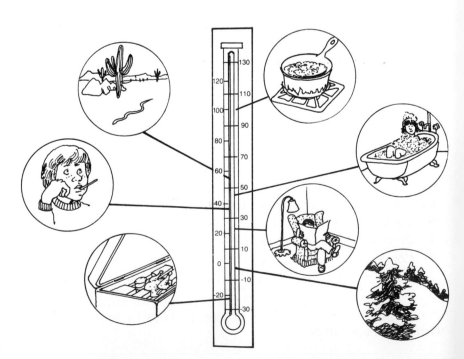

FIGURE 12-3. Some familiar reference points along the Celsius temperature scale are shown.

# 12:5   Kelvin Temperature

Temperatures do not appear to have an upper limit. The interior temperature of the sun ranges above $1.5 \times 10^7 °C$. Other stars may have even higher temperatures. However, temperatures do appear to have a lower limit. The random motion of particles is thought to approach zero at $-273°C$. At this temperature, known as **absolute zero,** the average kinetic energy of particles is zero. Since the average kinetic energy is zero, the temperature must also be zero. However, at this temperature, particles may still have energy. They can still exhibit rotational motion as well as other forms of internal energy not related to temperature.

Absolute zero serves as the basis of a temperature scale known as the kelvin scale. This scale is used extensively for work of a scientific nature in particular in association with the gas laws (Chapter 15). On this scale, temperatures are specified simply as kelvins (K) and no degree sign is used. Kelvin intervals are the same as the intervals on the Celsius scale but the zero point on this scale (0 K) is placed at absolute zero. Thus the freezing point of water (0°C) is 273 K* and the boiling point of water is 373 K. From this it is clear that any temperature on the Celsius scale can be changed to kelvins by adding 273 to it.

Although temperatures have no apparent upper limit, $-273°C$ appears to be the lower limit.

At $-273°C$, the motion of molecules approaches zero.

Zero degrees Celsius equals 273 kelvin.

**EXAMPLE: Converting Celsius to Kelvin Temperature**

Convert 20°C to kelvin.

*Solution:*
$$K = °C + 273$$
$$= 20° + 273 = 293 \text{ K}$$

**EXAMPLE: Converting Kelvin to Celsius Temperature**

Convert 50 K to degrees Celsius.

*Solution:*
$$K = °C + 273$$
$$\text{Thus,} \quad °C = K - 273$$
$$= 50 - 273 = -223°C$$

## PROBLEMS

1. Convert 40°C to kelvin.
2. Convert 40 K to degrees Celsius.
3. Convert 273°C to kelvin.
4. Convert 273 K to degrees Celsius.
5. Convert 200 K to degrees Celsius.
6. Convert these kelvin temperatures to Celsius temperatures.
   - **a.** 100 K
   - **b.** 22 K
   - **c.** 373 K
   - **d.** 323 K
   - **e.** 400 K

1. 313 K

3. 546 K

5. $-73°C$

*More precisely, 273.15 K.

7. a. 373 K  d. 293 K
   b. 173 K  e. 250 K
   c. 573 K

**7.** Convert these Celsius temperatures to kelvin temperatures.

    **a.** 100°C      **c.** 300°C      **e.** −23°C

    **b.** −100°C     **d.** 20°C

## 12:6   First Law of Thermodynamics

The first law of thermodynamics states that energy is conserved.

    The **first law of thermodynamics** states that *when mechanical energy, electric energy, or any other kind of energy is converted to heat, all energy is conserved.* This statement reaffirms the law of conservation of energy. Converting heat to any other form of energy develops exactly the same amount of energy as that originally used to develop the heat.

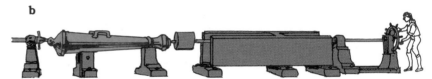

FIGURE 12-4. The type of apparatus used at the time of Count Rumford's cannon boring experiments.

Count Rumford performed the first experiments to determine the relationship between work and energy.

    The first experiments designed to establish a relationship between other forms of energy and thermal energy were performed by Count Rumford (1753-1814)*. Count Rumford was the Bavarian Minister of War, as well as a leading scientist. For one of his projects, Rumford conducted experiments concerned with the caloric theory of heat. As we pointed out earlier, the caloric theory of heat considered heat to be a fluid that flowed from hot to cold. However, the Count's experiments failed to show the existence of any such substance as a caloric fluid.

    One of the Count's most famous heat experiments took place while he was watching the boring of cannons at the arsenal in Munich. Cannons are made by pouring steel into large molds and then drilling, or boring, a hole down their centers. The drills were powered by two horses harnessed to long shafts. During the drilling, both cannon and drill became very hot due to friction. Rumford thought he could use this process to test the caloric theory. He ordered a cannon to be submerged in a large tub of water. He then had the cannon drilled while submerged and

*Count Rumford was born Benjamin Thompson in 1753 in Woburn, Mass., the son of a poor farmer. Almost entirely self-educated, he became a superb scientist, a count of the Holy Roman Empire (the name by which he came to be known), Minister of War of Bavaria, and an English Knight.

made frequent measurements of the temperature of the water. He found that as long as the drilling continued, heat was produced. This meant that if caloric fluid did exist, it could keep coming out of the cannon indefinitely. His finding was strong evidence that there can be no such thing as caloric fluid.

There was a more important result of this experiment. A relationship was established between the work done by the horses and the heat produced by the friction between drills and cannon. Rumford found that while the horses worked, the temperature of the water increased steadily. If the horses worked eight hours, the temperature of the water increased just twice as much as it did if they worked four hours. The temperature increased by the same amount every hour the horses worked. Rumford concluded that the heat added to the water was due to the work done by the horses and not the result of some mysterious fluid. This steady increase in temperature shows that heat is related to the energy output of the horses in a definite way.

James Prescott Joule (1818-1889) began a series of precise experiments to establish the equivalence of the various forms of energy. Joule carefully measured the work, *Fs*, required to drive an electric generator. Then, he measured the heat produced by electric current from the generator. He found consistently that the same amount of work put into the generator raised the temperature of one kilogram of water through one Celsius degree (4180 J). Thus, the energy needed to raise the temperature of one *gram* of water through one Celsius degree is assigned a value of 4.18 joules.

Joule performed many other experiments to measure the mechanical equivalent of heat. One of the best known is shown in Figure 12-5. The potential energy of a falling mass is used to turn a set of paddles submerged in a water-filled calorimeter. Joule assumed that the work done by the paddles on the water was equal to the loss of potential energy, *mgh*, of the falling

A definite relationship exists between heat and other forms of energy.

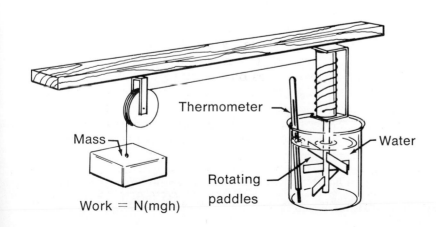

**FIGURE 12-5. Joule measured the energy transferred to the water by falling masses. He made corrections for the kinetic energy of the masses hitting the floor, the amount of stretch of the string, and energy losses in the pulleys. Joule's experiments were instrumental in establishing the principle of the conservation of energy.**

mass. The work done on the water by the paddles was converted to heat. As a result, the temperature of the water rose steadily. To cause a large change in the water temperature, Joule repeated the process several times. He found that the total work done on the water was equal to *N(mgh)* where *N* is the number of times the mass was allowed to fall.

By measuring the change in the temperature of the water, Joule again found that 4180 joules of work produced a temperature increase of one Celsius degree in a kilogram of water. Thus, it became possible to predict the quantity of heat that will be produced when other forms of energy are converted to heat. It also became clear that all forms of energy can be changed to other forms without energy loss. These statements are consistent with the law of conservation of energy.

## 12:7  Second Law of Thermodynamics

The second law of thermodynamics states that heat flows spontaneously from a hotter to a colder object, but not the reverse.

The quantity of heat an object supplies is not necessarily indicated by its temperature. Temperature indicates the direction heat will flow when two objects of different temperatures are brought together. For example, if a hot iron bar is placed in cold water, heat will travel from the metal bar into the water. The iron bar is "hot" because its atoms have a higher average kinetic energy than the molecules of water. Collisions between the water molecules and the more energetic iron atoms impart energy to the water molecules. The energy spreads into the entire system. However, the reverse process never occurs. The hot iron bar does not become hotter while the water becomes colder. This principle is the **second law of thermodynamics.** *Heat flows from hot to cold.* This law prohibits the transfer of energy from areas of low concentration to areas of high concentration.

**FIGURE 12-6. A heat pump runs in either direction depending on whether it is used in heating or cooling. In cooling, heat is extracted from the air in the house and pumped outside. In heating, heat is extracted from the outside air and pumped inside.**

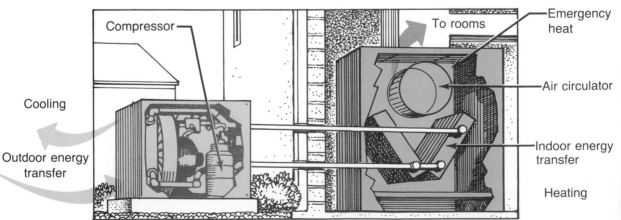

The second law of thermodynamics sometimes is stated in terms of entropy. **Entropy** (EN truh pee) is the "unavailability" of energy. Dissipated energy cannot be retrieved without additional energy input. Heat energy must always spread from areas of high concentration to areas of lower concentration. The entropy of the universe must, therefore, constantly increase.

It is interesting to note that the second law of thermodynamics is the result of probability and not some mysterious rule of nature. The motion of the particles in any object is completely random. Some particles move very fast, some slowly, and many at speeds in between. Temperature is a measure of the average kinetic energies of these particles. If you place a "hot" iron bar in cold water, it is not impossible for all the fast moving molecules in the cold water to just happen to be around the iron bar and cause an increase rather than a decrease in its temperature. However, the probability of this happening is so remote as to make the event effectively impossible. In the same manner, it is not forbidden mathematically for all the air molecules in your classroom at some given instant to be located within a centimeter of the floor. Fortunately for us, this situation is also, statistically, an extremely unlikely possibility.

> Entropy is the randomness of a system.

> Cold is a term that describes the heat energy of one object relative to the heat energy of another object.

## 12:8   Heat Units

The proper unit for all energy, including heat energy, is the joule. Thermal energy ($Q$) and the amount of thermal energy transferred from one place to another, or heat ($\Delta Q$), are both measured in joules.

For many years heat was measured in calories (cal). This unit still appears sometimes. A calorie is simply another way of saying 4.18 joules.

The calorie was put in use before it was understood that all energy should be measured in the same manner. With the adoption of SI units, the calorie has been dropped.

## 12:9   Specific Heat

The **specific heat** of a substance is the amount of heat needed to raise the temperature of a unit mass of that substance through one degree. In metric units, specific heat, C, is expressed in joules per gram Celsius degree, $J/g \cdot C°$, or kilojoules per kilogram Celsius degree, $kJ/kg \cdot C°*$. For example, 0.903 joules of heat are needed to raise the temperature of one gram of

> In the metric system, specific heat is the heat required to raise the temperature of a unit mass of a substance through 1 C°.

*The above notation, C° (Celsius degree), represents a temperature interval— the difference between two temperatures.

$$70°C - 45°C = 25 \ C°$$

aluminum through one Celsius degree. The specific heat of aluminum is 0.903 J/g·C°. A kilogram of aluminum contains one-thousand grams so this could be stated as 0.903 kJ/kg·C°.

**TABLE 12-1**

**Specific Heats of Common Substances**

| Material | Specific Heat (J/g·C°) | Material | Specific Heat (J/g·C°) |
|---|---|---|---|
| alcohol (ethanol) | 2.45 | ice | 2.06 |
| aluminum | 0.903 | iron | 0.450 |
| brass | 0.376 | lead | 0.130 |
| carbon | 0.710 | silver | 0.235 |
| copper | 0.385 | steam | 2.02 |
| glass | 0.664 | water | 4.18 |
| gold | 0.129 | zinc | 0.388 |

Notice that water has a high specific heat when compared to most other substances including ice and steam. Water requires 4.18 joules per gram to undergo a temperature increase of one Celsius degree. By comparison copper needs only 0.385 joule per gram for each Celsius degree temperature increase. The heat needed to raise the temperature of one gram of water one Celsius degree would raise the temperature of one gram of copper by about 11 Celsius degrees.

When the specific heat of a material is known, the amount of heat lost or gained by any given mass of that material as its temperature is changed can be calculated. The specific heat of water is 4.18 J/g·C°. When the temperature of one gram of water is increased 1 C°, the heat absorbed by the water must be 4.18 joules. When 10 grams of water are heated 5 C°, the heat absorbed, $\Delta Q$ must be

$$(10 \text{ g})(4.18 \text{ J/g·C°})(5 \text{ C°}) \text{ or } 210 \text{ joules.}$$

Thus, the quantity of heat gained or lost by a mass as it changes temperature is determined by the mass, change in temperature, and specific heat. This statement can be written

$$\Delta Q = mC\Delta T$$

Heat gained or lost by an object ($\Delta Q$) is the product of its mass, specific heat, and change in temperature.

where $\Delta Q$ is the heat gained or lost, $m$ is the mass of the substance involved, $C$ is the specific heat of the substance, and $\Delta T$ is the change in temperature.

**EXAMPLE: Heat Transfer**

A 400-g block of iron is heated from 20°C to 50°C. How much heat is absorbed by the iron?

*Solution:* $\Delta T$ is found by taking the difference between the two temperatures. The specific heat of iron is found in Table 12-1.

$$\Delta Q = mC\Delta T$$
$$= (400\text{ g})(0.450\text{ J/g·C°})(30\text{ C°}) = 5400\text{ J}$$

## PROBLEMS

**8.** How much heat is absorbed by 250 g of water when it is heated from 10°C to 85°C?

**9.** How much heat is absorbed by 60 g of copper when it is heated from 20°C to 80°C?

     9. 1400 J

**10.** A 38-kg block of lead is heated from −26°C to 180°C. How much heat does it absorb during the heating?

**11.** The cooling system of an automobile engine contains 20 liters of water.

     11. a. 10°C
           b. 21°C
           c. Water is the better coolant.

  **a.** What is the change in the temperature of the water if the engine operates until 836.0 kJ of heat are added?

  **b.** Suppose it is winter and the engine is filled with methanol having a specific heat of 2.48 kJ/kg·C°. The density of methanol is 0.8 g/cm$^3$. What would be the increase in the temperature of the methanol if it also absorbed 836.0 kJ of heat?

  **c.** Which is the better coolant, water or methanol?

**12.** A 400-g glass coffee cup at room temperature, 20°C, is plunged into hot dishwater, 80°C. If the temperature of the cup reaches that of the dishwater, how much heat does the cup absorb?

**13.** Five kilograms of ice cubes are moved from the freezing compartment of a refrigerator into a home freezer. The refrigerator's freezing compartment is kept at −4°C. The home freezer is kept at −17°C. How much heat does the freezer's cooling system remove from the ice cubes?

     13. 130 kJ

**14.** A 250-kg cast-iron car engine contains water as a coolant. Suppose the engine's temperature is 35°C when it is shut off. The air temperature is 10°C. The heat given off by the engine and water in it as they cool to air temperature is $4.4 \times 10^6$ J. What mass of water is used to cool the engine?

**15.** An 800-g block of lead is heated in boiling water, 100°C, until its temperature is the same as the water. The lead is then removed from the boiling water and dropped into 250 g of cool water at 12.2°C. After a short time, the temperature of both lead and water is 20°C.

     15. a. 8200 J
           b. 0.13 J/g·C°

  **a.** How much heat is gained by the cool water?

  **b.** On the basis of these measurements, what is the specific heat of lead?

## 12:10   Conservation in Heat Transfer

In an experiment 100 g of water at 10°C are mixed with 100 g of hot water at 90°C. The container in which they are mixed is well insulated to prevent heat loss. The hot water gives up heat to the cold water. The temperature of the mixture, when measured with a thermometer, is 50°C. The temperature of the cold water has increased by 40 Celsius degrees. The temperature of the hot water has decreased by 40 Celsius degrees.

To heat 100 g of water through one Celsius degree requires 418 joules. Thus, to heat 100 g of water through 40.0 Celsius degrees requires

$$40.0 \times 418 \text{ J} \quad \text{or} \quad 16 \ 700 \text{ J}$$

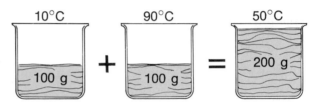

**FIGURE 12-7. Heat lost by the hot water is equal to the heat gained by the cold water.**

The cold water gained 16 700 joules of thermal energy. Similarly, the 100 g of hot water is cooled through 40.0 Celsius degrees. As a result, the hot water gave up

$$(40)(418 \text{ J}) \quad \text{or} \quad 16 \ 700 \text{ J of heat}$$

The heat gained by the cold water is equal to the heat lost by the hot water. This relationship is in full agreement with the first law of thermodynamics.

According to the first law of thermodynamics, the heat lost by one substance is equal to the heat gained by another.

To solve problems of heat transfer, assume that the heat lost by one substance is equal to the heat gained by the second substance. Heat lost or gained by a substance is equal to $mC\Delta T$. This statement is expressed as

$$\textit{Heat lost} = \textit{Heat gained}$$
$$(mC\Delta T)_{\text{substance 1}} = (mC\Delta T)_{\text{substance 2}}$$

### EXAMPLE: Conservation in Heat Transfer

A 500-g block of iron at 100°C is placed in 500 g of water at 20°C. What is the final temperature of the iron and water mixture? (The specific heat of iron is about 0.450 J/g·C°.)

*Solution:* The temperature of the iron decreases. Its temperature change ($\Delta T$) is ($100°C - T_2$) where $T_2$ represents the final temperature of the mixture. The temperature of the water increases. Its temperature change is ($T_2 - 20°C$). *Hence,*

$$\textit{Heat lost by iron} = \textit{Heat gained by water}$$
$$(mC\Delta T)_{\text{iron}} = (mC\Delta T)_{\text{water}}$$

The specific heats of iron and water are found in Table 12-1.

$$(500 \text{ g})(0.450 \text{ J/g} \cdot \text{C}°)(100°\text{C} - T_2) = (500 \text{ g})(4.18 \text{ J/g} \cdot \text{C}°)(T_2 - 20°\text{C})$$
$$225(100 - T_2) = 2090(T_2 - 20)$$
$$22\ 500 - 225\ T_2 = 2090\ T_2 - 41\ 800$$
$$64\ 300 = 2315\ T_2$$
$$T_2 = 27.8°\text{C}$$

**PROBLEMS**

**16.** A 200-g sample of water at 80°C is mixed with 200 g of water at 10°C. Assume no heat loss to surroundings. What is the final temperature of the mixture?

**17.** A 600-g sample of water at 90°C is mixed with 400 g of water at 22°C. Assume no heat loss to surroundings. What is the final temperature of the mixture?    17. 63°C

**18.** A 400-g sample of alcohol at 16°C is mixed with 400 g of water at 85°C. Assume no heat loss to surroundings. What is the final temperature of the mixture?

**19.** A 100-g mass of brass at 90°C is placed in a glass beaker containing 200 g of water at 20°C. Assume no heat loss to the glass or surroundings. What is the final temperature of the mixture?    19. 23°C

**20.** A 100-g mass of aluminum at 100°C is placed in 100 g of water at 10°C. The final temperature of the mixture is 25°C. What is the specific heat of the aluminum?

**21.** A 10-kg piece of zinc at 71°C is placed in a container of water. The water has a mass of 20 kg and has a temperature of 10°C before the zinc is added. What is the final temperature of the water and zinc?    21. 12.7°C

## 12:11   Latent Heats and Change of State

The particle nature of matter implies that some force holds the particles of a substance together. Otherwise, particles would drift apart and an object would not be able to retain its shape. The forces holding particles together are called **cohesive forces.** These forces help explain how a substance can absorb heat without an increase in temperature. For example, the specific heat of ice is 2.06 J/g·C°. If a gram of ice at −10°C absorbs 20.6 joules of heat, the temperature of the ice rises to 0°C. This temperature is the melting point of ice. At the melting point, the ice continues to absorb heat, yet it shows no increase in temperature. The ice at 0°C will absorb 334 joules of heat in becoming water at 0°C. The 334 joules of heat cause the change in state but not a change in temperature. The number of joules needed to bring about a change from the solid to liquid state of

Latent heat of fusion is the number of joules required to change the state of a substance from a solid to a liquid.

**FIGURE 12-8. Molecules of a solid behave as if they were held together by springs.**

**FIGURE 12-9. Graph of the heat absorbed by 1.0 g of ice as its temperature is raised from −50°C to 150°C. Notice that the slope of the graph is steeper from *a* to *b* and from *e* to *f* than it is from *c* to *d*. This is because the specific heats of ice and steam are less than the specific heat of water. The horizontal portions of the graph indicate that heat is being absorbed with no change in temperature.**

any substance is called its **latent heat of fusion.** The latent heat of fusion of ice is 334 J/g.

As the ice melts, the heat it absorbs is stored in a form other than as the kinetic energies of its molecules. If the kinetic energies of the molecules were increased, the temperature of the ice would increase. This temperature change does not occur because the absorbed energy is used to do work on the ice molecules. Since molecules attract one another, work is required to force them apart. As the molecules are forced apart, their potential energies are increased. The potential energy of each molecule increases in relation to all the molecules about it. However, the kinetic energy of the system remains the same.

As the space between ice molecules increases, the cohesive forces decrease. This decrease allows each individual molecule more freedom of movement. Eventually, the forces among the molecules are reduced such that the molecules slide easily over one another. This point is seen as melting.

After the ice has melted it may continue to absorb heat. The temperature of the water increases one Celsius degree for each 4.18 joules of heat it absorbs. As heat is added, the temperature will continue to rise until the water reaches a temperature of

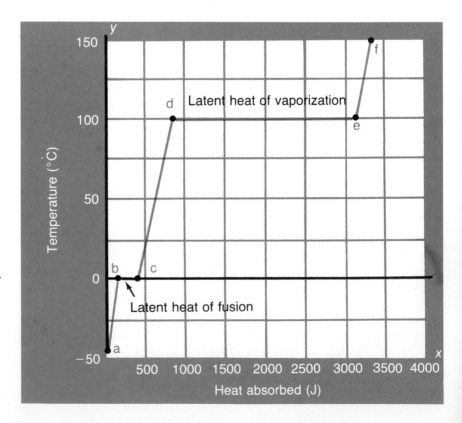

100°C. This temperature is the boiling point of water. Once the boiling point is reached, any heat absorbed is used to change the water from the liquid state to the vapor state. The amount of heat needed to change one gram of a liquid at its boiling point to vapor at the same temperature is called the **latent heat of vaporization.** For water, the latent heat of vaporization is 2260 J/g. Each substance has a characteristic latent heat of vaporization.

The latent heat of vaporization of water is considerably higher than the latent heat of fusion of ice. This difference in energy input serves to leave the molecules almost completely free of intermolecular cohesive forces.

The latent heat of vaporization is the number of joules required to change the state of a substance from a liquid to a gas.

### TABLE 12-2
### Latent Heats of Fusion and Vaporization of Common Substances

| Material | Latent Heat of Fusion (J/g) | Material | Latent Heat of Fusion (J/g) |
|----------|------------------------------|----------|------------------------------|
| alcohol | 109 | lead | 23.0 |
| copper | 205 | mercury | 11.5 |
| gold | 63.0 | silver | 105 |
| iron | 276 | water (ice) | 334 |

| Material | Latent Heat of Vaporization (J/g) | Material | Latent Heat of Vaporization (J/g) |
|----------|-----------------------------------|----------|-----------------------------------|
| alcohol | 878 | lead | 864 |
| copper | 4820 | mercury | 306 |
| gold | 1640 | silver | 2360 |
| iron | 6290 | water | 2260 |

### EXAMPLE: Latent Heat of Fusion

Heat is applied to 100 g of ice at 0°C until the ice melts and the temperature of the resulting water rises to 20°C. How much heat is absorbed?

*Solution:* First, find the amount of heat the ice absorbs to cause a change of state from solid to liquid water. Each gram requires 335 joules to bring about the change.

$$(100 \text{ g})(334 \text{ J/g}) = 33\ 400 \text{ J}$$

Next, calculate the amount of heat the water absorbs to raise its temperature from 0°C to 20°C.

$$\Delta Q = mC\Delta T$$
$$= (100 \text{ g})(4.18 \text{ J/g·C°})(20 \text{ C°}) \quad = 8360 \text{ J}$$

Total: 33 400 J + 8360 J = 41 760 J

Latent heat increases the potential energy between the molecules of a substance.

### EXAMPLE:  Latent Heat of Vaporization

A 100-g sample of water at 80°C is heated until it becomes steam at 130°C. How much heat did the sample absorb?

*Solution:* First, calculate the amount of heat the water absorbed to raise its temperature to 100°C.

$$\Delta Q = mC\Delta T$$

$$= (100\ \cancel{g})(4.18\ \text{J/g·}\cancel{C°})(20\ \cancel{C°})$$

$$= 8360\ \text{J}$$

Next, determine the amount of heat absorbed by the water at 100°C to become steam at 100°C. Each gram requires 2260 joules to cause the change.

$$(100\ \cancel{g})(2260\ \text{J/}\cancel{g}) = 226\ 000\ \text{J}$$

Finally, find the heat absorbed by the steam to raise its temperature from 100°C to 130°C. The specific heat of steam is 2.02 J/g·C°.

$$\Delta Q = mC\Delta T$$

$$= (100\ \cancel{g})(2.02\ \text{J/g·}\cancel{C°})(30\ \cancel{C°})$$

$$= 6060\ \text{J}$$

$$\text{Total: } 8360\ \text{J} + 226\ 000\ \text{J} + 6060\ \text{J} = 240\ 400\ \text{J}$$

### PROBLEMS

**22.** How much heat is needed to change 50 g of ice at 0°C to water at 0°C?

**23.** How much heat is needed to change 50 g of water at 100°C to steam at 100°C?

23. 110 000 J

**24.** How much heat is absorbed by 100 g of ice at −20°C to become water at 0°C? The specific heat of ice is 2.06 J/g·C°.

**25.** A 200-g sample of water at 60°C is heated to steam at 140°C. How much heat is absorbed?

25. $5.0 \times 10^5$ J

**26.** How much heat is needed to change 300 g of ice at −30°C to steam at 130°C?

**27.** How much heat is removed from 60 g of steam at 100°C to change it to 60 g of water at 20°C?

27. $1.6 \times 10^5$ J

**28.** The specific heat of mercury is 0.14 J/g·C°. Its latent heat of vaporization is 306 J/g. How much heat is needed to heat a kilogram of mercury from 10°C to its boiling point and vaporize it completely? The boiling point of mercury is 357°C.

**29.** Years ago, a block of ice with a mass of about 20 kg was used daily in a home icebox. The temperature of the ice was 0°C when delivered. As it melted, how much heat in joules did a block of ice of this size absorb?

29. $6.7 \times 10^6$ J

**Summary**

1. Heat is the measure of internal energy transferred from one object to another.  12:1
2. Internal energy refers to the kinetic and potential energies possessed by the particles of an object.  12:1
3. External energy refers to the kinetic and potential energy possessed by any given mass as a whole.  12:1
4. Internal kinetic energy is referred to as thermal energy.  12:1
5. The temperature of a substance is a measure of the average kinetic energy of its molecules.  12:2
6. Temperature is not a measure of internal energy. Internal energy is measured in joules.  12:2
7. Scientists use either the Celsius or kelvin temperature scales. A kelvin is the same as a Celsius degree.  12:4–12:5
8. The average kinetic energy of the molecules of a substance is zero at 0 K or −273°C. These temperatures are known as "absolute" zero.  12:5
9. The first law of thermodynamics restates the law of conservation of energy: Energy is conserved when thermal energy is transferred, when other forms of energy are changed to thermal energy, or when thermal energy is changed to other forms of energy.  12:6
10. According to the second law of thermodynamics, thermal energy is transferred from areas of high concentration to areas of low concentration (hot to cold).  12:7
11. Specific heat is the quantity of heat needed to raise the temperature of one gram of a substance through one Celsius degree. The specific heat of water is 4.18 joules per gram.  12:9
12. Latent heat of fusion is the quantity of heat required to change a unit mass of a solid to the liquid state.  12:11
13. Latent heat of vaporization is the quantity of heat required to change a unit mass of a liquid to the gaseous state.  12:11
14. The heat gained or lost during a change of state does not produce a change in temperature.  12:11

**Questions**

1. How is heat described in terms of the kinetic theory?
2. Distinguish between heat and temperature.
3. Why are the readings of thermometers of different diameters the same under identical conditions?
4. Describe the Celsius temperature scale.
5. How is the kelvin scale different from the Celsius scale?
6. Ten grams of aluminum and ten grams of lead are heated to the same temperature. The pieces of metal are placed on a block of ice. Which metal will cause more ice to melt?

7.  A wheel is stopped by a friction brake. The brake gets hot, and the internal energy of the brake is increased. The kinetic energy of the wheel is decreased by the same amount as the increase in internal energy of the brake. The first law of thermodynamics would be satisfied if the hot brake were to cool and give back its internal energy to the wheel causing it to resume rotation. This does not happen. Explain.

8.  Would the water at the bottom of a high waterfall be warmer or colder than the water at the top of the same falls? Explain.

9.  Will an ice cube lower the temperature of a glass of water or a glass containing an alcoholic beverage faster? Explain.

## Problems

1.  Convert these Celsius temperatures to kelvin temperatures.
    **a.** 50°C    **b.** 150°C    **c.** −200°C    **d.** 300°C

2.  Convert these kelvin temperatures to Celsius temperatures.
    **a.** 50 K    **b.** 150 K    **c.** 273 K    **d.** 300 K

3.  How much heat in joules is needed to raise the temperature of 50 kg of water from 4.5°C to 83°C?

4.  How much heat in joules must be added to 50 g of aluminum at 20°C to raise its temperature to 120°C?

5.  Suppose the same amount of heat needed to raise the temperature of 50 g of water through 100 C° is applied to 50 g of zinc. What is the temperature change of zinc?

6.  A copper wire has a mass of 165 g. An electric current runs through the wire for a short time and its temperature rises from 20°C to 38°C. What minimum quantity of heat is generated by the electric current?

7.  A 500-g sample of water at 90°C is mixed with 500 g of water at 30°C. Assume no heat loss to surroundings. What is the final temperature of the mixture?

8.  A 200-g sample of brass at 100°C is placed in a calorimeter cup which contains 260 g of water at 20°C. Disregard the absorption of heat by the cup and calculate the final temperature of the mixture. The specific heat of brass is 0.376 J/g·C°.

9.  A 100-g sample of tungsten at 100°C is placed in 200 g of water at 20°C. The mixture reaches equilibrium at 21.6°C. Calculate the specific heat of tungsten.

10. How much heat is added to 10 g of ice at −20°C to convert it to steam at 120°C?

11. A 40.0-g sample of chloroform is condensed from a vapor at 61.6°C to a liquid at 61.6°C. It liberates 9870 joules of heat. What is the latent heat of vaporization of chloroform?

**12.** A 50-g sample of ice at 0°C is placed in a glass beaker containing 400 g of water at 50°C. All the ice melts. What is the final temperature of the mixture? Disregard heat loss to the glass.

**13.** A 500-g block of metal absorbs 5016 joules of heat when its temperature changes from 20°C to 30°C. Calculate the specific heat of the metal.

**Applying Physics**

**1.** *Electrical Energy to Thermal Energy:* A 300-watt electric immersion heater is used to heat a cup of water. The cup is made of glass and its mass is 300 g. It contains 250 g of water at 15°C. How much time is needed for the heater to bring the water to the boiling point? The specific heat of glass is 0.84 J/g·C°. Assume the temperature of the cup to be the same as the temperature of the water at all times.

**2.** *Ecology:* A nuclear power plant on the Connecticut river produces 200 megawatts of power but also releases $1.0 \times 10^{11}$ kJ/day of waste thermal energy into the river. Assume that the average rate of flow of the river is $9.0 \times 10^4$ kg/s.

   **a.** What is the maximum temperature increase in the river water that could be caused by the plant's cooling system?

   **b.** The construction of four additional nuclear power plants along the river has been proposed. What is the total increase in the temperature of the river that could result if the plants are built? Could this change cause serious damage to the ecological structure of the river?

**3.** *Biophysics:* During a game, the metabolism of basketball players often increases by as much as 30 watts. How much perspiration will a player vaporize per hour to dissipate this extra thermal energy?

**4.** *Thermal Engineering:* Due to the rising cost of oil, a school in Pennsylvania converted its heating system from oil to coal. The school contains 17 000 kg of air and the heat of combustion of coal is $3.35 \times 10^4$ kJ/kg. How many kg of coal must be burned in the school's new furnace to bring the temperature of the unheated air in the school from −10°C to 24°C? The specific heat of air is 1.1 kJ/kg·C°. Assume that 50% of the heat produced by the coal actually serves to heat the air in the school.

**Readings**

Brown, Sanborn C., *Benjamin Thompson—Count Rumford.* Cambridge, Mass., M.I.T. Press, 1979.

Graves, C. K., "Rain of Trouble." *Science 80,* July/August, 1979.

Joule, James, "The Mechanical Equivalent of Heat" in Morris H. Shames, ed., *Great Experiments in Physics.* New York, Holt, Rinehart and Winston, Inc., 1959, Chapter 12.

National Geographic Society, *Powers of Nature.* Washington, D.C., Special Publications Division, 1978.

The kinetic theory attempts to explain the nature and behavior of matter. Matter can expand and contract with changes in temperature and pressure. A knowledge of how and why this occurs is important to these divers. Breathing compressed air at a normal rate prevents the divers' lungs from collapsing at increased pressure. How does the kinetic theory explain the gas bubbles rising to the surface?

Dennis Holloman/fpg

# Kinetic Theory 13

Gold and silver are easily shaped and bent. In contrast, chalk breaks when an attempt is made to bend it. Water and alcohol mix readily with one another. However, water and salad oil separate into layers after mixing. In general, an increase in temperature causes materials to expand. Gases expand more than liquids, and liquids expand more than solids with a given change in temperature. All of these properties can be understood if certain assumptions are made about matter.

**GOAL: You will gain knowledge and understanding of the kinetic theory and will interpret some common physical phenomena in terms of this theory.**

## 13:1  Assumptions of the Kinetic Theory

The kinetic theory of matter forms the basis of our understanding of heat. The following are the three basic assumptions of the kinetic theory.

The kinetic theory explains many aspects of the behavior of matter.

1. All matter is made of very small particles.
2. These particles are in constant motion.
3. A mutual force of attraction acts among particles of the same kind. This force is called a cohesive force. Cohesive forces are sometimes called van der Waals forces. Cohesive forces are strongest in solids, strong in liquids, and weak in gases.

Cohesion is the attraction between particles of the same kind.

These assumptions are supported by substantial evidence. For example, water placed in an open dish for a few days will slowly evaporate. Water must be made of many tiny particles in order to behave in this way.

Start

FIGURE 13-1. A model of Brownian motion. The time intervals between successive positions of the particle is the same. The particle changes motion when acted upon by a force (collision with a water molecule).

Brownian motion provides evidence that particles are in constant motion.

The motion of particles can be shown by a method used by the biologist Robert Brown in 1827. Brown suspended pollen grains in a drop of water. He then observed them under a microscope. The grains moved in a strange zigzag way. Their motion can be explained as follows. Water molecules constantly collide with pollen grains. A net force acts on a grain, changing its motion.

The detection of odors is further evidence of the motion of particles. The odor of perfume spreads throughout a room in a short time. Therefore, perfume must consist of tiny particles which move very fast.

The third assumption of the kinetic theory follows from the first two assumptions. If we assume matter is made of particles, some force must hold the particles together. Otherwise, an object would not have a shape. All materials would just drift apart. From experience, we know this situation does not occur. Thus, cohesive forces hold the particles together.

## 13:2  Thermal Expansion of Matter

Because liquids and gases flow, they are both considered to be fluids.

Most materials expand when heated and contract when cooled. The expansion of solids, liquids, and gases can be understood in terms of the kinetic theory. Consider a fluid. A **fluid** is any material which flows. The particles of the fluid are free to move throughout the material. Gases and liquids are fluids. As a fluid absorbs heat energy, the particles of the fluid collide more often and more violently than before. At higher temperatures, the particles rebound greater distances after collisions. The space between particles increases. Thus, a fluid expands when heated.

There is a second reason for the expansion of fluids. Consider what happens when a particle passes a second particle. A force of attraction exists between the particles. If the particles pass each other at high speed, this force of attraction has less time to be effective. Suppose the temperature of a fluid is raised. Then, the particles move faster. When the particles move faster, the force of attraction between particles becomes less effective and the substance tends to expand. On the other hand, suppose the temperature of the fluid is lowered. Then, the particles move more slowly. When the particles move more slowly, the force of attraction between particles becomes more effective and the fluid contracts.

In solids, the particles are not free to move about. Instead, they vibrate about fixed positions. When a solid is heated, the particles vibrate more violently, moving farther from their centers of vibration. This motion causes expansion of the solid. You can observe evidence of expansion and contraction caused by heating and cooling every day. Telephone wires expand in the summer and sag. They contract in the winter and do not sag between poles. Sections of railroad track contract and have more space between them in the winter than in the summer. Water in a pan filled to the brim will expand and overflow when heated.

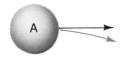

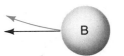

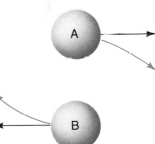

FIGURE 13-2. As molecule *A* passes molecule *B* at a high velocity, the attractive force between them is less effective than it is when the velocity of *A* is low.

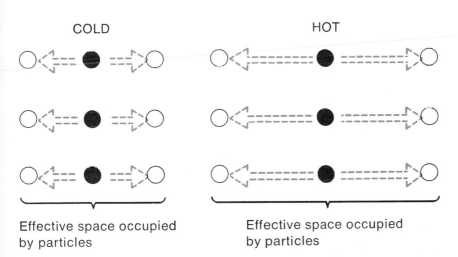

FIGURE 13-3. Molecules vibrate more vigorously and move farther from their fixed positions in hot solids than in cold solids.

A practical application of the expansion and contraction of fluids is found in systems for heating buildings. The air directly around a radiator expands as it is heated. In this way, it becomes less dense than the cool air above it. The warm air rises and the cool air moves in to take its place. This results in circulation of air. This kind of movement resulting from density difference and gravity is called a convection current. Through convection currents, air in a room may be quickly warmed.

**Convection currents in fluids are a result of the combined effects of gravity and difference in density.**

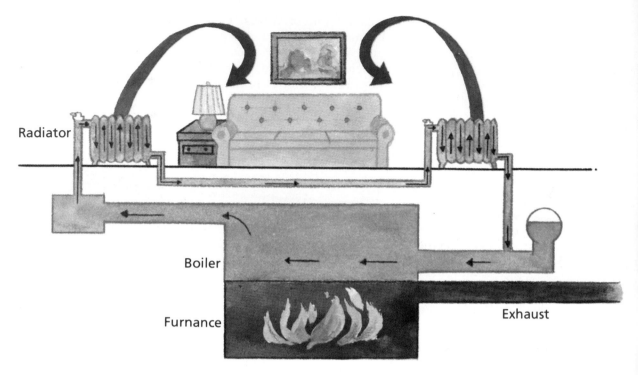

Radiator

Boiler

Furnance

Exhaust

**FIGURE 13-4. The air in a room can be warmed by a radiator and circulated by convection currents.**

Different materials expand at different rates. The expansion rates of gases and liquids are larger than those of solids. Engineers must consider these different expansion rates in designing structures. Steel bars are often used to reinforce concrete. These bars must expand at the same rate as the concrete. Otherwise, the structure may crack on a hot day. Bridges must be built with special joints to allow for expansion and contraction with temperature changes. For a similar reason, a dentist must use filling materials that expand and contract at the same rate as a tooth.

Sometimes, different rates of expansion are useful. Engineers have taken advantage of these differences to construct a useful device called a bimetallic (by muh TAL ik) strip. A **bimetallic strip** consists of two different metal strips. These two metals are either welded or riveted together. Usually, one strip is brass and the other is iron. When heated, brass expands more than iron. Thus, when the bimetallic strip of brass and iron is heated, the brass strip becomes longer than the iron strip. In this case, the bimetallic strip bends with the brass on the outside of the curve. If the bimetallic strip is cooled, it bends in the opposite direction. The brass is on the inside of the curve.

Thermostats that are used in the home usually contain a bimetallic strip. The bimetallic strip is arranged so that it bends toward an electric contact as the room cools. When the room

A bimetallic strip consists of two metal strips that expand and contract at different rates. Thus, a bimetallic strip bends when heated or cooled.

b

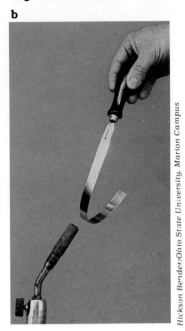

Thomas Russell

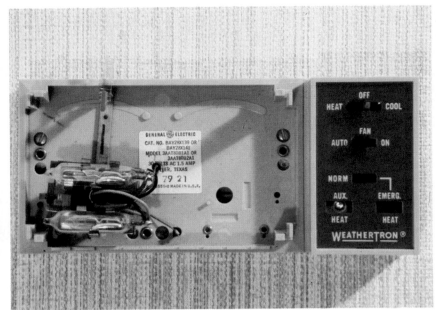

cools below the setting on the thermostat, the bimetallic strip bends enough to make electric contact with the switch which turns on the heater. As the room warms, the bimetallic strip bends the other direction. The electric contact is broken and the heater is switched off.

**FIGURE 13-5.** This thermostat (a) is controlled by the expansion of mercury in the glass tubes. When a room becomes too warm, the mercury expands and trips the tubes to the left breaking the electric circuit. The properties of a bimetallic strip (b) cause it to bend when heated.

# 13:3 Surface Tension

The cohesive force between like molecules leads to an effect known as **surface tension.** A liquid is made of molecules that attract each other. Beneath the surface of the liquid, Figure 13-6, each molecule is attracted equally in all directions by neighboring molecules. As a result, there is no net force acting on any of the molecules beneath the surface. At the surface, however, these molecules are attracted to the side and downward, but not upward. Thus, there is a net downward force acting on the top several molecular layers. This net force tends to increase the density (mass per unit volume) of the surface layer causing it to act as a film. The film is strong enough to support the weight of light objects. Water bugs can stand on the surface of quiet pools of water because of surface tension. The surface tension of water also supports an object such as a steel sewing needle even though the density of steel is seven times greater than that of water.

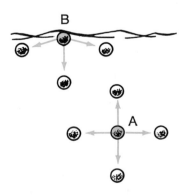

**FIGURE 13-6.** The net downward force on molecule *B* draws the surface molecules together.

a

b

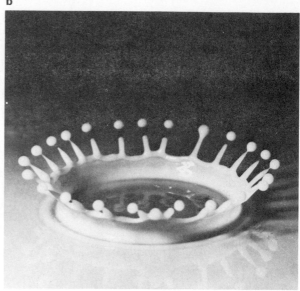

Sharon M. Kurgis

Courtesy of Harold E. Edgerton, Massachusetts Institute of Technology

**FIGURE 13-7. A water strider (a) can stand on water due to surface tension. The splashing milk drops (b) are spherical due to surface tension.**

Surface tension also accounts for the tendency of unconfined liquids to form drops. The force pulling the surface molecules into the liquid causes the surface to become as small as possible. The shape that has the least surface for a given volume is a sphere. Notice that a small drop of water tends to form a sphere when placed on a smooth surface. However, the water droplet usually tends to flatten out. Liquid mercury has a much stronger cohesive force between its molecules than water. Thus, small amounts of mercury form spherical drops even when placed on a smooth surface.

On the other hand, liquids such as alcohol or ether have very weak cohesive forces between their molecules. A drop of either of these liquids flattens when placed on a smooth surface. These two liquids also evaporate quickly because the forces between molecules are weak. A liquid which evaporates quickly is called a **volatile** (VAHL uht uhl) liquid.

A volatile liquid has weak cohesive forces between its molecules.

Adhesion is the attraction between molecules of different substances.

A force similar to cohesion is adhesion. **Adhesion** is the attractive force that often acts between molecules of different substances. If a glass tube with a small inside diameter is placed in water, the water rises inside the tube. The water rises because the adhesive force between glass and water molecules is stronger than the force between water molecules. The water rises in the tube until its weight counteracts the difference in forces. This phenomenon is called **capillary action.** A tube with a small diameter has a larger surface area per unit volume than a tube with a large diameter. Thus, the adhesive force is more effective in the tube with a small diameter. Water rises higher in a small-diameter tube than in a large-diameter tube.

Capillary action occurs when adhesive forces are stronger than cohesive forces.

a  b

Hickson-Bender Photography, Ohio Wesleyan University

**FIGURE 13-8.** Water climbs the wall of this capillary tube (a), while mercury is depressed in the tube (b). The force of attraction between mercury atoms is stronger than any adhesive force between the mercury and the glass.

Oil rises in the wick of a lamp because of capillary action. Paint moves up through the bristles of a brush for the same reason. It is also capillary action that causes water to move up through the soil to the roots of plants.

## 13:4 Vaporization

The molecules in a liquid move at random speeds. Some are moving rapidly while others are moving slowly. The temperature of a liquid is dependent upon the average speed of its molecules. Suppose a fast-moving molecule is near the surface of the liquid. If it can break through the tightly-packed surface layers, it will escape from the liquid. Since there is a net downward cohesive force at the surface, only the more energetic molecules can escape. Each time a molecule escapes from the liquid, the average kinetic energy of the remaining molecules decreases. A decrease in kinetic energy is a decrease in temperature. This result is the cooling effect of evaporation.

This effect can be demonstrated by pouring some rubbing alcohol into the palm of your hand. Alcohol molecules have weak cohesive forces (low surface tension). Alcohol molecules therefore evaporate easily. The cooling effect is quite noticeable.

The opposite process is also true. Vapor molecules above the surface of a liquid may strike the surface and be absorbed. This process is called condensation. Each time a vapor molecule is absorbed by the liquid, the average kinetic energy of the liquid is increased. Thus, the temperature of the liquid is increased. This result is the warming effect of condensation.

The cooling effect of evaporation occurs because the molecules which escape from the liquid are those with the highest KE.

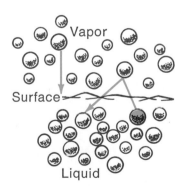

**FIGURE 13-9.** The vapor pressure above a liquid slows the rate of evaporation.

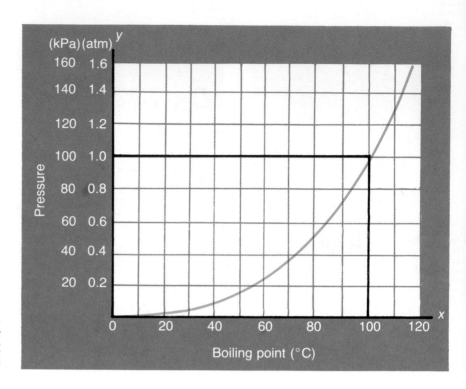

**FIGURE 13-10. This vapor-
ization curve for water
shows how the boiling
point varies with pressure.**

A pressure increase
reduces the chance for
molecules to escape from
a liquid. Thus, boiling
occurs at higher
temperatures when
pressure is raised.

A pressure decrease
makes it easier for
molecules to escape.
Thus, boiling occurs at
lower temperatures when
pressure is lowered.

An increase in pressure above a liquid makes it more difficult
for a molecule to escape from the liquid. Thus, increased pressure means that the molecules need a higher kinetic energy to
escape.

When a liquid boils, fast moving molecules form vapor pockets
within the liquid. Vapor pockets form because the average kinetic
energies of the molecules is so high that the absorption of additional energy requires the liquid to change to a gas. Usually
these vapor pockets form at the bottom of the container near the
source of heat. The vapor pockets then rise and leave the liquid
as a whole. At the boiling point, the pressure inside these pockets
is equal to the pressure above the liquid. Under increased pressure, a liquid must therefore reach a higher temperature before
boiling takes place.

At normal atmospheric pressure, water boils at 100°C. If the
pressure above water is decreased, boiling occurs at lower temperatures. People living in low pressure areas (high altitudes)
must alter cooking time for food due to the difference in boiling
point. To demonstrate (Figure 13-11), a small container of
warm water is placed inside a bell jar. The bell jar is attached to
a vacuum pump. Air is slowly removed from the jar with a
vacuum pump. As the pressure is lowered, the water boils, even
though its temperature is less than 100°C.

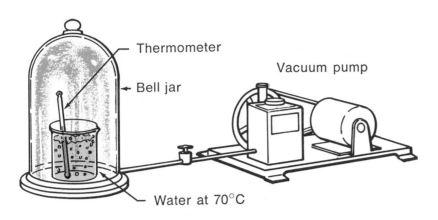

Thermometer

Bell jar

Vacuum pump

Water at 70°C

*George Anderson*

## 13:5  Solid State

When a liquid freezes, the particles of the liquid are no longer able to move freely. As the particles of a liquid slow down, the cohesive forces between them become more effective (Section 13:2). The particles assume relatively stable positions. However, the particles in a solid do not stop moving completely. Instead, each particle vibrates about a set position. The position of each particle is affected by the cohesive forces around it. Particles of the same material have similar cohesive attractions for one another. Therefore, the particles in a solid take a uniform arrangement in relation to one another. In this way, crystals are formed. Examples of materials with interesting crystal structures are snowflakes and diamonds.

**FIGURE 13-11. Water boils at low temperatures when the pressure is decreased. Body heat is sufficient to get the water to boil if the pressure is low enough.**

In a solid, each particle vibrates about a set position.

The crystalline structure of some solids is a result of similar cohesive forces between particles.

a          b          c

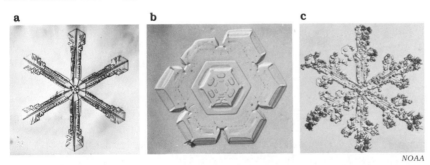

*NOAA*

**FIGURE 13-12. Ice crystals exhibit a variety of different shapes.**

As a liquid freezes, its particles usually fit more closely together than in the liquid state. Water is an exception. Water molecules in the solid state take up more space than they do as a liquid. Thus, water expands as it freezes causing ice to have a lower density than liquid water. If water contracted as it froze, ice would have a higher density than water and would sink. Lakes and rivers would freeze from the bottom up. In summer, the water above the ice would act as an insulator. Many lakes and rivers would never thaw completely.

Unlike most liquids, water expands as it freezes.

*Keith Turpie*

FIGURE 13-13. The expansion and contraction of water as it freezes and melts can cause extensive road damage.

An increase in the pressure on the surface of a liquid forces the particles closer. Then, the cohesive forces become stronger. For most liquids, an increase in surface pressure will raise the freezing point of the liquid. In general, the freezing point of a liquid increases as the pressure on the liquid increases. Again, water is the exception. Since water expands as it freezes, an increase in pressure prevents this expansion. The freezing point of

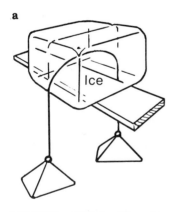

a

FIGURE 13-14. The ice melts as a result of the pressure exerted by the wire (a). An ice skater exerts a force on the skate blades. The melted ice allows the skater to glide (b).

b

*Young/Hoffhines*

water is lowered as the pressure on its surface is increased. Ice skating is based on this principle. Increased pressure from the skate blades causes the ice under the blades to melt. The water that forms acts as a lubricant to make skating easier and faster.

## 13:6  Plasma

We have studied the three common states of matter—solid, liquid, and gas. There is a fourth state of matter called plasma. There is very little plasma on the earth. However, more than 99 percent of the universe is made up of plasma. Stars and much of interstellar space consists of plasma.

In the plasma state, the particles have charges. Atoms have lost one or more of their electrons as a result of energetic collisions. An atom which has lost electrons has a net positive charge and is a positive ion. The electrons are negative particles. Gas that contains more than 5 percent ions can be classified as plasma. By this definition, fluorescent lamps contain plasma.

Ideal plasma, such as the plasma found in stars, consists of electrons and bare nuclei. The plasma then contains a swirling mass of positive ions and electrons. Although the ions themselves are charged, the plasma as a whole has no charge. It contains as many positive charges as negative charges. The main difference between a gas and a plasma is that a plasma can conduct an electric current. A gas cannot conduct an electric current.

Much of the sun consists of a glowing mass of plasma at temperatures in excess of 6000°C. Plasma is not limited to the sun's surface. Plasma from the sun extends for millions of miles into space. The earth is actually inside the sun's sphere of plasma. This plasma is mainly hydrogen plasma that leaves the sun and makes up the solar wind. The solar wind speeds by the earth at a rate of 1 500 000 km/h.

At the extreme temperatures in a star, hydrogen plasma fuses to form helium nuclei. This process is called **nuclear fusion.** Nuclear fusion is the source of all the sun's radiant energy. A small part of this radiant energy reaches the earth.

In about 10 billion years, the sun will run out of hydrogen fuel. Then, its helium will collapse under gravitational forces and higher temperatures will result. At these higher temperatures a new series of fusion reactions will take place. Heavier elements will be formed. Vast amounts of energy will be released. In some stars this event may result in enough radiant pressure to cause a violent explosion. The star could become a supernova. A **supernova** is a large bright star which lasts for a few days or weeks and then fades away.

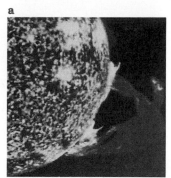

*NASA*

*NASA*

FIGURE 13-15. The sun (a) consists of plasma. This ion engine (b) operates by using electricity to produce mercury ions from mercury vapor. The charged ions are shown here in the stream of exhaust. Such engines can reach velocities over $1.6 \times 10^5$ km/h.

Plasma is the fourth state of matter.

Companion star

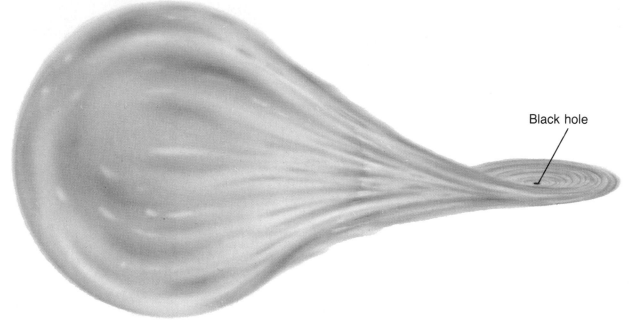

Black hole

**FIGURE 13-16. Black holes are detected by their gravitational effects on nearby stars. Gaseous matter from a nearby star is pulled into the black hole.**

**FIGURE 13-17. The fastest spinning pulsar known is located in the center of the Crab Nebula.**

A supernova leaves behind a very dense central core called a neutron star. **Neutron stars** result from the gravitational collapse of the original star. Usually they are only a few kilometers wide and have densities $10^{14}$ times that of the sun. The neutrons are formed as electrons and protons are pressed together during the collapse. Neutrons have no charge. Therefore, they can be compacted more than normal nuclei. The density of the star becomes huge.

Since momentum is always conserved, a neutron star must maintain a constant angular momentum. Therefore, the mass that collapses into the center of the star must rotate faster and faster as it nears the center. Electrons trapped in the rapidly rotating magnetic field of the star emit radio waves with great regularity. For this reason, some neutron stars are called **pulsars.** The radiowaves from the electrons sweep over us at regular intervals causing pulses of energy in detectors.

Stars of huge mass create neutron stars of unbelievable density. These stars literally crush themselves out of existence leaving behind an unusually strong gravitational

*Hale Observatories/fpg*

field called a **black hole.** The gravitational field of a black hole is so great that not even light can leave the star. In order to escape from a black hole, an object would have to be traveling faster than the speed of light. Black holes cannot be "seen." Instead, they are detected by their effects on nearby objects.

# 13:7  Electric Resistance and Superconductivity

The transfer of electric energy from place to place requires the use of conductors. Good **conductors** have low resistance to electron flow. Metallic solids such as copper and aluminum are good conductors.

Under normal conditions, all electric conductors show some resistance to electron flow. Thus, some of the energy produced by an electric generator must be used to force electrons through conducting wires. The energy used in this way does not appear as electric energy.

One theory that attempts to explain electric resistance is based on the kinetic theory and its assumption that the particles of a substance are in constant motion. In Figure 13-18, electrons are shown flowing through the crystalline lattice of a metallic conductor. Suppose nothing hinders the movement of the electrons through the space between the atoms that comprise the lattice. In this case, the electrons would move through the conductor without any resistance. In reality, the atoms vibrate as they occupy positions in the lattice. Thus, they hinder the flow of electrons through the conductor. According to the kinetic theory, vibration of atoms in the lattice results in resistance in electric conductors.

One theory of electric resistance is based on the kinetic theory.

From this explanation, it follows that temperature should affect the electric resistance of a conductor. If the solid is heated, its particles vibrate more energetically. They move farther from their centers of vibration. Thus, the particles hinder the electron flow more effectively. The electric resistance of a wire increases as it is heated. Conversely, cooling a conductor slows the vibration of the particles. There is less interference with the electron flow. The electric resistance of a wire decreases as it is cooled.

The vibratory motion of particles in a crystal lattice accounts for electric resistance.

When the temperature of certain conductors is reduced to near absolute zero, the particles in the lattice do not vibrate enough to interfere with the electrons. Thus, at very low temperatures, these conductors have zero electric resistance. This property is known as **superconductivity.** When electrons flow through a superconductor, there is zero energy loss. A current introduced into a superconductive circuit will flow around the circuit indefinitely.

When certain conductors are cooled to near absolute zero, they become superconducting.

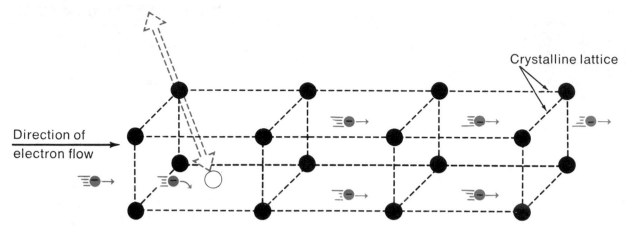

Direction of
electron flow

Crystalline lattice

**FIGURE 13-18. Vibration of particles in a lattice causes resistance to electron flow through the lattice.**

Some materials are superconductors at temperatures higher than absolute zero. A few materials become superconductive at about 20 K. Research is being done to develop materials that will be superconductors at still higher temperatures. Such materials could lead to large increases in available electric energy.

## 13:8  Studying the Unobservable

We have used the assumptions of the kinetic theory to explain different behaviors of matter. Scientists have not yet been able to construct a device that will allow us to directly observe the behavior of particles that compose matter.

**The kinetic theory has been tested and observable phenomena consistently agree with the predictions of the kinetic theory.**

The kinetic theory appears correct because it consistently provides a good explanation of the behavior of matter. Some scientists call this testing process an "if—then" process. If matter is made of particles that attract one another, then liquids should display surface tension. We do observe surface tension in liquids. Thus, the theory passes the test. If any uniform substance is made of similar particles, then solids should assume regular crystalline arrangements just as marbles in a jar assume a regular arrangement. Solids do form crystalline arrangements, and the theory again passes a test.

**Inference is useful when direct observation is not possible.**

The "if—then" process is an **inference process.** It is useful whenever we want to study behavior that we cannot observe directly. For example, we cannot observe directly the planetary systems orbiting distant stars. The light from a star interferes with any dim light which might be reflected from any of its orbiting planets. But, if there are planets near a star, then the star should wobble slightly from the gravitational attraction of its planets as it moves through space. Some stars do wobble slightly. Their wobbling is evidence that the planets we cannot observe directly are really there.

**Summary**

1. The kinetic theory is a valuable tool with which we can explain aspects of the behavior of matter.  13:1

2. The three basic assumptions of the kinetic theory are that matter is made of minute particles, these particles are constantly in motion, and a mutual force of attraction exists between them.  13:1

3. The force of attraction between like molecules is electric in nature and is referred to as "cohesive" and "van der Waals" forces.  13:1

4. Adhesion, the force of attraction between unlike particles, is responsible for capillary action.  13:3

5. The kinetic theory of matter explains thermal expansion, surface tension in liquids, the cooling effect of evaporation, crystalline structure of solids, the resistance of electrical conductors, and many other phenomena.  13:2

6. The states of matter are solid, liquid, gas, and plasma.  13:2, 13:4, 13:5, 13:6

7. Plasma consists of free electrons and nuclei that have been completely stripped of electrons and can conduct electricity. While plasma is not abundant on Earth, it makes up the vast majority of the universe.  13:6

8. When scientific phenomena cannot be studied directly, an inference process must be used.  13:8

**Questions**

1. Why does the pressure inside a container filled with a gas increase if its temperature increases?

2. If two baseballs collide in midair, much of their kinetic energy is changed to heat, and the balls become warmer but move more slowly. Why do two molecules of a gas not lose energy in the same way when they collide?

3. A razor blade is more dense than water. Yet, it can be made to float on the surface of water. Explain.

4. Atmospheric pressure at the top of Mt. Everest (elevation 8850 m) is approximately 0.316 atm (31.6 kPa). Use Figure 13-10 to find the approximate temperature at which water boils at the top of the mountain.

5. In a warm room, ammonia molecules have a velocity of about 607 m/s. At this velocity, what time would be needed for an ammonia molecule to travel 10.0 m? If a bottle of ammonia is opened at one end of a room, it takes several minutes for the odor to be detected at the other end? Why?

6. Denver, Colorado, has the highest altitude of any major city in the United States. How does atmospheric pressure in Denver compare with that at sea level? Why are pressure cookers widely used in Denver?

7. A drop of water, a drop of mercury, and a drop of naphtha (lighter fluid) are placed on a smooth, flat surface. The water and the mercury take a definite shape. The naphtha spreads out over the surface. What does this tell you about the cohesive forces between naphtha molecules? Explain why naphtha vaporizes readily.

8. Use your answer to Question 7 to explain why naphtha has a low boiling point.

9. In what way does a plasma differ from a gas? What portion of the universe consists of plasma?

10. Why does the resistance of electric conductors increase when they are heated?

11. Does a power company make more money in the summer or the winter? Explain.

12. Explain why electric companies do not use superconductors to transmit power to their customers.

## Problems

1. New 20-m lengths of railroad track are installed on a winter day when the temperature is 0°C. A meter of steel expands $1 \times 10^{-5}$ m when the temperature increases $1 C°$. If summer temperatures reach 35°C, what minimum distance must be left between each length of track?

2. A meter of brass expands at the rate of $2 \times 10^{-5}$ m/C°. What is the increase in the length of a 50-m brass rod if it is heated from 20°C to 50°C?

3. An icicle 0.80 m long is heated from −30°C to −10°C. If a meter of ice expands at a rate of $5.0 \times 10^{-5}$ m/C°, what is the new length of the icicle?

4. Using the vaporization curve of Figure 13-10, state the pressure under which water will boil at
   **a.** 80°C   **b.** 60°C   **c.** 45°C   **d.** 20°C

5. Assume that a quasar converts $5 \times 10^5$ kg of mass to radiant energy each second. Using the equation $E = mc^2$, find the energy in joules released each second by the quasar. (Recall that $c = 3 \times 10^8$ m/s.)

6. A 100-watt light bulb produces about 15 J of radiant energy each second. How many 100-watt light bulbs would be needed to produce the same radiant energy as the quasar of Problem 5?

**7.** A major manufacturer of light bulbs can produce 10 000 light bulbs per day. How many years would it take for this manufacturer to produce enough light bulbs to equal the brilliance of the quasar of Problem 5?

**1.** *Kinetic Energy and Temperature:* At a temperature of 25°C, an ammonia molecule of mass $2.8 \times 10^{-26}$ kg has a velocity of about $6.7 \times 10^2$ m/s.
   **a.** Calculate the KE of the molecule.
   **b.** How many ammonia molecules at this temperature would be needed to develop a total energy of one joule?
   **c.** The mass of an oxygen molecule ($O_2$) is about $5.4 \times 10^{-26}$ kg. At what velocity would an oxygen molecule have the same KE (temperature) as the ammonia molecule?

**2.** *Atomic Physics:* The fluorine nucleus is spherical and has a diameter of about $5.0 \times 10^{-13}$ cm. It contains 19 atomic particles, each of approximate mass $1.67 \times 10^{-27}$ kg.
   **a.** What is the volume of the fluorine nucleus?
   **b.** What is the density of the fluorine nucleus in grams per cubic centimeter?

**3.** *Space Travel:* You are traveling on a space mission far from Earth and due to instrument malfunction your spaceship of mass 2000 metric tons (1000 kg per ton) has wandered off course. You find that you are within 40 000 km of a very small neutron star of mass $1.0 \times 10^{28}$ kg.
   **a.** What gravitational force exists between your ship and the star?
   **b.** The maximum acceleration your rockets can give the ship is 400 m/s$^2$. Can you escape the gravitational field of the neutron star or is your ship in serious difficulty?

Mason, B. J., "The Growth of Snow Crystals." in, *The Physics of Everyday Phenomena.* W. H. Freeman and Co., 1979.

McDonald, James E., "The Shape of Raindrops." in, *The Physics of Everyday Phenomena.* W. H. Freeman and Co., 1979.

Overbye, Dennis. "The Wizard of Space and Time." *Omni,* February, 1979.

The construction of a hot air balloon requires an understanding of the properties of gases. The volume of the balloon is controlled by the temperature of the gas in the balloon. The balloon's buoyancy is a function of the density of the gas in the balloon. As a balloon rises, changes in air pressure occur. How does a balloonist compensate for changing air pressure? How does a decrease in air pressure affect the volume of a balloon?

# Gas Laws 14

Gas particles are distributed evenly throughout an enclosed container. Therefore, the volume of a gas is the volume of the container that encloses it. Three quantities are necessary to describe the condition of any given sample of a gas. These quantities are temperature, pressure, and volume. A change in one of these quantities always results in a change in at least one of the others.

**GOAL: You will gain knowledge and understanding of the laws governing the behavior of gases.**

Three quantities describe the condition of a gas—temperature, pressure, and volume.

## 14:1 Standard Pressure

**Pressure** is force per unit area. When speaking of pressure we think of the force as being spread uniformly over the area. The SI unit for pressure is the pascal (Pa). A **pascal** is a pressure of one newton per square meter.

$$1 \text{ Pa} = 1 \text{ N/m}^2$$

The newton is a rather small force (about the weight of a 100-g mass on Earth). A square meter is a good-sized area. Therefore, a pressure of 1 pascal is a very low pressure. For this reason the kilopascal (kPa) or 1000 pascals is a more useful unit.

$$1000 \text{ N/m}^2 = 1000 \text{ Pa} = 1 \text{ kPa}$$

Pressure is force per unit area.

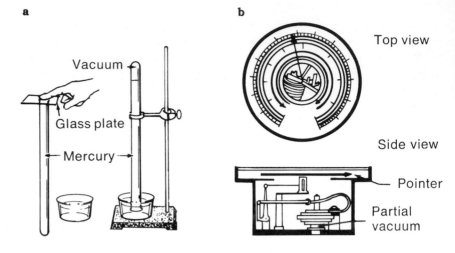

FIGURE 14-1. A mercury barometer (a) measures air pressure by using the height of a column of mercury supported by the atmosphere. The aneroid barometer (b) measures air pressure by means of changes in the size of an evacuated chamber.

Scientists have long found it convenient to relate pressure to what is known as **standard atmospheric pressure.** This is the average pressure of the atmosphere taken at sea level over a long period of time. This pressure turns out to be $1.01 \times 10^5$ newtons per square meter. Since a pascal is a pressure of one newton per square meter, this is $1.01 \times 10^5$ pascals, or 101 kilopascals.

There are several ways to measure atmospheric pressure. The method most frequently used in laboratories relates atmospheric pressure to the height of a column of mercury that it will support. Why this can be done is illustrated in Figure 14-1. Here a glass tube, sealed at one end and completely filled with mercury, is shown. If the filled tube is turned upside down (inverted) and placed in a dish of mercury, the mercury drops slightly in the tube. Since the tube was filled initially, the empty space at the top of the tube must be a vacuum. The pressure in a vacuum is zero, so the pressure at the top of the tube is zero. However, the pressure on the mercury in the dish is atmospheric pressure. This difference in pressure, under standard atmospheric conditions, will support a column of mercury 760 millimeters (76.0 cm) high. Thus, standard atmospheric pressure is referred to as 760 mm of mercury. To a scientist one atmosphere (1 atm) of pressure, or $1.01 \times 10^5$ N/m$^2$, or 101 kPa all mean the same thing.

The height of the column of mercury in the tube will increase or decrease with changes in air pressure. Therefore, the height of the column of mercury is a direct indication of pressure. **Barometers,** Figure 14-1, are used to measure pressure. Meteorologists watch barometric readings carefully since atmospheric pressure has a direct bearing upon weather conditions. During scientific experiments, tubes filled with mercury are often used to measure pressures. Scientists take readings in millimeters of mercury and then convert the readings to pascals or some other appropriate units.

Aneroid (AN uh royd) barometers, Figure 14-1, are also used to measure pressure. An aneroid barometer consists of a metal "can" that contains a vacuum. When the air pressure changes, the top of the can is displaced slightly. A needle is attached to the top of the can. Because the top of the can moves when air pressure changes, this needle can be used to indicate the air pressure. The scale of the barometer is usually calibrated in millimeters of mercury.

## 14:2  Boyle's Law

Figure 14-2a shows a gas-filled cylinder. A 1-kilogram mass rests on the piston. Due to its weight, this mass exerts a force on the piston which in turn exerts pressure on the gas. Gas molecules collide with the underside of the piston. These collisions produce an upward pressure on the piston. Even a small sample of gas has a large number of molecules. Thus, many collisions take place between the gas molecules and the piston in any given instant. The fact that there are many collisions guarantees (statistically) that the number of collisions taking place at any given instant is constant. Therefore, the upward pressure on the underside of the piston is constant.

In Figure 14-2b, two 1-kilogram masses are placed on the piston. Now the piston produces twice the pressure on the gas as it did in Figure 14-2a. Since molecular collisions account for the gas pressure on the underside of the piston, twice as many collisions per second must act on the underside of the piston before equilibrium is regained. Twice as many collisions per second will occur if the piston sinks to half its previous distance from the bottom of the cylinder. With the piston in this new position, the distance each molecule travels between collisions is reduced to one-half its former value. With only half the distance to travel, the molecules strike the underside of the piston twice as often. These collisions result in twice as much pressure on the piston.

Following this line of reasoning, three times the pressure on the top of the piston pushes the piston down to one-third its original height, Figure 14-2c. Four times the pressure pushes the piston down to one-fourth its original height. Thus, the kinetic theory predicts **Boyle's law:** *the volume occupied by a gas varies inversely with the applied pressure.* Therefore, the product of volume and pressure is a constant.

$$PV = k$$

If $P_1$ = initial pressure, $V_1$ = initial volume, $P_2$ = new pressure, and $V_2$ = new volume, then

$$P_1V_1 = k = P_2V_2$$

**FIGURE 14-2. The volume of a gas decreases as the pressure applied to it increases.**

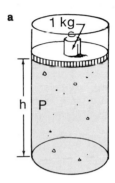

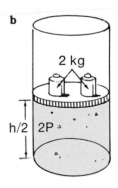

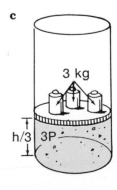

Boyle's law states that the volume and the pressure of a gas are inversely related.

Since $k$ is a constant, substitute $k = P_2V_2$ into the first equation.

$$P_1V_1 = P_2V_2$$

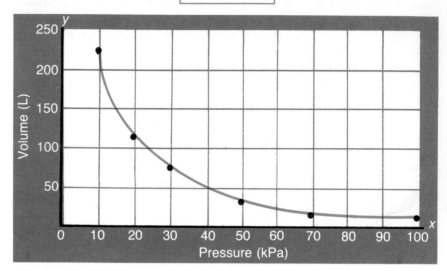

**FIGURE 14-3. A graph of the pressure of a gas versus its volume. The curve indicates an inverse relationship. Volume varies inversely with pressure.**

### EXAMPLE: Boyle's Law

Under a pressure of 200 kPa, a confined gas has a volume of 2.6 m³. The pressure acting on the gas is increased to 500 kPa. The temperature of the gas remains unchanged. What is the volume of the gas?

*Solution:*    $P_1V_1 = P_2V_2$    or    $V_2 = \dfrac{P_1V_1}{P_2}$

$$= \frac{(200 \text{ kPa})(2.6 \text{ m}^3)}{500 \text{ kPa}} = 1.0 \text{ m}^3$$

### PROBLEMS

1. 40 m³

**1.** Pressure acting on 60 m³ of a gas is raised from 236 kPa to 354 kPa. The temperature is kept constant. What new volume does the gas occupy?

**2.** A volume of 50 m³ of neon gas is compressed until its volume becomes 12.5 m³. The original pressure acting on the gas was 200 kPa. What is the final pressure acting on the gas?

3. 0.67 L

**3.** An inflated balloon occupies a volume of 2.0 liters. The balloon is tied with a string and weighted with a heavy stone. What is its volume when it reaches the bottom of a pond 20.8 m deep? Note: One atmosphere of pressure supports a column of water 10.4 m high. Assume the pressure acting on the balloon before it submerges is 1.0 atm.

4. A helium-filled balloon occupies a volume of 16 m$^3$ at sea level. The balloon is released and rises to a point in the atmosphere where the pressure is 0.75 atm. What is its volume?

5. A helium-filled balloon occupies a volume of 2.0 m$^3$ at sea level. The balloon then rises to a height in the atmosphere where its volume is 6.0 m$^3$. What is the pressure in kPa at this height?

5. 34 kPa

6. A diver works at a depth of 52 m in fresh water. A bubble of air with a volume of 2.0 cm$^3$ escapes from the diver's mouthpiece. What is the volume of the same bubble as it breaks the surface of the water? (See note in Problem 3.)

# 14:3   Charles' Law

Boyle's law assumes that the temperature of a gas remains constant. We will now consider the relationship that exists between the temperature and volume of a gas.

Jacques Charles (1746–1823) discovered that, at constant pressure, all gases expand the same amount for a given temperature change. Charles kept a gas at 0°C under a pressure of 101 kPa. He increased its temperature to 1°C and the gas expanded $1/273$ of its original volume. He increased the temperature to 2°C. Its volume increased $2/273$ of the first volume. At 273°C, the volume was twice the volume at 0°C. Charles obtained similar results when he reduced the temperature of the gas below 0°C. For each Celsius degree below 0°C, the volume of the gas was reduced by $1/273$ of its original volume. This discovery had startling implications. In theory, it meant that at −273°C a gas would have zero volume. However, a substance does not remain a gas as its temperature is lowered. A point is reached when a change of state occurs and the gas becomes a liquid. Then, a further decrease in temperature causes the liquid to follow a different rate of contraction.

Charles found that the volume change of a gas per kelvin is 1/273 of its volume at 0°C and 1 atm pressure.

Figure 14-4 plots the volume of a gas against its temperature. The volume of the gas at 0°C is the basic volume. Today, in the laboratory, it is possible to measure most of the data needed to plot such a graph. However, in Charles' day, it was not possible to attain temperatures much below −20°C. Charles extended the line of the graph down to temperatures below −20°C to see what lower limits might be possible. Extending a graph beyond measurable points is called **extrapolation.** Although extrapolation is not based on precise data, it can provide useful information upon which to draw conclusions.

Figure 14-4 indicates that the lowest possible volume of a gas occurs at −273°C. This fact leads to the conclusion that −273°C

FIGURE 14-4. A graph of the temperature of a gas versus its volume. The straight line indicates that the volume varies directly as the temperature. The constant of proportionality, taken from the slope of the graph, is $\Delta y/\Delta x$. What is the numerical value of the slope of this graph? What is 1/273 expressed as a decimal?

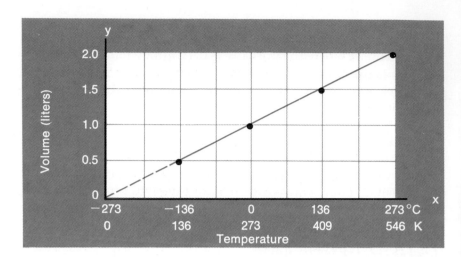

is the lowest possible temperature for a gas. Lord Kelvin chose this point as zero on what is called the kelvin temperature scale. The temperature $-273°C$ or 0 K is called absolute zero.

Through his work with gases, Charles accomplished two things. He postulated the point of absolute zero and found the relationship between the temperature and the volume of a gas. **Charles' law** states that, *under constant pressure, the volume of a gas varies directly with its kelvin temperature.*

Charles' law states that, at constant pressure, the volume and the temperature of a gas are directly related.

When using Charles' law, temperatures must be in kelvins.

$$\frac{V_1}{V_2} = \frac{T_1}{T_2} \qquad P \text{ is constant}$$

In calculations using Charles' law, temperature must be expressed in kelvins.

### EXAMPLE:  Charles' Law

A volume of 22.0 m³ of nitrogen gas at 20°C is heated under constant pressure to 167°C. What is the new volume of the nitrogen gas?

*Solution:* First, change the Celsius temperatures to kelvin.

$$T_1 = 20°C = 20° + 273 = 293 \text{ K}$$
$$T_2 = 167°C = 167° + 273 = 440 \text{ K}$$

Then,  $\dfrac{V_1}{V_2} = \dfrac{T_1}{T_2}$ and $V_2 = \dfrac{V_1 T_2}{T_1} = \dfrac{(22.0 \text{ m}^3)(440 \text{ K})}{293 \text{ K}} = 33.0 \text{ m}^3$

### PROBLEMS

7. 58 m³

   **7.** A volume of 30.0 m³ of argon gas is kept under constant pressure. The gas is heated from 20°C to 293°C. What is the new volume of the gas?

   **8.** Thirty liters of oxygen gas are kept under constant pressure. The gas is cooled from 20°C to $-146.5°C$. What is the new volume of the gas?

**9.** A gas at 60°C has a volume of 0.02 m³. Under constant pressure, it is heated to twice its original volume. What is the temperature of the gas?

**10.** A volume of 4.0 m³ of a gas is kept under constant pressure. Its temperature is increased from 40°C to 140°C. What is the new volume of the gas?

9. 666 K

# 14:4   Combined Gas Law

By combining Boyle's law and Charles' law, an equation can be derived which relates pressure, temperature, and volume of a gas.

$$\frac{P_1 V_1}{T_1} = \frac{P_2 V_2}{T_2}$$

This equation is called the **combined gas law.** It holds for gases at moderate pressures. However, under high pressures or low temperatures, the law is modified. The combined gas law reduces to Boyle's law if the temperature is constant. If the pressure is kept constant, it reduces to Charles' law. If the volume is kept constant, the pressure varies directly with the temperature.

The combined gas law relates temperature, pressure, and volume of a gas.

The combined gas law reduces to Boyle's law if $T$ is kept constant. It reduces to Charles' law if $P$ is kept constant.

**EXAMPLE:  Combined Gas Law**

Twenty liters of gas are kept under a pressure of 100 kPa at a temperature of 273 K. The gas temperature is lowered to 91 K. The pressure is increased to 150 kPa. What is the new volume of the gas?

*Solution:*    $\dfrac{P_1 V_1}{T_1} = \dfrac{P_2 V_2}{T_2}$    or    $V_2 = \dfrac{P_1 V_1 T_2}{P_2 T_1}$

$$= \frac{(100 \ \text{kPa})(20 \ \text{L})(91 \ \text{K})}{(150 \ \text{kPa})(273 \ \text{K})} = 4.4 \ \text{L}$$

**PROBLEMS**

**11.** Ten cubic meters of hydrogen gas are confined in a cylinder under a pressure of 205 kPa at a temperature of 91 K. The volume is kept constant but the temperature is increased to 182 K. What pressure does the gas exert on the walls of the container?

11. 410 kPa

**12.** Two hundred liters of gas at 0°C are kept under a pressure of 150 kPa. The temperature of the gas is raised to 273°C. The pressure is increased to 300 kPa. What is the final volume?

**13.** Fifty liters of gas are kept at a temperature of 200 K and under a pressure of 15 atm. The temperature of the gas is increased to 400 K. The pressure is decreased to 7.5 atm. What is the volume of the gas?

13. 200 L

**Summary**

1. Pressure is force per unit area and is expressed as pascals (newtons per square meter). The kilopascal (kPa) is 1000 Pa.   **14:1**
2. An important standard for pressure is the average pressure of the atmosphere at sea level. This value is 101 kPa.   **14:1**
3. Boyle's law states that the volume of a gas varies inversely with the applied pressure, provided the temperature remains constant.   **14:2**
4. Charles' law states that the volume of a gas varies directly with its kelvin (absolute) temperature provided the pressure remains constant.   **14:3**
5. The combined gas law combines Boyle's law and Charles' law. Kelvin temperatures must always be used when working with the gas laws.   **14:4**

**Questions**

1. State standard atmospheric pressure in four different terms.
2. When you use a straw to drink a soda, is the liquid drawn up the straw or pushed up the straw? Explain.
3. According to the combined gas law, what happens when the pressure acting on a gas is held constant but the temperature of the gas changes?
4. According to the general gas law, what happens when the temperature of a gas remains constant and pressure is changed?
5. If you made a barometer that was filled with a liquid one-third as dense as mercury, how high would the level of the liquid be on a day of normal atmospheric pressure?
6. Explain how Charles' experiments with gases indicated the possible location of absolute zero.

**Problems**

1. A bubble of air with a volume of 0.05 cm$^3$ escapes from a pressure hose at the bottom of a tank. The tank is filled with mercury to a height of 6.84 m. What is the volume of the air bubble as it reaches the surface of the mercury? Assume the pressure at the surface which acts on the bubble is 1.0 atm. The pressure at the bottom of the tank is the pressure due to the mercury plus the pressure at the surface.
2. The pressure acting on 50 cm$^3$ of a gas is reduced from 1.2 atm to 0.30 atm. What is the new volume of the gas if there is no temperature change?
3. The pressure acting on a volume of 50 m$^3$ of air is $1.01 \times 10^5$ N/m$^2$. The air is at a temperature of −50°C. The pressure acting on the gas is increased to $2.02 \times 10^5$ N/m$^2$. Then the gas occupies a volume of 30 m$^3$. What is the temperature of the air at this new volume?

**4.** Two cubic meters of a gas at 30°C are heated at constant pressure until the volume is doubled. What is the final temperature of the gas?

**5.** A cubic meter of gas at standard temperature and pressure is cooled to 91 K. The pressure is not changed. What volume does the gas occupy?

**6.** A cubic meter of gas at standard temperature and pressure is heated to 364°C. The pressure acting on the gas is kept constant. What volume does the gas occupy?

**7.** At 40 K, 10 $m^3$ of nitrogen is under 400 kPa pressure. The pressure acting on the nitrogen is increased to 2000 kPa. Its volume remains constant. What is the temperature of the nitrogen?

**8.** A balloon contains 200 $m^3$ of helium while on the surface of the earth. Atmospheric pressure is 1.0 atm. Temperature is 20°C. The balloon expands freely and rises to a height where the pressure is only 0.67 atm and the temperature is −50°C. What is the new volume of the balloon?

---

## Applying Physics

**1.** *Water Barometer:* Mercury has a specific gravity of 13.6 which means that mercury is 13.6 times more dense than water. If a barometer were constructed using water rather than mercury, how high (in meters) would the water rise under normal atmospheric pressure?

**2.** *Scuba Diving:* Suppose that a scuba diver filled her lungs to a capacity of 6.0 liters while at a depth of 10.3 m below the surface of a pond. To what volume would her lungs (attempt to) expand if she suddenly rose to the surface?

**3.** *Conservation Laws:* The volume of a confined gas is changed by applying a force $F$ to a piston and moving the piston a displacement $s$. Thus, work must be done on a gas to change its volume $V$ and pressure $P$ an amount $P\Delta V$. Ideally, if the gas is allowed to expand it should be able to do an equal amount of work. Therefore $P\Delta V$ and $Fs$ must be equivalent and have the same units. Recalling that pressure is force per unit area and that volume can be expressed as $m^3$ show that the work done on the piston must have the same units as does $P\Delta V$.

---

## Readings

Franklin, Kenneth, L., "Halley's Comet is Poised for its Regular 75.8-Year Appearance." *Science Digest*, April, 1980.

Greenwald and Olive E. Greenwald, "The Buoyancy of the Chambered Nautilus." *Scientific American*, October, 1980.

Hall, Marie, "Robert Boyle." *Scientific American*, August, 1967.

Hewitt, Paul, *Conceptual Physics*. Boston, Little-Brown and Company, 1980, Chapter 2.

The action of waves is familiar to you. You may have noticed waves at the beach, in a puddle, and even in the bathtub. Much of today's technology involves the use of waves. Television, radio, light bulbs, and microwave ovens are examples. One property of waves is their ability to transfer energy. How does a surfer use the energy of water waves? What are some other properties of waves?

# Waves and Energy Transfer 15

There are only two methods by which energy can be transferred between two points. The first method involves the transfer of matter. A falling weight can drive a stake into the ground. Electrons moving through a wire can transfer energy from one place to another.

The second method of energy transfer involves wave motion. All waves transfer energy. Sound waves transfer the energy of a vibrating string of a guitar to your ear. Light waves bring energy from the sun to the earth. Radio waves carry energy from a radio station to your home. Water waves can do tremendous amounts of damage during storms. Waves are a means of transferring energy.

The behavior of all waves follows the same general rules. For example, when a water wave is reflected from a barrier, the angle at which the wave is reflected is the same as the angle at which the wave approaches the barrier. Sound waves, light waves, and all other waves are reflected from barriers in exactly the same way. By learning the general rules of wave behavior, you can understand the behavior of all waves.

## 15:1 Types of Waves

**Mechanical waves** need a material medium through which they can travel as they transfer energy. Some examples of mechanical waves are water waves, sound waves, and the waves that travel along a spring or rope. The behavior of most mechanical waves can readily be observed.

**GOAL: You will gain knowledge and understanding of the general properties of waves.**

Energy can be transferred by particles or by waves.

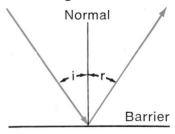

FIGURE 15-1. Different kinds of waves are reflected from barriers according to the law of reflection—the angle of incidence is equal to the angle of reflection.

NASA

**FIGURE 15-2. This experimental solar satellite could be used to beam energy to Earth in the form of microwaves. These electromagnetic waves need no medium to travel through.**

Mechanical waves need a medium.

Electromagnetic waves do not need a medium.

In a transverse wave, particles vibrate at right angles to the direction of the wave.

In a longitudinal wave, particles vibrate parallel to the wave direction.

**Electromagnetic waves** are a large and important family of waves. They need no medium to travel through as they transfer energy. Some examples of electromagnetic waves are light waves, radio waves, and X rays. We know that electromagnetic waves are both magnetic and electric in nature, but we cannot observe them directly. Studying mechanical waves can lead to an understanding of electromagnetic waves. We will use the information concerning mechanical waves in this chapter to explain the behavior of electromagnetic waves in later chapters.

Waves can be classified by the way in which they displace matter. There are two general types of waves—transverse waves and longitudinal waves. A **transverse wave** causes the particles of a medium to vibrate perpendicularly to the direction of the wave itself. Figure 15-3a shows a transverse wave. The wave moves along the spring. However, the spring moves perpendicularly to the motion of the wave. Thus, the amplitude of the wave is at 90° to the motion vector of the wave.

A **longitudinal wave** causes the particles of a medium to move parallel to the direction of the wave. Figure 15-3b shows a longitudinal wave. Note that the motion vector of the spring is parallel to the direction in which the wave is moving. Thus the difference between transverse and longitudinal waves is apparent. A sound wave is an example of a longitudinal wave.

a

*George Anderson*

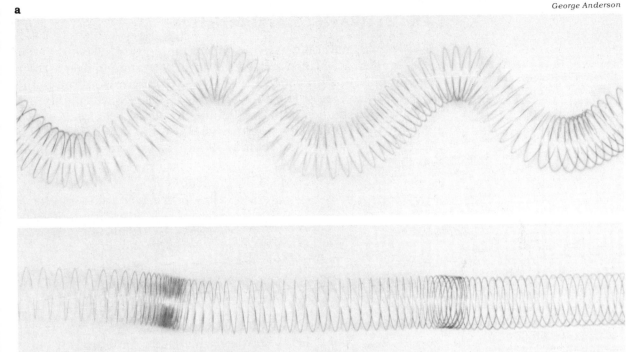

b

Sound waves are caused by vibrating objects. A vibrating object moves back and forth. As the object moves forward, it compresses the air on one side. When the object moves in the opposite direction, it rarefies the air on this same side. The process continues as the object swings to the other side of the rest (equilibrium) position. The positions of greatest compression and rarefaction correspond to the crests and troughs of a transverse wave. Sound waves cause particles of a medium to vibrate in the same direction as the movement of the wave.

Although the particles of a medium vibrate in response to a passing wave, they do not move along with the wave. The float on a fishing line will bob up and down as waves from a passing motorboat go by, but the float does not move with the wave. After a wave has passed through the spring of Figure 15-3, each coil is in the same position it occupied before the wave arrived. In the same way, the particles of the air in a classroom will vibrate in response to a sound wave, but they do not move with the wave.

A **pulse** is a single disturbance traveling through a medium. A pulse can be produced by applying a single sideways movement to one end of a spring. Any point which is undisturbed before the pulse arrives will be undisturbed after the pulse passes. A wave is composed of a series of pulses. When a wave passes, a given point will vibrate regularly in response to the wave.

**FIGURE 15-3. Two general types of waves are (a) the transverse wave and (b) the longitudinal wave.**

A medium vibrates in response to a wave but does not move with the wave.

A pulse is a single disturbance in a medium.

A wave is a series of pulses at regular intervals.

## 15:2  Wave Characteristics

There are several characteristics common to all waves. The **wavelength** ($\lambda$) of a wave is the linear distance between corresponding points on consecutive waves. In Figure 15-4, all points labeled $C$ are crests. Points $T$ are troughs. The wavelength of the wave is the distance from one Point $C$ to the next Point $C$, or one $T$ to the next $T$. Points $A$ and $A'$ are also one wavelength apart. You should notice that points $A$ and $A''$ are two wavelengths apart.

Wavelength is the linear distance between corresponding points on consecutive waves.

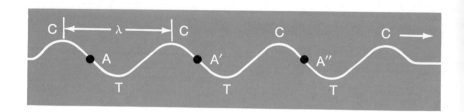

FIGURE 15-4. Points labeled $C$ represent wave crests; points labeled $T$ represent wave troughs.

Frequency is the number of waves which pass a given point per unit time.

The **frequency** of a wave is the number of wavelengths that pass a given point per second. Frequency is measured in hertz, (1 Hz = 1 wave/s). The frequency of a wave is the same as the frequency at which pulses are generated. For example, waves in a spring can be generated by hand. In such a case, the frequency of the wave is determined by the person generating the wave.

If the wavelength and frequency of a wave are both known, the velocity of the wave can be calculated. The equation is

The velocity of a wave is the product of its frequency and wavelength.

$$v = f \lambda$$

To understand why the velocity of a wave can be found in this way, consider the following example. Each car of a train is 20 meters long. The number of cars that pass a given point each

FIGURE 15-5. The frequency at which the train cars pass the observer is measured as the number of cars that pass per second. This frequency multiplied by the length of the cars is the velocity of the train.

second can be counted. If two cars pass per second, the velocity of the train must be 40 m/s. The length of one railroad car compares to the wavelength of a wave. The number of cars that pass each second is the frequency. The length of each railroad car multiplied by the number of cars per second gives the velocity of the train. In the same way, the velocity of a wave is frequency times wavelength. Wavelength can be measured in any convenient unit of length.

### EXAMPLE:  Velocity of a Wave

Transverse waves traveling along a rope have a frequency of 12.0 Hz and are 2.4 m long. What is the velocity of the waves?

*Solution:* $\quad\quad v = f\lambda$
$$= (12 \text{ Hz})(2.4 \text{ m}) = 28.8 \text{ m/s}$$

The period of a wave is the time required for one pulse to pass a given point. The frequency of the wave determines its period. For example, if the frequency of a wave is 10 hertz, ten pulses pass a given point per second. Thus, the time for one pulse to pass a given point must be $\frac{1}{10}$ s or 0.1 s. The period of a wave is the reciprocal of its frequency.

The period of a wave is the reciprocal of its frequency.

$$\boxed{T = \frac{1}{f}}$$

### EXAMPLE:  Period of a Wave

A sound wave has a frequency of 250 hertz. What is the period of the sound wave?

*Solution:* $\quad\quad\quad T = \frac{1}{f}$

$$= \frac{1}{250 \text{ Hz}} = 0.004 \text{ s}$$

The positions and motions of points along a wave indicate whether a wave is in or out of phase. Points that have the same displacement and are moving in the same direction at the same time are said to be inphase. Points $C$ in Figure 15-4 are in phase. Points which have opposite displacements and are moving in opposite directions are said to be 180° out of phase. Points $C$ and $T$ are 180° out of phase.

### PROBLEMS

1. Sound waves have a frequency of 250 hertz. The sound waves are 1.30 m in length. What is the speed of sound ?

1. 325 m/s

3. 29 cm/s

5. a. $1.5 \times 10^9$ Hz
   b. $6.7 \times 10^{-10}$ s

7. a. 0.44 m
   b. $1.3 \times 10^{-3}$ s

**2.** A radio wave has a frequency of $3.0 \times 10^7$ Hz. It is 10 m long. What is the speed of the radio wave?

**3.** Water waves in a small tank are 6.0 cm long. They pass a given point at the rate of 4.8 waves per second. What is the speed of the water waves?

**4.** What is the period of the waves in Problem 3?

**5.** Microwaves are electromagnetic waves. They travel through space at the rate of $3.0 \times 10^8$ m/s. A microwave has a wavelength of 0.20 m.
   **a.** What is the frequency of the microwave?
   **b.** What is the period of the microwave?

**6.** A sound pulse is directed toward a vertical cliff 660 m from the source. A reflected pulse is detected 4.0 s after the pulse is produced.
   **a.** What is the speed of sound in air?
   **b.** The sound pulse has a frequency of 500 Hz. What is its wavelength?
   **c.** What is the period of the pulse?

**7.** The speed of sound waves in air is 330 m/s. A sound wave has a frequency of 750 Hz.
   **a.** What is its wavelength as it travels through air?
   **b.** What is its period?

**8.** A typical light wave has a wavelength of 580 nanometers.
   **a.** What is the length of the light wave in meters?
   **b.** The speed of light is $3.0 \times 10^8$ m/s. What is the frequency of the wave?

## 15:3   Amplitude of a Wave

The energy content of a wave depends on its amplitude.

The amplitude of a wave is its maximum displacement from rest position.

The energy content of a wave is characterized by the wave's amplitude. The **amplitude** of a wave is its maximum displacement from the rest or equilibrium position. Figure 15-6 shows two waves traveling along identical ropes. The two waves have the same frequency, velocity, and wavelength, but their amplitudes are different. The source that generates wave *A* has the same frequency as the source that generates wave *B*. The source generating wave *A* puts more energy into the wave. This increased energy results in a wave of greater amplitude.

Since wave *A* has more energy input and a greater amplitude than wave *B*, wave *A* transfers more energy. Wave *A* can do more work than wave *B*. Suppose that water pumps are attached to each rope. The pumps lift water and transform the wave energy into useful work. Wave *A* can do more work per unit time than wave *B*.

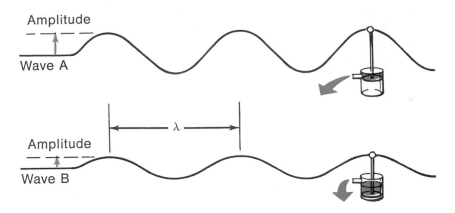

Wave A

Amplitude

Wave B

Amplitude

λ

**FIGURE 15-6. The relationship of the amplitude of a wave to the work it can perform is shown here. The greater the work done to create the wave, the greater the amplitude of the wave. The greater the amplitude of the wave, the more work it can do. Waves transfer energy.**

## 15:4 Wave Speed in a Medium

The speed at which waves travel through a medium depends on the properties of that medium. Figure 15-7 shows two waves produced at different times in the same medium. The wavelengths and the frequencies of the waves are different. However, their speeds are the same. Wave $B$ has a high frequency and a short wavelength. Wave $A$ has a low frequency and a long wavelength. In both cases, the product of the frequency and the wavelength results in the same speed. It makes no difference what frequency

The speed of a wave depends on the medium.

**FIGURE 15-7. Wave $B$ has a wavelength that is one half the wavelength of $A$. The frequency of $B$ is twice that of $A$.**

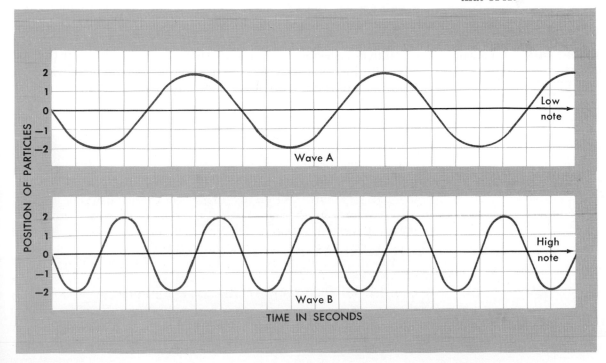

POSITION OF PARTICLES

Low note

Wave A

High note

Wave B

TIME IN SECONDS

wave is produced in the medium. The only result of a change in frequency is that the wavelength changes to keep the speed of the wave constant in the medium. The amplitude of the wave also has no effect on its speed. An increase in amplitude of a wave causes it to transfer more energy. However, an increase in amplitude does not change the speed of the wave. The medium determines the speed of the waves that pass through.

The speed of light in a vacuum is $3.0 \times 10^8$ m/s. All electromagnetic waves move through space at this speed. In the same way, all sound waves move through air at about 330 m/s. If all sound waves did not travel at the same velocity in air, musical instruments could not exist. Notes from the same instrument would overtake each other or fall behind their proper sequence. This would produce noise, not music. Fortunately all sound waves do have the same speed in air. Thus, we are able to enjoy music.

All electromagnetic waves travel at $3.0 \times 10^8$ m/s in a vacuum. All sound waves travel at about 330 m/s in air.

## 15:5 Behavior of Waves at Boundaries

Transverse waves are easier to draw and visualize than longitudinal waves. Therefore, transverse waves will be used as examples to discuss wave behavior. However, these rules of wave behavior apply to both transverse and longitudinal waves.

When a wave traveling through a medium reaches the boundary of a new medium, part of the wave will be reflected. The other part of the wave will be transmitted into the new medium. The part that is reflected depends on the difference between the two media. If the difference between the two media is slight, the amplitude of the reflected wave is small. The small amplitude indicates that most of the energy is transmitted.

The part of a wave reflected at a boundary depends on the difference between the two media.

**FIGURE 15-8. A pulse reaching a boundary between two media (a) is partially reflected and partially transmitted (b).**

a

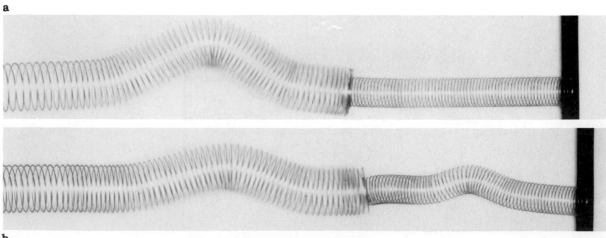

b

George Anderson

Consider a spring that is attached to a rigid object, such as a wall. The two media, the spring and the wall, are different from each other. Thus, when the pulse reaches the spring-wall boundary, most of the pulse is reflected. In theory, a small amount of the energy of the pulse does enter the wall. Figure 15-9 shows that the amplitude of the reflected pulse is almost equal to the amplitude of the incident pulse. However, the pulse is inverted upon reflection from the rigid wall. When a wave is reflected at the boundary of a more rigid medium, it undergoes inversion (180° change in phase).

When a wave is reflected from a more rigid medium, the reflected portion is inverted.

a

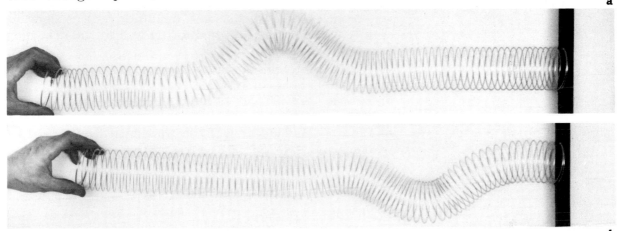

*George Anderson*

b

Now consider a spring that is supported by light threads, Figure 15-10. When a pulse reaches the end of the spring, it passes into a different medium. In this case, the new medium is air. The large difference in the two media causes nearly total reflection of the pulse. Because the pulse is reflected from the boundary of a medium less rigid than the one from which it came, the reflected pulse is erect (no change in phase).

**FIGURE 15-9. The pulse that is reflected from the rigid wall returns inverted. Notice that the amplitude of the reflected pulse is nearly equal to the amplitude of the incident pulse.**

When a wave is reflected from a less rigid medium, the reflected wave is erect.

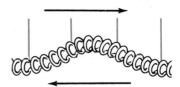

**FIGURE 15-10. A pulse reflected from an open-ended boundary returns erect.**

*George Anderson*

In all cases there is a reflected wave at a boundary. The amount of reflected energy depends on the difference in the properties of the two media. A pulse passing from a less rigid medium into a more rigid medium produces a reflected pulse that is inverted. A pulse entering a less rigid medium from a more rigid medium produces a reflected pulse that is erect.

## PROBLEMS

9. It is attached to the wall.

**9.** A long spring passes along the floor of a room and out a door. A pulse is sent along the spring. After a while, an inverted pulse of almost the same amplitude returns along the spring. Is the spring attached to the wall in the next room or is it lying loose on the floor?

**10.** A pulse is sent along a spring, Figure 15-11. The spring is attached to a light thread which ends at a wall.
   **a.** Describe the behavior of the pulse when it reaches *A*.
   **b.** Is the reflected pulse from *A* erect or inverted?
   **c.** Describe the behavior of the transmitted pulse when it reaches *B*.
   **d.** Is the reflected pulse from *B* erect or inverted?

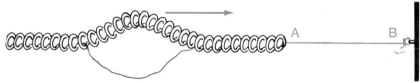

**FIGURE 15-11. Use with Problem 10.**

11. a. The pulse will be partially trans-mitted and partially reflected. It will be inverted.
   b. The pulse will be almost totally reflected. It will be inverted.

**11. a.** Describe the behavior of the pulse in Figure 15-12 when it reaches boundary *A*.
   **b.** Describe the behavior of the transmitted pulse when it reaches boundary *B*.

**FIGURE 15-12. Use with Problem 11.**

**12.** A light wave leaves a lamp and approaches a glass window.
   **a.** Describe the behavior of the light wave as it is reflected from the surface of the window.
   **b.** Part of the wave enters the window glass and travels through the glass. It is partly reflected again when it reaches the next surface of the glass. Describe the wave that is reflected from this surface.

**13.** To obtain waves of a longer wavelength, is wave frequency along a rope increased or decreased?

**14.** The left side of Figure 15-13 shows a pulse. The right side shows the transmitted pulse and reflected pulse. Describe the boundaries *A, B, C,* and *D.*

13. decreased

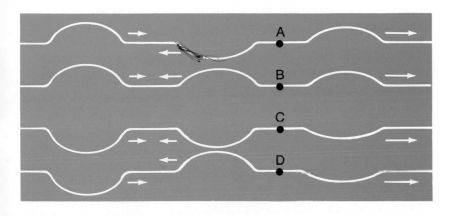

**FIGURE 15-13. Use with Problem 14.**

## 15:6  Transmitted Waves

The speed at which a wave travels through a medium depends on the medium. When a wave passes into a new medium, it has a different speed. The wave in the new medium is generated directly by the wave in the old medium. Thus, the frequency of the wave in the new medium is exactly the same as the frequency of the wave in the old medium. Because the speed of the transmitted wave changes and the frequency remains the same, the wavelength must change. This is true because $v = f\lambda$. Figure 15-14 shows a wave passing into a new medium. Since the speed in the new medium is greater, the wavelength is longer. Conversely, if the wave were to pass from the medium on the right to the medium on the left, its speed would be slower in the new medium. Thus, its wavelength would decrease.

When a wave passes into a new medium, its speed changes.

The wave must have the same frequency in the new medium as in the old medium. Thus, the wavelength adjusts so that $v = f\lambda$.

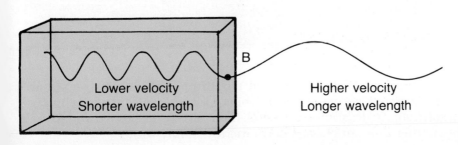

Lower velocity
Shorter wavelength

*B*

Higher velocity
Longer wavelength

**FIGURE 15-14. The speed and wavelength of a wave change when the wave enters a new medium at Point *B*.**

## 15:7   Interference

Suppose two or more waves travel through the same medium at the same time. When the waves meet, their displacements are superimposed. This process is called **interference.** Waves can interfere constructively or destructively.

Figure 15-15 shows the constructive interference of two equal pulses. When pulse $a$ and pulse $b$ meet, a stronger pulse $(a + b)$ is formed. The amplitude of this stronger pulse is the algebraic sum of the amplitudes of the two pulses. Note that once the two pulses have passed through each other, they are completely unaffected and retain their original form.

When two or more waves meet, their displacements add. This process is called interference.

Constructive interference occurs when two pulses combine to produce a pulse of greater amplitude.

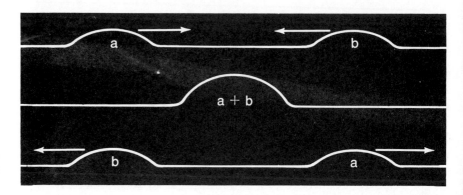

**FIGURE 15-15. Constructive interference of two equal pulses.**

Destructive interference occurs when two pulses combine to produce a pulse with smaller amplitude than either of the original amplitudes.

Figure 15-16 shows the destructive interference of two equal but opposite pulses. When pulse $a$ and pulse $b$ meet, a weaker pulse $(a + (-b))$ is formed. For an instant, the sum of the displacements is zero and the medium is completely undisturbed.

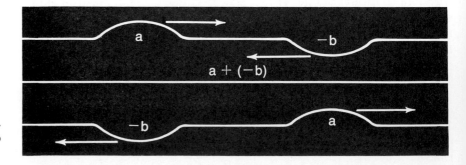

**FIGURE 15-16. Destructive interference of two equal pulses.**

After two pulses pass through one another, they return to their original form.

At that instant, the combined amplitude is zero. The pulses are not affected permanently by their momentary union. An important characteristic of waves is their ability to pass through one another and not change permanently in any way.

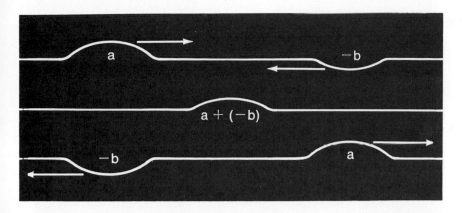

FIGURE 15-17. Interference of two pulses with the same wavelength but different amplitudes.

If the pulses that meet are of unequal amplitudes, their combined amplitude cannot equal zero, Figure 15-17.

## 15:8   Nodes

Suppose two pulses have identical shapes but opposite displacements and move toward each other in a medium. When they meet, there will be a point in the medium that is completely undisturbed at all times. This point is called a **node.** A node never undergoes a displacement. A nodal point is shown in Figure 15-18. Notice parts *b*, *c*, and *d* of the diagram. The amplitude of the part of the pulse above the nodal point is always the same as the amplitude of the part below the nodal point. Cancellation always takes place at the nodal point during the crossing of the two pulses.

A node is a point in a medium that never undergoes a displacement as waves pass through each other in the medium.

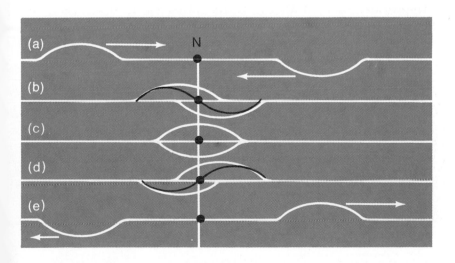

FIGURE 15-18. The nodal point is undisturbed during the meeting of two equal and opposite pulses.

When a wave train (series of waves) moving in one direction meets an identical wave train moving in the opposite direction, the same process occurs. Nodal points appear all along the path

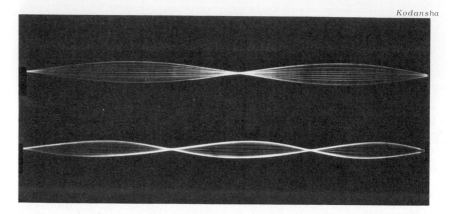

*Kodansha*

FIGURE 15-19. Standing
waves in a string.

A standing wave is the
result of identical waves
moving in opposite
directions.

of the waves. Between these nodal points, the waves interfere
constructively and destructively. Because of the two interfering
waves, the medium appears to be vibrating in segments. The
result is called a **standing wave.**

## 15:9   The Law of Reflection

The law of reflection
states that the angle at
which a wave approaches
a barrier is equal to the
angle at which the wave is
reflected.

Waves are reflected from a barrier at the same angle at which
they approach it. The **law of reflection** states that *the angle of
incidence is equal to the angle of reflection.*

Figure 15-20 shows a pulse sent toward a barrier. The direction
of the pulse is shown by a line drawn at a right angle to the wave
front. This imaginary line is called a **ray.** Wave behavior is often
shown by ray diagrams. Ray diagrams show only the directions
of the waves. They do not show the actual waves. The use of ray
diagrams in the study of light is known as **ray optics.**

FIGURE 15-20. Reflection
of a wave pulse by a bar-
rier. A ray indicates the
direction in which the
pulse is moving. The angle
which the incident ray
makes with the normal is
equal to the angle the reflected ray makes with
the normal.

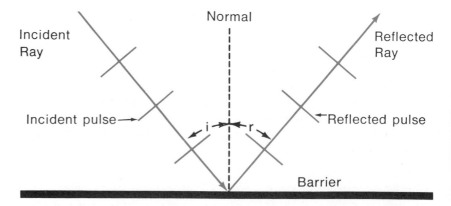

## 15:10   Refraction of Waves

Ripple tanks are used to
study wave behavior.

The behavior of waves as they move from one medium into
another can be observed in a ripple tank, Figure 15-21. The

*PSSC Physics. 2nd Edition. D.C. Heath and Company & Education Development Center. Newton, MA.*

**FIGURE 15-21. Straight waves enter a different medium (shallow water) head-on. Notice the change in wavelength. The change in media causes the waves to bend at the boundaries of the barrier. This is refraction.**

water above a glass plate placed in the tank is more shallow than the water in the rest of the tank. The shallow water acts like a different medium.

The velocity of waves is greater in deep water than in shallow water. To verify this statement, the edge of the glass plate is placed parallel to advancing wave fronts. A decrease in the wavelength of the waves is observed as they pass into the shallow water. Since the waves in the shallow water are produced by waves in the deep water, their frequency is exactly the same as the frequency of the waves in the deep water. The decrease in the wavelength of the waves indicates a lower velocity as shown by the relationship

$$v = f \lambda$$

When wavefronts approach a parallel boundary to another medium, they continue straight into the new medium. When wavefronts approach the boundary to another medium at an angle, their direction is changed. This change in the direction of waves at the boundary between two different media is known as **refraction.**

Refraction is the change of wave direction at the boundary between two media.

*George Anderson*

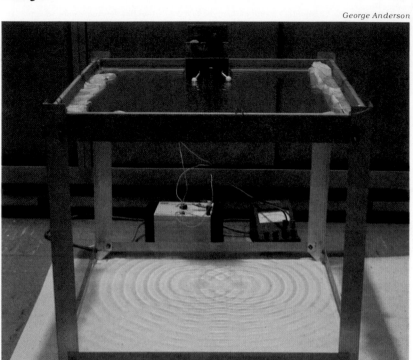

**FIGURE 15-22.** The ripple tank is a useful device for demonstrating wave behavior. Several types of waves and pulses can be generated. This photograph shows two circular waves. The image of the waves is shown on the white paper below the tank.

## 15:11    Diffraction of Waves

Diffraction is the bending of a wave around an object in its path.

**Diffraction** is the bending of a wave around obstacles placed in its path. Diffraction may be observed in a ripple tank by placing a small barrier in the path of straight waves. The waves bend around the edges of the barrier. They meet a short distance beyond the barrier. Thus, the barrier does not cast much of a "shadow."

**a**

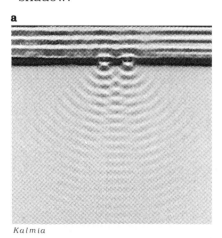

**b**

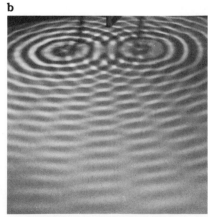

**FIGURE 15-23.** Waves are diffracted at two openings in the barrier (a). At each opening, circular waves are formed. The circular waves interfere with each other. Points of constructive interference are indicated by dashed lines. Two vibrating points can produce an interference pattern (b). Notice the areas of high amplitude and areas where the water remains almost undisturbed.

*Kalmia*

*Courtesy of Education Development Center, Newton, MA*

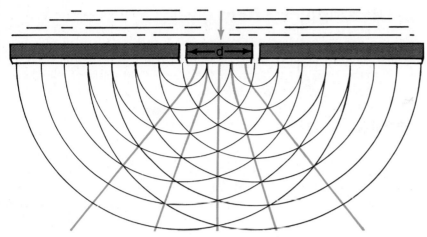

**FIGURE 15-24. Lines of reinforcement are shown where crest meets crest.**

A diffraction pattern may be created by placing three straight barriers in the path of the waves as shown in Figure 15-23a. The spaces between the barriers are smaller than the wavelength of the approaching waves. The diffraction of the waves around the edges of the openings causes each to produce new circular waves. The circular waves from the two openings interfere with one another. Along the points marked by lines, wave crests are superimposed. At these points the water is displaced doubly from its normal position. These points of reinforcement all lie along the same line. Between these lines of reinforcement are areas where a crest and a trough are superimposed. **Destructive interference** occurs and the water remains undisturbed. These undisturbed points lie in definite lines, called nodal lines.

The frequency of waves in the ripple tank can be varied. Thus, waves of different wavelengths can be sent toward the barriers. Each wavelength produces a diffraction pattern. By comparing the diffraction patterns for several different wavelengths, two facts are learned.

**1.** Different wavelengths produce similar diffraction patterns, but the lines of reinforcement are in slightly different places.

**2.** Regardless of the wavelength of the wave, the central line of reinforcement always falls in the center of the pattern.

Different waves pass through one another but do not change each other. Suppose several waves of different wavelengths are sent toward a barrier at the same time. Each wave produces its own independent diffraction pattern. A very strong central line of reinforcement is caused by these simultaneous diffraction patterns. To both sides of the central line is a cluster of lines of reinforcement. Each cluster has one line for each wavelength which falls on the barrier.

When circular waves from two side-by-side openings interfere, there will be undisturbed points in a medium which lie along definite lines, called nodal lines.

## 15:12 Doppler Effect

When a car goes by you at high speed and its horn is blowing you may have noticed a sudden drop in the pitch of the horn as the car passes you. This drop in pitch is an example of the **Doppler effect** named for the German physicist Christian Doppler (1803–1853).

The Doppler effect causes a change in the observed frequency of waves when a wave source and an observer are in relative motion. The wave source and the observer must move toward or away from each other. Figure 15-25a shows that the wavelength of the waves is shorter in front of the moving source, and longer behind the source. Figure 15-25b shows the effect more clearly. A vibrating point is drawn to the left across the surface of water in a ripple tank.

The Doppler effect is the change in the observed frequency of a wave when a source and an observer are in relative motion.

a

*Anne P. Layman/Tom Stack & Assoc.*

b

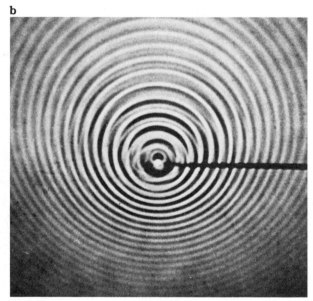

*The Ealing Corporation*

**FIGURE 15-25. The swans swimming on the surface of the water provide examples of the Doppler effect (a). The wavelength of the waves ahead of the swans is noticeably shorter than the wavelength of the waves behind the swans. A point source moving across a ripple tank can be used to show the Doppler effect (b).**

In the case of sound waves, a sound of higher frequency is heard when a source is moving toward a listener. The sound is higher in pitch because more waves reach the observer per second which means higher frequency. In sound, high frequency is high pitch. If the observer is moving toward the source, the result is the same. If both source and observer are moving toward each other the effect is even more pronounced. When the source passes the listener and moves away, a lower frequency is heard. This lower frequency appears as a sudden drop in pitch.

The Doppler effect is a characteristic of all waves. It explains why stars moving away from the earth display light of longer wavelengths. This phenomenon is known as the "red shift" because the longer wavelengths of light are red. The wavelengths observed coming from a star will show a shift toward the red, but they may not actually be red. The shift towards the longer wavelengths indicates that the stars are moving away from the earth. Astronomers have found that no matter what direction they look, all stars display the red shift. This observation means that all stars are moving away from the earth and from each other. The red shift is evidence that our universe is expanding. Imagine what will happen if you stick small stars all over a balloon and then blow up the balloon. The stars all move away from each other. An observer on any one star would see all other stars moving away from the observer's star. The red shift tells us that the universe must be behaving in the same way.

This clear evidence that the universe is expanding has led astronomers to develop a theory about the origin of the universe called the "Big Bang Theory." The theory states that the universe was once a huge compact mass that exploded and is still expanding away from that explosion. Astronomers are now searching for evidence that the universe will eventually stop expanding and begin to contract due to gravitational attraction. Perhaps the universe, like so many of the things in the universe, will expand and contract endlessly.

The Doppler effect explains how sonic booms are generated. Consider a bug swimming across a water surface. The bug causes waves to pile up in front of it and become drawn out behind it. The bug is causing a Doppler effect. The waves in front of the bug act as a barrier to its progress.

Should the bug swim fast enough it could break through the barrier and then swim through the water faster than the waves move through the water. It would have super water-wave speed. In that case, the bug would find smooth going. It would also generate a new wave pattern. Where the waves overlap they reinforce each other constructively and two lines of very strong waves are formed. If the moving source is a speedboat, a pair of strong bow waves appears. If it is a supersonic plane, a very strong sound wave sweeps along on either side of the plane. This is the "sonic boom" you have no doubt heard on occasion. Contrary to popular belief, such booms are continuous and do not happen only when the plane breaks through the sound wave barrier.

The Doppler shift in the wavelength of light coming from distant stars indicates an expanding universe.

**FIGURE 15-26. When a plane moves faster than the waves it creates, a strong sound wave sweeps along either side of the plane.**

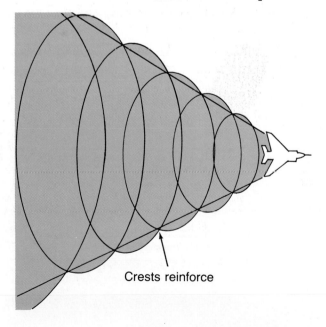

Crests reinforce

# Dimensions in Physics

The description of sound is partially physical and partially subjective; each listener hears a particular sound differently. To understand the subjective quality of sound, we begin by examining the physical properties of a sound wave with a frequency of 1000 Hz. The frequency of the wave is its pitch. The amplitude of the wave is interpreted as loudness. The length of time the wave is heard is the duration of the wave.

The 1000 Hz wave is an ideal case since an instrument does not emit a sound wave with a single frequency. When a flute produces a 1000 Hz tone, it also emits tones at 2000 Hz, 3000 Hz, 4000 Hz, and higher. Each higher tone is a whole number multiple of 1000 Hz and has a smaller amplitude than the 1000 Hz tone. This group of frequencies is called a harmonic series. The 1000 Hz tone is the fundamental frequency. In any harmonic series, the harmonic frequencies are whole number multiples of the fundamental frequency.

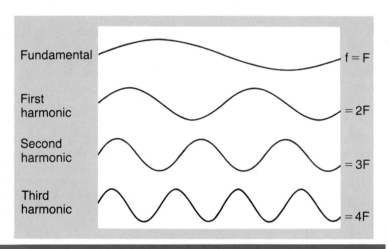

Fundamental $f = F$

First harmonic $= 2F$

Second harmonic $= 3F$

Third harmonic $= 4F$

The pitch of an instrument is the fundamental frequency of the note produced. When a piano and a flute have a pitch of 1000 Hz, they do not sound the same. They may have the same harmonic frequencies, but the amplitudes of the harmonics are different. The different harmonic structure gives each instrument its distinctive sound. The distinct sound of a note from a flute is called its timbre (TAM bur). Since a piano and a flute played at the same pitch produce different harmonics, they have different timbres.

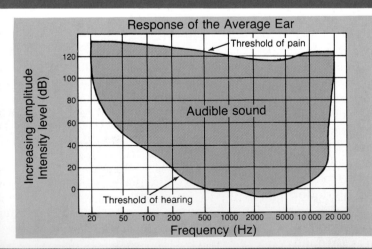

Response of the Average Ear

Threshold of pain

Increasing amplitude Intensity level (dB)

Audible sound

Threshold of hearing

Frequency (Hz)

Our ears respond to sound waves in varied manners. For example, we each hear loudness differently. The loudness heard depends on the response of our ears to sound in different frequency ranges. In general, people's ears are most sensitive to sounds with frequencies between 1000 Hz and 5000 Hz. These sounds seem louder than sounds above or below this frequency range but of the same intensity.

Individuals are sensitive to sounds in more specific frequency ranges. For example, an instrument may emit a tone at 1500 Hz with harmonic tones at 3000 Hz and 4500 Hz. If a listener's ear is more sensitive to the 3000 Hz tone than the fundamental (1500 Hz) tone, the harmonic tone will seem louder than it is. Since the harmonic tone seems louder, the listener hears a pitch that differs from the fundamental tone. In the same way, each of us is more sensitive to particular frequencies and hears sounds differently.

Larry Hamill

The Ohio Theatre. Columbus Assoc. for the Performing Arts/photo by Quicksilver

The duration of sound is affected by the reflection of sound waves from walls or other barriers. A sound can reach our ears directly from the source or indirectly after reflecting from an object. If the delay of reflected sound is short, it may add to and reinforce the directly transmitted sound— the sound we hear will be clearer and have a longer duration. On the other hand, if the delay due to reflection is long, the sound may be garbled. Multiple reflections, called reverberations, may interfere with speech, making it unclear. Reverberation can, however, make music more pleasant to hear— more vibrant and full.

Reflections are caused by the environment around the source of a sound. Architects must design buildings to make the best use of these reflections. A lecture hall may be designed with acoustical tiles to absorb and thus eliminate reflections. A concert hall uses sloped ceilings and uneven walls to redirect the sounds and their reflections, enhancing the music you hear.

The factors affecting the sounds we hear are based on physical properties. But no two people hear a sound in the same way due to the subjective characteristics of sounds. Harmonics, variations in loudness, and reflections are features of sound that are perceived differently by all people.

**Summary**

1. Waves transfer energy. Different types of waves follow similar behavior patterns making it possible to study waves in general.   Intro.

2. Mechanical waves such as sound waves and the waves in a spring require a medium. Electromagnetic waves do not require a medium. Light and radio waves are electromagnetic.  15:1

3. Transverse waves cause the particles of a medium to move perpendicularly to the direction of the wave. Longitudinal waves cause a medium to move parallel to the direction of the wave's motion.  15:1

4. Points along a wave train that have the same displacement and are moving in the same direction are said to be inphase.  15:2

5. The wavelength ($\lambda$) of a wave is the linear distance between corresponding points on consecutive pulses.  15:2

6. The frequency of a wave is the number of pulses that pass a given point per second. The period of a wave is the reciprocal of the frequency.  15:2

7. The velocity of a wave is its frequency multiplied by its wavelength ($v = f\lambda$).  15:2

8. Sound waves are generated by vibrating objects. A sound wave has 15:1 the same frequency as does the vibrating object that generates it.

9. The energy of a wave is proportional to its amplitude.  15:3

10. The speed of a wave depends upon the properties of the medium through which the wave is traveling. All waves of the same kind travel in a given medium at the same speed.  15:4

11. When waves reach the boundary of a medium they are always partially transmitted and partially reflected. The percentage of reflection depends upon the difference in the media involved.  15:5

12. When a wave reaches the boundary of a more rigid medium the reflected wave is inverted. When a wave reaches the boundary of a less rigid medium the reflected wave is erect.  15:5

13. When a wave passes into a new medium, it will have a new velocity. Since $v = f\lambda$ and $v$ changes, the wavelength must also change. The frequency cannot change because the wave in the new medium is generated by the wave in the old medium.  15:6

14. When waves meet, their displacements add algebraically. This behavior is called interference. Interference does not permanently af- 15:7 fect waves. After waves pass through one another they are unaffected.

15. When two waves of opposite phase (180° phase difference) meet, a point along the medium is not affected due to the cancelling effect of the two waves. This point is known as a nodal point.  15:8

16. The law of reflection states that when waves reach a boundary and 15:9 are reflected, the angle of incidence is equal to the angle of reflection.

**17.** The change in direction of a wave as it enters a new medium at some angle is known as refraction.  **15:10**

**18.** Diffraction is the bending of a wave around obstacles in its path.  **15:11**

**19.** The change in the frequency of a wave received by an observer when the wave source and the observer are in relative motion is called the Doppler effect.  **15:12**

**Questions**

**1.** How many general methods of energy transfer are there? Give two examples of each.

**2.** There are many kinds of waves. Why is it possible to learn the rules of wave behavior of all kinds of waves without an extensive study of each?

**3.** Distinguish between a mechanical wave and an electromagnetic wave.

**4.** How does a transverse wave differ from a longitudinal wave? Give an example of each.

**5.** If a pulse is sent along a rope, how does the rope behave at any given point after the pulse has passed?

**6.** A pulse differs from a wave. How?

**7.** Distinguish among the wavelength, frequency, and period of a wave.

**8.** Write an equation used to find the velocity of a wave.

**9.** What does the amplitude of a wave represent?

**10.** Waves are sent along a spring of fixed length. Can the speed of the waves in the spring be changed? How can the frequency of a wave in the spring be changed?

**11.** The top of a drum vibrates at a frequency that cannot be changed without altering the drum itself. Therefore, all sound waves coming from the drum must have the same frequency. If the drum is hit harder, what is different about the sound waves?

**12.** When a wave reaches the boundary of a new medium, part of the wave is reflected and part is transmitted. What determines the amount of reflection?

**13.** A pulse reaches the boundary of a medium more rigid than the one from which it came. Is the reflected pulse erect or inverted?

**14.** A pulse reaches the boundary of a medium less rigid than the one from which it came. Is the reflected pulse erect or inverted?

**15.** A light wave is reflected from the surface of a pond. Is the reflected wave erect or inverted?

**16.** When a wave passes into a new medium, what remains the same? What changes?

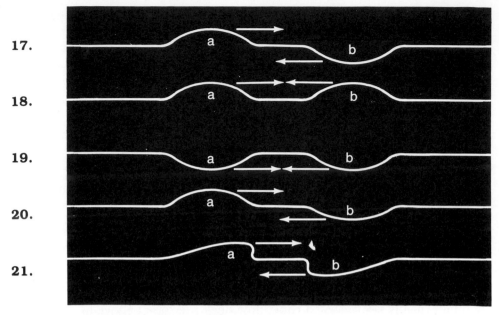

17.

18.

19.

20.

21.

*For Questions 17–21, sketch the result of wave a and wave b* **a.** *when they meet* **b.** *when they pass one another.*

22. In Questions 17–21:
    **a.** In which diagrams do the pulses produce constructive interference when they meet?
    **b.** In which diagrams do the waves produce destructive interference?

23. In Questions 17–21, in which diagrams are nodes formed as the pulses pass through one another?

24. List three different means of changing the direction of a wave.

25. State the law of reflection.

26. What is diffraction?

27. Name two facts about the diffraction patterns produced by waves of different wavelengths as they pass through the same pair of openings.

28. How do the waves in front of a moving source differ from the waves behind a moving source?

29. Contrary to popular belief, a seismic wave (tsunami) usually takes the form of a very fast-moving shallow wave that moves across the ocean's surface. A tidal wave could pass under a ship and hardly be noticed. Why does such a wave cause so much damage when it reaches land? (Hint: Consider the energy form of the wave at all times.)

**Problems**

1. What is the wavelength of a sound wave with a frequency of 50 Hz?

2. An ocean wave has a wavelength of 10 m. A wave passes by every 2.0 s. What is the speed of the wave?

**3.** A sonar signal (sound wave) of frequency 1000 Hz has a wavelength of 1.5 m in water.
   **a.** What is the speed of sound in water?
   **b.** What is the period of the sound wave in water?
   **c.** What is the period of the sound wave in air?

**4.** A sound wave in a steel rail has a frequency of 620 Hz and a wavelength of 10.5 m. What is the speed of sound in steel?

**5.** A light wave has a wavelength of $4.0 \times 10^{-7}$ m. The frequency of the wave is $7.5 \times 10^{14}$ Hz. What is the speed of light?

**6.** Waves of frequency 2.0 Hz are generated along a spring. The waves have a wavelength of 0.45 m.
   **a.** What is the speed of the waves along the spring?
   **b.** What is the wavelength of the waves along the spring if their frequency is increased to 6.0 Hz?
   **c.** If the frequency is decreased to 0.5 Hz, what is their wavelength?

**7.** Determine the frequency of a microwave 6.0 cm in length. (A microwave is an electromagnetic wave. It travels through space at a speed of $3.0 \times 10^8$ m/s.)

**8.** What is the period of the microwave in Problem 7?

**9.** A gamma ray has a period of $10^{-24}$ s.
   **a.** What is the frequency of the gamma ray?
   **b.** What is the wavelength of the gamma ray in meters? (A gamma ray is an electromagnetic wave. It travels through space at a speed of $3.0 \times 10^8$ m/s.)

**Applying Physics**

**1.** *Radio Wavelengths:* The AM radio signals are broadcast at frequencies between 550 kHz and 1600 kHz (kilohertz) and travel at $3.0 \times 10^8$ m/s.
   **a.** What is the range of wavelengths for these signals?
   **b.** FM frequencies range between 88 MHz and 108 MHz (megahertz) and travel at the same speed. What is the range of FM wavelengths?

**2.** *Sonar:* The speed of sound in water is 1498 m/s. A sonar signal is sent from a ship at a point just below the water surface and 1.80 s later the reflected signal is detected. How deep is the ocean beneath the ship?

**Readings**

Bascom, Willard, "Ocean Waves." in *The Physics of Everyday Phenomena.* San Francisco, W. H. Freeman Co., 1979.

Cousteau, Jacques, "The Traveling Wave." *Science Digest,* May, 1980.

Hutchins, C. M., *The Physics of Music.* San Francisco, W. H. Freeman and Co., 1978.

Light has intrigued people for many years. Some objects such as our sun produce their own light. Other objects such as the moon only reflect light from some other source. What is the source of the moon's light? Light travels in straight lines. How does this photograph show this fact? What are other properties of light?

# Nature of Light 16

Visible light waves have wavelengths that range from about $3.80 \times 10^{-7}$ m (the violet region) to $7.60 \times 10^{-7}$ m (the red region). Although visible light is only a small portion of the entire electromagnetic array of waves, there are many good reasons for us to study optical effects. Light is perhaps our most important means of learning about the physical nature of our world. Microscopes, telescopes, and the human eye are all important scientific tools. Also, a study of visible light is, in many ways, a study of all electromagnetic radiation.

**GOAL: You will gain knowledge and understanding of the wave and particle properties of light, the illumination of a surface by a point light source, and methods used to measure the speed of light.**

## 16:1 Light—An Electromagnetic Wave

The sun is a source of huge quantities of electromagnetic radiation. Such radiation is also emitted from incandescent lamps, fluorescent lamps, and flames. Some of this radiation can stimulate the retina of the human eye and is called **light.** Much of the radiation that comes from these sources is not detected by the eye and has other names such as infrared waves, ultraviolet waves, and radio waves. These waves can be detected by other means.

A **luminous body** is a body that emits light waves. An **illuminated body** reflects light waves. The sun is a luminous body. However, the moon is an illuminated body. The word luminous refers only to bodies that emit light waves. All warm bodies emit radiation, but not all emit visible light. The radiation that a hot stove emits cannot be seen but can be detected by other means.

Light is electromagnetic radiation capable of stimulating the retina of the eye.

A luminous body emits light. An illuminated body reflects light.

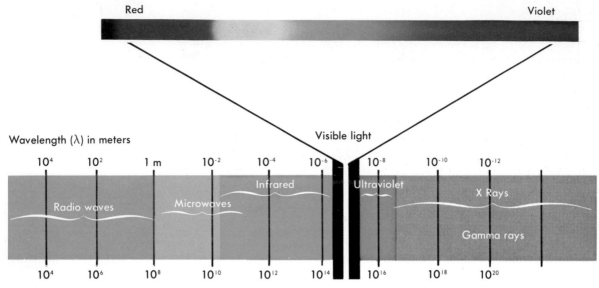

Red

Violet

Wavelength ($\lambda$) in meters

| $10^4$ | $10^2$ | 1 m | $10^{-2}$ | $10^{-4}$ | $10^{-6}$ | | $10^{-8}$ | $10^{-10}$ | $10^{-12}$ |

Visible light

Radio waves    Microwaves    Infrared    Ultraviolet    X Rays    Gamma rays

| $10^4$ | $10^6$ | $10^8$ | $10^{10}$ | $10^{12}$ | $10^{14}$ | | $10^{16}$ | $10^{18}$ | $10^{20}$ |

Frequency ( f ) in Hertz

**FIGURE 16-1. A chart of the electromagnetic spectrum. Note that the visible spectrum is only a very small portion of the whole electromagnetic spectrum. The broadcast band ranges from approximately 50 to 500 meters in wavelength.**

Light waves, like all electromagnetic waves, do not need a medium.

Light waves make up only a small part of the electromagnetic spectrum.

Electromagnetic waves require no medium. Light is an electromagnetic wave. But light waves represent only one small portion of electromagnetic radiations. The known spectrum (array) of electromagnetic waves is shown in Figure 16-1. Note that light waves account for only a small part of this spectrum.

All electromagnetic waves travel at the same speed in space. However, they differ in frequency, and therefore, in wavelength. Figure 16-1 shows the frequencies and wavelengths of various electromagnetic waves.

An electromagnetic wave has both electric and magnetic properties. An electric field and a magnetic field make up the wave. These fields vary in planes perpendicular to each other and perpendicular to the direction of the wave.

## 16:2   Transmission and Absorption of Light

Many materials transmit light without distorting the rays. Objects can be seen clearly through glass, quartz, air, and some other materials. These materials are called **transparent materials.** Other matter, such as smoked glass, transmits light but distorts the rays during transmission. These materials are called **translucent.** Lampshades and most light bulbs are translucent. Materials such as brick transmit no light. They absorb or reflect all light that falls on them. These materials are called **opaque.**

# 16:3   Speed of Light

The speed of light is not difficult to measure. The methods used to measure the speed of light are easily understood. The first rough measurement of the speed of light was made by the Danish astronomer Olaf Roemer (1644–1710). About 1676, Roemer was studying one of the moons of Jupiter. While the earth was in position $E_1$, he observed the moon move behind Jupiter, Figure 16-2, and emerge from the other side. Carefully, Roemer timed several of these eclipses. From his data, he made a table which predicted the occurrence of moon eclipses during the next few months. At first, Roemer's table was fairly accurate. However, as time passed, an error of increasing size gradually appeared. The eclipses occurred later than predicted. But after six months, the error began to decrease. At the end of twelve months the table was once again accurate. Roemer immediately understood the source of error. He had made the table while the earth was at position $E_1$. As the earth followed its orbit around the sun, it moved away from Jupiter. Jupiter, however, moved only a short distance along its orbit. The error occurred because the light from Jupiter's moon had to travel a greater distance to reach the observer on the earth as the months went by. At position $E_2$, the earth was $3 \times 10^{11}$ meters farther from Jupiter than it was at position $E_1$. At position $E_2$, the eclipse began about 1000 seconds later than predicted (in Roemer's table). Roemer assumed this 1000 second interval was the time needed for the light coming from Jupiter's moon to traverse the diameter of the earth's orbit. Therefore, the speed of light must be

$$v = \frac{s}{t} = \frac{3 \times 10^{11} \text{ m}}{1000 \text{ s}} = 3 \times 10^8 \text{ m/s}$$

Roemer made the first calculation of the speed of light using data from astronomical observations.

From his data, Roemer calculated a value of $3 \times 10^8$ m/s for the speed of light.

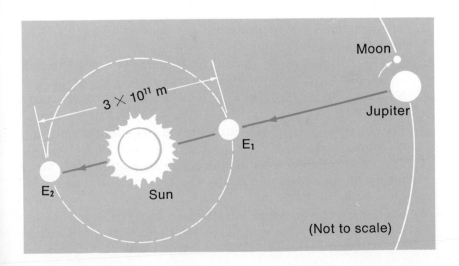

Moon

Jupiter

$3 \times 10^{11}$ m

$E_1$

$E_2$

Sun

(Not to scale)

**FIGURE 16-2.** Roemer's method of measuring the speed of light involved measuring the time of an eclipse for one of Jupiter's moons.

Michelson made an accurate land measurement of the speed of light.

    The first accurate land measurement of the speed of light was made by the American scientist Albert Michelson (1852–1931). Michelson timed the flight of a beam of light on a round trip between two mountains. To do this, he used a rotating octagonal mirror, Figure 16-3. A pulse of light was sent from the source S to the mirror A. The light then traveled the path shown. For the observer O to see the pulse, mirror B had to move into the exact position of mirror C in just the time it took the light to travel the path. The time required for B to move into position C was just one-eighth of the time needed for one revolution of the mirror. In practice, the octagonal mirror was turned by an electric motor. Starting from rest, the speed of the motor was adjusted until the light reflected from C was at maximum brightness. Then, with the rate of rotation of the mirror known, the speed of light was calculated. Michelson obtained a value of $3 \times 10^8$ meters per second for the speed of light in air.

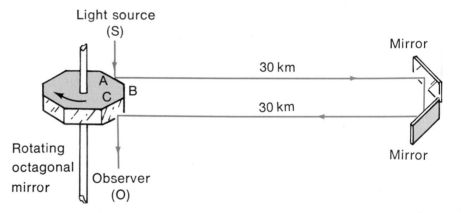

**FIGURE 16-3. Michelson's method of measuring the speed of light involved timing the flight of a light beam between two mountains.**

## PROBLEMS

1. $1.6 \times 10^{-3}$ s

3. a. $3 \times 10^5$ km/s
   b. $3 \times 10^8$ m/s

5. by starting to rotate the mirror from rest and increasing its rate of revolution to the first rate that gives the brightest reflected spot

**1.** The octagonal mirror in Figure 16-3 makes 625 rev/s. What time is required for one revolution?

**2. a.** For the octagonal mirror of Problem 1, what time is needed for B to move into position C?
   **b.** Using Figure 16-3, find the total distance the light travels in this time.

**3.** Use the solutions to Problem 2 to find the speed of light in
   **a.** km/s    **b.** m/s

**4.** The speed of the motor is increased until the mirror is rotating at the speed of 1250 rev/s. Will an observer see the pulse of light? Explain.

**5.** What steps can an observer take to be sure that the octagonal mirror does not rotate at some multiple of the proper number of rev/s?

## 16:4   Light Travels in a Straight Line

Light appears to travel in a straight line. For example, when the air contains many dust particles, the path of light coming from a flashlight can be seen. The light forms a "beam" of light. Also, an opaque object casts a sharp shadow when light falls on it. Shadows are further evidence that light travels in straight lines.

A small beam of light consists of a very large number of individual waves of many different wavelengths. The waves travel together in a straight line. This fact helps to explain much of the behavior of light. Since light travels in straight lines in the direction of the waves, lines can be used to represent the direction of the light waves. These lines are called rays. Using ray diagrams in studying light is called ray optics.

Since light travels in straight lines, the direction of light waves can be represented by rays.

**a**

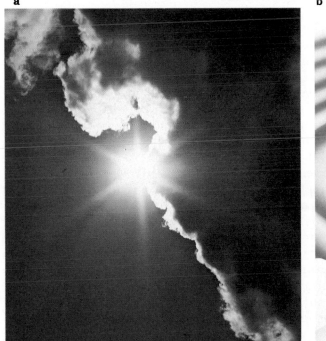

M.J. Manuell/Tom Stack & Assoc.

**b**

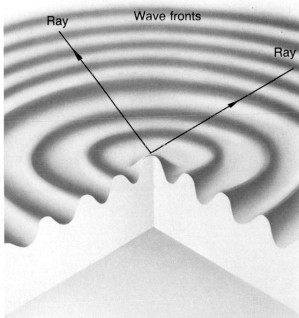

**FIGURE 16-4. Light travels in straight lines (a). A ray diagram showing the direction of propagation of a circular wave (b). Circular waves are propagated from a common center. Rays for circular waves are perpendicular to the wave fronts.**

## 16:5   Illumination by a Point Source

The light that comes from a light source consists of many short bursts of light emitted randomly by the atoms that make up the source. Since even a small light source consists of many billions of atoms, the net result is a smooth flow of light away from the source in all directions.

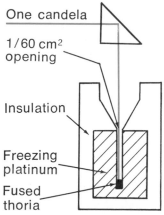

One candela

1/60 cm² opening

Insulation

Freezing platinum

Fused thoria

**FIGURE 16-5. The standard light source contains glowing thoria. The brightness of all other light sources is defined in terms of light emitted by this standard.**

The candela is the unit for luminous intensity.

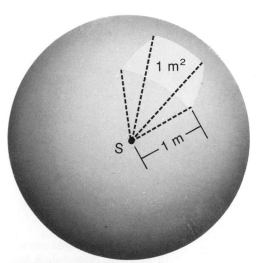

1 m²

S    1 m

**FIGURE 16-6. The lumen is the unit of luminous flux and is a measure of the rate of flow of light energy from a source.**

The lumen is the unit for luminous flux. It is a power unit.

The **luminous intensity,** *I,* of a light source is measured by comparing it with the international unit, the candela, cd. At first, the unit for luminous intensity was called a candle. An actual candle was made to meet certain specifications. However, even carefully made candles have an unsteady light intensity. Thus, a candle was not a good reference device.

At present, the standard source of luminous intensity is one sixtieth of a square centimeter of fused thoria.* At the temperature of freezing platinum, thoria is incandescent and emits a steady flow of light energy. One **candela** is defined to be the luminous intensity of this source.

The amount of light that a source gives out, its luminous intensity, depends on the amount of energy being put into the source. It also depends on how efficiently the source converts the energy input to light energy. Incandescent lamps are very inefficient sources of light. A fluorescent lamp produces about four times more light per watt than a typical light bulb. It is clear that a homeowner can reduce electric costs by using fluorescent lamps rather than incandescent lamps.

The flow of light energy from a source is called the **luminous flux.** The unit of luminous flux is called the lumen. Rate of energy flow is power. Thus, the lumen is a power unit.

In order to define the lumen, standards must be set up as to the area that light passes through and the intensity of the light. Imagine a hollow sphere with a radius of one meter. At the center of the sphere is a point light source of one candela intensity. A point light source is a very small light source that sends out light uniformly in all directions. Now, imagine four radii leaving the point source, each to form a corner of the surface of one square meter. The angle defined by the four radii is a unit solid angle. The luminous flux through any surface that would cap this unit solid angle at any point back to the source would be one lumen. If the four radii were all one meter in length, the surface area would be one square meter. The light energy flowing through that area would be one lumen. The **lumen** is, therefore, the rate at which light from a one-candela source passes through a solid angle of unit size.

The surface area of a sphere is $4\pi r^2$. The sphere of one meter radius has a total surface area of $4\pi(1 \text{ m})^2$ or $4\pi \text{ m}^2$. The rate at which light crosses the entire surface is accordingly $4\pi$ lumens. A two-candela source would emit $8\pi$ lumens, a three-candela source, $12\pi$ lumens, and so on. The energy flow in lumens from

*Thoria is a powdery white oxide of the element thorium.

a light source is directly proportional to the intensity of the source.

**Illuminance,** $E$, is the rate at which light energy falls on a unit area some distance from a light source. Illuminance is measured in lumens per square meter, lm/m$^2$ or lux (lx). One lumen per square meter (1 lux) is the illuminance of a surface located one meter from a one-candela source. A surface one meter from a 10-candela source receives illuminance of 10 lux or 10 lumens per square meter.

Illuminance is the rate at which light falls on a surface of unit area.

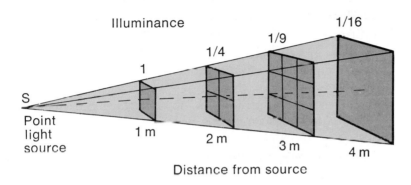

Distance from source

**FIGURE 16-7. The illuminance of a surface varies inversely as the square of its distance from a light source.**

Light from a point source radiates in all directions. Therefore, it spreads out with distance. Surfaces far from a light source receive less illumination than surfaces closer to the source. Figure 16-7 shows that the amount of illumination received by a surface varies inversely with the square of its distance from the source. A given amount of light energy falls on one square meter of a surface one meter away from a source. This same amount of energy spreads to cover an area of four square meters on a surface two meters from the source. Hence, the illumination of the surface two meters from the source is only one fourth that of the surface one meter from the source. In the same way, the source provides one ninth the illumination to a surface three meters away.

There are two ways to increase the illuminance of a surface. The luminous intensity of a light source can be increased. Or, the distance between the source and the surface can be decreased. Thus, the illuminance of a surface varies directly with the intensity of the light source and inversely with the square of its distance from the source. Let $I$ represent the luminous intensity of the source in candelas. Let $E$ represent the illuminance of the surface in lm/m$^2$ or lx. Then, the illuminance of any surface can be expressed as

Illuminance varies directly with the source intensity and varies inversely with the square of distance from the source.

The SI unit for illuminance is lux (lx).

One lux equals one lumen per square meter.

$$E = \frac{I}{d^2}$$

**EXAMPLE: Illumination**

A student's desk top is 2.5 m below a 150-cd incandescent lamp. What is the illumination of the desk top?

*Solution:*
$$E = \frac{I}{d^2}$$

$$= \frac{150 \text{ cd}}{\dfrac{1 \text{ cd}}{\text{lm}} (2.5 \text{ m})^2}$$

$$= 24 \text{ lm/m}^2 = 24 \text{ lx}$$

**PROBLEMS**

7. 1/9

**6.** Find the illumination 4.0 m below a 32-cd source of light.

**7.** A lamp is moved from 30 cm to 90 cm above the pages of a book. Compare the illumination of the book before and after the lamp is moved.

**8.** The intensity of illumination on a surface 3.0 m below a 150-watt incandescent lamp is 10 lx. What is the intensity of the lamp in candelas?

9. 450 cd

**9.** A light produces an illumination of 18.0 lx on a road. The light is suspended 5.0 m above the road. What is the intensity of the light source in candelas?

**10.** A public school law requires a minimum illumination of 160 lx on the surface of each student's desk. An architect's specifications call for classroom lights to be located 2.0 m above the desks. What must be the minimum intensity of the lights?

11. 125 cd

**11.** A screen is placed between two lamps of different intensities. The illumination is 20 lx on both sides of the screen. The smaller lamp has an intensity of 20 cd and is located 1 m from the screen. The larger lamp is 2.5 m from the screen. What is the intensity of the larger lamp?

# 16:6   Color and Light

Color is a property of light. Sunlight or white light from a lamp is dispersed into an array of different colors when it passes through a glass prism. White light is a combination of many colors of light. Each color corresponds to a different wavelength. Red light waves have the longest wavelengths. Violet light waves have the shortest wavelengths. When white light passes through a prism, these wavelengths are separated. Note that red and violet light are at opposite ends of the spectrum, Figure 16-8.

White light is composed of many colors.

Red and violet make up opposite ends of the visible light spectrum.

An object exhibits a particular color because it reflects light. A shirt is red because it reflects red light. When white light falls on

*Eastman Kodak Co., 1977*

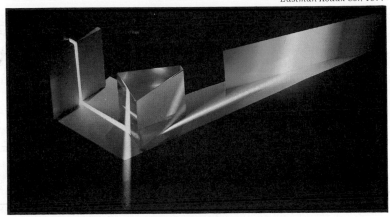

FIGURE 16-8. White light, when passed through a prism, is separated into a band of different colors.

the shirt, the pigments in the dye of the shirt absorb most of the light. However, the pigments do not absorb wavelengths in the red region of visible light. These wavelengths are reflected to the eye and the shirt looks red. Suppose that only blue light falls on the red shirt. The pigments in the dye would absorb all the blue light. No light would be reflected from the shirt. Thus, it would appear to be black. Black is the absence of color or light. Clothing, that is black in the presence of white light, absorbs all wavelengths. White objects reflect all wavelengths.

The color of an object depends on which wavelengths of light the object reflects.

a

b

c

*Larry Hamill*

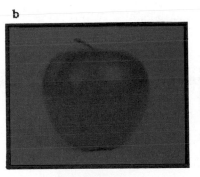

## 16:7 Light—Waves or Particles?

During Newton's lifetime a debate arose concerning the nature of light. Newton thought light consisted of minute particles. The Dutch scientist Christian Huygens (1629–1695) thought light consisted of waves. Both theories had strong arguments in their favor.

From observing the way light reflects from a surface, Newton reasoned that light consists of particles. Newton knew that when a beam of light strikes a surface, the angle of reflection is equal to the angle of approach. A particle is also reflected in this way.

FIGURE 16-9. An apple absorbs the colors of white light and reflects red (a). In red light, the apple still appears red (b). In blue light, the apple appears black (c). The blue light is absorbed.

The nature of light was a subject of much debate during Newton's lifetime.

A basketball bounces away from a gym floor at the same angle that it hits the floor. However, Huygens pointed out that waves act in the same way. When waves fall on a surface, the angle of reflection is equal to the angle of incidence. Since particles and waves are reflected from surfaces in the same way, the question of the nature of light remained.

Diffraction is the bending of waves around barriers placed in their path. Because waves bend around the edges of obstacles, they behave as shown in Figure 16-10. The waves pass through an opening in the barrier. As they pass through, they bend around the two edges and form new circular waves. The wave spreads out to both sides of the opening. Particles do not seem to act this way. In Figure 16-11a, a compressed air gun shoots pellets at a steel plate. The plate has a small circular opening in its center. The pellets cut a sharp, well defined image of the opening on a paper screen some distance from the plate. The pellets travel straight through the hole. No bending takes place at the edges. In Figure 16-11b, light seems to behave like the pellets. A street lamp casts a sharp image of a window on the wall of a room. Thus, it appears that light is not diffracted in the manner of waves and that, therefore, Newton was right. Light must consist of particles.

*The Ealing Corp.*

**FIGURE 16-10. Water waves are diffracted at openings.**

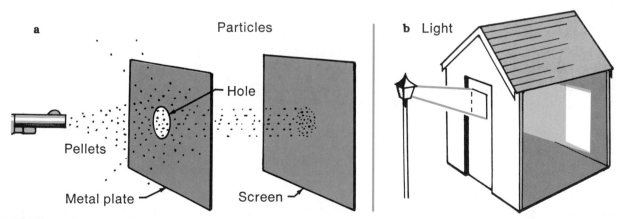

**FIGURE 16-11. Particles are not diffracted as they pass through openings (a). Light does not seem to be diffracted at large openings (b).**

The Italian physicist Francesco Grimaldi (1618–1663) did not agree with the idea that light casts sharp shadows. He said that if the edges of a shadow are examined closely, they appear to be slightly blurred. Light does bend around obstacles if only slightly. Grimaldi suggested that the diffraction was hardly noticeable because the light waves were very small. If the light rays had short wavelengths, then observable diffraction would take place only when the waves passed through very small openings.

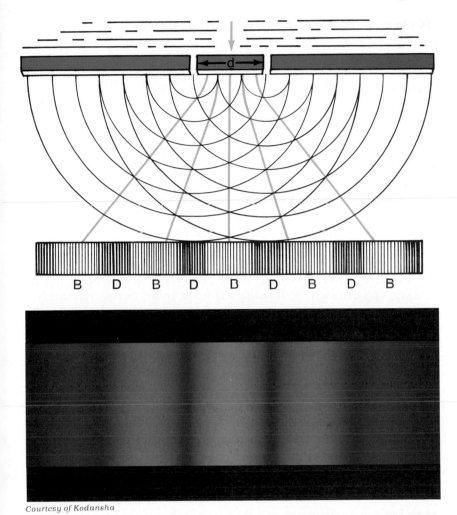

*Courtesy of Kodansha*

**FIGURE 16-12. If the two slits are small compared to the wavelength of the waves, an interference pattern is produced. Note the equal spacing between the bright bands.**

During the 18th century, Thomas Young tested Grimaldi's hypothesis. Young postulated that if light is diffracted as it passes through narrow openings, it should form a pattern like the one on Figure 16-12. He made two narrow slits in a screen. When he passed light through the slits, the pattern formed was similar to the pattern formed by the diffraction and interference of water waves. In this case, lines of constructive interference resulted in bright spots on a screen some distance from the slits. Between the bright spots were dark spots where destructive interference caused the light waves to cancel. Young concluded that since light can be diffracted and exhibits interference, it must consist of waves.

Light shining through a window appears to cast a well-defined image. But light is actually diffracted, or bent, when it moves past a barrier.

The diffraction and interference of light waves favor the wave theory of light.

## 16:8   Interference in Thin Films

The diffraction of light is not the only evidence favoring the wave theory of light. The colorful pattern often seen in soap films, soap bubbles, and oil slicks also shows the wave theory of light. If a soap film is held vertically, its weight makes it thicker at the bottom than at the top. In fact, the thickness of the film varies gradually from top to bottom. When a light wave strikes the film, part of it is reflected as shown by $R_1$ in Figure 16-13. Part of the wave is transmitted, as shown by the ray $T$. The transmitted wave travels through the film to the inner surface. Again, part of the wave is reflected, $R_2$. If the thickness of the film is 1/4 of the wavelength of the wave ($\lambda/4$), the "round trip" path length in the film is $\lambda/2$. It would appear that the wave returning from the inner surface would arrive back at the outer surface just one-half wavelength (180°) out of phase with the first reflected wave and that the two waves would cancel. However, remember from Chapter 15 that when a wave is reflected from a more dense medium, it undergoes inversion. Thus, the first reflected wave, $R_1$, is inverted upon reflection. The second reflected wave, $R_2$, returning from the boundary of a less dense medium, is not inverted. The wave reflected from the inner surface arrives back at the first surface inphase with the first reflected wave. Thus, reinforcement occurs. Wavelengths that do not meet the $\lambda/4$ wavelength requirement for this region of the film arrive back at the outer surface out of phase. They cancel or at least weaken the first reflected wave. The strongest light from any given region of the film is the wavelength that satisfies the $\lambda/4$ requirement.

**FIGURE 16-13. Each color is reinforced where the soap film is 1/4, 3/4, 5/4, etc., of the wavelength for that color. Since each color has a different wavelength, a series of color bands are seen reflected from the soap films.**

a.

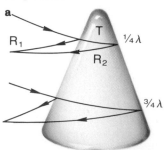

b

*Courtesy of Kodansha*

The individual colors of light have different wavelengths. Since the thickness of the film changes, the λ/4 requirement for different colors is met at intervals down the film. If the region of the film has a thickness of ¼ the wavelength of red light it appears to be red. Thus, white light falling on the film results in a rainbow of color.

When a point is reached where the thickness is 3λ/4 for the first color, the first color reappears. This point again gives a λ/2 path difference. Any odd multiple of quarter wavelengths, such as λ/4, 3λ/4, or 5λ/4, satisfies the conditions for reinforcement for a given color. If the film is λ/2 thick, or any multiple thereof, the returning wave cancels the wave reflected from the outer surface. There is no reflected wave for the wavelength at that point.

# 16:9   Polarization of Light

In Figure 16-14, waves sent along a rope pass through a slot. Under these circumstances, waves can be sent along the rope only if the waves are generated in the plane of the slot. Each slot permits only those waves with the proper orientation to pass through. The waves are said to be **polarized** to a particular plane, or plane polarized.

Waves oriented to a particular plane are plane polarized.

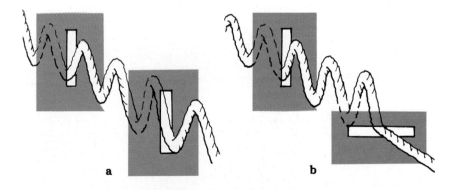

a               b

FIGURE 16-14. In (a) the waves are polarized with respect to the vertical plane. Vertically polarized waves (b) cannot pass through a horizontal polarizer.

A beam of light contains a huge number of waves vibrating in every possible plane. All of the waves can be resolved into vertical and horizontal components. Thus, it averages out as if half of the waves vibrate vertically and half vibrate horizontally. If a filter (polarizer), such as polaroid sunglasses, is placed in front of the beam of light, only those waves that vibrate parallel to the permitted plane pass through. Thus, half of the light rays are eliminated. Suppose a second sheet of polaroid material (analyzer) is placed in the path of the polarized light. If its permitted plane is perpendicular to the light that passed through the polarizer, almost no light will pass through.

Light can be polarized by passing it through a polaroid filter.

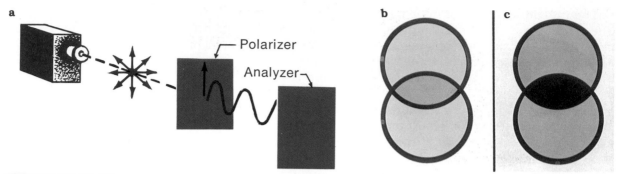

a

**FIGURE 16-15. The arrows show that unpolarized light vibrates in many planes (a). Plane polarized light vibrates in only one plane. Polarized light from the first polarizer (b) is absorbed by the analyzer (c).**

Light can be polarized by reflection.

The polarization of light gives evidence that light is a transverse wave.

Light can also be polarized by reflection. If you look through a piece of polaroid material at the light reflected by a sheet of glass and rotate the polaroid filter, you will notice that the light brightens and dims. Reflected light has been polarized upon its reflection. There will be one angle at which no light is able to pass through the polaroid. At the **angle of polarization,** the light which is reflected from the glass is completely polarized.

The fact that light can be polarized supports two ideas. First, light consists of waves. Particles would be unaffected by a polarizer. Secondly, light waves are transverse waves. Longitudinal waves would not be affected by a polarizer. For example, sound waves cannot be polarized.

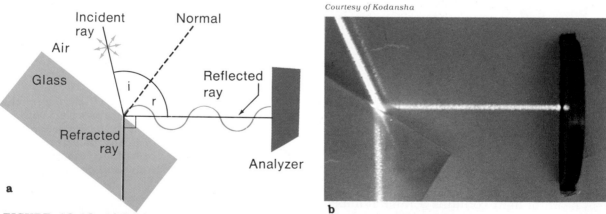

*Courtesy of Kodansha*

**FIGURE 16-16. Light becomes polarized when it is reflected from a smooth surface such as glass or water.**

The photoelectric effect is the ejection of electrons from a metal surface when light falls on it.

## 16:10   The Dual Nature of Light

Beyond all doubt, the diffraction, interference, and polarization of light demonstrate the wave properties of light. Now consider an effect that shows just as clearly that light consists of particles.

Light which falls on a metal surface, such as zinc or cesium, ejects electrons from the metal. This ejection of electrons is called the **photoelectric effect.** The electrons leave the metal with a kinetic energy that is dependent upon the frequency of the light, not its intensity. This means that light energy is not distributed evenly. Instead, it is concentrated in small packages or bundles of energy. The photoelectric effect is definitely not a property of waves but is a property of particles.

We have still not answered our question about the nature of light. Does light consist of waves or is it made up of particles? We can avoid the problem if we reword the question about light. Let us look at the possibility that light behaves as both waves and particles.

The photoelectric effect supports the particle theory of light.

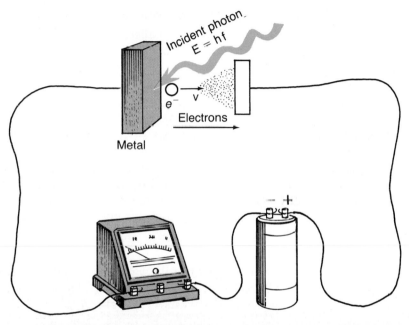

FIGURE 16-17. When an incident photon hits the surface of the metal, electrons are ejected from the surface. The meter detects a completed circuit.

The quantum theory of light was proposed by Max Planck. The quantum theory attempts to explain the dual nature of light. According to the quantum theory, light is emitted from a source in discrete packages. These packages are called **photons.** Each photon is related to a light wave of specific frequency. The energy of a photon is proportional to its wave frequency, in accordance with the equation proposed by Max Planck.

The quantum theory of light attempts to explain the fact that light behaves as both waves and particles.

Photons are small bundles of energy.

$$E = hf$$

In the equation, $E$ is the energy in joules. The symbol $h$ is Planck's constant $6.6 \times 10^{-34}$ J/Hz, and $f$ is the frequency of the photon.

**EXAMPLE: Energy of a Photon**

A photon of red light has a frequency of $5.0 \times 10^{14}$ Hz. How much energy does the photon have?

*Solution:* $E = hf$

$= (6.6 \times 10^{-34} \text{ J/Hz})(5.0 \times 10^{14} \text{ Hz}) = 3.3 \times 10^{-19}$ J

Each photon corresponds to a specific wave frequency. The ratio of energy to frequency is Planck's constant.

**Summary**

1. Electromagnetic radiation capable of stimulating the retina of the eye is called light. All bodies emit electromagnetic radiation most of which is not light.   16:1

2. White light is a combination of many colors of light. Each color has a different wavelength.   16:6

3. The speed of light is $3.0 \times 10^8$ m/s in air or in a vacuum. Light travels in straight lines.   16:3

4. The standard of luminous intensity is the candela.   16:5

5. The flow of light energy from a source is called luminous flux. The unit for luminous flux is the lumen.   16:5

6. Illuminance is the rate at which light energy falls on a unit area. Illuminance is measured in lux.   16:5

7. The illumination received by a surface varies inversely with the square of its distance from the light source involved.   16:5

8. The illumination received by a surface varies directly with the intensity of the source.   16:5

9. Light may be reflected, refracted, and diffracted. If light falls on two narrow slits, diffraction will cause the light waves to interfere and produce a diffraction pattern.   16:7

10. Light can cause interference effects by diffraction, by reflection from the outer and inner surfaces of thin films of soap or oil, and by reflection from irregular surfaces.   16:8

11. Waves are said to be plane polarized if only waves oriented to a particular plane are present. Very fine gratings can polarize light demonstrating that light is a wave and a transverse wave at that.   16:9

12. The diffraction, interference, and polarization of light clearly indicate the wave nature of light. The photoelectric effect clearly indicates that 16:10 light consists of particles. Light has both wave and particle properties.

13. The quantum theory attempts to explain the dual nature of light. It states that light is emitted from a source in discrete packages called quanta or photons. The energy of a photon is equal to its frequency multiplied by Planck's constant, or $E = hf$.   16:10

**Questions**

1. What determines whether an electromagnetic wave is a light wave?
2. Electromagnetic waves differ from mechanical waves. How?
3. Distinguish among transparent, translucent, and opaque.
4. Of what does white light consist?
5. Why does a red shirt look red?
6. Is black a color? Why does an object appear to be black?
7. Distinguish between a luminous body and an illuminated body.
8. In what unit is the intensity of a light source measured?

9. In what unit is the illumination of a surface measured?

10. To what is the illumination of a surface by a light source directly proportional? To what is it inversely proportional?

11. Explain why the reflection of light cannot be used as evidence that light is a wave or particle.

12. What theory of light does the diffraction of light support?

13. What theory of light does the polarization of light support?

14. The fact that light consists of transverse waves is supported by what phenomenon?

15. What theory of light is supported by the photoelectric effect?

16. To what is the energy of a photon proportional?

17. If light is a wave, why is there no apparent diffraction when light goes through large openings?

18. Fold a small piece of paper in half. Using a pair of scissors snip two or three slits along the folded edge of the paper. Unfold the paper and look through the slits at a bright light source. You may need to pull the slits apart slightly. Describe the pattern you observe.

**Problems**

1. An observer uses a 10-sided mirror to measure the speed of light. Maximum brightness occurs when the mirror is rotating at 2000 rev/s. The total path of the light pulse is 15 km. What is the speed of light?

2. Assume that the sun is $1.5 \times 10^8$ km from the earth. Calculate the time required for light to travel from the sun to the earth.

3. A radar signal is reflected from the moon. It is detected after a 2.58 s time lapse between sending and receiving. How far away is the moon?

4. A 64-cd point source of light is 3.0 m above the surface of a desk. What is the illumination of the desk's surface in lux?

5. A 100-cd point source of light is 2.0 m from screen *A* and 4.0 m from screen *B*. How does the illumination of screen *B* compare with the illumination of screen *A*?

6. The illumination of a tabletop is 20 lx. The lamp providing the illumination is 4.0 m above the table. What is the intensity of the lamp?

7. Two lamps illuminate a screen equally. The first lamp has an intensity of 100 cd and is 5.0 m from the screen. The second lamp is 3.0 m from the screen. What is the intensity of the second lamp?

8. A polaroid filter is placed over the light detecting surface of a light meter. The meter is then exposed to the sun on a clear day. The meter reads 500 lx. What actual illumination falls on the meter?

9. If the sun is $1.5 \times 10^8$ km away, what is the intensity of the sun as a light source? (Use the answer to Problem 8 and scientific notation.)

10. **a.** Calculate the illumination of a screen when it is located at the following distances from a 400-cd source; 5 m, 10 m, 15 m, 20 m, 25 m.
    **b.** Make a table to show the distances in the first column and the corresponding illuminations in the second column.
    **c.** Use graph paper to plot illumination versus distance. Plot the distance on the $x$ axis.
    **d.** Draw the curve that best fits these points. What is the resulting curve called? What does it indicate?

11. A radio wave has a frequency of $10^8$ Hz. Planck's constant is $6.6 \times 10^{-34}$ J/Hz. What energy is associated with the radio wave's photons?

12. A gamma ray has a frequency of $10^{20}$ Hz. What energy is associated with this photon?

13. Which has more energy, the radio wave or the gamma ray?

14. How thick is the first point near the top of a soap-film wedge that will reinforce light of wavelength $3.0 \times 10^{-7}$ m?

15. Light from an infrared heat lamp has a wavelength of $1 \times 10^{-5}$ m. Light from an ultraviolet sunlamp has a wavelength of $1 \times 10^{-8}$ m.
    **a.** Calculate the energy of each photon.
    **b.** Why is overexposure to ultraviolet radiation more hazardous than overexposure to infrared?

**Applying Physics**

1. *Space Travel:* Proxima Centauri, the nearest star (beyond the sun), is four light-years away. A round trip to this star by astronauts, even at the speed of light, would require eight years. Under current technological conditions, such a mission is impossible; not because we cannot attain high speeds, but because of radiation. A space craft traveling at speeds close to the speed of light would strike interstellar particles at these speeds. This would have the same result as though the craft were stationary and was being exposed to a constant stream of particles from a cyclotron. Hydrogen gas is thinly distributed throughout space so the primary particle encountered would be protons. Note that constant exposure to gamma radiation is highly lethal.
    **a.** Calculate the kinetic energy a proton would have if it had a velocity equal to 0.90 the velocity of light $c$.
    **b.** Upon being struck by the craft assume that the particle converts this energy to radiation. What frequency would result?
    **c.** Using Figure 16-1, identify the nature of the radiation.

**2.** *Astronomy:* A popular measure of interstellar distances amongst astronomers is the light-year which is the distance light travels in one year. Calculate this distance. Express your answer in
    **a.** meters    **b.** kilometers

**3.** Calculate the distance to Proxima Centauri. Express your answer in
    **a.** meters    **b.** kilometers

**4.** The Milky Way galaxy has a diameter of approximately 100 000 light years.
    **a.** Calculate this distance in kilometers.
    **b.** How long does it take a photon of light to move from one end of the galaxy to the other?

**Readings**

Amateur Scientist: "The Bright Colors in a Soap Film Are a Lesson in Wave Interference." *Scientific American*, September, 1978.

Bladow, Janel, "Luminicity." *Omni*, August, 1980.

Nassau, Kurt, "The Causes of Color." *Scientific American*, October, 1980.

Smay, Elaine, "Solar Goes Underground." *Popular Science*, May, 1980.

A rainbow is one of nature's most dynamic displays of reflection and refraction. In this chapter you will look closely at the way light behaves as it passes from one medium to another. Using your knowledge of how water waves behave when striking a barrier, you should be able to explain some of the interesting effects of reflection and refraction. For example, why is it possible to form a rainbow with materials such as water and glass?

# Reflection and Refraction 17

In our study of the nature of light, we found that light behaves both as waves and as particles. We also found that light travels in straight lines and at a very high speed. Let us now study some specific behaviors of light. What happens when light is bounced off a barrier? How does light behave when it passes from one medium into another medium?

**GOAL: You will gain knowledge and understanding of reflection, refraction, and the effects which result from these phenomena.**

## 17:1 The Law of Reflection

When a light ray is incident upon a surface, *the angle of incidence is equal to the angle of reflection.* Both of these angles are measured from a normal (perpendicular) to the surface at the point of incidence. The incident ray, the reflected ray, and the normal all lie in the same plane.

## 17:2 Diffuse and Regular Reflection

When a beam of light strikes most surfaces, it reflects in many directions. Most surfaces do not reflect light in a regular manner because they are not smooth. A painted wall or a page of a book appear to be smooth. Actually their surfaces are rough and have many small projections. Rays of light strike different parts of these projections. Each ray reflects according to the law of reflection and the rays are scattered in many different directions, Figure 17-2a. This scattering is known as **diffuse reflection.**

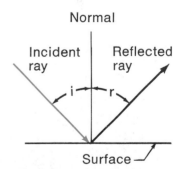

**FIGURE 17-1. The law of reflection: The angle of incidence is equal to the angle of reflection.**

Light reflected from an uneven surface is scattered in different directions.

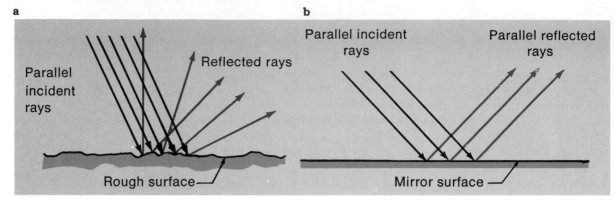

FIGURE 17-2. When parallel light rays strike an uneven surface, they are reflected randomly. When parallel light rays strike a mirror surface, they are reflected as parallel rays.

If a beam of light falls on a very smooth surface, the rays reflect in a regular way. Figure 17-2b shows a beam of parallel rays reflecting from a smooth, flat surface. Since each ray follows the law of reflection, the reflected rays are also parallel. The rays are arranged in the same order after they leave a smooth surface as they were before they approached the surface.

Refraction is the bending of light as it enters a new medium.

FIGURE 17-3. Comparison of the refraction of light at a boundary to the deflection of a car at the boundary of mud and pavement. Light is refracted toward the normal as it enters a more dense medium.

## 17:3 Refraction of Light

Light travels at different speeds in different media. For this reason, light bends as it moves from one medium to another. The bending of light at the boundary between two media is called **refraction.**

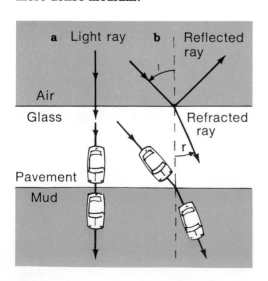

*Courtesy of Kodansha*

The incident ray falls on the boundary between two media. Once the ray enters a new medium, it is a refracted ray. The angle between the incident ray and a normal to the surface at the point of incidence is the angle of incidence, $i$. The angle between the refracted ray and the same normal is the angle of refraction, $r$. Refraction occurs only when the incident ray strikes the boundary between the two media at an angle. When the angle of incidence is zero (the ray is perpendicular to the surface), there is no refraction. The ray passes straight into the new medium.

Figure 17-3 shows a ray of light as it passes from air into glass at different angles of incidence. Part of the ray is reflected and part is transmitted. Notice that as the ray enters a medium in which it travels more slowly, the refracted ray bends toward the normal. The angle of refraction is smaller than the angle of incidence.

In Figure 17-4, a light ray passes from glass into air at different angles. A ray perpendicular to the surface is not refracted. Rays that strike the surface at an angle are refracted. They bend away from the normal. When a light ray passes into a medium in which it travels faster, the light ray refracts away from the normal. **Optical density** is the property of a medium that determines the speed of light in that medium. If a medium is optically dense, it slows light more than a medium which is less optically dense.

Figures 17-3 and 17-4 compare the refraction of light to a car entering or leaving a patch of mud. When the car enters the mud at an angle, Figure 17-3b, its right wheel enters the mud before the left wheel. The right wheel slows. As a result the car swings to the right or toward the normal. In Figure 17-4c, the car leaves the mud at an angle. The right wheel leaves the mud first and

The angle of incidence is measured from the normal to the incident ray. The angle of refraction is measured from the normal to the refracted ray.

Light is refracted only when it hits a boundary at an angle.

Light bends toward the normal if its speed is reduced as it enters the new medium; light bends away from the normal if its speed increases as it enters the new medium.

Optical density of a medium determines the speed of light in that medium.

**FIGURE 17-4. Light is refracted away from the normal as it enters a less dense medium.**

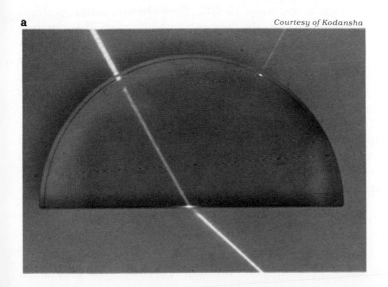

a

*Courtesy of Kodansha*

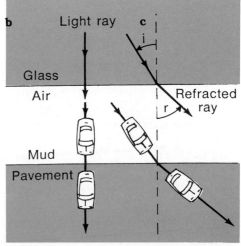

speeds up. The left wheel is still held back. Therefore, the car swings to the left or away from the normal. Keep this car analogy in mind until the behavior of light at various surfaces becomes more familiar to you.

**PROBLEM**

1. Find the path of the incident light ray through and beyond the medium in each case.

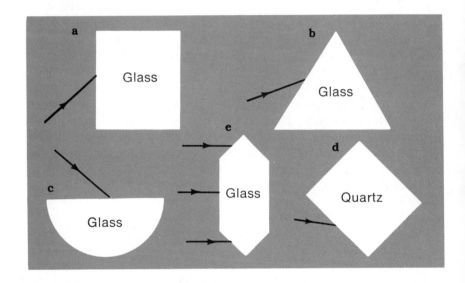

**FIGURE 17-5. Use with Problem 1.**

## 17:4 Snell's Law

Rays of light that travel from air into glass, or any other medium more optically dense than air, are refracted toward the normal. As the angle of incidence increases, the angle of refraction increases, Figure 17-3. However, the angle of refraction does not vary directly with the angle of incidence. Still, the increase in the angle of refraction as the angle of incidence increases suggests that a definite relationship exists.

The relationship between the angle of incidence and the angle of refraction was discovered by the Dutch scientist Willebrord Snell (1591–1626). **Snell's law** states that *a ray of light bends in such a way that the ratio of the sine of the angle of incidence to the sine of the angle of refraction is a constant.* For a light ray passing from air into a given medium, this constant (the ratio between the sines) is called the **index of refraction,** *n*, for that medium. Snell's law can be written

**Snell's law states that the ratio of the sine of the incident angle to the sine of the refracted angle is a constant.**

$$n = \frac{\sin i}{\sin r}$$

In this equation, $i$ is the angle of incidence, $r$ is the angle of refraction, and $n$ is the index of refraction of the medium. Note that this equation applies only to a ray traveling from air to another medium.

In general, for a ray traveling from any medium to another medium, Snell's law can be written

$$n_1 \sin i = n_2 \sin r$$

In this equation, $n_1$ is the index of refraction of the incident medium and $n_2$ is the index of refraction of the second medium.

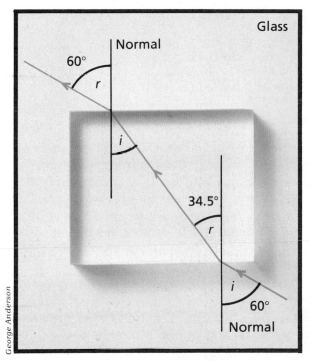
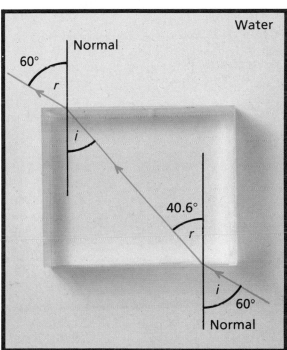

FIGURE 17-6. The index of refraction for glass is greater than that for water. If light enters both media at the same angle, the angle of refraction is greater for water. This result agrees with Snell's law.

**TABLE 17-1**

**Indices of Refraction**

| Medium | $n$ | Medium | $n$ |
|--------|-----|--------|-----|
| vacuum | 1.00 | polyethylene | 1.52 |
| air | 1.00* | crown glass | 1.52 |
| water | 1.33 | flint glass | 1.61 |
| alcohol | 1.36 | diamond | 2.42 |
| quartz | 1.46 | | |

*Index of refraction of air is 1.0003 which is higher than that of vacuum which is 1.0000. However, for practical purposes they are the same.

**EXAMPLE: Snell's Law**

A ray of light traveling through air is incident upon a sheet of crown glass at an angle of 30°. What is the angle of refraction?

*Solution:* Find the index of refraction from Table 17-1. Find the sine of 30° from Table B-1 of the Appendix. Use

$$n = \frac{\sin i}{\sin r}$$

$$\sin r = \frac{\sin i}{n} = \frac{0.5}{1.52} = 0.32$$

$$r = \text{arc sin } 0.32$$

$$\text{angle of refraction} = 19°$$

**PROBLEMS**

**2.** Light is incident upon a piece of crown glass at an angle of 45°. What is the angle of refraction to the nearest degree?

3. 22°

**3.** A ray of light passes from air into water at an angle of 30°. Find the angle of refraction to the nearest degree.

**4.** Light is incident upon a piece of quartz at an angle of 45°. What is the angle of refraction to the nearest degree?

5. a. 17°
   b. diamond

**5.** A ray of light is incident upon a diamond at 45°.
   **a.** What is the angle of refraction?
   **b.** Compare your answer to that for Problem 2. Does glass or diamond bend light more?

**6.** A ray of light travels from air into a liquid. The ray is incident upon the liquid at an angle of 30°. The angle of refraction is 22°.
   **a.** What is the index of refraction of the liquid?
   **b.** Look at Table 17-1. What might the liquid be?

7. a. should measure
      19°
   b. 30°
   c. away from

**7.** In the Example on this page, a ray of light is incident upon crown glass at 30°. The angle of refraction is 19°. Assume the glass is rectangular in shape. Construct a diagram to show the incident ray, the refracted ray, and the normal. Continue the ray through the glass until it reaches the opposite edge.
   **a.** Construct a normal at this point. What is the angle at which the refracted ray is incident upon the opposite edge of the glass?
   **b.** Assume the material outside the opposite edge is air. What is the angle at which the ray leaves the glass?
   **c.** Is the ray refracted away from the normal or toward the normal?

# 17:5   Index of Refraction and the Speed of Light

Refraction occurs because the speed of light depends on the medium in which the light is traveling. The index of refraction is a measure of the amount of bending (refraction). In this section, the relationship between the index of refraction and the speed of light in a medium will be derived.

*George Anderson*

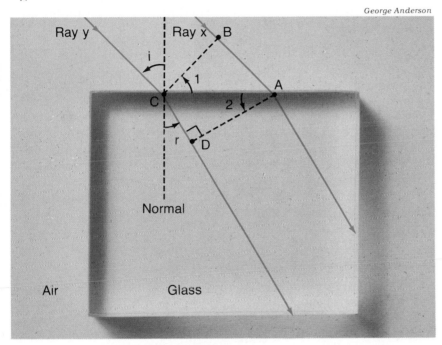

FIGURE 17-7. A diagram for the refraction of two parallel light rays incident on a piece of glass.

Figure 17-7 shows the behavior of two parallel rays of light that are incident upon a glass plate from air. The rays are refracted toward the normal. Consider the wave front *CB* as it approaches the glass plate. After a time interval, the wave front reaches position *DA*. Since the speed of the wave is slower in the glass, point *C* on ray *y* travels only distance *CD*. Point *B* on ray *x* travels distance *BA*. This difference causes the wave front to turn.

Point *B* on ray *x* travels to *A* in the same time that point *C* on ray *y* travels to *D*. Therefore, the ratio of *BA* to *CD* is the same as the ratio of the speed of light in vacuum, $v_v$, to the speed of light in glass, $v_g$.

$$\frac{BA}{CD} = \frac{v_v}{v_g}$$

Angle 1 in Figure 17-7 is equal to the angle of incidence of the ray. Angle 2 is equal to the angle of refraction of the ray (corresponding sides mutually perpendicular). The sine of angle 1 is

BA/CA. The sine of angle 2 is CD/CA. Using Snell's law, the index of refraction is

$$n_{glass} = \frac{\sin i}{\sin r} = \frac{\sin 1}{\sin 2} = \frac{BA}{CD} = \frac{v_v}{v_g}$$

Thus, the index of refraction of any substance is the speed of light in a vacuum divided by the speed of light in the medium.

The speed of light in air is assumed to be the same as the speed of light in a vacuum. Because this speed has a special significance, it is assigned the symbol c. The index of refraction for any substance is

$$\boxed{n_s = \frac{c}{v_s}}$$

where $v_s$ represents the speed of light in the medium.

The index of refraction of many transparent substances, such as water or glass, can be found by measurement. A small ray of light is caused to fall on the substance and the resulting angle of refraction is measured. The sine of the angle of incidence divided by the sine of the angle of refraction gives the index of refraction of the substance. The speed of light in a vacuum, $3.0 \times 10^8$ m/s, is known. Therefore, it is possible to calculate the speed of light in many substances by setting the index of refraction equal to $c/v_s$.

**EXAMPLE: Speed of Light in a Medium**

The index of refraction of water is 1.33. Calculate the speed of light in water.

*Solution:*    $v = \dfrac{c}{n} = \dfrac{3 \times 10^8 \text{ m/s}}{1.33} = 2.25 \times 10^8 \text{ m/s}$

**PROBLEMS**

8. Use Table 17-1 to find the speed of light in
   **a.** alcohol     **b.** quartz     **c.** polyethylene
9. The speed of light in a plastic is $2.0 \times 10^8$ m/s. What is the index of refraction of the plastic?
10. The speed of light in a glass plate is 196 890 km/s. Find the index of refraction of the glass.

# 17:6    Total Internal Reflection

When a ray of light passes from a dense medium into air, it is bent away from the normal. In other words, the angle of refraction is larger than the angle of incidence. The fact that the angle of refraction must be larger than the angle of incidence leads to

**The index of refraction of a medium is the ratio of the speed of light in a vacuum to the speed of light in the medium.**

9. 1.50

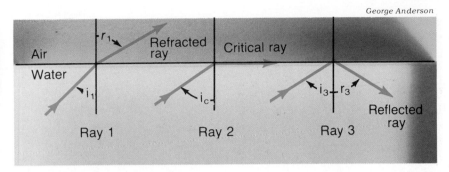

FIGURE 17-8. Ray 1 is refracted. Ray 2 is refracted along the boundary of the medium showing the critical angle. An angle of refraction greater than the critical angle results in the total internal reflection of Ray 3.

an interesting phenomenon known as total internal reflection. **Total internal reflection** occurs when light falls on the surface of a less optically dense medium at an angle so great that it cannot produce a refracted ray. Figure 17-8 shows such an occurrence. Ray 1 is incident upon the surface of the water at angle $i_1$. Ray 1 produces the angle of refraction, $r_1$. Ray 2 is incident at such a large angle, $i_c$, that the refracted ray lies along the surface of the water. The angle of refraction is 90°. The incident angle which causes the refracted ray to lie right along the boundary of the substance, angle $i_c$, is unique to the substance. It is known as the **critical angle** of the substance. Any ray which falls upon the surface of the water at an angle greater than the critical angle (ray 3) cannot be refracted. All of the light is reflected.

Total internal reflection causes some curious effects. Suppose an underwater swimmer looks at the surface of the water. The

In total internal reflection no light rays are transmitted into the new medium.

FIGURE 17-9. The passage of light through the reflecting prisms in a pair of binoculars shows total internal reflection (a). The angle of the prisms changes the path of the reflected rays (b).

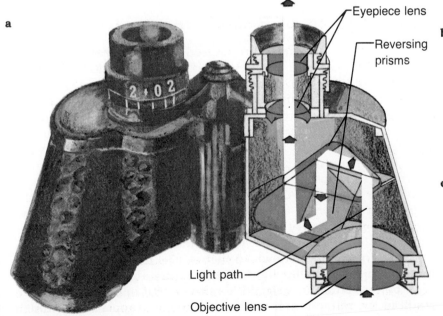

a

Eyepiece lens

Reversing prisms

Light path

Objective lens

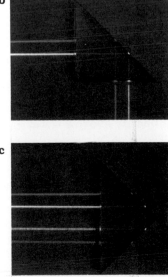

b

c

*Thomas Russell*

a

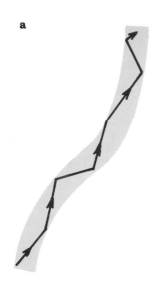

a

b

**FIGURE 17-10. Optical fibers exhibit total internal reflection along the inner surface of the fiber (a). Light transmitted through plastic fibers was used to create this sign (b).**

Fiber optics is an example of the practical application of total internal reflection.

legs of a second swimmer, seated on the edge of the pool, may appear to be higher than they actually are. Total internal reflection is important in the design of binoculars. It has also given rise to a field of optics known as fiber optics. Fiber optics promises to contribute much to the field of communications.

## 17:7  Effects of Refraction

Many interesting effects are caused by the refraction of light. The puddle-effect, the apparent shift in the position of objects immersed in liquids, and the lengthening of the day are examples.

The puddle effect is due to the gradual change in air density above a warm surface.

The puddle-effect can be observed along highways in summer. A driver looking down the road sees what looks like a puddle of water. However, the puddle disappears as the car approaches because the air next to the surface of the road is heated sooner than the air above it. This heated air expands. As the distance above the road increases, the air gradually becomes cooler. As a result, the density of the air gradually increases. Therefore, the index of refraction of the air also increases with distance above the road. As a ray of light moves toward the road, it passes through air of increasingly lower index of refraction. The ray bends in the manner shown in Figure 17-11. To an observer, the refracted light looks like light reflected from a puddle.

A similar phenomenon occurs above hot stoves and radiators.

An object viewed in a liquid is not where it appears to be. As a result of the refraction of light, an object may appear to be much

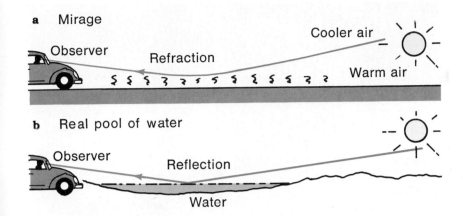

**a** Mirage

Observer

Refraction

Cooler air

Warm air

**b** Real pool of water

Observer

Reflection

Water

**FIGURE 17-11. Refraction of light in air of different densities (a) produces an effect similar to the reflection of light off a pool of water (b).**

closer to the surface of the liquid than it really is. This same effect makes a spoon placed in a glass of water appear broken.

Light travels at a slightly slower speed in air than it does in the near vacuum conditions of outer space. As a result, sunlight is refracted by the atmosphere. In the morning, this refraction causes sunlight to reach the earth before the sun actually comes up. In the evening, the sunlight is bent over the horizon after the sun has actually set. Thus, daylight is extended in the morning and evening because of the refraction of light.

# 17:8 Dispersion of Light

When a beam of light from the sun or a light bulb falls on the surface of a glass prism, the light disperses. The light emerges from the prism as an array of different colors. Early scientists thought that the colors were produced somehow inside the glass. Sir Isaac Newton disproved this assumption. Newton allowed a beam of sunlight (white light) to fall on a prism. Then he allowed the emerging colored light to fall on a second, inverted prism. The colored light rays recombined to form white light once again. Newton was the first to understand that white light is made of many colors.

All electromagnetic waves travel through space at the speed of light, $3.0 \times 10^8$ m/s. However, in all other media, these waves travel more slowly, and waves of different frequencies travel at slightly different speeds. Therefore, the index of refraction is slightly different for each wavelength of light. When white light falls on a prism, the waves of each color bend by different amounts and the light disperses.

White light is dispersed into an array of colored light when it passes through a prism.

**FIGURE 17-12. White light directed through a prism is dispersed into a band of different colors.**

Red light has the longest wavelength and the highest speed for visible light in a medium. Violet light has the shortest wavelength and the lowest speed.

**FIGURE 17-13. Newton showed that white light can be dispersed into a spectrum of colors and that the white light can be reconstituted by sending the dispersed light through a second prism.**

A visible spectrum is a display of color formed when a light beam of multiple wavelengths is bent and spread by passing through a prism.

A rainbow shows the various components of white light.

As light emerges from a prism, the various colors are in a distinct arrangement. Red light is refracted the least by the prism because red light has the fastest speed in the glass. Violet light is always refracted the most because violet light has the slowest speed in the glass.

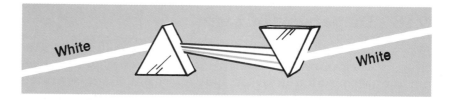

The array of different colors that emerges from a prism is called a **spectrum.** If the prism is placed between the light source and a screen, the spectrum produced by the source will fall on the screen. Different light sources produce different spectra. Light from an incandescent solid produces all visible wavelengths of light. When this light passes through the prism, a continuous spectrum is seen. Sunlight passing through a prism or through raindrops will cause a spectrum of this sort, commonly called a rainbow.

A rainbow is an example of refraction and internal reflection. The incident light is reflected off the interior surface of a water drop as shown in Figure 17-14b.

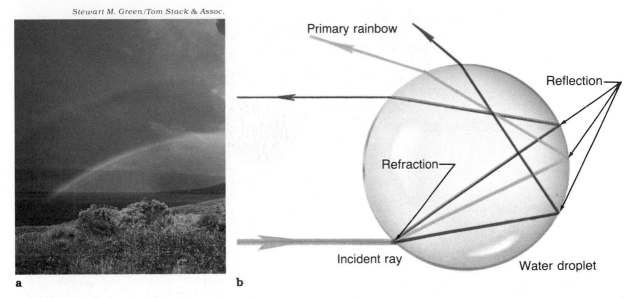

Stewart M. Green/Tom Stack & Assoc.

a                     b

**FIGURE 17-14. This rainbow is a result of the dispersion of white light by water droplets in the air (a). Refraction occurs at the outside surface of a water drop. Reflection occurs at the inside surface (b).**

**Summary**

1. Light rays follow the law of reflection. This law states that the angle of incidence is equal to the angle of reflection.   **17:1**
2. Refraction is the bending of light rays at the boundary between two media. Refraction occurs only when the incident ray strikes the boundary of a new medium at an angle.   **17:3**
3. Snell's law states that when a light ray passes from air into a more optically dense medium at an angle, the ratio of the sine of the angle of incidence to the sine of the angle of refraction is a constant. This ratio is given the symbol $n$ and called the index of refraction.   **17:4**
4. Light waves of different frequencies are refracted by slightly different amounts. Thus, when light falls on a prism, waves of each color bend by different amounts. A spectrum of colored light is produced.   **17:8**

**Questions**

1. How does regular reflection differ from diffuse reflection?
2. If a light ray does not undergo refraction at a boundary between two media, what is its angle of incidence?
3. How does the angle of incidence compare with the angle of refraction when a light ray passes from air into glass at an angle?
4. How does the angle of incidence compare with the angle of refraction when a light ray leaves glass and enters air?

**5.** State Snell's law.

**6.** Write two equations for finding the index of refraction of a medium. To do this, use two different sets of symbols.

**7.** What is the "critical angle" of incidence?

**8.** Explain the "puddle effect."

**9.** Explain how white light is dispersed by a prism.

**10.** Which travels fastest in glass: red, green, or blue light?

**11.** What type of spectrum is the spectrum of sunlight?

**12.** Why is the lettering on the fronts of some vehicles, such as ambulances, printed in a reverse manner?

**FIGURE 17-15. Use with Question 12.**

ƎƆNA⅃U8MA

## Problems

**1.** A ray of light strikes a mirror at an angle of 53° to the normal.
   **a.** What is the angle of reflection?
   **b.** What is the angle between the incident ray and the reflected ray?

**2.** A ray of light incident upon a mirror makes an angle of 36° with the mirror. What is the angle between the incident ray and the reflected ray?

**3.** In each of the diagrams of Figure 17-16, a ray of light is incident upon the surface of a glass prism. Trace the diagrams on a separate sheet of paper. Extend each ray to show how it travels through the prism and beyond.

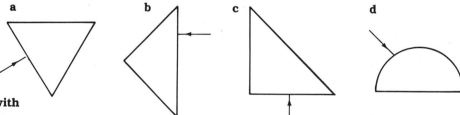

**FIGURE 17-16. Use with Problem 3.**

**4.** A ray of light is incident at an angle of 60° upon the surface of a piece of glass ($n = 1.5$). What is the angle of refraction?

**5.** A light ray strikes the surface of a pond at an angle of incidence of 36°. At what angle, to the nearest degree, is the ray refracted?

**6.** Light is incident at an angle of 60° on the surface of a diamond. Find the angle of refraction.

**7.** A light ray is incident at an angle of 45° on one surface of a 10-cm glass cube ($n_g = 1.5$). At what angle with the normal does the ray emerge from the other side of the cube?

**8.** By what amount is the emergent ray of Problem 7 shifted from the path of the incident ray?

**9.** The speed of light in a clear plastic is $1.90 \times 10^8$ m/s. A ray of light enters the plastic at an angle of 22°. At what angle is the ray refracted?

**1.** *Optical Engineering:* A ray of light is incident upon a 60-60-60 glass prism ($n = 1.5$) as shown in Figure 17-17a.
  **a.** Using Snell's law determine the angle $r$ to the nearest degree.
  **b.** Using elementary geometry determine the value of angles $A$, $B$, and $C$.
  **c.** Angle $C$ is actually the angle of incidence on the other side of the prism. However, the reversability of light rays tells us that if angle $D$ were the incident angle, angle $C$ would be the angle of refraction. Assume this statement is true and determine angle $D$.

**2.** *Optical Effects:* A light source, $S$, is located 2 m below the surface of a swimming pool and 1.5 m from one edge of the pool. The pool is filled with water ($n = 1.33$) to its top.
  **a.** At what angle does the light reaching the edge of the pool leave the water?
  **b.** Does this cause the pool to appear to be deeper or less deep than it actually is? (Note: This problem illustrates the reversability of light rays. If angle $r$ were the angle of incidence, then angle $i$ would be the angle of refraction. Solve the problem by reversing the identity of the two angles.)

**FIGURE 17-17.**

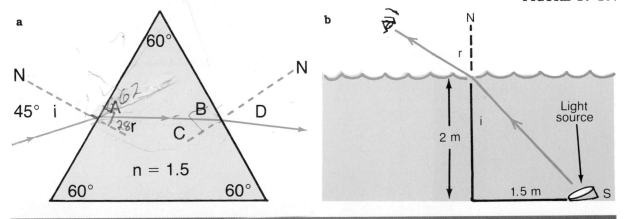

Free, John, "Fiber Optics Start a Communications Revolution." *Popular Science,* May, 1980.
Lyttleton-Smith, David, "Cyberforms." *Omni,* April, 1980.
Margon, Bruce, "The Bizarre Spectrum of SS 433." *Scientific American,* October, 1980.
*Scientific American,* September, 1968. Entire issue deals with light. Several fascinating articles.

Mirrors reflect light. In contrast, lenses transmit light. Mirrors and lenses may be curved or flat, and both produce images. The type of image produced depends on the shape of the mirror or lens. An image may be larger or smaller than the original object. The image may be upright or inverted. This glass of water acts as a lens. What type of image is formed in the glass? How are mirrors and lenses useful to you?

# Mirrors and Lenses 18

We have studied the behavior of light when it is reflected from a surface. We have also studied light as it moves from one medium into another. These properties of reflection and refraction have many practical uses. Mirrored surfaces are based on reflection. Eyeglasses and magnifying glasses are based on refraction. Microscopes and cameras make use of both mirrors and lenses. Let us look at the way in which different mirrors and lenses reflect or transmit light. In this way, we can better understand how they can be put to practical use.

GOAL: You will gain knowledge and understanding of mirrors and lenses of various shapes, and the types of images they form.

## 18:1 Plane Mirrors

The regular reflection of light rays enables us to see the images of objects in mirrors. In Figure 18-1a, object A is illuminated by a light source. A large number of the light rays that fall on object A are reflected in all directions. Thus, object A can be seen from any direction. If some of the rays that leave A fall on a mirror, they will be reflected from the mirror. Since the surface of the mirror is smooth, the rays are reflected in a regular way. Looking at the mirror produces an effect similar to looking at A. Because the directions of the rays are changed as they are reflected from the mirror, the image of A appears to be behind the mirror.

A plane mirror reflects light rays in the same order that they approach it.

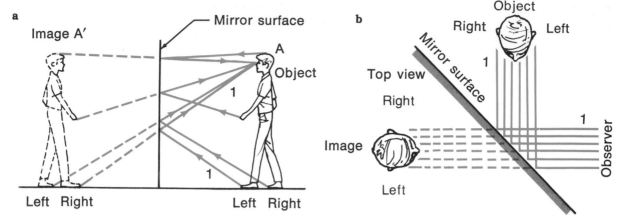

**a**

Image A'

Mirror surface

A

Object

1

1

1

Left  Right

Left  Right

**b**

Object

Right    Left

Mirror surface

Top view

Right

1

Image

Left

1

Observer

**FIGURE 18-1. Formation of an image in a plane mirror. The image is the same size as the object and is the same distance behind the mirror as the object is in front of it. The image is also erect but reversed right for left.**

The image in a plane mirror is reversed left to right.

One interesting effect of mirror-images is the apparent reversal of the image from left to right. In Figure 18-1b an observer looks into the mirror. The right ear of the person is seen as the right ear of the image. However, in facing the same direction as the image the right ear is on the left side of the image.

Suppose an object is located at point *P*, Figure 18-2a. Light rays extend in every direction from point *P*. The rays that strike the mirror at points $M_1$ and $M_2$ are reflected to the eye of an observer. By extending the two reflected rays behind the mirror, point *P'* is located. Triangles *PBM* and *P'BM* are congruent. Point *P'* appears to be as far behind the mirror as point *P* is in front of the mirror. If the same method is used to locate a second point next to *P*, the eye will also interpret that point to be as far

**FIGURE 18-2. Ray diagram for finding an image in a plane mirror is shown in (a). Two rays from the object are traced to the point behind the mirror at which they intersect. Locating an image shows it to be behind the mirror (b).**

**b**

*Courtesy of Kodansha*

**a**

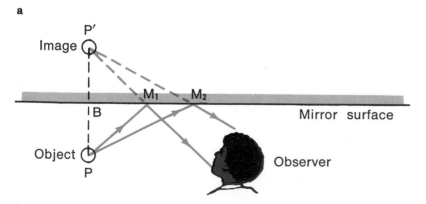

P'

Image

$M_1$    $M_2$

B

Mirror  surface

Object

P

Observer

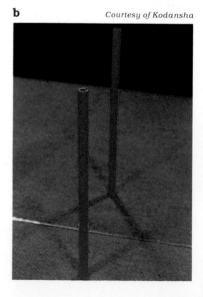

behind the mirror as it is in front of the mirror. Thus, points all along the image appear to have the same relation to each other as do their corresponding points on the object. The image will be the same size as the object.

In summary, the image observed in a plane mirror is the same size as the object. It is as far behind the mirror as the object is in front of the mirror. It also appears to be reversed.

The image is the same size as the object and the same distance behind the mirror as the object is in front of the mirror.

## 18:2   Converging Mirrors

Figure 18-3 represents a spherical concave mirror. Remember, an actual spherical mirror is 3-dimensional. The inside of a spoon is a concave mirror. A spherical mirror has a geometric center or vertex, *A*. A radius perpendicular to a tangent to this point passes back through the center of curvature of the mirror, *C*. This radius is called the **principal axis.**

The principal axis is an imaginary line extending from the geometric center of a spherical mirror to its center of curvature *C*.

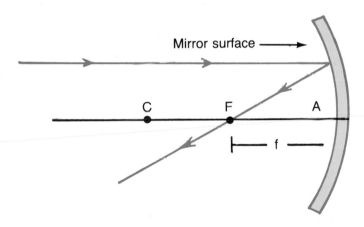

FIGURE 18-3. The focus of a concave spherical mirror is located halfway beween the center of curvature and the center of the mirror surface. Rays reflected by this spherical mirror converge at the focal point.

A spherical concave mirror can be thought of as an infinite number of plane mirrors arranged in a spherical fashion, Figure 18-4. When parallel rays of light are sent to the mirrors, each ray follows the law of reflection. The point where the rays converge or meet is the focal point, *F*, of the mirror. For a spherical mirror, the focal point is located halfway between the center of curvature, *C*, and the vertex, *A*.

It is important to remember two rules concerning concave mirrors.

A concave mirror is a converging mirror.

The focal point *F* of a converging mirror is the point where parallel rays of light meet after being reflected from the mirror.

1. Any light ray approaching the mirror parallel to the principal axis is reflected through the focal point.
2. Any ray that approaches the mirror through the focal point is reflected parallel to the principal axis.

If the principal axis of a small concave mirror is pointed at the sun, all rays that fall on the mirror are parallel to each other and to the principal axis. Rays from the sun travel more than $1.5 \times 10^8$ kilometers to reach the mirror. Any rays leaving the sun that are not parallel to the principal axis would be far from the mirror by the time they travel this distance. In fact, the rays from any distant object that fall on the mirror would be parallel for all practical purposes. Therefore, to determine the focal point, allow light from a fairly distant source to fall on the concave mirror. Move a piece of paper toward and away from the mirror to find the sharpest point of focus. This is the focal point. The distance from the focal point to the vertex of the mirror is the **focal length,** $f$, of the mirror.

The focal length $f$ is the distance from $F$ to $A$.

**FIGURE 18-4. This collection of plane mirrors is an experimental setup being used to concentrate solar energy.**

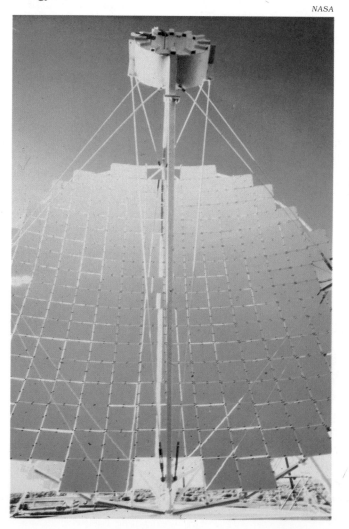

*NASA*

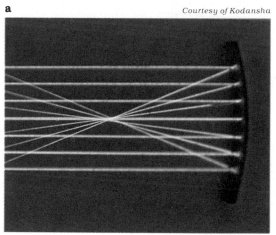

*Courtesy of Kodansha*

**a**

**b**

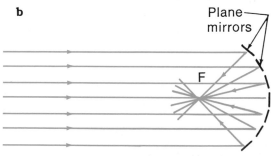

Plane mirrors

F

**FIGURE 18-5. Each ray striking a plane mirror follows the law of reflection (a). If the mirrors are arranged in the proper curve, all the rays intersect at a single point called the focal point (b).**

## 18:3   Spherical Aberration

In a truly spherical mirror, some rays that approach the mirror parallel to the principal axis are not reflected through *F*. Those rays that strike the mirror along its outer edge miss *F* slightly. This effect is called **spherical aberration** (ab uh RAY shuhn). To avoid spherical aberration, parabolic mirrors are used to focus light instead of spherical mirrors.

Spherical aberration occurs because rays that strike a spherical mirror along its outer edge are not reflected through *F*.

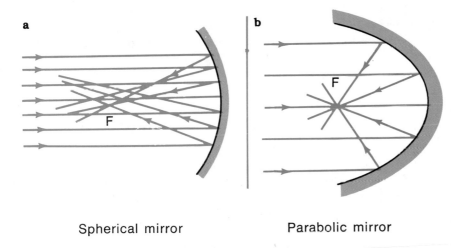

Spherical mirror                    Parabolic mirror

**FIGURE 18-6. In a concave spherical mirror, some rays converge at other points than the focus (a). A parabolic mirror focuses all rays at a sharp point (b).**

A parabolic mirror can be used for cooking. If a cooking pot is placed at the focal point of a large concave mirror, sunlight can be concentrated upon the pot. The intense heat produced can be used to cook food where fuel is scarce. Parabolic mirrors are also used to produce parallel beams of light by flashlights, car headlights, and searchlights. In this case, the light source is placed at *F* and the reflected rays leave the device as a parallel beam.

## 18:4   Real and Virtual Images

The image seen in a plane mirror appears to be behind the mirror. Because light rays do not pass through the image seen in a plane mirror, it cannot be cast upon a screen. Thus, it is called a **virtual image.**

When a concave mirror reflects the sun's rays, the reflected rays meet at the principal focus of the mirror. Thus, they produce an image of the sun at this point. A bright point of light that falls on a piece of paper placed at the principal focus of a concave mirror is a very small image of the sun. This image is actually where it appears to be and can be cast upon a screen. Thus, it is called a **real image.**

An image is virtual when light rays do not pass through it.

An image is real when light rays actually do meet to reproduce the object.

## 18:5   Images Formed by Converging Mirrors

Ray diagrams can be used
to locate images
graphically.

In this section "ray diagrams" will be drawn. The diagrams will show how converging mirrors cause real images to appear outside the mirrors. They will also aid in locating the image.

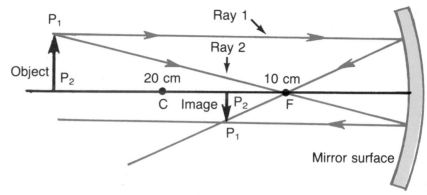

**FIGURE 18-7. Finding the real image formed by a concave spherical mirror when the object is located beyond the center of curvature C of the mirror.**

Figure 18-7 shows how a concave mirror forms an image. Consider an object that is farther from the mirror than C. This object is said to be "beyond C." When light falls on it, light rays are reflected in all directions. Therefore, rays can be drawn from the object to the mirror in any direction.

In a ray diagram, Ray 1 is
drawn parallel to the
principal axis and then is
reflected through F; Ray 2
is drawn through F and
then is reflected parallel
to the principal axis.

To construct a ray diagram, first select a point on the object, $P_1$. Draw two rays from this point to the mirror. Draw ray 1 parallel to the principal axis. Ray 1, therefore, reflects through F. Draw ray 2 so that it passes through F on its way to the mirror. This ray reflects parallel to the principal axis. The two rays from $P_1$ converge beyond F. If two rays are drawn from point $P_2$ in the same way, they meet at point $P_2$ on the image. Other points on the object send out rays that meet at corresponding points forming the image. The object is placed with one end on the principal axis. A ray goes straight to the mirror and straight back. Thus, the bottom of the image is also located on the principal axis.

Figure 18-7 shows an object that is beyond C. The image is between C and F. It is a real image because the rays actually come together to form it at this point. It is also inverted and smaller than the object. Figure 18-7 also shows that when an object is placed in the position of the image, its image is formed in the position of the object. Thus, if the object is between C and F, the image will be beyond C, inverted, real and larger.

As the object is moved in toward C from beyond C, the image position also approaches C. The image and the object meet at C. In this case, the image is inverted, real, and the same size as the object. If the object then is moved between C and F, the image moves out beyond C. Object and image positions are interchangeable, Figure 18-11a, b, c.

Suppose the object distance and the focal length of the mirror are given. The position of the image can then be calculated from the mirror equation.

$$\frac{1}{d_o} + \frac{1}{d_i} = \frac{1}{f}$$

The mirror equation can be used to locate the image.

Here, $d_o$ is the distance from the object to A; $d_i$ is the distance from the image to A; and $f$ is the focal length of the mirror. Also, the ratio of the size of the image and the size of the object equals the ratio of the image distance and the object distance. The ratio of the image size to the object size is called the **magnification** of the mirror.

$$\frac{S_i}{S_o} = \frac{d_i}{d_o}$$

**EXAMPLE: Real Image From a Converging Mirror**

An object 2.0 cm high is 30 cm from a concave mirror. The focal length of the mirror is 10 cm. **a.** What is the location of the image? **b.** What is the size of the image?

*Solution:* **a.** Use the mirror equation to determine the image distance.

$$\frac{1}{d_o} + \frac{1}{d_i} = \frac{1}{f}$$

$$\frac{1}{30 \text{ cm}} + \frac{1}{d_i} = \frac{1}{10 \text{ cm}}$$

$$\frac{1}{d_i} = \frac{1}{10 \text{ cm}} - \frac{1}{30 \text{ cm}}$$

$$= \frac{2.0}{30 \text{ cm}}$$

$$d_i = 15 \text{ cm}$$

**b.**
$$\frac{S_i}{S_o} = \frac{d_i}{d_o}$$

$$S_i = \frac{S_o d_i}{d_o}$$

$$= \frac{(15 \text{ cm})(2.0 \text{ cm})}{30 \text{ cm}} = 1.0 \text{ cm}$$

**PROBLEMS**

*Needed: a compass, a metric ruler, a sharp pencil.*

1. An object is 15 cm from a spherical concave mirror having a 20-cm radius. Locate the image by means of
   **a.** a ray diagram   **b.** the mirror equation

1. a. ray diagram
   b. 30 cm

**2.** Solve the Example in Section 18:5 by constructing a ray diagram. The problem states that the focal length of the mirror is 10 cm. Focal length is always half the radius of curvature, so the radius of the mirror is 20 cm. Draw to scale if necessary.

3. a. ray diagram
   b. 15 cm
   c. 4.5 cm

**3.** An object 3.0 cm high is 10 cm in front of a spherical concave mirror having a 12-cm radius. Locate the image by means of
   **a.** a ray diagram    **b.** the mirror equation
   **c.** What is the height of the image?

**4.** An object 1.5 cm in height is 12 cm from a spherical concave mirror having a 12-cm radius. Locate the image by means of
   **a.** a ray diagram    **b.** the mirror equation
   **c.** What is the height of the image?

5. a. ray diagram
   b. 4 cm
   c. 1 cm

**5.** An object 3.0 cm high is 12 cm from a concave mirror having a 6-cm radius. Locate the image by means of
   **a.** a ray diagram    **b.** the mirror equation
   **c.** What is the height of the image?

**6.** An image of an object is 30 cm from a spherical concave mirror having a 20-cm radius. Locate the object.

7. 60 cm

**7.** An image of an object is 30 cm from a concave mirror having a 20-cm focal length. Locate the object.

## 18:6   Virtual Images in a Converging Mirror

The object in Figure 18-8 is located between *F* and the mirror. It is 5 cm in front of a mirror of 20 cm focal length. To locate the image of the object, construct the same two rays used in previous examples. Ray 1 leaves the object and follows the path it would have followed if it had started at *F*. This ray is reflected parallel to the principal axis. Ray 2 approaches the mirror parallel to the

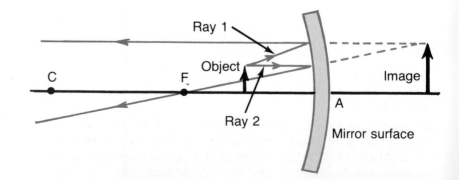

**FIGURE 18-8. Finding the virtual image formed by a concave spherical mirror when the object is located between the mirror and *F*.**

principal axis. It is reflected through the focal point. Note that rays 1 and 2 diverge when reflected. Hence, the rays cannot come together to form a real image. On the other side of the mirror, the rays are traced back to their apparent origin. The image is virtual, erect, and larger than the object.

When an object is placed between the vertex and the focal point of a concave mirror, the result of the mirror equation is a negative image distance. The negative distance means the image is located behind the mirror and is a virtual image.

A negative image distance indicates a virtual image.

**EXAMPLE:  Virtual Image From a Converging Mirror**

Find the location of the image in Figure 18-8 if the object is 5.0 cm in front of a concave mirror of focal length 10 cm.

*Solution:*  $d_o = 5.0$ cm, $f = 10$ cm

$$\frac{1}{d_o} + \frac{1}{d_i} = \frac{1}{f}$$

Solving the equation for $d_i$ yields,

$$d_i = \frac{d_o f}{d_o - f}$$

$$= \frac{(5.0 \text{ cm})(10 \text{ cm})}{5.0 \text{ cm} - 10 \text{ cm}} = \frac{50 \text{ cm}^2}{-5.0 \text{ cm}} = -10 \text{ cm}$$

**PROBLEMS**

 **8.** An object is 4.0 cm in front of a spherical concave mirror of 12-cm radius. Locate the image.

 **9.** An object is 6.0 cm in front of a concave mirror having a focal length of 10 cm. Where is the image?

 9.  $-15$ cm

 **10.** An object is 10 cm from a concave mirror having a focal length of 16 cm. The object is 4.0 cm high.
   **a.** Locate the image.
   **b.** What is the height of the image?

# 18:7  Diverging Mirrors

A **convex mirror** is a spherical mirror which is reflective on its outer surface. For example, the inside of a spoon is a concave mirror. The outside of the spoon is a convex mirror. Convex mirrors cause rays to spread out or diverge. Thus, convex mirrors never form real images. The focal point, $F$, of a convex mirror is behind the mirror. The focal length, $f$, of a convex mirror is negative.

A convex mirror is a diverging mirror.

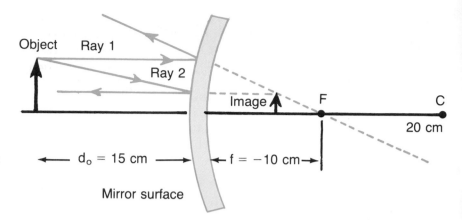

**FIGURE 18-9. Convex spherical mirrors cause reflected light rays to diverge.**

Images formed by diverging mirrors are always virtual, erect, and smaller than the object.

The image seen in a convex mirror is always virtual, behind the mirror, erect, and smaller than the object. Figure 18-9 shows how a convex mirror forms a virtual image. Follow the paths of the two principal rays. Ray 1 approaches the mirror parallel to the principal axis and is reflected. The path of the reflected ray, extended behind the mirror (dotted line), passes through *F*. Ray 2 approaches the mirror on a path that, if extended behind the mirror, would pass through *F*. Ray 2's reflected ray is parallel to the principal axis. The two reflected rays when traced back to their point of apparent intersection behind the mirror indicate an erect, smaller, virtual image.

Divergent mirrors are used when a large field of view is needed. Rear-view mirrors on vehicles and mirrors used in stores to watch for shoplifters are some uses.

*Philip M. Jordain*

**FIGURE 18-10. Diverging mirrors are used to show a large field of view.**

**a**

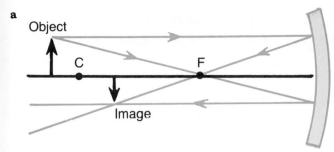

Object beyond C. Image is between C and F, inverted, real, and smaller than the object.

**b**

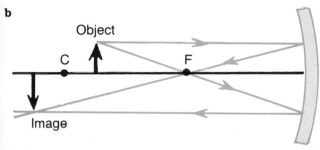

Object is between C and F. Image is beyond C, inverted, real, and larger than the object.

**c**

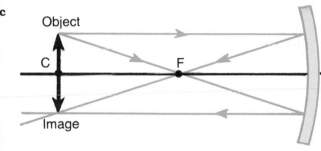

Object is at C. Image is at C, inverted, real, and the same size as the object.

**d**

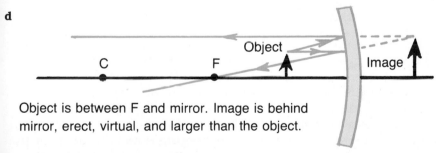

Object is between F and mirror. Image is behind mirror, erect, virtual, and larger than the object.

**e**

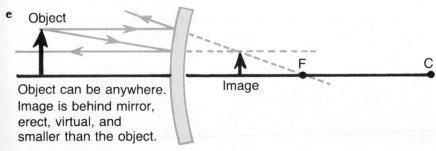

Object can be anywhere. Image is behind mirror, erect, virtual, and smaller than the object.

**FIGURE 18-11. Formation of images in curved mirrors.**

**EXAMPLE: Image From a Diverging Mirror**

Calculate the position of the image in Figure 18-9. Use the mirror equation.

*Solution:*    $d_o = 15$ cm, $f = -10$ cm

$$\frac{1}{d_o} + \frac{1}{d_i} = \frac{1}{f}$$

$$d_i = \frac{d_o f}{d_o - f}$$

$$= \frac{(15 \text{ cm})(-10 \text{ cm})}{15 \text{ cm} - (-10 \text{ cm})}$$

$$= \frac{-150 \text{ cm}^2}{25 \text{ cm}} = -6.0 \text{ cm}$$

**PROBLEMS**

11. −8.6 cm

**11.** An object is 20 cm in front of a convex mirror with a −15-cm focal length. Locate the image.

**12.** A convex mirror has a focal length of −12 cm. An object is placed 60 cm in front of the mirror. Locate the image.

13. −38 cm

**13.** A mirror used to watch for shoplifters in a department store has a focal length of −40 cm. A person stands in an aisle 6.0 m from the mirror. Locate the person's image.

**14.** Shiny lawn spheres placed on pedestals are convex mirrors. One such sphere has a focal length of −20 cm. A robin sits in a tree 10 m from the sphere. Locate the robin's image.

# 18:8 Lenses

Lenses are an essential part of telescopes, eyeglasses, cameras, microscopes, and other optical instruments. A lens is usually made of glass, although some are made of transparent plastic. Many precision optical instruments use quartz lenses.

The two main types of lenses are converging lenses and diverging lenses. A **converging lens** is thickest at its middle and becomes thinner at the edges. A **diverging lens** is thinnest at its middle and becomes thicker at the edges, Figure 18-12. Converging lenses are often called **convex lenses.** Likewise, diverging lenses are often called **concave lenses** because their surfaces

A converging lens is thick in the center and thin at the edges.

A diverging lens is thin in the center and thick at the edges.

A convex lens is a converging lens. A concave lens is a diverging lens.

**FIGURE 18-12. Ray diagrams for the path of light through a converging lens (a) and diverging lens (b).**

a
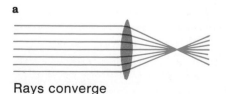
Rays converge

b
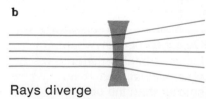
Rays diverge

are concave. A converging lens refracts light rays so they meet. A diverging lens refracts light rays so they spread out.

## 18:9  Converging Lenses

The principal axis of a lens is a line perpendicular to the plane of the lens through the midpoint. Light rays that approach a converging lens parallel to the principal axis will, upon refraction, converge at a point. This point is called the focal point, $F$, of the converging lens. The distance from the focal point to the lens is the focal length, $f$. Symmetrical lenses, such as the one in Figure 18-13, have a focal point on each side of the lens. The focal length of a converging lens depends on two factors. These are the shape of the lens and the index of refraction of the lens material.

**The focal point of a converging lens is the point where rays that approach the lens parallel to the principal axis meet after being refracted by the lens.**

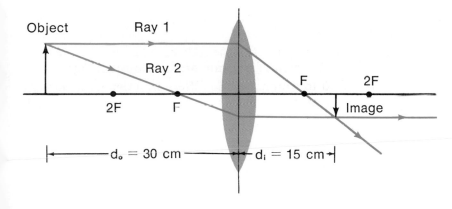

**FIGURE 18-13. Finding the real images formed by a converging lens when the object is located beyond the principal focus $F$ of the mirror.**

An important position along the principal axis of a lens is twice the focal length, $2F$. An object is placed at a distance greater than $2F$ in Figure 18-13. Two rays are drawn to locate the image. Ray 1 is parallel to the principal axis. It refracts and passes through $F$ on the other side of the lens. Ray 2 passes through $F$ on its way to the lens. It leaves the lens parallel to the principal axis. The two rays converge between $F$ and $2F$. The point where the rays converge is the image location. Rays selected at other points on the object would converge at corresponding points on the image. The image is real, inverted, and smaller than the object.

**The focal length of a lens depends on its shape and its index of refraction.**

Suppose an object is placed at the image position. The image appears at the original position of the object because light rays are reversible. Thus, if the object is located between $F$ and $2F$, the image would appear beyond $2F$ on the other side of the lens. The image would be real, inverted, and larger than the object.

If an object is placed at $2F$, the image appears at $2F$ on the other side of the lens. It is real, inverted, and the same size as the object.

**FIGURE 18-14. If an object is located at a distance greater than 2F, the image in the lens appears inverted.**

The lens equations can be used to find the size and location of an image.

A straight line can be drawn to represent a lens when making ray diagrams for lens problems. To find the size and location of the image mathematically, use these lens equations.

$$\frac{1}{d_o} + \frac{1}{d_i} = \frac{1}{f}$$

$$\frac{S_o}{S_i} = \frac{d_o}{d_i}$$

The lens equations are exactly the same as the mirror equations.

Note that these equations are the same as those used with mirrors. The equations are derived in Section 18:12, page 311.

**EXAMPLE: Real Image From a Converging Lens**

In Figure 18-13, the object is 30 cm from a converging lens of 10-cm focal length. Use the lens equation to locate the image.

*Solution:*

$$\frac{1}{d_o} + \frac{1}{d_i} = \frac{1}{f}$$

$$d_i = \frac{d_o f}{d_o - f}$$

$$= \frac{(30 \text{ cm})(10 \text{ cm})}{30 \text{ cm} - 10 \text{ cm}}$$

$$= 15 \text{ cm}$$

*Craig Kramer*

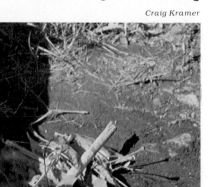

**FIGURE 18-15.** This camper is using a converging lens to start a fire in this pile of leaves.

## PROBLEMS

**15.** Use a ray diagram to find the image position of an object 30 cm from a convex lens with 10-cm focal length. (Let 1 cm equal 2 cm.)

**16.** An object 1.0 cm high is 15 cm from a convex lens of 10 cm focal length. Find the distance and size of the image
**a.** using a ray diagram   **b.** mathematically

**17.** An object 3.0 cm high is 10 cm in front of a convex lens of 6.0 cm focal length. Find the image distance and height.

**18.** An object 1.5 cm high is 12 cm from a convex lens of 6.0 cm focal length. Find the height and position of the image
**a.** using a ray diagram   **b.** mathematically

**19.** An object 3.0 cm high is 12 cm from a convex lens of 3.0 cm focal length. Locate the image.

**20.** An image is 12 cm from a convex lens of 4.0 cm focal length. Locate the object.

**21.** A camera lens having a focal length of 8.0 cm is 10.0 cm from the film. What distance from the lens should a flower be placed to obtain a sharp photograph?

15. ray diagram

17. 15 cm, 4.5 cm

19. 4 cm

21. 40 cm

## 18:10   Virtual Images Formed by a Converging Lens

If an object is placed between a converging lens and its focal point, the rays do not meet on the other side of the lens. Instead, the image appears on the same side of the lens as the object. As Figure 18-16 shows, the image is erect, larger, and virtual.

If an object is placed between a converging lens and its focal point, a virtual, enlarged image is produced.

To understand how a converging lens forms a virtual image, look at Figure 18-16. The object is between $F$ and the lens. Ray 1 is drawn from the tip of the object to the lens. It follows the same path it would have followed if it had started at $F$. Therefore, ray 1 is refracted in a way that it leaves the lens parallel to the principal axis. Ray 2 is drawn parallel to the principal axis. When refracted, ray 2 travels through the focal point on the other side of the lens. Note that when rays 1 and 2 leave the other side of the lens they diverge. Therefore, they cannot join to form a real image. However, if the two rays are traced back to their apparent origin, a larger virtual image is seen on the same side of the lens as the object. This image is magnified. A convex lens used in this way is a magnifier.

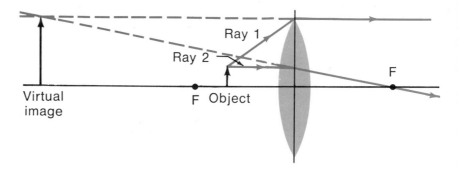

**FIGURE 18-16. Finding the virtual image formed by a converging lens when the object is placed between the lens and the principal focus $F$.**

**EXAMPLE:  Virtual Image From a Converging Lens**

An object is 4.0 cm from a converging lens of 6.0 cm focal length. **a.** Locate its image. **b.** What kind of image is formed?

*Solution:* **a.** Solve the lens equation for $d_i$. Then substitute the values above.

$$d_i = \frac{d_o f}{d_o - f} = \frac{(4.0 \text{ cm})(6.0 \text{ cm})}{4.0 \text{ cm} - 6.0 \text{ cm}} = -12 \text{ cm}$$

**b.** Since the image distance is negative, the image is virtual. It is on the same side of the lens as the object.

**PROBLEMS**

**22.** The focal length of a convex lens is 20 cm. A newspaper is 6.0 cm from the lens. Find the image distance.

23. a. −6 cm
    b. 3 cm

**23.** A magnifying glass has a focal length of 12 cm. An object is placed 4.0 cm from the lens. The object is 2.0 cm high.
   **a.** Locate the image.     **b.** How high is the image?

**24.** An object is 8.0 cm from a lens. What focal length must the lens have to form a virtual, erect image 16 cm from the lens?

## 18:11 Diverging Lenses

All images seen through diverging lenses are virtual and erect. Figure 18-17 shows how a concave lens forms these images. Ray 1 approaches the lens parallel to the principal axis. Upon refraction, ray 1 appears to originate at the focal point. Ray 2 passes through the center of the lens. Ray 2 is refracted as it enters the lens. It is refracted again as it leaves the lens. The two refractions cancel and ray 2, in effect, passes straight through the lens. Notice that the two rays are divergent and appear to originate at *i*.

**Images formed by diverging lenses are always virtual and erect.**

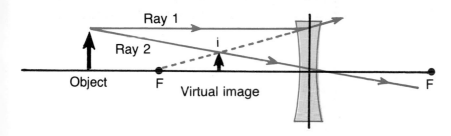

**FIGURE 18-17. Formation of a virtual image by a diverging lens.**

## 18:12 Derivation of the Lens Equation

We can mathematically derive the expression for the lens equation using Figure 18-18. Triangles *APO* and *DGO* are similar triangles. For similar triangles, the ratios of corresponding sides are equal.

$$\frac{S_o}{S_i} = \frac{AP}{DG} = \frac{OP}{OG} = \frac{d_o}{d_i} \quad \text{and} \quad \frac{S_o}{S_i} = \frac{d_o}{d_i}$$

Also, triangles *FGD* and *FOB* are similar. Thus,

$$\frac{OF}{GF} = \frac{BO}{DG} = \frac{d_o}{d_i} \quad \text{so,} \quad \frac{OF}{GF} = \frac{d_o}{d_i}$$

Since $OF = f$ and $OG = d_i$, the length of $GF$ can be found by

$$GF = d_i - f$$

Substituting $f$ for $OF$ and $d_i - f$ for $GF$ yields

$$\frac{OF}{GF} = \frac{f}{d_i - f} = \frac{d_o}{d_i} \qquad fd_i + fd_o = d_i d_o$$

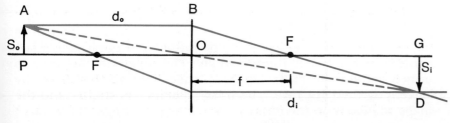

**FIGURE 18-18. Diagram for derivation of lens equation.**

Dividing both sides of the equation by $fd_id_o$ gives the lens equation.

$$\frac{1}{d_o} + \frac{1}{d_i} = \frac{1}{f}$$

## 18:13   Chromatic Aberration

Light is refracted when it falls on a lens. Upon passing through a medium, such as glass, different wavelengths of light refract at slightly different angles. Thus, the light that passes through a lens is slightly dispersed. Any object observed through a lens appears ringed with color. This effect is called chromatic aberration. **Chromatic aberration** is one factor that limits the sharpness of an image on the film of a camera.

**Chromatic aberration limits the sharpness of an image.**

**Newton invented the reflecting telescope because of this lens defect.**

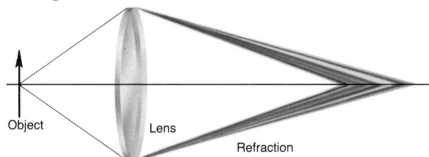

**FIGURE 18-19. Chromatic aberration occurs when light passing through a lens is dispersed. An object appears ringed with color.**

The chromatic aberration of a lens cannot be eliminated, but it can be corrected. The lens can be coated with a material having a different index of refraction from the lens. The new material disperses light but in an opposite way from the lens. The dispersion caused by the lens is cancelled. A lens prepared in this way is called an **achromatic lens.**

## 18:14   Optical Devices

**Corrective glasses, microscopes, and telescopes are important uses of lenses.**

For normal vision, the lens of the eye must focus the image of an object on the retina. If the shape of the lens of the eye is distorted, external lenses, eyeglasses, are needed to adjust the image distance. The adjustment allows the image to focus on the retina. The eye lens of a nearsighted person is too thick. Thus, images are formed in front of the retina. Concave lenses correct this defect by diverging the light rays so that the image distance is greater. The image will focus on the retina. The eye lens of a farsighted person is not thick enough. The image in this case is formed behind the retina. Convex lenses correct this defect by converging the light rays. The image distance is shorter and the image will focus on the retina.

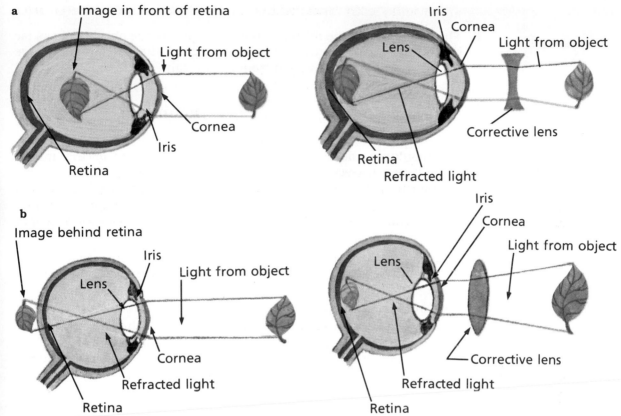

**a** Image in front of retina · Light from object · Cornea · Iris · Retina

Iris · Cornea · Lens · Light from object · Corrective lens · Retina · Refracted light

**b** Image behind retina · Iris · Lens · Light from object · Cornea · Refracted light · Retina

Iris · Cornea · Lens · Light from object · Corrective lens · Refracted light · Retina

Most microscopes use two converging lenses. An object is placed close to the lower lens, called the objective lens. This lens produces a real image. The real image is located between the second lens called the eyepiece and its focal point. The eyepiece produces a greatly magnified virtual image of the real image.

A simple refracting telescope also uses two converging lenses. However, the objective lens of a telescope has a longer focal length. The objective lens of a telescope forms a real, inverted image of a star or other distant object. As in the microscope, the image is located between the focal point of the eyepiece and the eyepiece itself. The viewer sees an enlarged, virtual, and inverted image.

**FIGURE 18-20. A far-sighted person cannot see close objects. The image is focused behind the retina. A concave lens corrects the problem by refracting light to focus the image on the retina (a). A nearsighted person cannot see distant objects. The image is focused in front of the retina. A convex lens can correct this defect (b).**

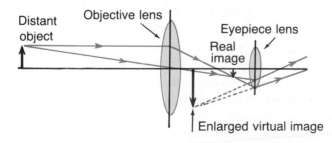

Distant object · Objective lens · Eyepiece lens · Real image · Enlarged virtual image

**FIGURE 18-21. The lens system of a refracting telescope has two converging lenses.**

**Summary**

1. The image in a plane mirror is the same size as the object. It is as far behind the mirror as the object is in front of the mirror. The image is virtual, erect, and reversed from left to right.   18:1

2. The focal point of a spherical mirror is halfway between the center of curvature of the mirror and the center of the mirror.   18:2

3. The distance from the focal point to the center of the mirror is the focal length of the mirror.   18:2

4. An imaginary radius that passes from the center of the mirror through the center of curvature and beyond is called the principal axis of the mirror.   18:2

5. Truly spherical mirrors have an inherent defect called spherical aberration. Light rays that fall on the outer edges of the mirror do not pass through the focal point of the mirror.   18:3

6. A virtual image is not located where it appears and cannot be cast upon a screen. A real image is located where it appears and can be cast upon a screen.   18:6

7. All virtual images are erect. All real images are inverted.   18:5, 18:6

8. Concave mirrors produce real, inverted images if the object is farther from the mirror than the focal point. If the object is between the focal point and the mirror, an enlarged, virtual image is formed behind the mirror.   18:6

9. Convex mirrors always produce virtual images.   18:7

10. Lenses that are thinner at their outer edges than at their centers are called converging or convex lenses. Lenses which are thicker at their outer edges are diverging or concave lenses.   18:8, 18:9, 18:10, 18:11

11. Chromatic aberration is a lens defect caused by the dispersion of the different wavelengths of light as they pass through the lens.   18:13

12. The location of an image can be determined by using the lens or mirror equation as the case may be. The equation is the same in either case.   18:5, 18:9, 18:12

**Questions**

1. Describe the image of a person seen in a plane mirror.

2. An object is located beyond the center of curvature of a spherical concave mirror. Locate and describe the image of the object.

3. Locate and describe the image produced by a concave mirror when the object is located at the center of curvature.

4. An object is located between the center of curvature and the principal focus of a concave mirror. Locate and describe the image of the object.

5. How does a virtual image differ from a real image?

6. An object produces a virtual image in a concave mirror. Where is the object located?

7. Describe the image seen in a convex mirror.

8. Describe the properties of a virtual image.

9. What factor, other than the curvature of a lens, determines the location of its focal point?

10. Locate and describe the image produced by a convex lens if an object is placed some distance beyond $2F$.

11. What causes an inherent defect of a concave spherical mirror?

12. What causes an inherent defect of lenses?

13. To project an image from a movie camera onto a screen, the film is placed between $F$ and $2F$ of a converging lens. This arrangement produces an inverted image. Why do the actors appear to be erect when the film is viewed?

14. Convex mirrors are used on the front of school buses. Why are these mirrors used?

## Problems

1. An object is 20 cm from a spherical concave mirror of 8.0 cm focal length (16 cm radius). Locate the image
   a. using a ray diagram   b. mathematically

2. An object 3.0 cm high is placed 25 cm from a concave mirror of 15 cm focal length. Find the location and height of the image
   a. using a ray diagram   b. mathematically

3. An object is 30 cm from a concave mirror of 15 cm focal length. The object is 1.8 cm high.
   a. Locate the image.   b. How high is the image?

4. A jeweler inspects a watch of diameter 3.0 cm by placing it 8.0 cm in front of a concave mirror of 12.0 cm focal length.
   a. Where will the image of the watch appear?
   b. What will be the diameter of the image?

5. A convex mirror has a focal length of $-16$ cm. How far behind the mirror does the image of a person 3.0 m away appear?

6. An object is 8.0 cm in front of a concave mirror having a focal length of 30 cm. Locate the image.

7. How far behind the surface of a convex mirror of $-6.0$ cm focal length does an object 10 m from the mirror appear?

8. The convex lens of a copy machine has a focal length of 25.0 cm. A letter to be copied is placed 40.0 cm from the lens.
   a. How far from the lens is the copy paper located?
   b. The machine was adjusted to give an enlarged copy of the letter. How much larger will the copy be?

9. An object is 40 cm from a convex lens of 10 cm focal length.
   **a.** Find the position of the image using a ray diagram.
   **b.** Find the image position mathematically.
   **c.** The object is 3.0 cm high. How high is the image?

10. An object is 25 cm from a convex lens having a focal length of 12.5 cm. Locate the image.

11. To develop a sharp image on a screen, the convex lens of the projector is moved until the film is 21 cm from the lens. The focal length of the lens is 20 cm.
    **a.** How far is the screen from the lens?
    **b.** How many times larger is the image on the screen than the picture on the film?

---

**Applying Physics**

1. *Optical Systems:* A microscope slide of an onion cell is placed 12 mm from the objective lens of a microscope. The focal length of the objective lens is 10.0 mm.
   **a.** How far from the lens is the image formed?
   **b.** What is the magnification of this image?
   **c.** The real image thus formed is located 10.0 mm beneath the eyepiece lens of the microscope. If the focal length of the eyepiece is 20 mm, where does the final image appear?
   **d.** What is the final magnification of this compound system?

2. *Optics in Medicine:* A dentist uses a small mirror of radius 40 mm to locate a cavity in a patient's tooth. If the mirror is concave and is held 16 mm from the tooth, what is the magnification of the resulting image?

3. Camera lenses are described in terms of their focal length. A 50 mm lens has a focal length of 50 mm.
   **a.** A camera is focused on an object 3 m away using a 50 mm lens. Locate the position of the image.
   **b.** A 1000 mm lens is focused on an object 125 m away. Locate the position of the image.

**FIGURE 18-22. Comparing the focal lengths of two lenses. Note the difference in the size of the image for each lens. Use with Applying Physics 3.**

a    Focal length 25 mm

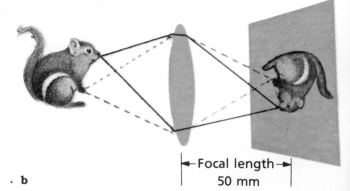

· b    |←Focal length→|
       50 mm

**4.** The 50 mm lens in Problem 3 is focused on a dog 0.5 m high. What is the size of the image?

**5.** A 1000 mm lens is used to focus on a football that is 75 m away. The length of the football is 28 cm. What is the position and length of the image?

**Readings**

Berman, Arthur, "Word From a Lonely Planet." *Science Digest,* July, 1980.
Edelhart, Mike, "New Sun." *Omni,* April, 1980.
Mullaney, James, "Binoculars in Astronomy." *Science Digest,* April, 1980.
Stepler, Richard, "Solar Collector Converter." *Popular Science,* June, 1980.

Light has the same property as water waves in that it bends around the edges of a barrier. This photograph was taken with a special diffraction filter. Its surface contains many cross-hatched lines. Light passing through the filter bends around the edges of these lines to produce the star effects shown. Diffracted and refracted light can be separated to form spectra. How does diffraction differ from refraction?

# Diffraction of Light 19

We have learned that light travels in straight lines. In most cases, this appears to be so. When light passes through a large opening, the shadow that is cast looks quite sharp. However, when light passes through a small opening, the edges of the shadow cast look blurred. This blurring effect can be understood if we think of light as bending around barriers. The bending of light as it passes the edge of a barrier is called diffraction. Diffraction can be explained in terms of the wave nature of light.

## 19:1 Diffraction and Interference

Light waves are diffracted as they pass through narrow slits. Figure 19-1 shows the arrangement used by Thomas Young to show the diffraction of light waves. Young placed a barrier with a single slit in front of a light source. Any wave that falls on a narrow slit is diffracted. Another barrier with two narrow slits was placed between the first barrier and a screen. The single slit acts as a source of new uniform waves that strike the double slit at the same time. The double slit acts as two sources of new waves. The two waves interfere constructively at points where crests overlap. They interfere destructively where a crest and a trough meet. In Figure 19-1, the semicircles represent wave crests moving outward from the sources. Midway between the crests are the troughs.

GOAL: You will gain knowledge and understanding of the interference and diffraction of light waves, and of the methods used to measure wavelength.

Diffraction occurs when light bends around the edges of a barrier.

An interference pattern is set up when light falls on two narrow slits that are close together.

**319**

Antinodal lines pass
through points where
waves interfere con-
structively.

Nodal lines pass through
points where waves
interfere destructively.

The solid lines in the diagram pass through points of constructive interference (crests meet crests). These lines are called antinodal lines. At points where the antinodal lines fall on the screen, bright bars of light appear. Note that a bright spot of light appears on the screen directly opposite the midpoint between the two slits. On both sides of this central bright spot are other spots of light. These spots correspond to the other antinodal lines.

The dotted lines in Figure 19-1 pass through points of destructive interference. These lines are called nodal lines. The nodal lines trace paths where the light waves cancel each other and light is, in effect, absent. Dark spots appear at the points where nodal lines fall on the screen.

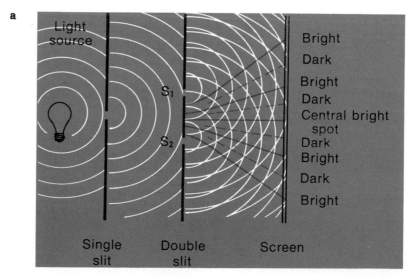

*Courtesy of Kodansha*

**FIGURE 19-1. Formation of a diffraction pattern from an incandescent light source (a). The single slit acts as a source of uniform waves. The double slit produces the interference pattern in (b).**

When white light passes
through a double-slit, a
continuous spectrum is
produced.

Every wavelength of light
gives its own interference
pattern, independent of
any others that may be
forming.

When white light is used as the source for a double-slit diffraction pattern, the light is dispersed into a continuous spectrum, Figure 19-1b. A white light source emits several hundred thousand wavelengths at the same time. Thus, many wavelengths approach the slits together. However, one of the basic rules of wave behavior is that waves can pass through each other without changing one another. Each wavelength of light produces its own interference pattern. This pattern is not affected by the other patterns around it.

Each wavelength produces a bright line at the center of the pattern. The addition of all wavelengths at the central bright line produces a line of white light. On both sides of the central bright line, the bright lines for each color do not fall in exactly the same place. Each wavelength produces a pattern that is slightly different from that of the other wavelengths. Thus, white light is separated into a continuous spectrum of colors on each side of the central bright line.

## 19:2 Measuring the Wavelength of a Light Wave

An interference pattern can be used to measure the wavelength of light waves. In Figure 19-1, the pattern produced by only one of the wavelengths from a light source is shown. Choose an antinodal line other than the central line. Select any point along one of these lines where two crests meet. Count the wavelengths back to $S_1$. Then from the same point, count the wavelengths back to $S_2$. The difference is always a whole number of wavelengths. For the first antinodal line to both the right and the left of the central line, the path difference is one wavelength. For the second antinodal line, the path difference is two wavelengths. For the third line, the difference is three wavelengths, and so on. Any point on an antinodal line is always a whole number of wavelengths farther from one slit than the other. Thus, waves arrive at that point in phase and reinforce each other.

Along the first antinodal line, the path difference is always one wavelength. Thus, the distance to the first bright line where this wavelength falls on the screen, *P*, is just one wavelength farther from $S_1$ than from $S_2$. This situation is shown in Figure 19-2.

From the use of interference patterns, wavelengths of light can be determined.

In double-slit interference, each point on a line of reinforcement is a whole number of wavelengths farther from one slit than from the other.

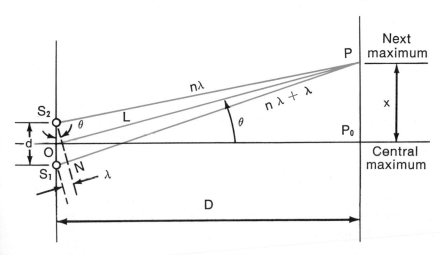

**FIGURE 19-2. Schematic diagram for analysis of double-slit interference.**

First-order lines appear to both sides of the central bright line. They are located one wavelength farther from one slit than from the other.

Here, $P_o$ is the central bright line. $P$ is the point where the first bright line of light appears on the screen. $L$ is the distance from the center of the two slits to $P$, and $x$ is the distance from the central bright line to $P$.

During an actual trial, a group of bright lines appears on the screen at $P$. Each of these represents one wavelength of light emitted by the source. These lines are called first-order lines. **First-order lines** can be seen both to the right and to the left of the central bright line. Some distance away, a second group of lines can be found. These lines are called **second-order lines.**

The distance between the two slits is marked $d$ in Figure 19-2. The distance from the central line to any bright line of reinforcement on the screen is $x$. The distance from $S_1$ to $P$ is one wavelength longer than the distance from $S_2$ to $P$. Thus, in right triangle $S_1NS_2$, the side $S_1N$ equals the wavelength, $\lambda$. This triangle is similar to triangle $PP_oO$. These triangles are similar because the sizes of their angles are equal. Therefore, the ratios of corresponding sides of these similar triangles are the same.

$$\frac{x}{L} = \frac{\lambda}{d}$$

Solving this equation for $\lambda$, we obtain the equation

$$\lambda = \frac{xd}{L}$$

By using interference patterns, the wavelengths of light waves can be measured with considerable precision. It is not unusual for wavelength measurements to be precise to six digits. In addition to wavelengths, the speed of light is also known. Frequencies of light waves are then calculated by using the relationship

$$c = f\lambda$$

### EXAMPLE:  Wavelength of Light

Red light falls on two small slits $1.9 \times 10^{-4}$ cm apart. A first-order line appears 22.1 cm to the left of the central bright line on a screen opposite the slits. The distance from the center of the slits to the first-order line is 60.0 cm. What is the wavelength of the red light?

*Solution:* Use Figure 19-2 as a model to assign the values given in the problem. The distance between slits, $d = 1.9 \times 10^{-4}$ cm. The distance between lines $x = 22.1$ cm. The length $L = 60.0$ cm.

$$\lambda = \frac{xd}{L}$$
$$= \frac{(22.1 \text{ cm})(1.9 \times 10^{-4} \text{ cm})}{(60 \text{ cm})}$$
$$= 7.0 \times 10^{-5} \text{ cm}$$

**PROBLEMS**

1. Violet light falls on two small slits $1.9 \times 10^{-4}$ cm apart. A first-order line appears 13.2 cm from the central bright spot on a screen opposite the slits. The distance from the center of the slits to the first-order violet line is 60 cm. What is the wavelength of the violet light?

2. Yellow light of wavelength $6.0 \times 10^{-5}$ cm is used instead of the violet light of Problem 1. The distance from the center of the slits to the first-order line for the yellow light is measured and found to be 58.0 cm. How far from the central bright spot on the screen is the first-order yellow line?

3. Green light falls on a pair of slits $1.9 \times 10^{-4}$ cm apart. A first-order line appears 28.4 cm to the left of the central bright line. The distance between the center of the slits and the first-order line is 100 cm. What is the wavelength of the light?

4. Blue light falls on a pair of slits 0.02 cm apart. A first-order line appears 0.184 cm from the central bright line on a screen opposite the slits. The distance from the midpoint between the slits to the first-order line is 80.0 cm. What is the wavelength of the blue light?

5. When the screen of a two-slit arrangement is replaced with a photographic plate, electromagnetic waves outside the visible region can be detected. An ultraviolet source produces a line on the film 0.072 cm from the central bright line. The slits are 0.02 cm apart and arranged so that the midpoint between them is 40.0 cm from the line appearing on the plate. What is the wavelength of the ultraviolet light?

1. $4.2 \times 10^{-5}$ cm

3. $5.4 \times 10^{-5}$ cm

5. $3.6 \times 10^{-5}$ cm

# 19:3   Single-Slit Diffraction

When a light passes through one narrow slit, a diffraction pattern appears on a distant screen. This single-slit diffraction pattern differs from the double-slit pattern. The spacing between the bright lines lacks the regularity found in a double-slit diffraction pattern. Also, the central bright band is much larger and brighter than when two slits are used.

To observe single-slit diffraction, fold a small piece of paper and make a cut along its folded edge with a pair of scissors. Unfold the paper and peer through the slit at a light source. You will see a diffraction pattern. You can vary the width of the slit by pulling on the opposite edges of the paper. Observe the effect of the change in slit width on the diffraction pattern.

A diffraction pattern results when light passes through a single narrow slit.

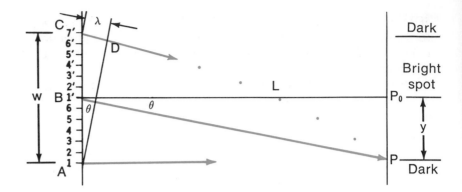

**FIGURE 19-3. Schematic diagram for analysis of single-slit diffraction.**

Monochromatic light is light of one wavelength.

Figure 19-3 shows how a single slit can cause a diffraction pattern. Here, monochromatic (mahn uh kroh MAT ik) light falls on a slit. **Monochromatic light** is light of only one wavelength. Because the slit is very narrow, all points of the wave along the slit are in phase. The diffraction pattern falls on a screen placed some distance from the slit. $P_o$ is the wide central bright band on the screen. $P$ is a dark band. $L$ is the distance from the center of the slit to $P_o$ and $w$ is the slit width. $L$ is so much larger than $w$ that all rays falling on $w$ are, in effect, the same distance from $P_o$. It follows that the band at point $P_o$ is very bright because all waves arriving at that point from $w$ are in phase. Point $P$, however, is exactly one wavelength farther from point 7′ on the slit than it is from point 1 on the slit. Therefore, point $P$ is one-half wavelength farther from point 1′ than it is from point 1. Hence, waves from points 1 and 1′ arrive 180° out of phase at point $P$ and cancel. The same is true for points 2 and 2′, points 3 and 3′, and so on down the slit. Therefore, no light is observed at point $P$. In our example, we used only six points along the slit. In reality, there are an infinite number of points acting in this way.

In Figure 19-3, triangles $ADC$ and $BP_oP$ are similar. Because $L$ is so large when compared to $w$, you can approximate the corresponding sides of similar triangles. That is, $BP$ and $L$ are very nearly equal. Thus, in the equation showing the equality between ratios of corresponding sides of the similar triangles,

$$\frac{BP}{y} = \frac{w}{\lambda}$$

We can substitute $L$ for $BP$ so that

$$\frac{L}{y} = \frac{w}{\lambda}$$

Solving for $\lambda$, we obtain the equation

$$\lambda = \frac{yw}{L}$$

If $w$ is very small, the bright central band will be large. If $w$ is one wavelength, then $\lambda/w = 1$. In the language of trigonometry, $\sin \theta = 1$, *and* $\theta$ is 90°. The bright band will then spread over 180° and no dark lines will be observed on the screen.

With other slit widths, second-order dark bands will appear on the screen below the point $P$. In keeping with our explanation of the first-order dark bands, second-order bands appear where angle $\theta$ is large enough to cause $CD$ to equal $2\lambda$. When $CD$ is equal to $3\lambda$ or some other multiple of $\lambda$, another dark band will appear.

a

*Courtesy of Kodansha*

b

c

**FIGURE 19-4. These diffraction patterns for (a) red light, (b) blue light, and (c) white light were produced with a slit of width 0.02 cm.**

**EXAMPLE: Single-Slit Diffraction**

Monochromatic orange light falls upon a single slit of width $1.0 \times 10^{-2}$ cm. The slit is located 100 cm from a screen. If a first-order dark band is observed 0.6 cm from the center of the central bright band, what is the wavelength of the orange light?

*Solution:*
$$\lambda = \frac{yw}{L}$$
$$= \frac{(6.0 \times 10^{-1} \text{ cm})(1.0 \times 10^{-2} \text{ cm})}{1 \times 10^{2} \text{ cm}}$$
$$= 6.0 \times 10^{-5} \text{ cm}$$

**PROBLEMS**

**6.** Monochromatic green light falls on a slit 0.01 cm wide and produces a first-order dark band 0.55 cm from the center of the central bright band on a screen 100 cm away. Find the wavelength of the green light.

7. 0.21 cm

7. Violet light of wavelength $4.0 \times 10^{-5}$ cm falls on a slit 0.015 cm wide. The screen is located 80 cm from the slit. How far from the central band will the first-order dark band appear?

8. Yellow light from a sodium vapor lamp falls upon a single slit 0.0295 cm wide. A screen 60 cm away reveals a first-order dark band located 0.120 cm from the center of the bright central band. What is the wavelength of the yellow light?

9. 0.012 cm

9. Light of wavelength $4.8 \times 10^{-5}$ cm passes through a single slit and falls on a screen 120 cm away. What is the width of the slit if the center of the first-order dark band is 0.5 cm away from the center of the bright central band?

## 19:4 Resolving Power of Lenses

When the light from two objects that are close together falls on a lens, the light is diffracted. The lens acts in the same way as a slit. It causes the diffracted light from the two objects to overlap. As a result, the width of a lens limits its ability to distinguish between two images. To reduce the effects of diffraction, a wide lens must be used. In the case of the objective lens of a microscope, it is not possible to use a wide lens. In a microscope, diffraction is reduced by using a light of a shorter wavelength. As a result the same effect as using a wider lens can be achieved. For this reason, biology classes often use blue or violet lamps when working with microscopes.

## 19:5 Diffraction Gratings

**FIGURE 19-5. This diffraction grating can be used to create an interference pattern.**

In practice, double and single-slit diffraction is not used as a method of analyzing light. Instead, diffraction gratings are used. **Diffraction gratings** are made by making very fine lines on glass with a diamond point. The spaces between the lines where the glass is undisturbed serve as slits. Gratings that have as many as 10 000 lines per centimeter are in common use today.

Essentially, diffraction gratings serve exactly the same purpose as double-slits with the added advantage of permitting much more light to pass through. This produces stronger images of the spectral lines. Many lines which may be too faint to be visible by means of a double-slit are clearly visible when a grating is used.

In Section 19:2 the expression used for the calculation of the wavelengths of light using a double-slit was given as

$$\lambda = \frac{xd}{L}$$

*Hickson-Bender Photography*

This same expression can be used when a grating is employed rather than a double-slit. However, careful inspection of Figure 19-2 shows that $x/L$ is actually sin $\theta$. Therefore, the wavelength can also be expressed as $\lambda = d$ sin $\theta$.

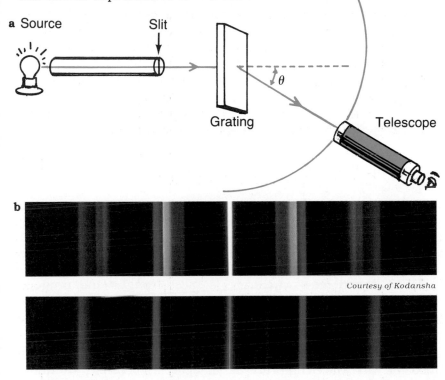

a Source    Slit

$\theta$

Grating    Telescope

*Courtesy of Kodansha*

b

**FIGURE 19-6. A spectrometer is used to measure the wavelengths of light emitted by a light source (a). A grating was used to produce these interference patterns for white light and red light (b).**

The wavelengths of light from any source are measured quickly and efficiently by the use of a device known as a spectrometer, Figure 19-6. The source emits light that falls on a slit and then passes through a grating. To the left and right of the central bright line, $O$, a cluster of lines appears representing the various first-order wavelengths from the source. Each of these lines is actually an image of the slit. The position of a movable telescope is then adjusted until a spectral line is in strong focus. The angle $\theta$ is then read directly from the calibrated base of the spectrometer. Since $d$ is known, $\lambda$ is just $d$ sin $\theta$. Each wavelength emitted by the source can be measured in the same manner.

**Summary**

1. When light falls on two very narrow slits which are close together, it is diffracted as it passes through the slits. The circular waves produced in this way interfere with each other both constructively and destructively.   **19:1**

2. The interference due to a double slit causes alternating dark and bright spots to appear on a screen some distance from the slits.   **19:1**

3. The diffraction pattern obtained by using double slits can be analyzed geometrically to obtain the wavelengths of the light passing through the slits. **19:2**

4. When wavelength is known the frequency of light waves can be obtained by using the relationship $c = f\lambda$. **19:2**

5. Narrow single slits will also cause diffraction patterns to appear on a screen some distance from the slit. **19:3**

6. In practice, gratings with large numbers of evenly spaced slits are used to obtain diffraction patterns. **19:5**

## Questions

1. Explain why the central bright line resulting from the diffraction of light by a double slit cannot be used to measure the wavelength of light waves.

2. Using a compass and a ruler, construct a diagram of the interference pattern that results when waves 1 cm in length fall on two slits which are 2 cm apart. The slits may be represented by two dots spaced 2 cm apart and kept to one side of the paper. Draw a line through the central line of reinforcement and through all other lines of reinforcement. Draw dotted lines where crests meet troughs and produce nodal lines.

3. If you are using light of a known wavelength in a double-slit experiment, how can you find the distance between the slits?

4. More accurate measurements of light waves can be made if the lines obtained for each wavelength are as far apart as possible. We know that $\lambda = xd/L$. How can the value of $x$ be increased?

5. How does a single-slit diffraction pattern differ from the pattern obtained by using two slits?

6. What happens to a single-slit diffraction pattern when the width of the slit approaches the wavelength of the light falling on it?

7. How do lenses make it difficult to distinguish between two objects that are very close together?

## Problems

1. Light falls on a pair of slits $1.9 \times 10^{-4}$ cm apart. The slits are 80 cm from a first-order bright line. The first-order line is 19 cm from the central bright line. What is the wavelength of the light?

2. Light of wavelength $4.0 \times 10^{-5}$ cm falls on a pair of slits. First-order bright lines appear 4.0 cm from the central bright line. The first-order lines are 200 cm from the center of the slits. How far apart are the slits?

3. A good diffraction grating has 2500 lines per centimeter. What is the distance $d$ between two lines in the grating?

**4.** Using the grating of Problem 3, a red line appears 16.5 cm from the central bright spot on a screen opposite the grating. The distance from the center of the grating to the red line is 100 cm. What is the wavelength of the red light?

**5.** Light of frequency $6.0 \times 10^{14}$ Hz falls on a pair of slits that are $2.0 \times 10^{-4}$ cm apart. The center of the slits is 50 cm from the screen. How far from the central bright line will the first-order bright lines appear?

**6.** Light falls on a single slit 0.01 cm wide and develops a first-order dark band 0.59 cm from the center of the central bright band on a screen 100 cm away. Calculate the wavelength of the light.

**7.** Light that falls on the slit described in Problem 6 develops a first-order dark band 0.48 cm from the bright central band.
   **a.** Calculate the wavelength of the light.
   **b.** Compare the distance between the central bright band and the first-order dark band with the wavelength of the light in this problem and in Problem 6 as well. What relationship exists? Can the wavelengths of the light waves be read directly from the screen in an arrangement of this sort?

**8.** When light of wavelength $4.0 \times 10^{-5}$ cm falls on a single slit, the two first-order dark bands are located 0.043 cm from the bright central band. If the slit is 86 cm from the screen, what is its width?

**1.** *Acoustics:* Sound waves of frequency 550 Hz fall on a window 1.2 m wide. The window is in the exact center of one wall of a theater 24 m × 12 m. The window is 12 m from the opposite wall along which is a row of seats filled with people. The theater is acoustically prepared to prevent the reflection of sound waves and the speed of sound is 330 m/s. Two people in a row along the wall hear no sound. Where are they sitting?

**2.** *Communications:* A radio station employs two antennas and broadcasts at 600 kHz.
   **a.** What is the wavelength of the signals emitted by the station?
   **b.** The occupants of a home that is located 17 500 m from one antenna and 19 500 m from the other antenna have their receiver tuned to the station. Is their reception good or poor?

**Applying Physics**

Chartrand, Mark, "Stars." *Omni*, June, 1980.
Connes, Pierre, "How Light Is Analyzed." *Scientific American*, September, 1968.
Waldemar, L., "The Arctic Mirage." *Science Digest*, April, 1980.

**Readings**

In previous chapters, you have examined the characteristics and behavior of light and other electromagnetic radiation. How is light produced? To find out, you will need to review the basic properties of atoms. After studying this chapter, describe how the atoms which compose the fluorescent screen of this radar scanner give off light. How do these atoms differ in properties from those that form the lighted dials?

# Origin of Light 20

The work of Michael Faraday and others led James Clerk Maxwell to develop a theory about the origin of electromagnetic waves. Maxwell's theory, based on mathematics, predicted that any accelerated charged particle should generate an electromagnetic wave. Note that the theory says the charged particle must be accelerated, not just moving.

**GOAL: You will gain knowledge and understanding of the origin of light, the means by which atoms can be excited, spectra, and the laser.**

## 20:1  Charged Particles Generate Light

By the year 1855, the German physicist Heinrich Hertz verified Maxwell's theory. Hertz actually generated and detected an electromagnetic wave. To generate the wave, he caused electrons to accelerate back and forth in a wire loop. The radio waves coming from the loop were detected by a second wire loop on the other side of his laboratory. It was known that radio waves differ from light waves only in their wavelengths and frequencies. Thus, it became clear that light waves must also be developed by accelerating charged particles.

Today Maxwell's theory includes all electromagnetic waves. Electromagnetic waves, including light waves, are generated by the acceleration of charged particles. Light waves usually are produced by the acceleration of electrons within an atom.

The acceleration of charged particles produces electromagnetic waves.

The charged particle must be accelerating and not just moving.

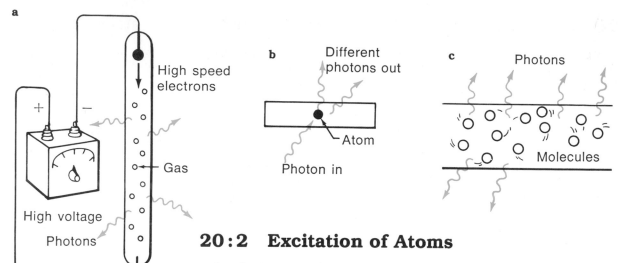

**a**

High speed electrons

Gas

High voltage

Photons

+

−

**b** Different photons out

Atom

Photon in

**c** Photons

Molecules

**FIGURE 20-1. Photons are emitted by excited atoms. Atoms can be excited in three ways: (a) electron excitation, (b) photon excitation, and (c) thermal excitation.**

**FIGURE 20-2. Brilliant colors of fireworks (a) result from thermal excitation of atoms. The light from neon signs (b) results from electron excitation.**

## 20:2 Excitation of Atoms

An electron can be given energy to raise it from a lower energy level to a higher energy level within an atom. When this happens, the atom is said to be excited. Excited atoms remain excited for only a fraction of a second. Then the electron drops from the higher energy level to its normal energy level. However, energy is absorbed by the atom when its electron is raised to a higher energy level. By the law of conservation of energy, this energy must be accounted for. When the electron returns to its lower energy level, electromagnetic radiation is emitted. The energy content of the radiation is exactly equal to the energy absorbed by the atom when its electron was raised to a higher energy level. This process is the origin of light waves.

**a**

**b**

# 20:3  Means by Which Atoms Are Excited

Atoms can be excited in three ways, thermal excitation, electron collision, or photon collision. Thermal excitation takes place when two atoms collide. As a fast-moving atom collides with another atom, it transfers energy to that atom. The added energy can raise an electron to a higher energy level within the atom. Since the atoms in a hot material move very fast, collisions take place more often and with more energy than in a cool material. Therefore, a hot material emits more light as a result of thermal excitation than a cool material. Heating a substance often causes it to glow or emit light. The filament of a light bulb and a glowing coal emit light in this way.

An atom absorbs energy when an electron moves to a higher energy level. The atom is then said to be excited.

An electron emits energy as it drops to a lower energy level.

When an electron collides with an atom, it often causes an electron within the atom to move to a higher energy level than it normally occupies. When this electron returns to its normal energy level, it emits radiation. The light from fluorescent lamps and neon signs is produced in this way. To make electrons flow through the tubes at a high speed, a high voltage is placed across the terminals of the tube. As the electrons pass through the tube, many collisions occur between the atoms and the electrons. Thus, the atoms are excited and emit light. Neon and fluorescent lamps are highly efficient because almost all of the electric energy input is used to produce light. On the other hand, incandescent lamps produce more heat than light. A 30-watt fluorescent lamp produces more light than a 100-watt incandescent lamp.

An atom can be excited upon collision with another atom.

An atom can be excited upon collision with an electron.

When a photon collides with an atom, a photon of radiation enters the atom and its energy is absorbed. The energy of the photon raises an electron to a higher energy level. When the electron returns to its normal energy level, one or more photons leave the atom. The reflectors on car bumpers contain atoms which are easily excited by photons. When light from another car shines on the reflector, its atoms are excited and emit light.

An atom can be excited upon collision with a photon.

# 20:4  Fluorescence and Phosphorescence

Both fluorescent and phosphorescent materials contain atoms which are easily excited. The two types of substances differ in the time it takes their excited atoms to return electrons to their normal energy levels. When an atom of a **fluorescent** material is in the excited state the electrons return to their normal energy levels at once. The electrons have no stability in the higher energy levels. The atoms of a **phosphorescent** material contain atoms which, once excited, can retain electrons in higher than normal energy levels for some time. Thus, a fluorescent reflector on an automobile will glow only while it is being irradiated by the photons from the

Fluorescent materials emit light only when light strikes them.

Phosphorescent materials continue to emit light after the external light source is removed.

*Sea Sports/Robert G. Bachand*

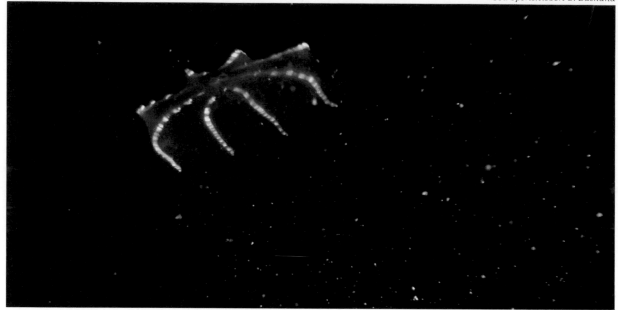

**FIGURE 20-3. In a luminescent organism, enzymatic chemical reactions cause the excitation of molecules to a high energy state. The return to the ground state results in the emission of visible light. The color of light produced is determined by the enzyme protein.**

headlights of another automobile. But, a phosphorescent toy held near a lamp so that it is irradiated by photons will glow for some time.

In a TV picture tube, electrons strike a screen painted with fluorescent materials. Wherever an electron strikes the screen, excitation causes the atoms of the materials to emit light. The amount of light that comes from any part of the screen is governed by the number and energy of electrons striking that part of the screen. A picture is formed on the screen by the varying amount of light emitted from different parts of the surface of the tube.

A doctor's fluoroscope works in the same way as the TV picture tube, with one exception. In the fluoroscope, X rays are used instead of electrons to bombard the screen and excite atoms. The X rays (high energy photons) pass through the patient and strike the fluorescent screen. Some X rays are able to pass through bones and other dense materials of the body. The result is a picture of the bone structure or body organs.

Phosphorescence is a matter of degree. Some phosphors are nearly fluorescent. Electrons are retained in higher energy levels only a bit longer than in fluorescent substances. There is no sharp dividing line between fluorescence and phosphorescence. Generally, if an electron remains in a higher energy level for $10^{-3}$ seconds or longer, the substance is a "phosphor." The fluorescent lamps used in our homes and businesses are coated with "phosphors" that absorb ultraviolet photons from the mercury arc inside the tube. The phosphors then emit visible light.

Different substances produce different colors of light as they fluoresce. These colors are due to the different allowed transitions as electrons move from higher to lower energy levels as explained in the next section. Many posters show attractive colors when flooded with light. Often such posters appear quite drab in white light but become very colorful when exposed to violet light. This is because the violet waves are the more energetic wavelengths of light and produce many more excited atoms in the materials than do the lower energy red and green wavelengths.

## 20:5  Allowed Transitions

The absorption of energy by electrons within an atom is **discrete.** This means that an electron within an atom can absorb only the exact amount of energy needed for the electron to move from one energy level to another. Otherwise it will not absorb the energy at all. This situation is somewhat similar to a ballplayer trying to throw a baseball into the air and having the ball refuse to leave the player's hand because it was not given the right amount of energy to raise it to a specific height.

An electron makes transitions only between exact energy levels.

Just as atoms must absorb energy in exact quantities so, too, atoms can emit energy only in exact, or discrete packages. Energy is **quantized.**

Energy is quantized.

The electrons in an atom can make a certain number of transitions between energy levels. These transitions are called **allowed transitions.** The energy levels within the atoms of each element are unique to that element. Therefore each element has a set of allowed transitions peculiar to that element. Figure 20-4 is a representative chart of the energy levels of a typical atom.

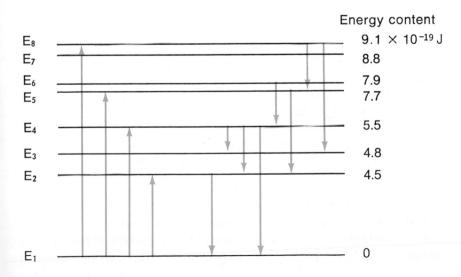

FIGURE 20-4. Each line represents an energy transition from one level to another.

A wave model of the atom is useful in explaining energy levels.

To understand why electrons occupy only certain levels, a wave model of the atom is helpful. The wave model assumes that as an electron moves about the nucleus, it follows a path that is a whole number multiple of its wavelength. (The wave properties of electrons are discussed further in Section 28:9.) The electron then continually reinforces itself and its energy remains constant. At any level that does not provide for a path length that is a whole number multiple of the wavelength, the wave will interfere with itself. As a result, the electron would lose energy. Theory and experiment strongly indicate that an electron occupies only the energy levels in which it can keep a constant energy. Thus, when an electron moves from one energy level to another, it moves only between exact levels.

When an electron returns from a higher energy level to a lower energy level, only certain transitions are allowed. As Figure 20-4 shows, these transitions need not be the same transitions as those that increased the energy of the atom. Therefore, any fluorescent material can be flooded with light of one color and emit light of a different color. Atoms in color TV screens are excited by electron collision. The color each atom emits depends on the favored down-transitions of its electrons.

Each element has its own set of allowed transitions. Thus, under normal conditions, each element emits only certain wavelengths of light. For this reason, every element has its own spectrum.

## 20:6   Emission Spectra

The emission spectrum of each element is unique to that element and serves to identify it.

If the atoms of an element in its gaseous state are excited, the gas emits a limited number of wavelengths. The group of wavelengths emitted by an element is always the same and is called the **emission spectrum** of that element. Each element's spectrum is different from all other spectra. Thus, the spectrum can be used as a sort of "fingerprint" of the element. The composition of a substance can be identified by this fingerprint. To analyze a substance, a sample of the substance can be heated in an electric arc until it becomes a gas and emits light. From the wavelengths present in the light, the composition of the substance can be determined.

One way to observe the spectra of elements is shown in Figure 20-5. A glass tube containing neon gas is equipped with electrodes at both ends. When a high voltage is applied to the tube, electrons pass through it and cause the neon atoms to emit light. The light passes through a slit and then through a prism. Each wavelength of light forms an image of the slit, or lines, that can be observed by looking at the prism through a telescope. Each line corresponds to a particular wavelength of neon. Suppose a different gas such as helium, argon, or nitrogen is contained in the tube, and you want to find out which gas the tube contains. Each gas emits light of characteristic wavelengths. Thus the gas is easily identified by noting the lines present in the spectrum. Some spectra are shown in Figure 20-5.

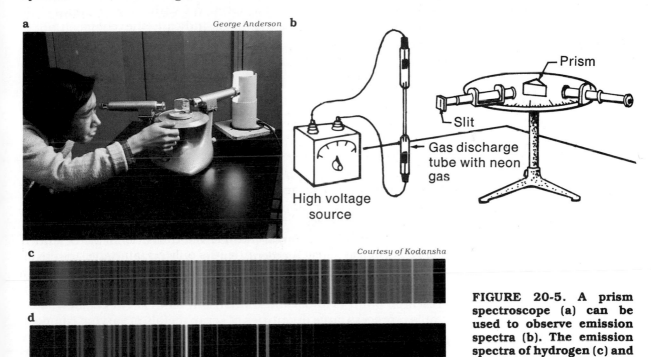

a  *George Anderson*  b

Prism

Slit

Gas discharge tube with neon gas

High voltage source

c  *Courtesy of Kodansha*

d

FIGURE 20-5. A prism spectroscope (a) can be used to observe emission spectra (b). The emission spectra of hydrogen (c) and neon (d) are shown.

The device shown in Figure 20-5 is called a **spectroscope.** When the spectrum of a substance is photographed, the lines on the photograph indicate both the elements present and their relative amounts. If the substance being examined contains a large amount of any particular element, the lines for that element on the photographic plate are stronger. By comparing the strengths of the lines, the percentage composition of the substance can be determined. An emission spectrum is a useful analytical tool.

## 20:7 Absorption Spectra

Absorption spectra are another method used to detect the composition of a substance. To obtain an **absorption spectrum,** white light is sent through a gas and into a prism. The result

The identity of an element can also be determined by observing the wavelengths that it absorbs.

is a continuous spectrum that has several dark lines along its length. These lines show that some wavelengths are missing. By comparison, it is found that the lines of the emission spectrum of the gas and the dark lines on the absorption spectrum occur at the same wavelengths. Gaseous elements absorb the same wavelengths that they emit. An atom that emits blue light absorbs blue light easily. White light, sent through an unknown gas, produces a continuous spectrum with missing lines. The wavelengths of the missing lines indicate the composition of the gas.

*For a gaseous element, absorption and emission lines appear at the same wavelengths.*

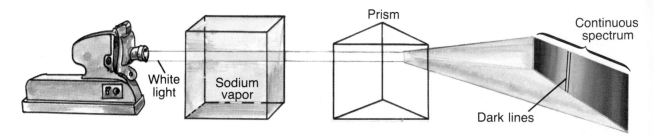

**FIGURE 20-6. This apparatus is used to produce the absorption spectrum of sodium.**

Both emission and absorption spectra are valuable scientific tools. Because each element emits a characteristic spectrum chemists are able to analyze materials by observing the spectra they emit. Not only is this method important in the field of research but it is important industrially as well. For example, steel mills reprocess large quantities of scrap metals of varying compositions. When a quantity of scrap has been melted a sample is sent to the lab for spectral analysis and its exact composition is determined in a matter of minutes. The composition of the steel can then be adjusted to suit commercial specifications. Aluminum, zinc, and other metal processing plants employ the same method.

*Courtesy of Kodansha*

**FIGURE 20-7. The emission spectrum of sodium (a) and the absorption spectrum of sodium (b).**

The study of spectra is a branch of science known as **spectroscopy. Spectroscopists** are scientists who specialize in this field and are employed throughout the research and industrial sectors.

It was not long before scientists recognized that the spectra of each element must be related to the structure of the atoms of each element. In other words, it became clear that a thorough study and analysis of the electromagnetic radiations, or photons, emitted by each element should tell us a great deal about the structure of atoms. For this reason, the spectra of the elements have been studied in great detail and much has been learned about atomic structure and chemical bonding as well. The entire field of chemistry has profited greatly through spectroscopic studies. The first important work along these lines was done by the Danish physicist, Niels Bohr. His work is discussed in more detail in Chapter 28.

## 20:8   Fraunhofer Lines

While examining the spectrum of sunlight, Fraunhofer noticed some dark lines. The dark lines he found in the sun's spectrum are called Fraunhofer lines. To account for these lines, he assumed that the sun has an atmosphere of hot gaseous elements. As light leaves the sun, it passes through these gases. As a result, the gases absorb light at their characteristic wavelengths. Thus, these wavelengths are missing from the sun's spectrum. By comparing the missing lines with the known lines of the various elements, the composition of the sun is determined. The same method can be used to find the composition of the stars.

By comparing absorption lines of sunlight to known spectra, the composition of the sun can be determined.

*Courtesy of Kodansha*

**FIGURE 20-8. Fraunhofer lines in the absorption spectrum of the sun.**

## 20:9   Lasers and Masers

Light is emitted randomly by atoms of an incandescent source. Each atom emits light of different wavelengths at different times and in different directions. Such light is called incoherent. Coherent light consists of light waves of the same wavelength joined inphase to produce an intense beam. Scientists thought a coherent light source could not be developed. Today lasers produce coherent light.

Coherent light results when light waves of the same frequency are in phase.

The word **laser** is an acronym. It stands for **L**ight **A**mplification by the **S**timulated **E**mission of **R**adiation. The first laser was a short ruby rod ($Al_2O_3$) containing about 0.1 percent chromium atoms as an impurity.

The laser is capable of emitting coherent light.

Excited atoms have an interesting property upon which the principle of the laser depends. Should an atom be in the excited state and a photon enter that atom it can cause (or stimulate) the electron in the higher energy level to return to its normal level at once. But this will only occur if the photon that enters the atom has the same wavelength as does the photon emitted by the electron as it makes its down-transition.

**a**  *Larry Hamill*

**b**  *Ad Image*

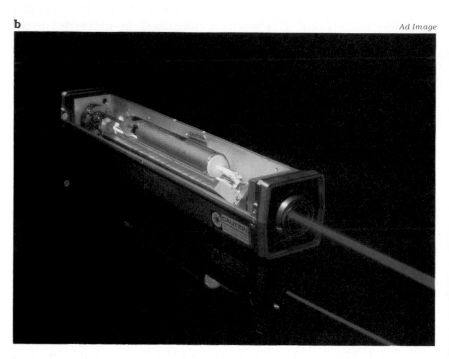

**FIGURE 20-9. Ruby rods (a) are used to make lasers. A laser (b) produces a beam of coherent light.**

Often a photon of the proper wavelength enters an atom and stimulates the emission of radiation. A small bit of material contains many excited atoms that are at the same energy level. However, the effect is usually not large enough to be noticed. A photon that has been amplified can lose its excess energy to the next atom it enters if the next atom is not in the excited state. In a laser, most of the atoms are in the excited state. Thus, the photons are likely to increase their energy each time they enter a new atom. This energy increase can produce an intense beam of coherent light.

Figure 20-10 shows one laser arrangement. A ruby rod is flooded with X rays. X rays are high energy photons. The flooding of the rod is called pumping. Pumping excites a great number of atoms in the rod. A mirror is placed at each end of the rod. The mirror on one end partly transmits and partly reflects.

Pumping or flooding a laser with X rays puts atoms in their excited states.

(a) Unexcited chromium atoms (solid circles) are arranged in a regular pattern within the crystalline structure of a ruby rod.

(b) The ruby rod is flooded or "pumped" with X rays to raise most of the atoms to the excited state (open circles).

(c) During the down-transitions of the electrons, energy in the form of red light is emitted. Photons of red light not parallel with the edges of the rod pass out of the rod.

(d) Photons parallel with the edges of the rod stimulate down-transitions in adjacent atoms and thus produce more photons of the same frequency.

(e) The light travels back and forth between the mirrored ends of the rod, causing an avalanche of down-transitions.

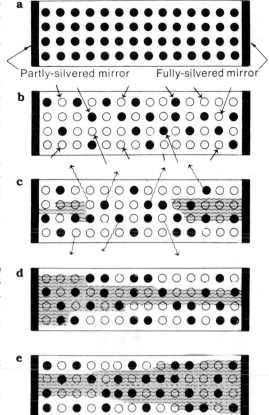

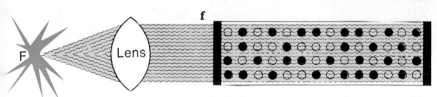

(f) The light bursts forth from the partially silvered mirror, producing an extremely intense flash of light.

**FIGURE 20-10. The lasing action in a ruby rod takes less than one millionth of a second.**

The mirror on the other end reflects only. When a photon enters an excited atom, it stimulates the electron to make its down-transition. Thus, the photon is amplified. This amplification takes place in many atoms at the same time. The amplified photons pass on to other excited atoms. Thus, photon intensities continue to increase. The photons are reflected by the two mirrors. They repeat the process back and forth between the two mirrors. In a short time, there is an avalanche of down-transitions. As a result, a short burst of intense, coherent light leaves the end of the ruby rod. This beam may be diffracted by a pair of slits. The diffraction pattern shows that laser light is coherent. The laser beam may be focused with a lens to provide a more intense and accurately placed spot of coherent light.

Several solids and gases can also be made to "lase." Helium and neon gas can emit continuous laser beams. The radiation emitted does not have to be in the visible region. A **maser** emits radiation in the microwave region. Masers are useful in communications. The word maser is also an acronym. It stands for **M**icrowave **A**mplification by the **S**timulated **E**mission of **R**adiation.

The unique aspect of the light from a laser is that it is a coherent narrow beam of a single frequency. The laser has many useful applications as a result of this property. Lasers were rapidly developed as surgical tools. The narrow intense beam can be used to destroy localized tissue or it can be used to weld tissue such as detached retinas. Lasers are used increasingly to destroy cancerous cells and often to cauterize wounds.

Recently close to 1000 km of narrow plastic fibers were installed as telephone lines in a high-traffic communications area in California. Using total internal reflection (Chapter 17), each fiber carries laser beams long distances without significant loss. Each fiber is capable of carrying up to 3000 calls. Plastic fiber is considerably less expensive than copper wire. By means of laser beams, plastic fiber can carry more calls. It is likely that lasers will be our principal means of communication in the future.

**FIGURE 20-11. Lasers have many practical uses in industry, communications, agriculture, and medicine.**

*Courtesy of Bell Laboratories*

*Courtesy of Ranco Control Division*

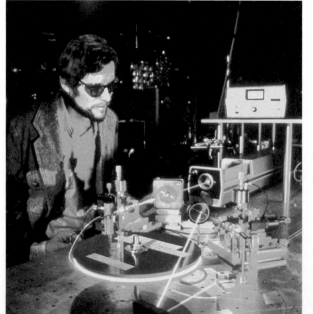

In the field of communications, lasers are also being used to operate video-discs. These discs enable the individual to play pre-recorded programs on home television sets. Home libraries of selected films, plays, and concerts are now a reality.

Not to be overlooked is the extreme straightness of laser beams. Surveyors use laser beams to line up boundaries with great precision. The new tunnels under San Francisco Bay were laid out by means of laser beams.

## 20:10 Origin of Electromagnetic Radiation

Principally this chapter has dealt with the generation of light, which is electromagnetic radiation in the visible region. However, visible light constitutes less than one percent of known electromagnetic radiations. We tend to think of the universe as largely empty space. It is actually an immense ocean of dense radiation in which bits of matter appear at large intervals. The vast majority of this radiation is not in the visible region.

All objects in the universe—stars, comets, rocks, trees, you—are continually radiating electromagnetic energy because accelerating charged particles radiate electromagnetic energy. Atoms and molecules are constantly bumping into one another causing their electrons to vibrate and radiate energy. The frequencies of the radiation emitted are related to the absolute temperature of the material. Thus, the speed at which molecules are moving when they collide determines the energy with which their electrons vibrate and a wide range of emissions results. If the temperature is high enough, some of the emitted radiation is in the visible region. Objects of lower temperature tend to emit radiation that is principally in the infrared region. A black woodstove emits mostly infrared radiation, but also emits visible light waves although not enough to be detected by the eye. It even emits some wavelengths in the broadcast band, but not enough to interfere with the operation of your radio or TV set.

Objects at even lower temperatures generally emit radiation of lower frequency. An iceberg emits wavelengths that are chiefly in the microwave region. The Navy has developed a method of tracking icebergs by using special microwave receivers.

When high speed electrons are rapidly decelerated by colliding with other ions or larger objects, radiation of very high frequency can result. X rays are generated in this manner. Even higher frequency radiations are created during nuclear reactions as evidenced by the emission of dangerous and highly penetrating gamma rays during such reactions.

Here is a good question to ask at this point. If all objects are constantly radiating energy, why doesn't the universe cool off,

Visible light is less than one percent of electromagnetic radiation.

All objects in the universe are continually radiating electromagnetic energy.

Accelerating charged particles radiate electromagnetic energy.

and become cold and dead? Most objects also absorb much of the radiation that constantly falls on them and more or less manage to maintain equilibrium.

Not all radiation is due to electron oscillation. All objects contain charged atoms (ions) and/or molecules which collide. In the process, these particles are accelerated. These ions generate radiations of their own. The vast majority of matter in the universe consists of swirling masses of plasma which are always electrically charged and therefore constantly generating radiation.

Every cubic meter of "empty space" in the universe is continually crisscrossed by electromagnetic radiation. Rough estimates place the available energy per cubic meter of space at $4 \times 10^{-14}$ joules. Most of the radiation that falls on the earth comes from the sun. If none of this radiation were absorbed by the atmosphere, each square centimeter of the earth's surface would receive about 8 joules of radiant energy per minute when the sun is directly overhead.

**Summary**

**1.** James Clerk Maxwell developed a theory which states that all electromagnetic radiation is due to the acceleration of charged particles.   20:1

**2.** An electron can be raised to a higher energy level within an atom. When this change occurs, the atom is said to be excited. The atom emits electromagnetic radiation when the electron returns to its normal energy level.   20:2

**3.** An atom can be excited by thermal excitation, electron collision, or photon collision.   20:3

**4.** A material is fluorescent if its electrons return to their normal energy levels immediately. A material is phosphorescent if its electrons can remain in higher energy levels for some time.   20:4

**5.** Different light sources produce different spectra in accord with their allowed transitions.   20:5

**6.** If white light passes through a gas, the gas will absorb the same wavelengths that it would ordinarily emit. When the emergent white light is sent through a prism, an absorption spectrum is produced.   20:7

**7.** Lasers are capable of producing coherent light. Coherent light consists of photons of the same wavelength emitted inphase.   20:9

**Questions**

**1.** Name three methods by which an atom can be excited.

**2.** Why does a hot material emit light?

**3.** Explain why a TV picture tube is coated with a fluorescent material rather than a phosphorescent material.

**4.** Why do different fluorescent materials emit different colored light when illuminated with the same ultraviolet light source?

**5.** Explain why electrons make transitions between specific energy levels only.

**6.** Explain the operation of a laser.

**7.** Can a laser put out more energy than is put into it? Explain.

**8.** What are absorption spectra?

**9.** What objects in the universe do not emit radiation? Explain.

---

**Problems**

In previous chapters we studied two important equations that can tell us a great deal about photons.

$E = hf$ (Where $h$ is Planck's constant $6.6 \times 10^{-34}$ J·s.)
$c = f\lambda$ (Where $c$ is the speed of light, $3 \times 10^8$ m/s.)

*Use these equations and the theory presented in this chapter to solve the following problems.*

**1.** Calculate the frequency and wavelength of the photon emitted when an electron makes the down-transition $E_5$ to $E_2$ in Figure 20-4.

**2.** What will be the frequency and wavelength of the photon emitted by the down-transition $E_4$ to $E_1$ in Figure 20-4?

**3.** At what rate must electrons be made to vibrate in a wire if the wire is to emit radio waves 10 m in length?

---

**Applying Physics**

**1.** *Solar Energy:* Current research indicates that we can effectively convert 20% of the radiation that falls on the earth to useful power. What power could be obtained from the roof of a factory building having an area of 80 m by 60 m when the sun is directly overhead? Assume no radiation is absorbed by the atmosphere before reaching the roof. Express your answer in kilowatts.

**2.** *Photography:* The wavelengths of visible blue light and red light are about $4.5 \times 10^{-7}$ m and $6.5 \times 10^{-7}$ m respectively. The silver compound used in photographic film is "exposed" when its molecules are dissociated by photons of energy content greater than $3.5 \times 10^{-19}$ J. Show by calculation why it is safe to use a red lamp in a photographer's darkroom but not a white or a blue lamp.

---

**Readings**

Bova, Ben, *The Amazing Laser.* The Westminister Press, 1974.
Free, John, "Video-Disc Players, Optical vs Mechanical." *Popular Science,* July, 1980.
Giacconi, Riccardo, "The Einstein X-ray Observatory." *Scientific American,* February, 1980.
Sheffield, Charles, "Earth Scans." *Omni,* June, 1980.

All matter in the universe contains positive and negative electric charges. These charges play a major role in all aspects of the behavior of matter. Lightning is an impressive display of the tremendous voltages electric charges can develop. Lightning is an example of static electricity. What other effects of static electricity have you observed? How is static electricity related to the internal structure of an atom?

# Static Electricity 21

For many centuries it has been known that electric charges can accumulate on objects. You have experienced an electric shock after walking across a rug or sliding from the seat of an automobile. Your clothes may stick together after they are taken from a dryer. All of these effects, and many others, are due to static electric charges which are charges that collect in one place. A close look at the structure of the atom will lead to an explanation of the existence of these charges.

GOAL: You will gain knowledge and understanding of static charges and the forces between them, and will be introduced to the concept of an electric field.

## 21:1 Microstructure of Matter

Models of the atom place the protons and neutrons in its center or nucleus. The protons have a positive electric charge. The charge is exactly the same on each proton. Neutrons are neutral and have no electric charge. Located outside the nucleus of the atom is a "cloud" of electrons. Each electron has a negative charge equal in magnitude to the charge of a proton. The magnitude of the charge is the same on all electrons and protons. The charge on an electron or proton is the **elementary unit of charge.** An atom contains the same number of electrons as protons. Thus, an atom is electrically neutral. Electric charges appear when this balance is disturbed.

The proton is firmly "locked" in the nucleus of the atom. It can be dislodged only by methods used in nuclear physics. The electron is the mobile particle of the atom. Thus, all electric phenomena are due to the movements of electrons.

The nucleus of an atom contains protons (positively charged) and neutrons (no charge).

About the nucleus is a "cloud" of electrons (negatively charged).

Electron movements cause electric phenomena.

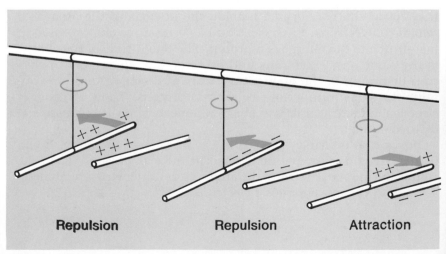

FIGURE 21-1. Objects become charged through a gain or loss of electrons. A neutral object (a) has equal numbers of electrons and protons. The negative object (b) has excess electrons. The positive object (c) is deficient in electrons.

Neutral

Negative charge

Positive charge

A neutral object has the same number of electrons as protons.

When a neutral object gains electrons, it gains a net negative charge.

When a neutral object loses electrons, it has a net positive charge.

An electrically-charged object has a static charge.

FIGURE 21-2. A charged rod, when brought close to another suspended rod, will attract or repel the suspended rod.

## 21:2   Charging Objects

Because electrons move easily, negative and positive charges can be produced on objects. A neutral object contains equal numbers of electrons and protons. It is possible to add electrons to a neutral object. When electrons are in excess, the object has a net negative charge. If electrons are removed from a neutral object, the object has a net positive charge. The object contains an excess of protons. In both cases, the protons remain in the nucleus. When an object is charged by adding or removing electrons, the charge stays on the object for a short time. The object has a static charge. **Static** means "at rest."

If a glass rod is rubbed with a piece of silk, electrons will leave the glass and move onto the silk. The glass rod then has a net positive charge while the silk has a negative charge.

If two glass rods are rubbed with a silk cloth, both have a positive charge. If one of the rods is suspended and the second rod

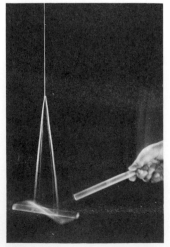

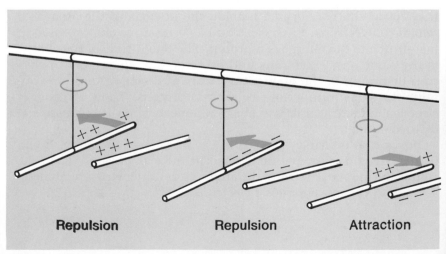

**Repulsion**          **Repulsion**          **Attraction**

*PSSC Physics, D.C. Heath & Co., Lexington.* 1965

brought close to it, the suspended rod will be repelled. Thus, two positively charged objects repel one another. In the same way, two rubber rods can be charged negatively by rubbing them with fur or wool. If one of the rubber rods is suspended, it is repelled by the second rubber rod. Thus, two negatively charged objects repel one another. However, if the negatively charged rubber rod is brought close to the suspended, positively charged rod, attraction occurs. In summary, there are three important facts you should know about static electric charges.

1. Electric charges are of two distinct kinds, positive and negative.
2. Like charges repel. Unlike charges attract.
3. Charges exert forces through a distance.

## 21:3   Electrostatics

Many demonstrations support the theory that static charges are due to the transfer of electrons. The device in Figure 21-3 is an **electroscope.** The rod is insulated from the ground by a glass flask. Electrons do not flow easily through glass. Thus, charges placed on the rod will stay on the rod. Two leaves of silver or aluminum foil hang from one end of the metal rod. When a charged rod is brought close to the top of the electroscope, the leaves diverge. A negatively charged rod repels the mobile electrons down into the leaves, giving both leaves a negative charge. Thus, the leaves repel each other, as shown in Figure 21-3a. A positively charged rod attracts the electrons into the top of the electroscope. Both leaves have a net positive charge. Again, repulsion takes place, as shown in Figure 21-3b. In both cases, when the rod is removed, the electrons redistribute themselves at once and the leaves fall.

Electroscopes are used to detect the presence of static charges.

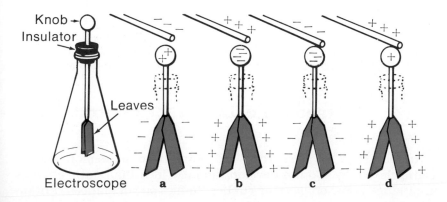

FIGURE 21-3. Electroscope with accompanying diagrams of possible charge distributions.

A negatively charged rod brought into contact with the top of the electroscope repels electrons from the knob down to the leaves. The top of the electroscope has a net positive charge and draws electrons from the negative rod. The electroscope gains an overall excess negative charge, Figure 21-3c. When the negative rod is removed, the leaves remain in a diverged position.

When a positively charged rod is brought into contact with the top of the electroscope, an overall excess positive charge develops. The rod produces this excess positive charge by drawing electrons from the electroscope, Figure 21-3d.

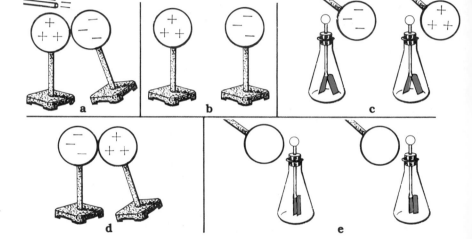

**FIGURE 21-4.** Metal spheres can be used to transfer charges. If oppositely charged spheres touch, they will become neutral. Uncharged spheres do not affect the leaves of the electroscope.

If a negatively charged rod is brought close to two insulated metal spheres that are touching, electrons will be repelled from the sphere nearest the rod to the sphere farthest away. If the spheres are then separated, one is charged negatively and the other positively. Each sphere, when brought close to the knob of an electroscope, causes the leaves to diverge. The two spheres are charged equally and oppositely. If the spheres touch, the excess electrons flow from the negative sphere to the positive sphere. The result is that both spheres become neutral. To show that the spheres no longer bear a charge, they are brought close to the knob of an electroscope. The uncharged spheres do not affect the leaves.

## 21:4 Charged Objects Attract Neutral Objects

Rubber rods or glass rods are often used in demonstrating static electricity. Do not develop the false idea that static charges are induced only on glass or rubber. In fact all substances contain electrons, and all substances can gain a static charge. For example, a charged rubber rod held near a stream of water pulls the stream to one side, Figure 21-5. The negative rod repels electrons from the side of the stream closest to it to the other side of the stream. Thus, the surface of the stream nearest the rod becomes positive. The positive water is attracted to the negative rod and the stream of water bends.

In the same way, a comb can be used to pick up small bits of paper even though the paper is neutral. A comb run through hair gains a negative charge. The negatively charged comb repels electrons from the side of the paper closest to it. This side of the paper is then positive, and the comb attracts it. The paper is drawn to the comb. However, almost at once, the paper is repelled by the comb. The paper is repelled because the negative comb gives electrons to the positive side of the paper. The paper itself becomes negative.

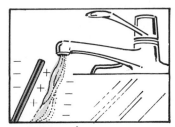

**FIGURE 21-5. A negatively charged rod can be used to deflect a stream of water.**

Any substance can be given a static charge.

## 21:5  Grounding

Suppose an insulated metal sphere is charged negatively and then touched to a second neutral sphere. The charged sphere repels electrons from the surface it is touching. Then it feeds electrons onto the now positive side of the second sphere. If the metal sphere is touched to a second sphere of equal size, the charge is shared equally. Both spheres indicate they are charged when held near an electroscope. However, they do not indicate as intense a charge as the one initially possessed by the first sphere. If the sphere is touched to a much larger sphere, it does not stop feeding the charge into the larger sphere until both spheres have the same electrical potential energy. In other words, the size of the charge on the small sphere is greatly reduced. An electroscope is affected only slightly, if at all, by either sphere.

**FIGURE 21-6. A charged sphere (a) shares charges equally with a neutral sphere of equal size (b). It gives much of its charge to a larger neutral sphere (c), and gives virtually all of its charge to a grounded object (d).**

Insulated metal sphere

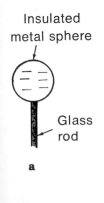

Glass rod

**a**

Metal spheres of equal size

**b**

Metal spheres of unequal size

**c**

Grounded metal sphere

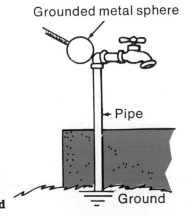

Pipe

Ground

**d**

Now consider what happens if the sphere is touched to the earth. The sphere tries to share its charge with the earth itself. In effect, the sphere feeds all of its charge into the earth and becomes neutral. The earth is so large that no net charge develops on it. Both objects are neutral. Touching a charged object to the earth as a means of eliminating the charge from the object is called **grounding.** Many electric devices such as clothes dryers, washing machines, and refrigerators are grounded when they are installed to prevent the buildup of annoying static charges.

*Grounding allows a charged object to feed all of its excess charge into the earth.*

## 21:6  Conductors and Insulators

All materials can be charged electrostatically. However, all materials do not conduct electrons well. A rubber rod can be charged, but its charge does not move along the rod. A glass rod acts in the same manner. Therefore, rubber or glass rods are used for electrostatic experiments. The failure of such materials to conduct electricity makes them good insulators.

*Materials which do not conduct electricity well are insulators.*

*Metals are good electric conductors.*

All metals are good conductors of electricity. The atoms of a metallic solid are packed closely together. The outermost electrons of the atoms in metals are almost as close to the attractive force of the positive nuclei of surrounding atoms as they are to the attractive force of their own nuclei. As a result, the outermost electrons form a pool of electrons and are able to move through metal. This effect is prominent in metals such as gold, silver, and copper which have only one electron in their outermost levels. The large number of free electrons in metals is often referred to as the electron gas. These electrons move easily back and forth through the metal. Thus, metals are good electric conductors. Silver is the best conductor. However, it has a limited supply thus making it expensive to use. Copper and aluminum are the most suitable conductors for commercial use.

A metal rod can be charged by rubbing it with fur or wool. As a good conductor, the metal quickly sends its excess charge to ground through the person holding the rod. (The person's body is also a good conductor.) In order to maintain a charge on metal, it must be placed on an insulating support.

## 21:7  Concentration of Charge

*Electrons are distributed over the outer surface of a charged object.*

Since electrons repel each other, any charged object distributes its charge over its outer surface. In this arrangement, the electrons are farthest from each other. The electrons distribute themselves in such a way as to bring about equilibrium over the surface. Therefore, any pointed or angular surface has a high concentration of charge to establish equilibrium. Charge per unit area along a pointed surface increases as the object narrows as shown in Figure 21-7. This increase is due to the decrease in surface area along the point. More charges are needed in less area to push against the repulsive force of the larger areas. The concentration of charge becomes extreme at the tip.

 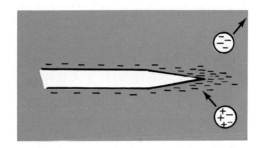

**FIGURE 21-7.** Electrons are concentrated around sharper surfaces of an object. They become so concentrated on pointed surfaces that they can leak off the object.

The charge can become so intense that it repels the electrons in the air molecules around the point to the side farthest from the point. Thus, the sides of the molecules that face the point have a positive charge. The molecules are attracted to the point immediately. When the molecules touch the point, they gain electrons and become negatively charged. Then, the molecules are repelled from the point. This process occurs so efficiently that it causes the rapid discharge of the entire object of which it is a part. To prevent loss of charge from devices designed to hold static charges, the surfaces are rounded. For example, the knob on an electroscope and metal spheres used to hold charges serve this purpose.

The fact that any pointed surface can cause a rapid electric discharge must be kept in mind when any electric component is designed. Should you study electronics in the future, you will find that all circuit parts are rounded and never pointed.

## 21:8   The Coulomb

The quantity of electric charge that exists on a charged object is measured in coulombs. A coulomb of charge is analogous to measuring water in liters. A liter of water could be defined as a specific number of water molecules. In much the same way, a **coulomb** (C) is defined as the electric charge on $6.25 \times 10^{18}$ electrons or protons. This definition came from early experiments in which electric charge was measured in terms of the amount of silver deposited on a plate during silver-plating. The existence of electrons and protons was not established until later. Once these particles were discovered it became possible to find the number of electrons or protons in one coulomb.

The coulomb is the charge found on $6.25 \times 10^{18}$ electrons or protons. The charge on a single proton or electron is therefore $1/6.25 \times 10^{18}$ or $1.60 \times 10^{-19}$ coulomb. This value is the **elementary unit of charge.** Since it is not possible to visualize a quantity of this magnitude, think of a coulomb as a certain quantity of charge just as a liter of water is a certain quantity of water.

## 21:9   Coulomb's Law

Electric forces hold together the particles that make atoms. Therefore, an understanding of the nature of electric force is the key to understanding atomic structure.

In 1785, Charles Coulomb (1736–1806) measured the force between two small charged spheres. He used a very sensitive torsion balance, Figure 21-8. The force needed to twist the thin wire through any given angle was carefully measured. A rod with a small sphere at either end was then suspended from the wire. The charged sphere, *B*, was touched to sphere *A* so that the two spheres, being equal in size, shared the charge equally. Coulomb varied the distance, *r*, between *A* and *B* and observed the deflection of *A* from its rest position. The deflection caused the wire to twist. Coulomb measured the angle of twist and used it to find the force between the two spheres. He then related this force to the distance between the spheres.

After a series of measurements, Coulomb touched *A* with his finger and grounded it. He touched *B* to *A* a second time. The charges on both *A* and *B* became half their former charge. He repeated the process. The spheres had one fourth their former charge. After many careful experiments, Coulomb stated his law. *The force between two charged objects varies directly with the product of their charges and inversely with the square of the distance between them.* **Coulomb's law** is expressed as

$$F \propto \frac{qq'}{r^2}$$

The charges on the objects *q* and *q'*, are separated by a distance *r*. Note that this expression is similar to the one for gravitational force, Section 9:2.

When charge is expressed in coulombs, distance in meters, and force in newtons, the equation used to calculate electric force is

$$F = K\frac{qq'}{r^2}$$

Coulomb's law describes the force between two charged objects.

The electric force between two charged objects varies directly with the product of their charges.

The electric force varies inversely with the square of distance between two charged objects.

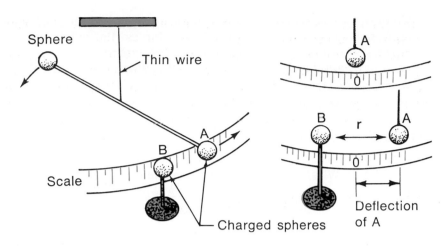

**FIGURE 21-8. Coulomb used this type of apparatus to measure the force between two spheres. He observed the deflection of *A* while varying the distance between *A* and *B*.**

The constant $K$ is found by measuring the force $F$ (in newtons) between two known charges $q$ and $q'$ (in coulombs) that are a known distance (in meters) apart. The constant turns out to be

$$K = 9.0 \times 10^9 \frac{\text{N} \cdot \text{m}^2}{\text{C}^2}$$

**EXAMPLE: Coulomb's Law—Like Charges**

A positive charge of $6.0 \times 10^{-6}$ C is 0.03 m from a second positive charge of $3.0 \times 10^{-6}$ C. Calculate the force between the charges.

*Solution:* $F = K\dfrac{qq'}{r^2}$

$$= \left(9.0 \times 10^9 \frac{\text{N} \cdot \text{m}^2}{\text{C}^2}\right) \frac{(6.0 \times 10^{-6} \text{ C})(3.0 \times 10^{-6} \text{ C})}{(0.03 \text{ m})^2}$$

$$= \left(9.0 \times 10^9 \frac{\text{N} \cdot \text{m}^2}{\text{C}^2}\right) \frac{(18 \times 10^{-12} \text{ C}^2)}{9.0 \times 10^{-4} \text{ m}^2} = 180 \text{ N}$$

The positive force between the charges indicates repulsion.

*A positive force between charges indicates repulsion.*

**EXAMPLE: Coulomb's Law—Unlike Charges**

What force exists between a positive charge of $1.5 \times 10^{-5}$ C and a negative charge of $-6.0 \times 10^{-6}$ C which are 5 cm apart?

*Solution:* $F = K\dfrac{qq'}{r^2}$

$$= \left(9.0 \times 10^9 \frac{\text{N} \cdot \text{m}^2}{\text{C}^2}\right) \frac{(1.5 \times 10^{-5} \text{ C})(-6.0 \times 10^{-6} \text{ C})}{(0.05 \text{ m})^2}$$

$$= -324 \text{ N}$$

The negative force between the charges indicates attraction. Note the large forces involved between electric charges given in millionths of a coulomb.

*A negative force indicates attraction.*

Coulomb's law is useful when working with atomic and sub-atomic particles. It helps to explain the forces that exist between electrons, protons, and the other particles within the atom. Coulomb's law applies accurately to them. When two fairly large charged objects are close together, Coulomb's law applies only with modification.

**PROBLEMS**

1. 1.3 N

3. $-4.4 \times 10^3$ N

5. $3.0 \times 10^{-6}$ C

1. Two positive charges of $6.0 \times 10^{-6}$ C are separated by 0.50 m. What force exists between the charges?

2. A negative charge of $2.0 \times 10^{-4}$ C and a negative charge of $8.0 \times 10^{-4}$ are separated by 0.30 m. What force exists between the two charges?

3. What is the force between a positive charge of 0.0008 C and a negative charge of 0.0003 C separated by 0.70 m?

4. Determine the force between two positive charges of 1.0 C each separated by 1.0 m.

5. A negative charge of $6.0 \times 10^{-6}$ C exerts an attractive force of 64.8 N on a second charge 0.05 m away. What is the magnitude of the second charge?

6. A positive charge of $2.0 \times 10^{-6}$ C is 0.06 m from a second positive charge of $4.0 \times 10^{-6}$ C. Find the force between the two charges.

**FIGURE 21-9. Lines of force are drawn perpendicularly away from the positive object and perpendicularly into the negative object.**

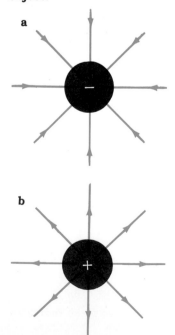

a

b

## 21:10 Electric Fields

The **electric field** concept is used to describe the behavior of any charged object when it is near another charged object. The electric field is not, in itself, an explanation of electric forces.

To plot an electric field, a small positive test charge is placed at different points within the field. Its behavior is then studied. The force on the positive test charge is always found to be toward a negatively charged object and away from a positively charged object. Figure 21-9 shows vectors representing the forces acting on a test charge in two situations. In all cases the vectors are perpendicular to the charged object. For this reason, the field about a charged object is sometimes described by drawing lines of force about and perpendicular to the object. These lines represent the force field, but they do not actually exist. Note that the lines get farther apart as the distance from the charged object increases. The increased spacing indicates a weakening of the field with distance in accord with Coulomb's law.

Figure 21-10 shows the patterns taken by the lines of force when the fields between charged objects are plotted. Lines of force serve only to describe the behavior of a positively charged test object placed in the field. The direction of an electric field is the direction of the force on a positive charge placed in the field. This direction is always away from a positive charge and toward a negative charge. Electric fields run from positive to negative.

The direction of an electric field is always away from a positive charge and toward a negative charge.

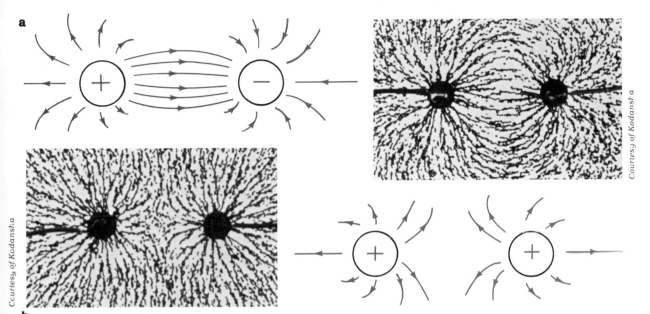

**FIGURE 21-10.** Lines of force between unlike charges (a), and between like charges (b) describe the behavior of a positively charged object in a field.

## 21:11   Electric Field Intensity

If a small positive test charge is placed in an electric field it will immediately experience a force. This force is, of course, an electric force and is a result of the interaction between the electric field about the small charge and the electric field in which the charge is placed.* The magnitude of the force on the small charge will be proportional to the intensity (strength) of the field at the point of location of the test charge. Therefore, if the force acting on the charge is measured in newtons and the magnitude of the charge in coulombs, the field intensity, $\vec{E}$, can be stated

Electric field intensity is electric force per unit charge.

$$\vec{E} = \frac{\vec{F}}{q}$$

---

*All interactions, or forces, are field interactions. For example, the force on a kilogram mass hanging some distance above the surface of the earth is actually the result of an interaction between the earth's gravitational field and the gravitational field about the mass.

**EXAMPLE:  Electric Field Intensity**

A positive test charge of $4.0 \times 10^{-5}$ C is placed in an electric field. The force acting on it is 0.60 N. What is the magnitude of the electric field intensity at the point where the charge is placed?

*Solution:*     $\vec{E} = \dfrac{\vec{F}}{q} = \dfrac{0.60 \text{ N}}{4.0 \times 10^{-5} \text{ C}} = 1.5 \times 10^4 \text{ N/C}$

Note: If the charge is negative, the field intensity is still measured the same way. However, the charge experiences a force in the opposite direction.

**PROBLEMS**

7.  50 N/C

**7.** A positive test charge of $8.0 \times 10^{-5}$ C is placed in an electric field. It experiences a force of $4.0 \times 10^{-3}$ N. What is the intensity of the field at this point?

**8.** Suppose the test charge of Problem 7 is located in the field of a charge considered to be a point charge. It is moved to a distance twice as far from the charge. What force does the field exert on it?

9.  $-3 \times 10^6$ N/C

**9.** A negative charge of $2.0 \times 10^{-8}$ C experiences a force of 0.060 N when in an electric field. What is the magnitude of the field intensity at the point where the charge is located?

**10.** A positive test charge of $5.0 \times 10^{-4}$ C is in an electric field which exerts a force of $5.0 \times 10^{-4}$ N on it. What is the magnitude of the electric field at the location of the test charge?

# 21:12   Electric Field between Two Parallel Plates

Point charges are used chiefly in the study of the structure of matter. However, the field that exists between two charged parallel plates has more practical uses. The field is uniform in the region between two such plates, except at the edges of the plates. A test charge would find the same force at any point in the space between the plates.

The electric field between two charged plates is uniform.

**FIGURE 21-11. The diagram of electric field between two parallel plates of opposite charge is shown. The lines of force are drawn from the positive plate to the negative plate.**

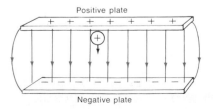

Positive plate

Negative plate

1. The neutral atoms of a material contain as many negative electrons as positive protons.   **21:1**

2. The negative electrons are located outside the nucleus and move easily. The positive protons are locked in the nuclei of atoms.   **21:1**

3. Because electrons move easily, negative and positive charges can be created on objects. An object is charged negatively by adding electrons to it. The removal of electrons leaves behind excess protons thus creating a net positive charge.   **21:2**

4. Like electric charges repel, unlike electric charges attract.   **21:2**

5. A charged object brought near a neutral object will induce a charge on the neutral object and attract it.   **21:4**

6. A charged object will attempt to share its charge with any object with which it comes in contact. If the second object is considerably larger, the charged object loses much of its charge.   **21:5**

7. If a charged object is touched to the earth, the object will share its charge with the earth effectively losing all charge.   **21:5**

8. The coulomb is the standard for electric charge. One coulomb is the charge found on $6.25 \times 10^{18}$ electrons or protons.   **21:8**

9. The charge on a single electron or proton is $1/6.25 \times 10^{18}$ C or $1.60 \times 10^{-19}$ C.   **21:8**

10. Coulomb's law states that the force between two charged objects varies directly with the product of their charges and inversely with the square of the distance between the charges.   **21:9**

11. A charged object can produce a force on a second charged object through a distance. The electric field concept is used to describe the behavior of a charged object near another charged object.   **21:10**

12. Electric fields are described as having the direction taken by a small positive test charge.   **21:11**

13. Electric fields run from positive to negative.   **21:10**

**Summary**

1. List the three major particles of the atom. State the electric charge of each.

2. Explain how the leaves of an electroscope are made to diverge by the near presence of a rod charged
   **a.** positively      **b.** negatively

3. A charged object can attract a neutral object. Describe how a negatively charged rod attracts a neutral bit of paper.

4. Why does a charged object lose its charge when it is touched to the ground?

5. A charged rubber rod placed on a table maintains its charge for some time. Why does the charge not "ground" immediately?

**Questions**

6. What is the charge on a single electron or proton?
7. State Coulomb's law.
8. Diagram the field between
   a. two like charges       b. two unlike charges
9. How is the direction of an electric field determined?

## Problems

1. A positive charge of $1.8 \times 10^{-6}$ C and a negative charge of $1.0 \times 10^{-6}$ C are 0.04 m apart. What is the force between the two particles?
2. Two negative charges of $5.0 \times 10^{-5}$ C are 0.20 m from each other. What force acts on the particles?
3. A positive charge of $1.5 \times 10^{-5}$ C and a negative charge of $1.5 \times 10^{-5}$ C are separated by 15 cm. Find the force between the two particles.
4. What force exists between two negative charges of $1.2 \times 10^{-3}$ C separated by 1.0 m?
5. The most common isotope of hydrogen contains a proton and an electron separated by about $5.0 \times 10^{-11}$ m. Use $1.6 \times 10^{-19}$ C as the elementary unit of charge to determine the force of attraction between the two particles.
6. The mass of a proton is approximately $1.7 \times 10^{-27}$ kg. The mass of the electron is approximately $9.0 \times 10^{-31}$ kg.
   a. Use Newton's law of universal gravitation to calculate the gravitational force between the electron and proton in the hydrogen atom.
   b. Compare this solution to the solution of Problem 5. How many orders of magnitude greater is the electric force between the two particles than the gravitational force between the two particles?
7. Two pith balls shown in Figure 21-12a have a mass of 1.0 g each and have equal charges. One pith ball is suspended by an insulating thread. The other charge is brought to within 3 cm of the suspended ball ($r = 0.03$ m). The suspended pith ball is deflected from its rest position until the thread forms an angle of 30° with the vertical. At this angle, the ball is in equilibrium. Equilibrium exists because $F_E$ and $mg$ add vectorially to yield the equilibrant of $T$. Calculate
   a. $mg$       b. $F_E$       c. the charge on the pith balls

**FIGURE 21-12. Use with Problems 7 and 8.**

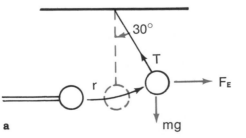

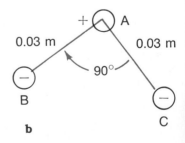

8. Charges of $6.0 \times 10^{-6}$ C exist on the three spheres in Figure 21-12b. Find the magnitude of the resultant force on sphere *A*.

9. A charge of $2.0 \times 10^{-4}$ C is placed in the electric field around a larger object which has a negative charge. The force acting on the charge is $8.0 \times 10^{-4}$ N.
   a. What is the intensity of the electric field at the position of the test charge?
   b. Is the field directed toward or away from the larger object?

10. What net force acts on a test charge of $4.0 \times 10^{-3}$ C when it is in an electric field at a point where the field intensity is 20 N/C?

11. What charge exists on a test charge that experiences a force of $1.0 \times 10^{-8}$ N at a point where the electric field intensity is $2.0 \times 10^{-4}$ N/C?

12. A positive test charge of $3.0 \times 10^{-4}$ C is placed between a pair of parallel plates. One is positive and the other is negative. The force acting on the test charge is 0.9 N.
   a. What is the intensity of the field at the location of the charge?
   b. The charge is moved 2.0 cm closer to the positive plate. What force acts on it?

---

1. *A Gram of Electrons:* The mass of a single electron is $9.1 \times 10^{-31}$ kg.
   a. Express the mass of the electron in grams.
   b. How many electrons are in a gram of electrons?
   c. What charge, in coulombs, would a gram of electrons carry?
   d. What force of repulsion would exist between a gram of electrons located on the moon and a gram of electrons located on the earth, $4.0 \times 10^5$ km away?

2. *The Nucleus:* Early experiments with cyclotrons indicated that the force needed to overcome the nuclear force between two protons inside a nucleus is 9.2 N. The nuclear force is the force that restrains the electric (coulomb) force from causing the nucleus to fly apart. Assuming that the nuclear force is just equal to the coulomb force, calculate the distance between two protons in a nucleus. The proton carries a single positive elementary unit of charge, $1.6 \times 10^{-19}$ C.

**Applying Physics**

---

Clarke, Arthur C., "Electronic Tutors." *Omni*, June, 1980.
Moore, A. D., "Electrostatics." *Scientific American*, March, 1972.
Seegar, Raymond J., *Benjamin Franklin*. Pergammon Press, 1974.
Walsh, William J., "Advanced Batteries for Electric Vehicles." *Physics Today*, June, 1980.

**Readings**

The availability of large, inexpensive supplies of electricity is important to the development of a nation. Without electricity, industry would grind to a halt, communications would cease, and our food supply would be seriously affected. The utilization of electric current allows us to enjoy our present standard of living. How is electric current controlled? What is involved in the design of high voltage transmission lines that allow current to flow with a minimum of energy loss?

# Electric Currents 22

The most important aspect of electricity is its ability to transfer energy. The large amounts of natural potential and kinetic energy possessed by such resources as Niagara Falls are of little use to an industrial complex one hundred kilometers away unless that energy can be transferred efficiently. Electricity provides the means to transfer large quantities of energy great distances with little loss.

Many devices that we now consider vital would not operate at all were it not for electric technology. Among these devices are radio, television, computers, telephones, automobiles, and a great many machines of a medical nature upon which life itself can depend.

## 22:1 Electric Potential Energy

When a mass is raised to a height above the surface of the earth, the earth-mass system has energy it previously did not have. If the mass falls back to the earth, this energy can be used to do work. The system has energy because the earth and the mass attract one another. Work is done to lift the mass from the surface of the earth against the attractive force. This work is reclaimed as the mass returns to the surface of the earth.

363

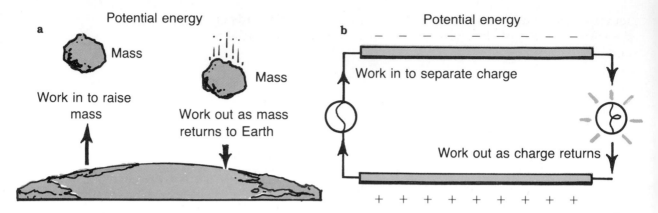

Potential energy

Mass

Work in to raise
mass

Mass

Work out as mass
returns to Earth

b

Potential energy

Work in to separate charge

Work out as charge returns

**FIGURE 22-1. Gravitational potential difference (a) and electric potential difference (b) are both found by multiplying field intensity by distance moved.**

Work must be done to separate charges.

Separated charges possess potential energy.

If charges are separated so that one object has an excess of electrons and another object lacks electrons, the situation is similar to the one just described. Electrons must be forced from the positive plate through some distance onto the negative plate. Work is done to separate the charges. The work is reclaimed when the charge moves back to the positive plate. While on the negative plate, the electrons have potential energy with respect to the positive plate. When the electrons flow from the negative plate to the positive plate, the flow is an electric current. Therefore, electric currents deliver energy.

Electric potential energy is more complex than gravitational potential energy. The gravitational force between the earth and a mass is always attractive. Electric forces are both attractive and repulsive. Also, the gravitational force acting on a unit mass near the surface of the earth is almost the same everywhere on the earth. The electric force acting on a unit charge depends on the charge intensity on the plates involved. Gravitational potential energy and electric potential energy are similar in that work is done to create the potential energy. Also, in both cases the same amount of work is done when the potential energy is used.

In order to have electric potential energy, it is not necessary to have both a negatively charged object and a positively charged object. Electrons always flow from areas of higher concentration to areas of lower concentration. Thus, if a wire connects two negatively charged objects, electrons flow from the object of higher electron concentration to the object of lower electron concentration. Likewise, electrons flow from a negatively-charged object to a neutral object or from a neutral object to a positively-charged object. When a wire connects two objects having different concentrations of electrons, electrons flow from the higher concentration to the lower.

Objects with different concentrations of electrons have a difference in potential between them. Thus, the two objects are a

**FIGURE 22-2. Electrons always flow from an area of higher electron concentration to an area of lower electron concentration.**

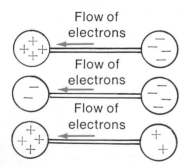

Flow of
electrons

Flow of
electrons

Flow of
electrons

source of potential energy. The difference in potential depends on the concentration of electrons on each. Difference in potential is measured in volts, V.

## 22:2 Difference in Potential and Field Intensity

The magnitude and direction of any field is measured by placing a standard unit in the field and measuring the force that acts on it. For example, the earth's gravitational field close to the earth has an intensity of 9.8 N/kg. That is, the earth exerts a force of 9.8 N on each kilogram near its surface. The intensity of the gravitational field on the moon is 1.6 N/kg.

To lift 1 kg of mass one meter above the surface of the earth requires a force of 9.8 N acting through a distance of 1 m. This means that 9.8 J of work are done on the mass to lift it one meter. The mass then has 9.8 J of potential energy. Thus, the difference in potential between a point on the surface of the earth and a point one meter above the surface of the earth is 9.8 J/kg. The difference in potential between two points in a field is the work needed to move a unit of whatever is affected by the field between the two points. Note that the potential difference is found by multiplying the field intensity by the distance moved.

*The potential difference between two points in a field is the work required to move a unit charge between the two points.*

$$Potential\ difference = Field\ intensity \times Distance$$
$$9.8\ \text{J/kg} = (9.8\ \text{N/kg})(1\ \text{m})$$

Electric fields affect electric charges. To measure the intensity of an electric field we place a standard charge in the field and measure the force acting on it. Thus, electric field intensity (Chapter 21) is measured in newtons per coulomb (N/C).

Suppose that a coulomb of charge is placed in an electric field. If the field produces a force of 1 N on the charge, the field intensity is 1 N/C. If a force of 1 N is applied to the charge and moves it 1 m against the field, 1 J of work is done on the charge. The coulomb of charge has gained 1 J of potential energy. Thus, the difference in potential between the two points one meter apart is a joule per coulomb. A joule per coulomb is called a **volt.** Note that the potential difference $V$ is found by multiplying the field intensity $E$ by the distance $d$. This is the same method used to find gravitational potential difference. Thus, for electric potential difference

*The potential difference between two points in an electric field is measured in joules per coulomb, or volts.*

*Potential difference is found by multiplying electric field intensity by the distance a charge is moved against the field.*

$$Potential\ difference = Field\ intensity \times Distance$$
$$\boxed{V = Ed}$$

In practice, electric fields are usually more intense than 1 N/C. Also, parallel plates are closer together than 1 m. The Example shows a typical situation.

### EXAMPLE: Potential Difference Between Parallel Plates

Two parallel plates are 0.03 m apart. The electric field intensity between them is 3000 N/C. What is the difference in potential between the plates?

*Solution:*

$$V = Ed$$
$$= (3000 \text{ N/C})(0.03 \text{ m})$$
$$= 90 \text{ N} \cdot \text{m/C}$$
$$= 90 \text{ J/C}$$
$$= 90 \text{ V}$$

### EXAMPLE: Electric Field Intensity Between Two Parallel Plates

A voltmeter shows a difference in potential of 50 V between two parallel metal plates. The plates are 0.05 m apart. What is the field intensity?

*Solution:* $\quad V = Ed \quad$ or $\quad E = \dfrac{V}{d}$

$$= \frac{50 \text{ V}}{0.05 \text{ m}}$$
$$= \frac{50 \text{ J/C}}{0.05 \text{ m}}$$
$$= \frac{50 \text{ N} \cdot \text{m/C}}{0.05 \text{ m}}$$
$$= 1000 \text{ N/C}$$

### PROBLEMS

1. 400 V

**1.** The electric field intensity between two charged metal plates is 800 N/C. The plates are 0.5 m apart. What is the difference in potential between them?

**2.** The field intensity between two plates is 2000 N/C. What is the difference in potential between one parallel plate and a point halfway to a second parallel plate 0.06 m away?

3. 25 000 N/C

**3.** A voltmeter reads 500 V when placed across two parallel plates. The plates are 0.02 m apart. What is the field intensity between them?

**4.** Two plates are 0.008 m apart. The potential difference between them is 200 V. What is the field intensity between the plates?

5. 125 V

**5.** What voltage is applied to two metal plates 0.05 m apart if the field intensity between them is 2500 N/C?

## 22:3   Work and Energy

A difference in potential of 1 volt between two plates means that 1 J of work must be done to transfer 1 C of charge between the plates against the electric field. To transfer 1 C of charge through a potential difference of 100 V against the field, 100 J of work must be done on the charge. To transfer 2 C of charge between the 100-V difference in potential, 200 J of work must be done on the charge. The work done to move a charge against an electric field is given by the expression

$$W = Vq$$

The work done on the charge is stored as electric potential energy. Suppose 1 C of charge flows back between the plates under the influence of the electric field. It delivers exactly the same energy that was used to move it against the field. For example, to move 1 C of charge through a potential difference of 100 volts, 100 J of work are exerted on the charge. When the charge returns through the field, it delivers 100 J of energy. Suppose the charge passes through an electric motor on its return through the field. Then it delivers 100 J of energy to the motor. Thus, the motor is able to do 100 J of work.

*The work done in moving a charge against an electric field is equal to the product of charge and potential difference.*

*Work done to move a charge is stored as electric potential energy.*

**EXAMPLE:  Work Done to Move a Charge Against an Electric Field**

A 5-C charge is transferred through a potential difference of 90 V. **a.** What work is done on the charge? **b.** What is the potential energy of the charge as a result of the transfer?

*Solution:* **a.**    $W = Vq$
$$= (90 \text{ J/}\cancel{C})(5 \ \cancel{C}) = 450 \text{ J}$$

**b.** By the law of conservation of energy, the potential energy is equal to the work done on the charge. Thus,

$$PE = 450 \text{ J}$$

### PROBLEMS

**6.** A generator transfers 1.0 C of charge through a potential difference of 110 V.
   **a.** What work does the generator do?
   **b.** What is the potential energy of 1.0 C of charge after the transfer?

**7.** What work is done by the chemical energy of a dry cell to transfer 5.0 C of negative charge from its positive plate to its negative plate? The dry cell is rated at 1.5 V.

7.  7.5 J

**8.** How much work does the chemical energy of a 90-V battery do to transfer 30 C of charge between its plates?

**9.** A generator transfers 50 C of charge through a potential difference of 110 V.

**9. a. 5500 J**
**b. 1100 J/s**
**c. 1100 W**
**d. 1.1 kW**

   **a.** What work does the generator do to transfer this charge?
   **b.** The generator accomplishes this work in 5.0 s. How much work does it do per second?
   **c.** What power does the generator deliver in watts?
   **d.** What is the power of the generator in kilowatts?

## 22:4   Electric Circuits

An electron flow takes place if two plates having a difference in potential are connected by a conductor. The flow of electrons is an **electric current.** To be useful, the current must be maintained. The only way to maintain a current is to maintain a charge on the two plates that are at different potentials. To maintain a potential difference, some device must pump the electrons back to the plate with higher electron concentration as soon as they arrive at the plate with lower concentration. Several devices can pump electrons. Voltaic cells (batteries) and generators are the most common.

Electric current can be maintained only if electrons are returned to areas of high electron concentration.

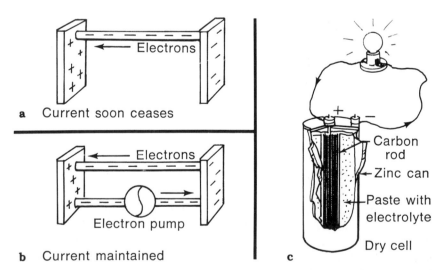

**FIGURE 22-3. Electrons flow from the negative to the positive plate (a). A generator (b) pumps electrons back to the negative plate allowing current to continue to flow. A diagram of an ordinary battery (c).**

A flashlight battery is actually a single cell consisting of a zinc plate and a carbon rod. They are separated by a paste containing an oxidizing agent. The chemical reaction between the oxidizing agent and the zinc causes the plates to maintain an electric charge. Essentially, this reaction is the same as burning a fuel to provide energy.

## 22:5 General Plan of an Electric Circuit

Electric energy is produced by changing an available, natural source of energy to electric energy. In Figure 22-4, the kinetic energy of falling water turns a waterwheel (turbine). The wheel gains kinetic energy. Kinetic energy from the wheel is transferred to the generator by a belt. When the generator turns, electrons are pulled from the positive plate and pushed onto the negative plate. Recall that electrons are attracted by a positive plate and repelled by a negative plate. The generator forces the electrons to move from the positive to the negative plate. The energy of the source is being used to do work on the electrons and charge the plates. The concentration of charge on the plates constitutes electric potential energy. The potential energy stored on the plates is equal to the work done on the generator by the falling water.

A generator forces electrons from a positive plate to the negative plate and gives them electric potential energy.

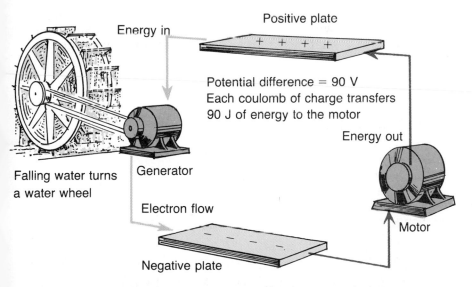

Positive plate

Energy in

Potential difference = 90 V
Each coulomb of charge transfers
90 J of energy to the motor

Energy out

Falling water turns a water wheel

Generator

Electron flow

Motor

Negative plate

**FIGURE 22-4.** This diagram shows the production and use of electric current. Electric potential energy is converted to kinetic energy of the turning motor.

If a wire is connected between the two plates, electric current appears in the wire. Electrons begin to move from the negative plate to the positive plate through the wire. The electrons are said to "fall back through the field" because the situation is similar to a weight falling through the earth's gravitational field to the surface of the earth.

If an electric motor is connected between the two plates, the electric potential energy given up by the electrons as they move from the negative plate to the positive plate will be used to make the motor turn. The electric energy is converted to the kinetic energy of the turning motor.

Electric potential energy can be changed to the kinetic energy of a spinning motor as electrons return to the positive plate.

If the difference in potential between the two plates is 90 V, the generator must do 90 J of work on every coulomb of charge that it transfers from the positive plate to the negative plate. Thus, every coulomb of charge that moves from the negative plate back to the positive plate through the motor delivers 90 J of energy to the motor. Note that electricity serves as a way to transfer the kinetic energy of falling water to the kinetic energy of a turning motor. In practice, the two plates are not necessary. The wires themselves serve the same purpose.

## 22:6  Ampere and Electric Power

The unit used for quantity of electric charge is the coulomb. Thus, the rate of flow of electric charge, or electric current, is measured in coulombs per second. In electrical terms, a flow of a coulomb per second is called an **ampere,** A.

**Electric current is measured in amperes.**

$$1 \text{ C/s} = 1 \text{ A}$$

Suppose that the current through the motor of Figure 22-4 is 3 C/s (3 A). The potential difference of 90 V means that each coulomb of charge supplies the motor with 90 J of energy. The energy delivered to the motor per second is

$$(90 \text{ J/}\mathcal{C})(3 \text{ }\mathcal{C}\text{/s}) = 270 \text{ J/s} = 270 \text{ watts}$$

Clearly, the power used by any electric device is found by multiplying the voltage $V$ by the current $I$.

**Electric power is the product of current and potential difference.**

$$\boxed{P = VI}$$

**EXAMPLE: Electric Power**

A 6-V battery delivers 0.5 A of current to an electric motor connected across its terminals. **a.** What is the power of the motor? **b.** What energy does the motor use in 5.0 min?

*Solution:* **a.**                    $P = VI$

$$= (6 \text{ J/}\mathcal{C})(0.5 \text{ }\mathcal{C}\text{/s}) = 3 \text{ J/s} \quad = 3 \text{ W}$$

**b.** Three watts is equal to 3 J/s. Thus,

$$Energy \ used = (3 \text{ J/s})(300 \text{ s}) \quad = 900 \text{ J}$$

**PROBLEMS**

10. The current through a light bulb connected across the terminals of a 120-V outlet is 0.5 A. At what rate does the bulb use electric energy?

11. 180 W

11. A 90-V battery causes a current of 2.0 A to flow through a lamp. What is the power of the lamp?

12. A toaster connected to a 120-V source uses 4.0 A of current. What power does the toaster use?

**13.** A light bulb uses 1.2 A when connected across a 120-V source. What is the wattage of the bulb?

**14.** What current flows through a 75-W light bulb connected to a 120-V outlet?

**15.** The current through a motor connected to a 60-V battery is 2.0 A. What energy in joules does the motor use in 5.0 min?

**16.** A lamp is connected across a 24-V difference in potential. The current flowing through the lamp is 4.0 A.
   **a.** What power does the lamp use?
   **b.** How much electric energy does the lamp use in 10 min?

**17.** A lamp draws 0.5 A from a 120-V generator.
   **a.** How much power does the generator deliver?
   **b.** How much energy does the lamp use in 5 minutes?

13. 144 W

15. 36 000 J

17. a. 60 J/s
    b. 18 000 J

## 22:7  Ohm's Law

The German scientist Georg Simon Ohm (1787–1854) discovered that the ratio of the potential difference between the ends of a wire and the current flowing through the wire is a constant. This ratio is known as the **resistance** of a wire. It is constant for any given wire. This relationship, known as Ohm's law states that *the current flowing through a given wire varies directly with the applied voltage.*

$$I = \frac{V}{R}$$

The electron current flow $I$ is in amperes. The potential difference $V$ is in volts. The resistance of the conductor $R$ is given in ohms. An **ohm,** $\Omega$, is the resistance which permits a current of 1 A to flow through a potential difference of 1 V.

A higher voltage causes a greater current flow between the ends of a conductor. To obtain a higher voltage, a more intense charge must be placed on the plates. This higher voltage (greater potential difference) causes the electric field between the plates to become more intense. This more intense field moves a greater number of electrons per unit time between the plates.

**EXAMPLE: Ohm's Law**

What current flows between a potential difference of 120 V through a resistance of 30 $\Omega$?

*Solution:*

$$I = \frac{V}{R}$$

$$= \frac{120 \text{ V}}{30 \text{ }\Omega} = 4 \text{ A}$$

$$I = \frac{V}{R}$$

$$= \frac{30 \text{ V}}{10 \text{ }\Omega}$$

$$= 3A$$

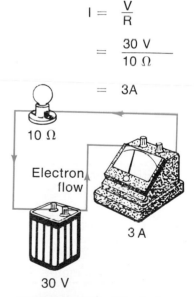

10 $\Omega$

Electron flow

3 A

30 V

**FIGURE 22-5. Ohm's law is illustrated in calculating the current between a potential difference of 30 volts and a resistance of 10 ohms.**

The current in an electric circuit varies directly with the applied voltage and inversely with the resistance.

**PROBLEMS**

**18.** A resistance of 30 Ω is placed across a 90-V battery. What current flows in the circuit?

**19. 5 A**

**19.** A voltage of 75 V is placed across a 15-Ω resistor. What current flows through the resistor?

**20.** A current of 0.5 A flows through a lamp when it is connected to a 120-V source.
**a.** What is the resistance of the lamp?
**b.** What is the wattage of the lamp?

**21. 120 V**

**21.** A motor with an operating resistance of 30 Ω is connected to a voltage source. The current in the circuit is 4.0 A. What is the voltage of the source?

**22.** A transistor radio uses 0.2 A of current when it is operated by a 3-V battery. What is the resistance of the radio circuit?

**23. 24 V**

**23.** A resistance of 60 Ω allows 0.4 A of current to flow when it is connected to the terminals of a battery. What is the voltage of the battery?

## 22:8   Diagramming Electric Circuits

Figure 22-6 shows a simple electric circuit and a diagram of the same circuit. The jagged line in the diagram represents the resistance (device being operated). The alternate long and short lines represent a battery. The short lines indicate negative terminals. The long lines indicate positive terminals.

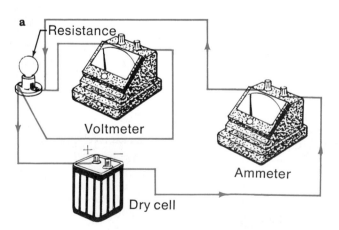

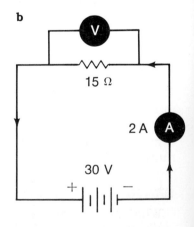

**FIGURE 22-6. A simple electric circuit is represented both pictorially (a) and schematically (b).**

A **voltmeter** measures the drop in potential across the resistance. The voltmeter is connected to each side of the resistance. The voltmeter is said to be in parallel with the resistance. An **ammeter** measures the current flowing in the circuit. It is connected directly into the circuit, and the entire current flows through the ammeter. The ammeter is said to be in series with the resistance.

The resistance in the circuit shown is a light bulb. In a precise measurement, the resistance of the connecting wires must also be included. However, the resistance of such wires is usually low enough to overlook.

**PROBLEMS**

**24.** Draw a diagram to show a circuit that indicates a 90-V battery, an ammeter, and a resistance of 60 Ω. What does the ammeter read?

**25.** Draw a circuit diagram to include a 60-V battery, an ammeter, and a resistance of 12.5 Ω. Indicate the ammeter reading.

**26.** Draw a circuit diagram to include a 16-Ω resistor, a battery, and an ammeter that reads 1.75 A. Indicate the voltage of the battery.

25.  4.8 A

## 22:9  Controlling Current in a Circuit

There are two ways to control the current that flows in a circuit. Since $I = V/R$, $I$ can be changed by varying either $V$, $R$, or both. Figure 22-7 shows a simple circuit. When $V$ is 60 V and $R$ is 30 Ω, the current flow is 2.0 A. This value may be more current than the resistance should have flowing through it for proper use. To reduce the current, the 60-V battery could be replaced with a 30-V battery, Figure 22-7b. The current can also be reduced by increasing the resistance to 60 Ω by adding a 30 Ω resistor to the circuit, Figure 22-7c. Both of these methods will reduce the current to 1.0 A. Resistors used to control the current flow in electric circuits are control resistors. Control resistors are used to send the proper amount of current through circuits or parts of circuits. Radios use such resistors.

Current in a circuit can be controlled by adjusting either voltage or resistance.

**FIGURE 22-7. The current flow through a simple circuit (a) can be regulated by removing some of the dry cells (b), or by increasing the resistance of the circuit (c).**

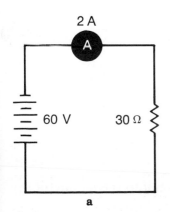

a

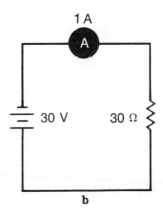

b

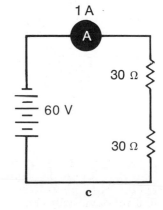

c

Sometimes it is necessary to vary the current flow through a resistor. The electric motors used on ripple tanks are usually arranged so that the current through them can be varied. As a result, the motor can run at different speeds by adding a variable resistor to the circuit, Figure 22-8. A **variable resistor** consists of a coil of wire and a sliding contact point. By moving the contact point to various positions along the coil, the amount of wire added to the circuit is varied. With more wire placed in the circuit, the resistance of the circuit increases. Thus, less current flows, in accordance with Ohm's law. In this way, the speed of the motor can be adjusted. The same type of device controls the speed of electric fans, electric mixers, and other appliances.

The resistance of a resistor can change during use. Sometimes the temperature of a resistor increases during use. This temperature change causes its resistance to change. Light bulbs increase in resistance after they have been on for a while. If the resistance of a circuit changes while it operates, the current flow changes accordingly.

**FIGURE 22-8. A variable resistor can be used to regulate current in an electric circuit.**

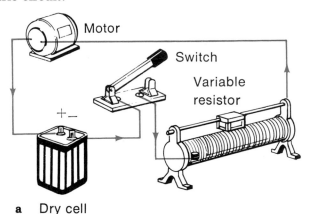

**a**   Dry cell

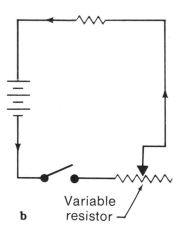

**b**   Variable resistor

## 22:10   Heating Effect of Electric Currents

The power (energy per unit time) used by an electric circuit is equal to the voltage multiplied by the current. From Ohm's law we know that $V = IR$. Substituting this expression into the equation for electric power

$$P = VI$$
$$= IR \times I$$
$$= I^2R$$

The power used by a resistor varies directly with the square of current in the resistor.

The power used by a resistor is proportional to the square of the current that passes through it and its resistance.

The power supplied to a circuit can be used in different ways. A motor converts electric energy into mechanical energy. An electric light generates light. However, not all of the electric energy used by a motor or an electric light ends up as work or light. All electric devices also generate heat. Some devices are designed for the purpose of supplying heat.

The energy supplied to a resistor is the power used by the resistor multiplied by the time of its operation.

$$Energy = Pt$$
$$= (watts)(seconds)$$
$$= (J/s)(s)$$
$$= J$$

The expression for power is $I^2R$. The total energy supplied to any device, $Pt$, is $I^2Rt$.

The heat developed by a heating coil, assuming 100 percent of the electric energy is converted to heat, equals the energy consumed during the time it is operated. Thus,

$$\Delta Q = I^2Rt$$

*The power also varies directly with the resistance.*

*The total energy supplied to any device is the product of power and time.*

*The heat energy developed in a resistor is given by the equation $\Delta Q = I^2Rt$.*

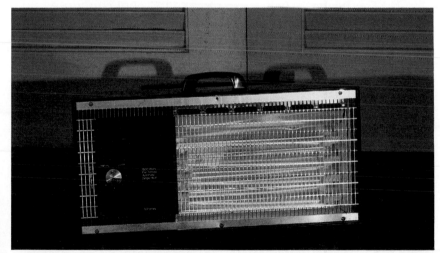

**FIGURE 22-9. The coils of this space heater are an example of the conversion of electric energy to heat.**

*Philip M. Jordain*

**EXAMPLE:  Heat Produced by an Electric Current**

A heating coil has a resistance of 10 $\Omega$. It is designed to operate on 120 V. **a.** What current flows through the coil? **b.** What thermal energy in joules is supplied by the heater in 10 s?

*Solution:* **a.**       $I = \dfrac{V}{R} = \dfrac{120 \text{ V}}{10 \text{ }\Omega} = 12 \text{ A}$

**b.**       $\Delta Q = I^2Rt$
$$= (12 \text{ A})^2(10 \text{ }\Omega)(10 \text{ s}) = 14\ 400 \text{ J}$$

**PROBLEMS**

27. a. **8 A**
    b. **2.9 × 10⁴ J**
    c. **2.9 × 10⁴ J**

**27.** A 15-Ω electric heater operates on a 120-V outlet.
    **a.** What current flows through the heater?
    **b.** How much energy is used by the heater in 30 seconds?
    **c.** How much heat is liberated by the heater in this time?

**28.** A 30-Ω resistor is connected to a 60-V battery.
    **a.** What is the current in the circuit?
    **b.** How much energy is used by the resistor in 5 minutes?

29. a. **20 A**
    b. **1.3 × 10⁵ J**
    c. **18 C°**

**29.** The resistance of an electric stove element at operating temperature is 11 Ω.
    **a.** 220 V are applied to it. What current flows through the element?
    **b.** How much energy does the element use in 30 s?
    **c.** The element is being used to heat a kettle containing 1.20 kg of water. Assume that 70% of the heat is absorbed by the water. What is its increase in temperature during the 30 s?

**30.** An electric heater is rated at 500 W.
    **a.** How much energy does the heater use in half an hour?
    **b.** The heater is being used to heat a room containing 50.0 kg of air. If the specific heat of air is 1.1 kJ/kg·C° (1100 J/kg·C°) and 50% of the heat effectively heats the air in the room, what is its change in temperature?

31. a. **1.2 × 10³ J**
    b. **4.8 × 10³ J**

**31.** A 100-W light bulb is 20% efficient.
    **a.** How many joules does the light bulb convert into light each minute it is in operation?
    **b.** How many joules of heat does the light bulb produce each minute?

**32.** How much energy does a 60-W light bulb use in half an hour? If the light bulb is 25% efficient, how much heat does it generate during the half hour?

## 22:11 Transmission of Current over Long Distances

The large sources of available energy found at places such as Niagara Falls and Hoover Dam are not always located near areas where electricity is in greatest demand. Accordingly, electric energy must often be transmitted over long distances. Clearly, it is important to accomplish this transfer with as little energy loss as possible.

The relationship $\Delta Q = I^2Rt$ points out that when a current flows through electric conductors, heat must result. All electric conductors generate heat. The heat produced is proportional to the resistance of the conductor and to the square of the current flowing through the conductor.

Except in the case of electric heaters, which are specifically designed to develop heat, the heat loss of an electric conductor serves no useful purpose and is wasted energy. In the case of a conductor of low resistance such as an ordinary lamp cord, the heat developed is negligible. However, the resistance of an electric conductor increases with length. This statement means that when electric energy must be transmitted great distances, the energy loss in the form of heat can be considerable. This energy loss is referred to by electrical engineers as the "$I^2R$" loss.

It is clearly to the advantage of power companies and in the interest of consumers to keep the $I^2R$ loss to a minimum during transmission. Reducing the $I^2R$ loss is done in two ways. Obviously, the conductors used to transmit electric energy must have the lowest possible resistance. Cables of high conductivity and large diameter fit this purpose well. However, since the loss is also proportional to the square of the current in the conductors, it is of even greater importance to keep the current in the lines at a very low value.

The energy transmitted per second (power) that moves by way of long-distance transmission lines follows the relationship $P = VI$. By keeping the voltage across these lines very high, it is possible to transmit large amounts of energy per second and keep the current in the lines at a low value. This low current reduces the $I^2R$ loss by keeping the $I^2$ factors low. Long-distance transmission lines always operate at high voltages to reduce this loss.

High-voltage lines are needed to transmit electric energy over long distances with minimum energy loss.

*Frank Cezus/Alpha*

**FIGURE 22-10. High-voltage transmission lines carry electricity over long distances.**

## 22:12   The Kilowatt Hour

While electric companies are often called "power" companies it is energy that they provide. When you pay your electric bill you are paying for energy, not power.

The electric energy used by any device is its rate of energy consumption in joules per second (watts) times the number of seconds it is operated. That is, joules per second times seconds (J/s × s) equals total joules of energy.

**The kilowatt hour is a rate of energy consumption (power) multiplied by the time, one hour.**

The joule is a relatively small amount of energy. For that reason electric companies measure their energy sales in a large block of joules called a kilowatt hour, kWh. A kilowatt hour is the energy represented by 1000 watts delivered continuously for 3600 seconds, which is one hour. It is, therefore,

$$1 \text{ kWh} = (1000 \text{ J/s})(3600 \text{ s}) = 3.6 \times 10^6 \text{ J}$$

Not many devices in the home other than heaters and hair dryers draw 1000 watts. Ten 100-watt light bulbs operating all at once would use a kilowatt hour of energy if left on for a full hour.

**FIGURE 22-11. Watthour meters (a) measure the amount of electric energy used by a consumer. The more current being used at a given time, the faster the horizontal disk in the center of the meter turns. Meter readings are then used in calculating the cost of energy use (b).**

a                                                        *William Maddox*

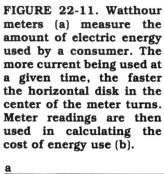

b                                                        *Thomas Russell*

### EXAMPLE:   The Cost of Operating an Electric Device

A color television set draws 5.0 A when operated on 120 V. **a.** How much power does the set use? **b.** If the set is operated for an average of 10 hours per day, what energy in kWh does it consume per month (30 days)? **c.** At $0.08 per kWh what is the cost of operating the set per month?

*Solution:* **a.** $P = VI$

$$= (120 \text{ J/C})(5.0 \text{ C/s}) = 600 \text{ W}$$

**b.** $Energy = Pt$

$$= (600 \text{ J/s})(3600 \text{ s/h})(10 \text{ h/day})(30 \text{ days})$$

$$= 6.48 \times 10^8 \text{ J}$$

$$= \frac{6.48 \times 10^8 \text{ J}}{3.6 \times 10^6 \text{ J/kWh}} = 180 \text{ kWh}$$

**c.** $(180 \text{ kWh})(\$0.08/\text{kWh}) = \$14.40$

## PROBLEMS

**33.** An electric space heater draws 15.0 A on a 120-V line. It is operated, on the average, for 5.0 h each day.
  **a.** How much power does the heater use?
  **b.** How much energy in kWh does it consume per month (30 days)?
  **c.** At $0.08 per kWh, what does it cost to operate the heater per month?

**34.** A digital clock has an operating resistance of 4600 $\Omega$ and is plugged into a 115-V outlet.
  **a.** How much current does it draw?
  **b.** How much power does it use?
  **c.** If the owner of the clock pays $0.07 per kWh, what does it cost to operate the clock for a month (30 days)?

**Summary**

**1.** An electric current transfers energy from place to place.  *Intro.*

**2.** To create a potential difference, work must be done to move a charge against an electric field.  **22:1**

**3.** The work done on the charge is measured in joules per coulomb which are called volts.  **22:2**

**4.** As charge flows back from the negative plate to the positive plate it gives up its potential energy. The energy released equals the work done to give the charge potential energy.  **22:3**

**5.** One ampere is a current flow of one coulomb per second.  **22:6**

**6.** Electric power is found by multiplying voltage by current ($V \times I$).  **22:6**

**7.** Ohm's law states that the current flowing in a circuit varies directly with the applied voltage and inversely with the resistance of the circuit.  **22:7**

**8.** The current in a circuit can be varied by varying the voltage or by varying the resistance of the circuit.  **22:9**

**9.** A kilowatt hour, kWh, is an energy unit. It is equal to $3.6 \times 10^6$ J.  **22:12**

## Questions

1. Define a volt in terms of work done against an electric field.
2. How is gravitational difference in potential expressed? How is electric difference in potential expressed?
3. If 120 joules of work must be done to move one coulomb of charge from a positive plate to a negative plate, what voltage exists between the plates?
4. In Europe, electric outlets provide 220 V. In North America, home outlets provide 120 V.
   a. What would happen if a tourist from North America took an electric razor to Europe and plugged it into an outlet at a hotel?
   b. What would happen if a tourist from Europe brought an electric razor to a North American hotel and plugged it in?
5. Electric space heaters are manufactured in a variety of different designs. When purchasing such a heater what information should you look for to decide if it will adequately heat the area you have in mind?
6. A 12-V battery is connected to a 4-Ω resistor.
   a. What current flows in the circuit?
   b. State two ways to reduce the current to 1.5 A.
7. What quantities must be kept small to transmit electric energy over long distances economically?

## Problems

1. The electric field intensity between two charged plates is 1500 N/C. The plates are 0.08 m apart. What is the difference in potential between them in volts?
2. A voltmeter indicates that the difference in potential between two plates is 50 V. The plates are 0.02 m apart. What field intensity exists between them?
3. What voltage is applied to a pair of parallel plates 0.04 m apart to develop a field intensity of 2500 N/C?
4. How much work is done to transfer 1.0 C of charge through a potential difference of 220 V?
5. A generator transfers 20 C of charge through 90 V.
   a. How much work does the generator perform?
   b. The generator accomplishes this transfer in 60 s. How much work does it do per second?
   c. How much power does the generator deliver in watts?
6. A 60-V battery transfers 22 C of negative charge from its negative plate to its positive plate. How much work is done?
7. How much work is done to transfer 6.0 C of charge through 1.5 V?
8. A force of 50 N is needed to move a negative charge of 1.0 C from a positive plate to a negative plate.
   a. What is the intensity of the electric field between the two plates?

**b.** How much work is done to move the charge between the two plates if they are 5.0 cm (0.05 m) apart?

**c.** What is the potential energy in joules of the charge after it is moved between the plates?

**d.** What is the difference in potential between the plates in J/C?

**e.** What is the difference in potential between the plates in volts?

**9.** A 12-V battery is connected to an electric motor. The current through the motor is 2.0 A.

  **a.** How many joules of energy does the battery deliver to the motor each second?

  **b.** What power does the motor use in watts?

  **c.** How much energy does the motor use in 10 min?

**10.** A 20-$\Omega$ resistor is connected to a 30-V battery. What current flows through the resistor?

**11.** What voltage is applied to a 4-$\Omega$ resistor if the current is 1.5 A?

**12.** What voltage is placed across a motor of 15 $\Omega$ operating resistance to deliver 8.0 A of current?

**13.** A 6-$\Omega$ resistor is connected to a 15-V battery.

  **a.** What is the current in the circuit?

  **b.** How much heat is produced in 10 minutes?

**14.** A heating coil has a resistance of 4.0 $\Omega$ and operates on 120 V.

  **a.** What current flows through the coil while it is operating?

  **b.** What energy is supplied to the coil in 5.0 min?

  **c.** If the coil is immersed in an insulated container holding 20.0 kg of water what will be the increase in the temperature of the water? Assume that 100% of the heat is absorbed by the water.

**Applying Physics**

**1.** *Electrical Engineering:* An electric motor operates a pump which irrigates a farmer's crop by pumping 10 000 L of water a vertical distance of 8.0 m into a field each hour. The motor has an operating resistance of 22.0 $\Omega$ and is connected across a 110-V source.

  **a.** What current does it draw?    **b.** How efficient is the motor?

**2.** *Electronics:* A transistor radio operates by means of a 9.0-V battery that supplies it with 50 milliamperes (0.050 A) of current.

  **a.** If the cost of the battery is $0.90 and it lasts for 300 h what is the cost per kWh to operate the radio in this manner?

  **b.** The same radio, by means of a converter, is plugged into a household circuit by a homeowner who pays $0.08 per kWh. What does it now cost to operate the radio for 300 hours?

**Readings**

Kocivar, Ben, "Sun-Powered Planes." *Popular Science,* July, 1980.

Overbye, Dennis, "The Ears of Socorro." *Discover,* October, 1980.

Solomon, Stephen, "Amazing Machines." *Science Digest,* Nov/Dec, 1980.

How resistors are connected into an electric circuit determines the total resistance in a circuit. How electronic devices, which are part of the total circuit, are connected also determines the way the system will function. What components of this computer circuit do you recognize? What are the advantages of connecting the resistors in series? In parallel?

# Series and Parallel Circuits 23

You have flipped a switch to turn on an electric light. You may also have pushed a button to turn on a record player or an iron. In each case, you completed an electric circuit. When a circuit is complete, an electric current flows through the circuit.

The way in which parts of a circuit are arranged affects the flow of current through the circuit. There are two basic types of circuits. One type is a series circuit. The other is a parallel circuit. A break in a **series circuit** stops the current flow in the whole circuit. A break in a **parallel circuit** stops the current flow in only a portion of the circuit. Let us take a closer look to see why these two types of circuits function as they do.

GOAL: You will gain knowledge and understanding of series and parallel circuits, and of the function of ammeters and voltmeters.

## 23:1  Series Circuits

When resistors are connected in series, current travels through each resistor one after the other. Figure 23-1 shows a series circuit. The electron current in the circuit passes through each appliance (resistance) in succession. The current through each resistance is exactly the same. The current flowing in a series circuit is the same everywhere along the wire.

In a series circuit, the current is the same at all points along the wire.

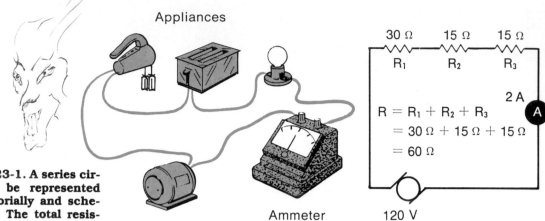

Appliances

Generator

Ammeter

120 V

$$R = R_1 + R_2 + R_3$$
$$= 30\ \Omega + 15\ \Omega + 15\ \Omega$$
$$= 60\ \Omega$$

**FIGURE 23-1. A series circuit can be represented both pictorially and schematically. The total resistance of a series circuit is equal to the sum of the individual resistances.**

The total resistance in a series circuit is the sum of the individual resistances.

The current encounters resistance by each resistor in turn. Thus, it is opposed by the sum of the resistances. The total resistance $R$ of a series circuit is equal to the sum of the individual resistances in the circuit.

$$R = R_1 + R_2 + R_3 + \cdots$$

To find the current flowing in the circuit, first find the total resistance of the circuit. Then apply Ohm's law.

**EXAMPLE:  Current Flowing in a Series Circuit**

Four 15-$\Omega$ resistors are connected in series across a 30-V battery. What current flows in the circuit?

*Solution:* Find the total resistance of the circuit.

$$R = R_1 + R_2 + R_3 + R_4$$
$$= 15\ \Omega + 15\ \Omega + 15\ \Omega + 15\ \Omega = 60\ \Omega$$

Then apply Ohm's law to the circuit.

$$I = \frac{V}{R} = \frac{30\ \text{V}}{60\ \Omega} = 0.5\ \text{A}$$

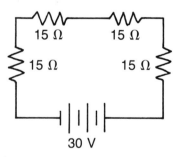

15 $\Omega$    15 $\Omega$

15 $\Omega$    15 $\Omega$

30 V

**FIGURE 23-3. Use with the Example.**

1. a. 60 $\Omega$
   b. 2 A

**PROBLEMS**

**1.** Three 20-$\Omega$ resistors are connected in series across a 120-V generator.
   **a.** What is the total resistance of the circuit?
   **b.** What current flows in the circuit?

**2.** A 10-$\Omega$ resistor, a 15-$\Omega$ resistor, and a 5-$\Omega$ resistor are connected in series across a 90-V battery.
   **a.** What is the total resistance of the circuit?
   **b.** What current flows in the circuit?

**3.** Ten Christmas tree bulbs have equal resistances. When connected to a 120-V outlet, a current of 0.5 A flows through the bulbs.

  **a.** What is the total resistance of the circuit?

  **b.** What is the resistance of each bulb?

**4.** A 16-Ω resistor, a 14-Ω resistor, and a 30-Ω resistor are connected in series across a 45-V battery.

  **a.** What is the total resistance of the circuit?

  **b.** What current flows in the circuit?

**5.** A lamp having a resistance of 10 Ω is connected across a 15-V battery.

  **a.** What current flows through the lamp?

  **b.** What resistance must be connected in series with the lamp to reduce the current to 0.5 A?

**6. a.** What current flows through a 60-W bulb when it is connected across a 120-V outlet?

  **b.** What is the resistance of two 60-W bulbs connected in series?

  **c.** What current flows through the two bulbs when connected in series and placed across a 120-V outlet?

**3. a.** 240 Ω
  **b.** 24 Ω

**5. a.** 1.5 A
  **b.** 20 Ω

## 23:2   Voltage Drops in a Series Circuit

The total resistance of the circuit in Figure 23-3 is

$$10 \ \Omega + 20 \ \Omega + 30 \ \Omega, \text{ or } 60 \ \Omega.$$

By Ohm's law, the current in the circuit is

$$\frac{120 \text{ V}}{60 \ \Omega} = 2 \text{ A}$$

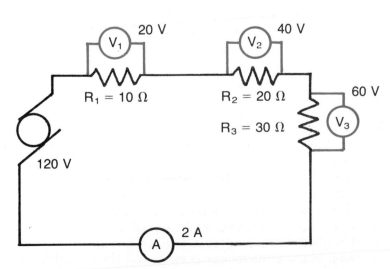

FIGURE 23-3. A series circuit diagram showing the voltage drops across the resistors.

When resistors are connected in series, each resistor uses a part of the voltage applied to the circuit. According to Ohm's law, the voltage used is proportional to the resistance. To determine the voltage drop across each resistor, multiply the current in the circuit by the resistance. Thus, in Figure 23-3

$$V_1 = IR_1 = (2 \text{ A})(10 \text{ } \Omega) = \quad 20 \text{ V}$$
$$V_2 = IR_2 = (2 \text{ A})(20 \text{ } \Omega) = \quad 40 \text{ V}$$
$$V_3 = IR_3 = (2 \text{ A})(30 \text{ } \Omega) = \quad 60 \text{ V}$$
$$V = 120 \text{ V}$$

**In a series circuit, the sum of the voltage drops equals the voltage drop across the entire circuit.**

The voltage drops are 20 V, 40 V, and 60 V respectively. The sum of the voltage drops across the resistors is equal to the voltage drop across the entire circuit, in this case, 120 V.

$$V = V_1 + V_2 + V_3$$

**EXAMPLE: Voltage Drops in a Series Circuit**

A 5-$\Omega$ resistor and a 10-$\Omega$ resistor are connected in series and placed across a 45-V potential difference. **a.** What is the total resistance of the circuit? **b.** What current flows through the circuit? **c.** What is the voltage drop across each resistor? **d.** What is the total voltage drop across the circuit?

*Solution:* **a.** $\qquad\quad R = R_1 + R_2$

$$= 5 \text{ } \Omega + 10 \text{ } \Omega = 15 \text{ } \Omega$$

**b.** $\qquad\quad I = \dfrac{V}{R} = \dfrac{45 \text{ V}}{15 \text{ } \Omega} = 3 \text{ A}$

**c.** The voltage drop across $R_1$ is

$$V_1 = IR_1$$
$$= (3 \text{ A})(5 \text{ } \Omega) = 15 \text{ V}$$

The voltage drop across $R_2$ is
$$V_2 = IR_2$$
$$= (3 \text{ A})(10 \text{ } \Omega) = 30 \text{ V}$$

**d.** $\qquad\quad V = V_1 + V_2$
$$= 15 \text{ V} + 30 \text{ V} = 45 \text{ V}$$

**PROBLEMS**

7. a. 50 $\Omega$
   b. 2 A
   c. 40 V, 60 V
   d. 100 V

**7.** A 20-$\Omega$ resistor and a 30-$\Omega$ resistor are connected in series and placed across a 100-V potential difference.
   **a.** What is the total resistance of the circuit?
   **b.** What current flows through the circuit?
   **c.** What is the voltage drop across each resistor?
   **d.** What is the total voltage drop across the circuit?

**8.** Three 30-Ω resistors are connected in series and placed across a difference in potential of 135 V.
   **a.** What is the total resistance of the circuit?
   **b.** What is the current flowing in the circuit?
   **c.** How much voltage is dropped across each resistance?
   **d.** What is the total voltage drop across all three resistors?

**9.** Three resistors of 3 Ω, 5 Ω, and 4 Ω are connected in series across a 12-V battery.
   **a.** What is the combined resistance of the three resistors?
   **b.** What current flows in the circuit?
   **c.** What is the voltage drop across each resistor?
   **d.** What is the total voltage drop across the circuit?

9. a. 12 Ω
   b. 1 A
   c. $V_1 = 3\,V, V_2 = 5\,V,$
      $V_3 = 4\,V$
   d. 12 V

**10.** Four resistors of 6 Ω each are connected in series and placed across a voltage source. The current flowing in the circuit is 1.6 A.
   **a.** What is the total resistance of the circuit?
   **b.** What is the voltage of the source?
   **c.** What is the voltage drop across each of the resistors?

**11.** A 10-Ω resistor and a variable resistor are connected in series and placed across a 12-V source. The variable resistor is adjusted until the current flowing in the circuit is 0.6 A.
   **a.** At what resistance is the variable resistor set?
   **b.** What are the voltage drops across the resistor and across the variable resistor?

11. a. 10 Ω
    b. $V_1 = 6\,V, V_2 = 6\,V$

**12.** A 40-Ω resistor and a variable resistor are connected in series across a 120-V outlet. Using the currents that follow determine the value at which the variable resistor is set.
   **a.** 2 A   **b.** 0.5 A

# 23:3  Parallel Circuits

Figure 23-4 shows three resistors connected in parallel across a 120-V potential difference. The wires running from the generator to points *A* and *B* have very little resistance and are not considered resistors.

Each line from *A* to *B* is a complete circuit across the generator and behaves as if the other lines are not present. A 60-Ω resistor across a difference in potential of 120 V allows a current of 2 A to flow.

In a parallel circuit, each resistor provides a new path for electrons to flow.

$$I = \frac{V}{R} = \frac{120\ V}{60\ \Omega} = 2\ A$$

Each 60-Ω resistor in Figure 23-4 allows 2 A of current to flow between points *A* and *B*. Thus, the total current between the two points is 6 A.

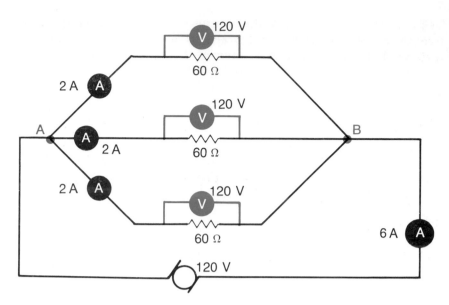

**FIGURE 23-4. In a parallel circuit, the reciprocal of the total resistance is equal to the sum of the reciprocals of the individual resistances. Here you see three 60-ohm resistors connected in parallel. For each resistor, the voltage drop is 120 volts and the current is 2 amperes.**

In terms of Ohm's law, the circuit as a whole has a total resistance of only 20 Ω.

$$R = \frac{V}{I} = \frac{120 \text{ V}}{6 \text{ A}} = 20 \text{ } \Omega$$

Placing resistors in parallel always decreases the total resistance of the circuit. The total resistance decreases because each new resistor provides an additional path for the electrons to follow between points *A* and *B*. Notice that the total resistance of the circuit is less than the resistance of any single resistor in the circuit. This statement is true of all parallel circuits.

**The total resistance of a parallel circuit decreases as each new resistor is added.**

The total resistance of a parallel circuit may be calculated in advance by using the equation

$$\frac{1}{R} = \frac{1}{R_1} + \frac{1}{R_2} + \frac{1}{R_3} + \cdots$$

The total resistance of the circuit shown in Figure 23-4 is

$$\frac{1}{R} = \frac{1}{60 \text{ } \Omega} + \frac{1}{60 \text{ } \Omega} + \frac{1}{60 \text{ } \Omega} = \frac{3}{60 \text{ } \Omega}$$

$$R = 20 \text{ } \Omega$$

According to Ohm's law, the current in the circuit is

$$\frac{V}{R} = \frac{120 \text{ V}}{20 \text{ } \Omega} = 6 \text{ A}$$

This current is the total current. It is found by adding together the 2-A currents in each of the three resistors. The total current in a parallel circuit is the sum of the currents in the separate branches.

**Total current in a parallel circuit is the sum of the currents in its branches.**

$$I = I_1 + I_2 + I_3 + \cdots$$

In Figure 23-4, the voltage drop across each resistor is the difference in potential between A and B. It is the same across each resistor. This voltage drop is the voltage of the generator, or 120 V.

### EXAMPLE:   Total Resistance and Current in a Parallel Circuit

Three resistors of 60 $\Omega$, 30 $\Omega$, and 20 $\Omega$ are connected in parallel across a 90-V difference in potential, Figure 23-5. **a.** Find the total resistance of the circuit. **b.** Find the current flowing in the entire circuit. **c.** Find the current flowing through each branch of the circuit.

*Solution:* **a.**
$$\frac{1}{R} = \frac{1}{R_1} + \frac{1}{R_2} + \frac{1}{R_3}$$

$$\frac{1}{R} = \frac{1}{60\ \Omega} + \frac{1}{30\ \Omega} + \frac{1}{20\ \Omega}$$

$$\frac{1}{R} = \frac{6}{60\ \Omega} \qquad R = 10\ \Omega$$

**b.**
$$I = \frac{V}{R} = \frac{90\ \text{V}}{10\ \Omega} = 9\ \text{A}$$

**c.** The voltage drop across each resistor is 90 V.

$$(\text{for } R_1)\quad I_1 = \frac{V}{R_1} = \frac{90\ \text{V}}{60\ \Omega} = 1.5\ \text{A}$$

$$(\text{for } R_2)\quad I_2 = \frac{V}{R_2} = \frac{90\ \text{V}}{30\ \Omega} = 3\ \text{A}$$

$$(\text{for } R_3)\quad I_3 = \frac{V}{R_3} = \frac{90\ \text{V}}{20\ \Omega} = 4.5\ \text{A}$$

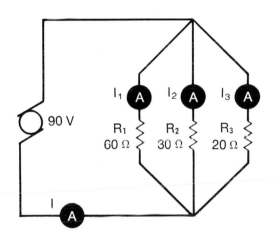

**FIGURE 23-5. Use with the Example.**

The sum of the current in the lines is 9 A as predicted by Part b. Dividing the voltage by the sum of the currents yields the total resistance of the circuit. The same solution is found as was found in Part a.

## PROBLEMS

**13.** Three 15-$\Omega$ resistors are connected in parallel and placed across a difference in potential of 30 V.
   **a.** What is the total resistance of the parallel circuit?
   **b.** What current flows through the entire circuit?
   **c.** What current flows through each branch of the circuit?

13. a.  5 $\Omega$
    b.  6 A
    c.  2 A

**14.** Two 10-$\Omega$ resistors are connected in parallel and placed across the terminals of a 15-V battery.
   **a.** What is the total resistance of the parallel circuit?
   **b.** What current flows in the circuit?
   **c.** What current flows through each branch of the circuit?

**15.** A 120-Ω resistor, a 60-Ω resistor, and a 40-Ω resistor are connected in parallel and placed across a potential difference of 120 V.
 **a.** What is the total resistance of the parallel circuit?
 **b.** What current flows through the entire circuit?
 **c.** What current flows through each branch of the circuit?

**16.** A 6-Ω resistor, an 18-Ω resistor, and a 9-Ω resistor are connected in parallel and placed across a 36-V potential difference.
 **a.** What current flows through each resistor?
 **b.** What total current flows in the circuit?
 **c.** What is the total resistance of the circuit?

**17.** A 75-Ω heater and a 150-Ω lamp are connected in parallel across a potential difference of 150 V.
 **a.** What current flows through the 75-Ω heater?
 **b.** What current flows through the 150-Ω lamp?
 **c.** What current flows through the entire circuit?
 **d.** What is the total resistance of the entire circuit?
 **e.** Divide the voltage by the total resistance. Does the result agree with the solution to Part c?

## 23:4   Characteristics of Parallel Circuits

Figure 23-4 showed three 60-Ω resistors connected in parallel across a 120-V source. Two amperes of current flowed through each resistor, and the total current in the circuit was 6 A. Figure 23-6 shows the same circuit but it has an open switch in one of the lines. Since the voltage across the lines remains 120 V, the current flowing through each of the two remaining resistors is 2 A. The total current in the circuit is 4 A. According to Ohm's law, the total resistance has increased from 20 Ω to 30 Ω.

This example demonstrates an important fact about parallel circuits. Each resistor in the circuit can be operated independently. If one of the lines is opened so that no current flows

*In a parallel circuit, each resistor can be operated independently.*

**FIGURE 23-6. Three 60-ohm resistors are connected in parallel and one switch is open. The current through each of the connected resistors is the same as when all three resistors are connected.**

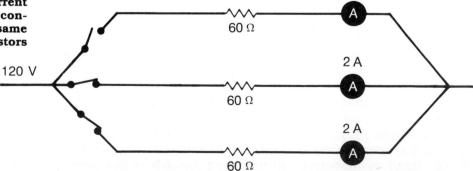

through it, the current in the other branches of the circuit is not affected in any way. In contrast, when a switch is opened or a resistor burns out at any place in a series circuit, current does not flow anywhere in the circuit. Therefore, a series circuit is not practical for house wiring. A house wired in series would require every device to be on in order to use any one of them.

**Parallel circuits are used for house wiring.**

Figure 23-7 shows a general plan of house wiring. Generators at the power station provide a source of 120 volts. Two lines run from this outside source to the house. At wall outlets, when appliances and lamps are plugged in, the circuit between these two lines is completed and current flows.

**a**

*Hickson-Bender Photography*

**b**

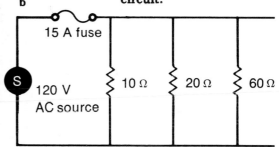

15 A fuse

S

120 V
AC source

10 Ω    20 Ω    60 Ω

**FIGURE 23-7. The wiring arrangement in this house (a) will permit the use of one or more appliances at the same time. This wiring diagram (b) indicates the parallel nature of the circuit.**

Three resistors are connecting two wires of the diagram. One resistor is a 10-Ω heater, another a 20-Ω refrigerator, and the third a 60-Ω lamp. Each device forms a complete circuit across the 120-V source. Each device operates independently of the others in the circuit. However, if all three devices operate at the same time, the total resistance is

$$\frac{1}{R} = \frac{1}{60 \ \Omega} + \frac{1}{20 \ \Omega} + \frac{1}{10 \ \Omega} = \frac{10}{60 \ \Omega}$$

$$R = 6 \ \Omega$$

The current flowing through the lines is

$$I = \frac{V}{R} = \frac{120 \text{ V}}{6} = 20 \text{ A}$$

Notice that 20 A exceeds the capacity of the 15 A fuse. This will cause the fuse to "blow," cutting off current to the entire circuit.

Fuses and circuit breakers are automatic switches in the line that act as safety devices. They prevent circuit overloads which can occur when too many appliances are turned on at the same time. When appliances are connected in parallel, each additional

**The current flowing into a house increases as additional appliances are turned on.**

a

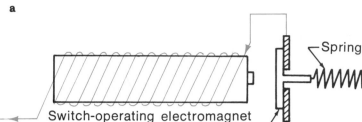

Switch-operating electromagnet

Spring

Electron flow

Iron bar

b

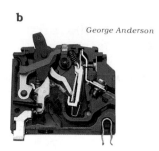

*George Anderson*

**FIGURE 23-8. When the current in a circuit is too great, the metal bar in this circuit breaker is pulled away from its contact points. The current stops flowing.**

Fuses and circuit breakers are safety devices which prevent too much current from flowing in a circuit.

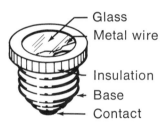

Glass

Metal wire

Insulation

Base

Contact

Melted wire

**FIGURE 23-9. The metal wire in a fuse melts when the circuit is overloaded. The fuse must then be replaced.**

Ohm's law can be used on each separate part of a series—parallel circuit.

appliance placed in operation causes more current to flow through the lead lines. This current increase may produce a heating effect ($I^2R$) in the lines large enough to cause a fire.

A **fuse** is a short piece of metal which melts when the heating effect of the current reaches a set magnitude. A **circuit breaker** is an automatic switch that cuts off when the current reaches some set value. If an overload occurred in the circuit shown in Figure 23-7, the fuse would melt. Then no current would flow anywhere in the circuit. Usually, houses are wired so that separate circuits are located in different parts of the house. Such an arrangement tends to prevent a circuit overload.

A short circuit occurs when a low resistance of any sort is included in the circuit causing the current in the circuit to become very large. This large current could start a fire if there were no fuse or circuit breaker in the circuit. For example, if a lamp cord becomes frayed, its wires could be accidentally brought together. A piece of copper wire in the lamp cord might have a resistance of 0.01 Ω. When placed across 120 V, this resistance draws

$$\frac{120 \text{ V}}{0.01 \text{ Ω}} \text{ or } 12\ 000 \text{ A}$$

The fuse or circuit breaker immediately blows. Thus, the wire is prevented from becoming hot and starting a fire.

## 23:5   Series-Parallel Circuits

Often a circuit consists of both series and parallel connections. To determine how the current or the potential difference is distributed in the various parts of the circuit, Ohm's law is used. Ohm's law is applied to each part of the circuit as well as to the entire circuit.

**EXAMPLE: Series-Parallel Circuit**

In Figure 23-10a, a 30-Ω resistor is connected in parallel with a 20-Ω resistor. The parallel connection is placed in series with an 8-Ω resistor, and the entire circuit is placed across a 60-V difference of potential. **a.** What is the total resistance of the parallel portion of the circuit? **b.** What is the resistance of the entire circuit? **c.** What current flows in the circuit? **d.** What is the voltage drop across the 8-$\Omega$ resistor? **e.** What is the voltage drop across the parallel portion of the circuit? **f.** What current flows through each line of the parallel portion of the circuit?

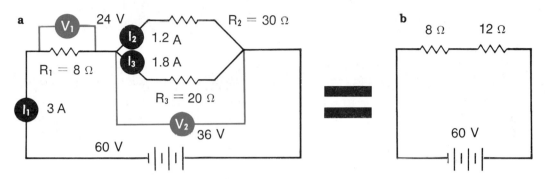

FIGURE 23-10. Use with the Example.

*Solution:* **a.** $R_2$ and $R_3$ are connected in parallel. Their combined resistance is

$$\frac{1}{R} = \frac{1}{R_2} + \frac{1}{R_3} = \frac{1}{30\ \Omega} + \frac{1}{20\ \Omega} = \frac{5}{60\ \Omega} \qquad R = 12\ \Omega$$

**b.** The circuit is now a series circuit with an 8-$\Omega$ resistor and a 12-$\Omega$ resistor in series, Figure 23-10b.

$$R = R_1 + R_{2.3}$$
$$= 8\ \Omega + 12\ \Omega = 20\ \Omega$$

**c.** The current flowing in the circuit is

$$I = \frac{V}{R}$$
$$= \frac{60\ V}{20\ \Omega} = 3\ A$$

**d.** The voltage drop across the 8-$\Omega$ resistor is

$$V = IR_1$$
$$= (3\ A)(8\ \Omega) = 24\ V$$

**e.** The parallel portion of the circuit behaves as a 12-$\Omega$ resistor. Therefore, the voltage drop across it is

$$V = IR_{2.3}$$
$$= (3\ A)(12\ \Omega) = 36\ V$$

**f.** The 36-V drop across the parallel portion of the circuit is the same across all parts of the parallel circuit. Therefore, the current through the 30-$\Omega$ resistor is

$$I = \frac{V}{R_2}$$
$$= \frac{36\ V}{30\ \Omega} = 1.2\ A$$

The current through the 20-$\Omega$ resistor is

$$I = \frac{V}{R_3}$$

$$= \frac{36 \text{ V}}{20 \text{ }\Omega} = 1.8 \text{ A}$$

The total current through the parallel part of the circuit is

$$1.2 \text{ A} + 1.8 \text{ A, or } 3 \text{ A}$$

This total agrees with the value for current calculated in Part c.

## PROBLEMS

**18.** Two 60-$\Omega$ resistors are connected in parallel. This parallel arrangement is connected in series with a 30-$\Omega$ resistor. The entire circuit is then placed across a 120-V potential difference.
   **a.** What is the resistance of the parallel portion of the circuit?
   **b.** What is the resistance of the entire circuit?
   **c.** What current flows in the circuit?
   **d.** What is the voltage drop across the 30-$\Omega$ resistor?
   **e.** What is the voltage drop across the parallel portion of the circuit?
   **f.** What current flows in each branch of the parallel portion of the circuit?

19. a. 5 $\Omega$    d. 30 V
    b. 15 $\Omega$   e. 15 V
    c. 3 A      f. 1 A

**19.** Three 15-$\Omega$ resistors are connected in parallel. This arrangement is connected in series with a 10-$\Omega$ resistor. The entire circuit is then placed across a 45-V difference in potential.
   **a.** What is the resistance of the parallel portion of the circuit?
   **b.** What is the resistance of the entire circuit?
   **c.** What current flows in the circuit?
   **d.** What is the voltage drop across the 10-$\Omega$ resistor?
   **e.** What is the voltage drop across the parallel portion of the circuit?
   **f.** What current flows in each branch of the parallel portion of the circuit?

**20.** Three 15-$\Omega$ resistors are connected in parallel. They are connected in series to a second set of three 15-$\Omega$ resistors, also connected in parallel. The entire circuit is then placed across the terminals of a 12-V battery.
   **a.** What is the total resistance of the circuit?
   **b.** What current flows through the circuit?
   **c.** What current flows through each resistor?

# 23:6  Ammeters and Voltmeters

An **ammeter** is used to measure the current in a circuit. An ammeter is placed in a circuit in series with the resistors. Therefore, the resistance of an ammeter must be very low. Otherwise it would change the total resistance of the circuit in which it is placed. If the total resistance of the circuit were changed, the current flowing in the circuit would also be altered. Thus, the ammeter would defeat its own purpose.

A **voltmeter** is used to measure the voltage drop across a part of a circuit or an entire circuit. A voltmeter is placed in parallel with the resistor where voltage drop is to be measured. A voltmeter must have a very high resistance so that it does not affect the resistance of that part of the circuit where the voltage is being measured. A low-resistance voltmeter placed in parallel with a resistor would constitute a parallel circuit of lower resistance

An ammeter measures current in a circuit.

A voltmeter measures voltage drop across a circuit.

**FIGURE 23-11. An engineer is checking integrated circuits on an experimental computerized battery tester for electric cars (a). A voltmeter is used to check for proper voltage levels (b). Ammeters are placed in series with resistors in measuring current flow (c). Voltmeters are connected in parallel with resistance in measuring potential difference (d).**

a

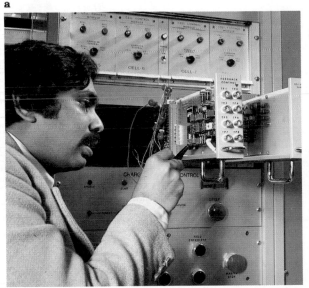

General Motors Research Laboratory

b

George Anderson

c

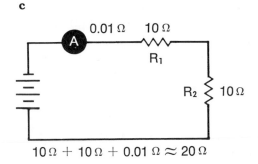

$$10\,\Omega + 10\,\Omega + 0.01\,\Omega \approx 20\,\Omega$$

d

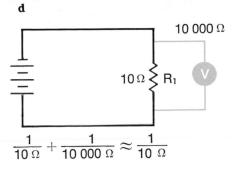

$$\frac{1}{10\,\Omega} + \frac{1}{10\,000\,\Omega} \approx \frac{1}{10\,\Omega}$$

than that of the resistor. The lower resistance would cause an increase of current in the circuit. The voltage drop across the resistor would increase. A low-resistance voltmeter would defeat its own purpose. The resistance of a voltmeter is usually a minimum of 10 000 $\Omega$. A 10 000-$\Omega$ resistance placed in parallel with a 10-$\Omega$ resistance keeps that part of the circuit resistance at 10 $\Omega$.

Ammeters and voltmeters have many everyday uses. For example, the condition of a car battery is tested with a special ammeter. A voltmeter is used to check TV circuits and the circuits of other electronic devices.

**PROBLEM**

**21.** $I_1 = 3$ A, $I_2 = 1.5$ A, $I_3 = 1.5$ A, $I_4 = 1.8$ A, $I_5 = 1.2$ A, $V_1 = 15$ V, $V_2 = 36$ V, $V_3 = 9$ V

**21.** Determine the reading of each ammeter and voltmeter in Figure 23-12.

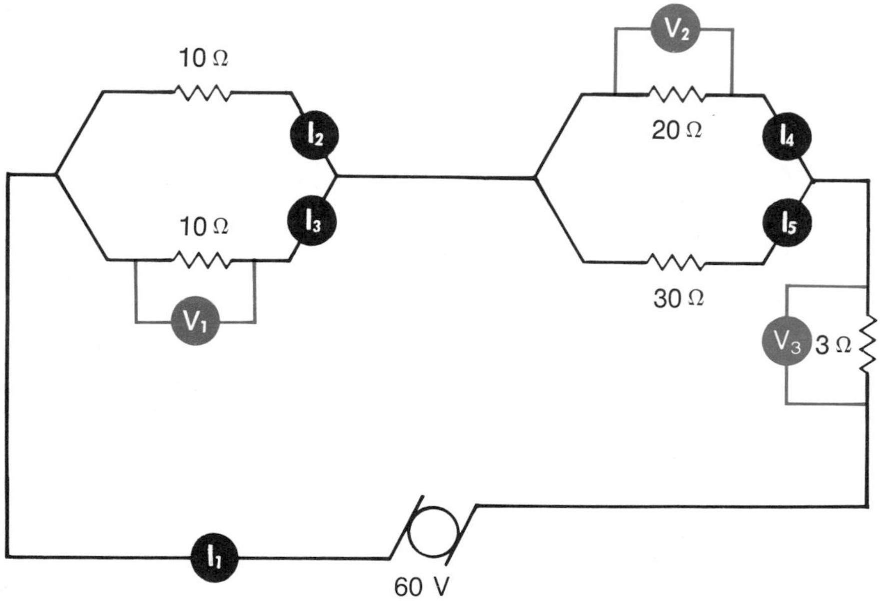

**FIGURE 23-12. Use with Problem 21.**

---

**Summary**

1. When resistances are connected in series, the total resistance of the circuit is equal to the sum of the individual resistances. **23:1**
2. The current is the same everywhere in a series circuit. **23:1**
3. When resistors are connected in parallel, the voltage is the same across all branches of the circuit. The current in each branch is inversely proportional to its resistance. **23:3**
4. The reciprocal of the total resistance of a parallel circuit is equal to the sum of the reciprocals of the individual resistances. **23:3**
5. The sum of the currents in the branches of a parallel circuit is equal to the total current in the circuit. **23:3**

**6.** If any branch of a parallel circuit is opened so that no current flows in the branch, the current in the remaining branches is unchanged.  **23:4**

**7.** Often a circuit is a combination of series and parallel connections. To determine the voltages and currents throughout the circuit and in parts of the circuit, Ohm's law is applied.  **23:5**

**8.** An ammeter is used to measure the current in a circuit or in a branch of a circuit. An ammeter is always connected in series.  **23:6**

**9.** A voltmeter measures the potential difference (voltage) across any part of a circuit or across the entire circuit. A voltmeter is always connected in parallel.  **23:6**

**Questions**

**1.** Circuit *A* contains three 60-$\Omega$ resistors in series. Circuit *B* contains three 60-$\Omega$ resistors in parallel. How does the current flowing in the second 60-$\Omega$ resistor change if a switch cuts off the current to the first 60-$\Omega$ resistor in
   **a.** circuit *A*?     **b.** circuit *B*?

**2.** Why is there a difference in total resistance between three 60-$\Omega$ resistors connected in series and three 60-$\Omega$ resistors connected in parallel?

**3.** An engineer needs a 10-$\Omega$ control resistor and a 15-$\Omega$ control resistor. But, there are only 30-$\Omega$ resistors in stock. Must new resistors be bought? Explain.

**4.** The total current flowing through a parallel circuit is equal to the sum of the current flowing through its branches: $I = I_1 + I_2 + I_3$, and so on. Since the voltage across each branch of a parallel circuit is the same, this equation written in Ohm's law form is $\frac{V}{R} = \frac{V}{R_1} + \frac{V}{R_2} + \frac{V}{R_3}$. Remember that the voltages are all equal. Rewrite this equation in a simplified form.

**5.** For each part of this question, write the form that applies: series circuit or parallel circuit.
   **a.** The current is the same throughout.
   **b.** The total resistance is equal to the sum of the individual resistances.
   **c.** The voltage drop is the same across each resistor.
   **d.** The voltage drop is proportional to the resistance.
   **e.** Adding a resistor decreases the total resistance.
   **f.** Adding a resistor increases the total resistance.
   **g.** If one resistor is turned off or broken, no current flows in the entire circuit.
   **h.** If one resistor is turned off, the current through all other resistors remains the same.
   **i.** Suitable for house wiring.

**6.** Explain the function of a fuse in an electric circuit.

**7.** Why does an ammeter have a very low resistance?

**8.** Why does a voltmeter have a very high resistance?

**9.** What is a short circuit? Why is a short circuit dangerous?

## Problems

**1.** Two resistors of 5 $\Omega$ and 7 $\Omega$ are connected in series across a 12-V battery.
   **a.** What is the total resistance of the circuit?
   **b.** What current flows through the 5-$\Omega$ resistor?
   **c.** What current flows through the 7-$\Omega$ resistor?
   **d.** What is the voltage drop across each resistor?

**2.** Two 6-$\Omega$ resistors and a 3-$\Omega$ resistor are connected in series. A potential difference of 6 V is applied to the circuit.
   **a.** What is the total resistance of the circuit?
   **b.** What current flows in the circuit?
   **c.** What is the voltage drop across each resistor?

**3.** A light bulb has a resistance of 2 $\Omega$. It is connected in series with a variable resistor. A difference in potential of 6 V is applied to the circuit. An ammeter indicates that the current of the circuit is 0.5 A. At what resistance is the variable resistor set?

**4.** What resistance is connected in series with an 8-$\Omega$ resistor that is connected to a 60-V generator if the current through the resistors is 4 A?

**5.** Ten Christmas tree lights are connected in series. When they are plugged into a 120-V outlet, the current flowing through the lights is 0.75 A. What is the resistance of each light?

**6.** A 20-$\Omega$ lamp and a 5-$\Omega$ lamp are connected in series and placed across a difference in potential of 50 V.
   **a.** What is the total resistance of the circuit?
   **b.** What current flows in the circuit?
   **c.** What is the voltage drop across each resistor?

**7.** A 20-$\Omega$ lamp and a 5-$\Omega$ lamp are connected in parallel and placed across a difference in potential of 50 V.
   **a.** What is the total resistance of the circuit?
   **b.** What current flows in the circuit?
   **c.** What current flows through each resistor?
   **d.** What is the voltage drop across each resistor?

**8.** A 16-$\Omega$, a 20-$\Omega$, and an 80-$\Omega$ resistor are connected in parallel. A difference in potential of 40 V is applied to the combination.
   **a.** Compute the total resistance of the parallel circuit.
   **b.** What total current flows in the circuit?
   **c.** What current flows through the 16-$\Omega$ resistor?

9. A household circuit contains six 240-$\Omega$ lamps (60-W bulbs) and a 10-$\Omega$ heater. The voltage across the circuit is 120 V.
   a. What current flows in the circuit when four lamps are on?
   b. What current flows when all six lamps are on?
   c. What current flows in the circuit if all six lamps and the heater are operating?

10. Determine the reading of each ammeter and each voltmeter in Figure 23-13.

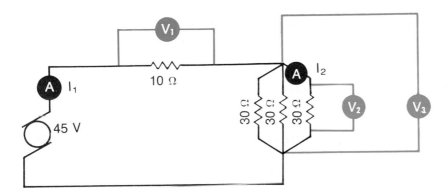

**FIGURE 23-13. Use with Problems 10 and 12.**

11. Find the reading of each ammeter and each voltmeter in Figure 23-14.

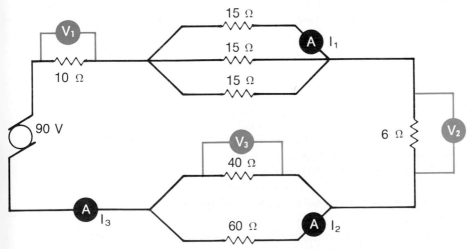

**FIGURE 23-14. Use with Problem 11.**

12. Determine the power in watts consumed by each resistance shown in Figure 23-13.

<table>
<tr><td>**Applying Physics**</td></tr>
</table>

**1.** *Electric to Thermal Energy:* During a laboratory exercise you are supplied with the following apparatus:

    **1.** a battery of potential difference $V$

    **2.** two heating elements of low resistance which can be placed in water

    **3.** an ammeter of negligible resistance

    **4.** a voltmeter of extremely high resistance

    **5.** wires of negligible resistance

    **6.** a beaker which is well insulated and has negligible heat capacity

    **7.** The beaker is partially filled with 100 g of water at 25°C.

  **a.** By means of a diagram, using the symbols given above, show how these components should be connected to heat the water as rapidly as possible.

  **b.** If the voltmeter reading holds steadily at 50.0 V and the ammeter reading holds steadily at 5.0 A estimate the time in seconds required to completely vaporize the water in the beaker. Use 4.2 J/g·C° as the specific heat of water and 2300 J/g as the heat of vaporization of water.

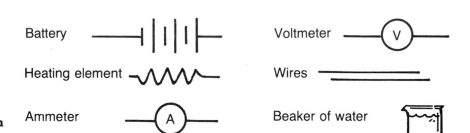

Battery

Heating element

Ammeter

Voltmeter

Wires

Beaker of water

**FIGURE 23-15. Use with Applying Physics 1.**

**2.** *Line Drops in Home Circuits:* A typical home circuit is diagrammed in Figure 23-15. Note that the lead lines to the kitchen lamp have very low resistances. The lamp contains a typical 60-W incandescent bulb of resistance 240 Ω. Although the circuit is a parallel circuit, the lead lines are in series with the components of the circuit.

  **a.** Compute the total resistance of the circuit consisting of just the light and the lead lines to and from the light. We will assume that the power saw and wall outlets are not in use.

  **b.** Show that the current to the bulb is essentially 0.5 amperes and that the bulb is a 60-W device.

  **c.** Since the current in the bulb is 0.5 A the current in the lead lines must also be 0.5 A. Calculate the voltage drop due to the two leads.

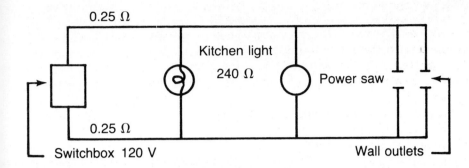

**FIGURE 23-16. Use with Applying Physics 2 and 3.**

**3.** A power saw is operated by an electric motor. When electric motors are first turned on they have very low resistances. We will study why the resistance is low in Chapter 25. Once in full operation, the resistance of an electric motor is greatly increased.

  Suppose that the kitchen light discussed in Problem 2 is on and the power saw (perhaps located in the basement) is suddenly turned on. If the saw plus the lead lines between the saw and the light have an initial total resistance of 6.0 $\Omega$:

  **a.** compute the total resistance of the light-saw parallel circuit.
  **b.** what current flows through the two leads to the light?
  **c.** what is the total voltage drop across the two leads to the light?
  **d.** what voltage remains to operate the light? Will this voltage cause the light to dim temporarily? (You may have noticed this effect many times.)

Matisoo, Juri, "The Superconducting Computer." *Scientific American,* May, 1980.

"Microelectronics." *Scientific American,* September, 1977. (Entire Issue.)

**Readings**

As a child you have probably played with small magnets. You know that opposite poles of a magnet attract while like poles repel. The Fermilab accelerator contains one thousand magnets. The magnets are used to control the paths of charged atomic particles moving through the accelerator. Particles with energies up to 500 billion electronvolts are directed at a target in the hopes of unlocking the secrets of the atom. What are some other uses of magnets?

*Dan McCoy from Rainbow*

# Magnetic Fields 24

Magnetism plays an important role in any study of electricity. In fact, whenever an electric current appears, magnetism also appears. The two cannot be separated. The operation of many devices such as radios, TV sets, motors, and electric meters depends on the magnetic effects of electric currents.

GOAL: You will gain knowledge and understanding of permanent magnets, electromagnets, magnetic fields, and the forces exerted on charged particles.

## 24:1  General Properties of Magnets

Let us begin our study of magnetic fields by reviewing some elementary principles of magnetism.

1. A magnet has polarity. The end of a suspended magnet that points north is the **north-seeking pole** (N pole) of the magnet. The end that points south is its **south-seeking pole** (S pole). These poles are distinct. However, they cannot be separated.

2. Like magnetic poles repel one another. Unlike poles attract one another.

Unlike poles attract, like poles repel.

3. Iron, cobalt, and nickel are important magnetic substances. Permanent magnets are made from these metals. **Permanent magnets** retain their magnetism for a long time.

4. Iron, cobalt, and nickel are magnetized by induction. When a magnetic substance is close to or touches a magnet, it becomes a magnet also. These substances become temporary magnets. When removed from the magnet, temporary magnets quickly lose their magnetic properties.

5. A **compass** is a small, suspended, needle-shaped magnet. The north-seeking pole of the compass needle points north. The magnetic north pole of the earth and the geographic north pole of the earth are not in the same place. A compass needle points toward the magnetic north pole.

*Philip M. Jordain*

**FIGURE 24-1. Magnetic tools are useful in working with small intricate parts.**

## 24:2  Magnetic Fields around Permanent Magnets

The presence of a magnetic field around a permanent magnet can be shown by covering the magnet with a piece of paper and sprinkling small iron filings onto the paper. The iron filings will arrange themselves in lines running from pole to pole, Figure 24-2. These lines are called **field lines** or **magnetic flux lines.**

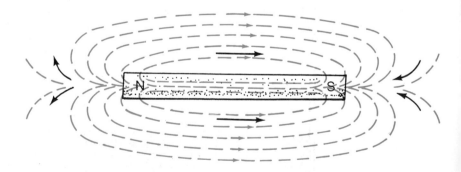

**FIGURE 24-2. Magnetic flux lines extend from the N pole to the S pole outside the magnet and from the S pole to the N pole inside the magnet.**

Magnetic flux lines are imaginary lines which indicate the direction and magnitude of the field about a magnet.

Magnetic flux density is magnetic flux per unit area.

Magnetic flux lines are actually imaginary lines. The whole group of lines together is called magnetic flux. The **magnetic flux** shows the magnetic field around the magnet. The magnetic flux density is the number of lines per unit area. The strength of the magnetic field is proportional to the flux density.

The direction of the magnetic field lines is the direction the N pole of a compass points in the magnetic field. Outside the magnet, the field lines run from the N pole of the magnet to its

S pole. Field lines always form closed loops. Inside the magnet, the field lines run from the S pole to the N pole of the magnet. These rules are important when studying the behavior of charged particles in magnetic fields.

Magnetic field lines never overlap. In fact, they repel one another and follow well-defined paths. Field lines leave the N pole and enter the S pole. The lines are most concentrated at the poles. The field is strongest at the poles of the magnet.

While magnetic fields cannot be literally "seen" it is possible to observe the behavior of these fields under different circumstances by using iron filings. If a piece of paper is placed over a bar magnet, iron filings may be sprinkled on the paper. The filings, each of which becomes a small magnet by induction, will align themselves along the bar magnet's field lines producing an excellent pattern of the field about the magnet. This effect is often enhanced if the paper is tapped slightly.

The behavior of fields may be observed by covering the like poles (N and N, or S and S) of two magnets with paper. If the like poles are held close together and sprinkled with iron filings, field lines form. Notice in Figure 24-3a that the field lines from the like poles clearly repel one another. Like poles repel. By contrast, two unlike poles (N and S) placed close together show the opposite effect. The filings show that the field lines between the magnets run directly from one magnet to the other. Unlike poles attract.

Magnetic fields outside a magnet run from north pole to south pole.

**a**

**b**

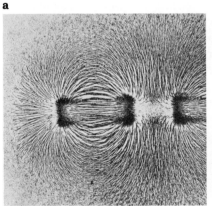
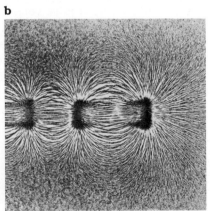

*Courtesy of Bell Telephone Laboratories*     *Courtesy of Bell Telephone Laboratories*

**FIGURE 24-3. The field lines for the repulsion of like poles is shown in (a) and unlike poles in (b).**

# 24:3  Electromagnetism

In 1820, the Danish physicist Hans Christian Oersted (1777-1851) made a very important discovery about magnetism. While experimenting with electric currents in wires, Oersted noticed

a

*Paul Chesley*

b

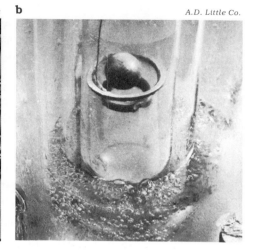

*A.D. Little Co.*

**FIGURE 24-4. This experimental train (a) is magnetically levitated. Moving along a magnetic cushion allows the train to reach extremely high speeds. The lead sphere (b) floats between two lead rings that carry electric currents when the temperature is near absolute zero. The repulsion between magnetic fields of the sphere and rings balances the sphere's weight so that it floats.**

Magnetic fields are the result of electric currents.

**FIGURE 24-5. The magnetic field produced by current in a straight-wire conductor is shown.**

that one of his wires was lying across the top of a small compass. He observed that each time he sent a current through the wire, the compass needle moved. A compass needle is a small magnet. The magnetic field around a magnet will interact only with another magnetic field. Thus, the presence of an electric current in the wire was somehow causing a magnetic field to appear around the wire. Further studies by Oersted showed that *any wire carrying an electric current has a magnetic field around it.* Electric currents produce magnetic fields.

The magnetic field around a current-bearing wire can easily be studied by placing a wire vertically through a piece of cardboard. An electric current is passed through the wire. Iron filings are sprinkled on the cardboard around the wire. As the cardboard is tapped the filings form a pattern around the wire. The pattern consists of concentric circles (circles with a common center) around the wire.

a

Electron flow      Electron flow

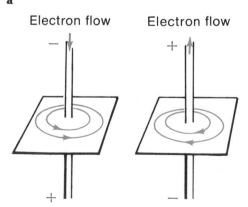

b

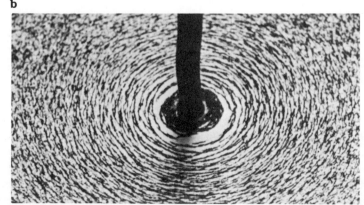

*Courtesy of Kodansha*

The circular lines indicate that the magnetic field lines form closed loops. The strength of the magnetic field around the wire varies directly with the magnitude of the current flowing in the wire.

The **left-hand rule** can be used to find the direction of the magnetic field around a current-bearing straight wire. *Grasp the wire with the left hand. Keep the thumb of that hand pointed in the direction of electron flow. The fingers of the hand circle the wire pointing in the direction of the magnetic field.*

## 24:4  Magnetic Field around a Coil

When an electric current flows through a single circular loop of wire, a magnetic field appears all around the loop. By applying the left-hand rule as in Figure 24-7b, it can be shown that the direction of the field inside the loop is always the same. In the case shown in the diagram, it is always up out of the page. Outside the loop it is always down into the page.

Suppose wire is looped several times to form a coil. When a current flows through the coil, the field around all loops will be in the same direction. The result is a smooth magnetic field inside the coil which acts in a single direction. The field outside the coil will also be uniform, but will act in the opposite direction.

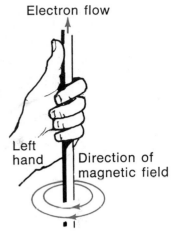

Electron flow

Left hand

Direction of magnetic field

**FIGURE 24-6. The left-hand rule for a current bearing straight wire shows the direction of the magnetic field.**

When current flows through a coil, a magnetic field is produced inside the coil. This field acts in one direction only.

a

*Courtesy of Kodansha*  **b**

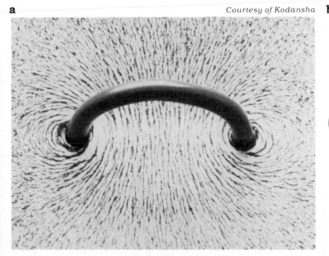

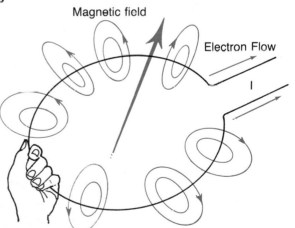

Magnetic field

Electron Flow

I

When an electric current flows through a coil of wire, the coil acts like a permanent magnet. When one end of this current-bearing coil is brought close to a suspended bar magnet, one end of the coil repels the north pole of the magnet. The other end of the coil attracts the north pole of the magnet. Thus, the current-bearing coil has a north and south pole and is itself a magnet. This type of magnet is called an **electromagnet.**

**FIGURE 24-7. The magnetic field about a circular loop of current-carrying wire is shown.**

An electromagnet is a current-carrying coil of wire that acts like a magnet.

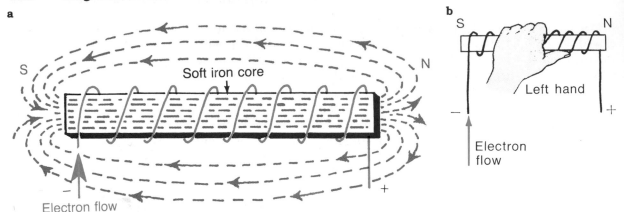

FIGURE 24-8. The second left-hand rule can be used to determine the polarity of an electromagnet.

A second left-hand rule can be used to find the north and south poles of an electromagnet.

The strength of the field about an electromagnet can be increased by placing an iron core inside the coil.

The strength of the field about an electromagnet varies with the current.

The field about an electromagnet also varies with the number of loops in the coil.

The polarity of an electromagnet may be found by using a **second left-hand rule.** *Grasp the coil with the left hand. Curl the fingers around the loops in the direction of electron flow. The thumb points toward the N pole of the electromagnet.*

The strength of an electromagnet can be increased by placing a soft iron core inside the coil. The iron is influenced by the field inside the coil. The iron core is magnetized by the magnetic field existing inside the coil. The strength of the core then adds to the strength of the electromagnet producing a much stronger magnet.

The strength of the magnetic field around a current-bearing wire is proportional to the current flowing in the wire. Likewise, the strength of the field around an electromagnet is proportional to the current flowing through the wire. Also, note that each loop of a coil produces the same field as any other loop. These individual fields are in the same direction and can be added. Thus, increasing the number of loops in an electromagnet increases the strength of the field. The strength of an electromagnet's magnetic field is proportional to the current, the number of loops, and the nature of the core.

## 24:5 Theory of Magnetism

The magnetism of a permanent magnet is due to the spinning motion of electrons in atoms.

The behavior of an electromagnet is similar to that of a permanent bar magnet. Can this be explained? In the early 19th century, a theory of magnetism was proposed by Andre Ampere (1775-1836). Ampere knew that the magnetic effects of an electromagnetic coil result when an electric current flows through its loops. Knowing this, he reasoned that the effects of a bar magnet must result from tiny "loops" of current within the bar. In essence, Ampere's reasoning was correct. The magnetic effect of a permanent magnet results from the spinning of electrons on their axes as they move in atoms. Thus, the behavior of an electromagnet is very similar to that of a permanent bar magnet.

The atoms in a magnet are not independent of surrounding atoms. Instead, the atoms act in groups or domains. Within each domain, the atoms are coupled and lined up in the same direction. The magnetic effects of the atoms of one domain act together to make a tiny magnet. Although domains are much larger than individual atoms, they are still very small. Thus, even a small sample of iron contains a huge number of domains. Usually, the domains are not lined up. As a result, their magnetic fields cancel one another. Therefore, a piece of iron does not always show magnetic effects. However, if an iron bar is placed in a strong magnetic field, the domains tend to align with the external field. Iron, cobalt, nickel, and their alloys often keep this domain alignment after being removed from the external field. Thus, they become permanent magnets.

**Atoms within a permanent magnet are arranged in domains.**

**All the atoms in a domain are lined up in the same direction.**

FIGURE 24-9. A model of the domain theory shows magnetic properties appear only when domains align.

## 24:6 Interaction of Magnetic Fields

Ampere did other experiments with magnetic fields. He observed two parallel wires carrying current in the same direction. He found that the wires attract one another. He also observed two parallel wires carrying current in opposite directions. These wires repel one another. These forces of attraction and repulsion result from the magnetic fields around the wires.

The strength of a magnetic field is called **magnetic induction.** Magnetic field strength might seem to be a better term for this quantity. However, to avoid confusion with other terms used with magnetic fields, we will use the term magnetic induction. Magnetic induction is a vector quantity. The symbol for magnetic induction is $\vec{B}$.

**Magnetic induction, the strength of a magnetic field, is a vector quantity.**

**Magnetic induction is another name for magnetic flux density.**

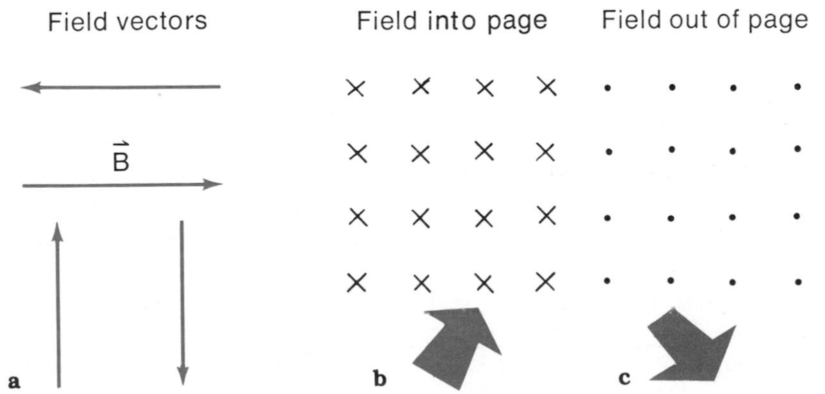

Field vectors        Field into page        Field out of page

$\vec{B}$

a                          b                          c

FIGURE 24-10. Directions of magnetic fields are indicated (a) by directional arrows when the field is in the same plane as the page, (b) by crosses when the field is into the page, and (c) by dots when the field is out of the page toward you.

Magnetic field vectors are shown pointing in several different directions in Figure 24-10a. In Figure 24-10b, magnetic field vectors are directed into the plane of the page. Those directed into the page are indicated by crosses. In Figure 24-10c, magnetic field vectors are directed out of the page. Those directed out of the page are indicated by dots. Think of the vectors as a flight of arrows. The dots represent points approaching the reader head-on. The crosses represent tail feathers going away from the reader. This convention is used when three dimensions are considered.

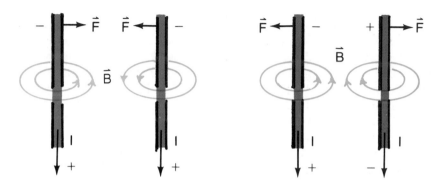

**FIGURE 24-11. Two current-bearing conductors (a) are attracted when the currents are in the same direction, and (b) are repelled when the currents are in opposite directions.**

**FIGURE 24-12. Force is directed upward on a current-carrying wire in a magnetic field when current is into the page (a). The force is directed downward when the current is out of the page (b).**

Figure 24-11 shows that the direction of the magnetic field around each of the current-bearing wires follows the left-hand rule. In Figure 24-11a, we see that the fields between the wires are in opposition. Since magnetic fields add vectorially, the field between the wires is weak. The field outside the wires remains normal strength. Thus, the wires are forced together, or attract each other.

In Figure 24-11b, we see the opposite situation. Here, the fields between the wires act in the same direction. Thus, the field between the wires is strengthened. Outside the wires, the fields are

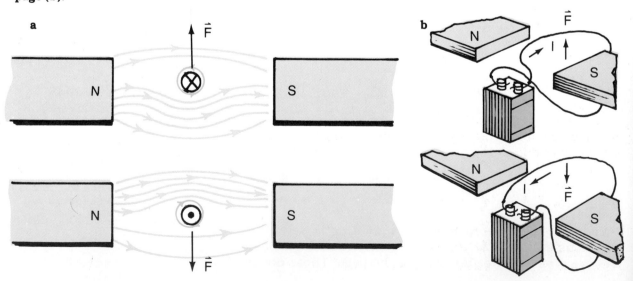

at normal strength. Thus, the wires are forced apart by the stronger field between them.

The behavior of a small segment of wire placed at right angles to an external magnetic field is of interest. As a current is sent through the wire, a magnetic field appears around the wire. The two magnetic fields interact. In Figure 24-12a, the field due to the current in the wire is directed counterclockwise. Above the wire, the field due to the current opposes the field due to the magnets. Below the wire, the two fields are in the same direction, and the resultant field is strengthened. The result is a net upward force. This force is perpendicular to both the external field and the direction of the current in the wire. In Figure 24-12b, the electrons flow in the opposite direction in the wire. The field around the wire is directed clockwise. Therefore, the wire is forced down.

The direction of the force due to an external magnetic field can be found using a **third left-hand rule.** *Point the fingers of the left hand in the direction of the magnetic field. Point the thumb in the direction of the electron flow of the wire. The palm of the hand then faces in the direction of the force acting on the wire.*

A third left-hand rule is used to determine the direction of force on a current-bearing wire placed in a magnetic field.

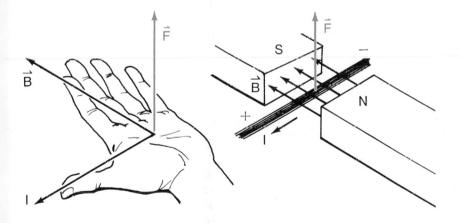

FIGURE 24-13. The third left-hand rule is used to determine the direction of force when the current and magnetic fields are known.

## 24:7 Measuring the Force on a Wire

Michael Faraday (1791–1867) discovered that when a current-bearing wire and a magnetic field are at right angles, a force acts on the wire due to the interaction of the fields. The force is proportional to three factors.

**1.** the magnetic induction or strength $B$ of the field

**2.** the current $I$ in the wire

**3.** the length $L$ of the wire that lies in the magnetic field

If $B$ is in the proper units, the expression is

$$F = BIL$$

**The unit for magnetic induction is the newton/ampere-meter (N/A·m).**

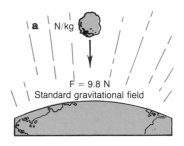

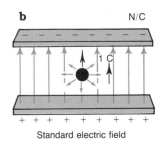

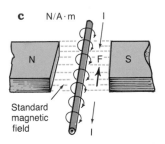

There need not be 1 m of wire in the field. The force on 10 cm can be measured and then multiplied by 10 to yield the force that would act on 1 m of wire.

**FIGURE 24-14. Gravitational, electric, and magnetic forces are the result of field interactions.**

Solving for $B$,

$$B = \frac{F}{IL}$$

The strength, or induction, of a magnetic field is measured in newtons per ampere-meter, N/A·m. That is, the strength of a magnetic field is measured in terms of the force of its interaction with a standard magnetic field. The standard magnetic field is the field found about a wire one meter long carrying a current of one ampere. Thus, the magnetic induction $B$ of a magnetic field indicates the force that field can produce when it interacts with the standard field around one meter of wire carrying one ampere of current.

To help understand what is intended by the term newtons per ampere-meter, consider how the intensities of other fields are measured. For example, gravitational fields are rated as newtons per kilogram. The earth's gravitational field intensity is 9.8 N/kg close to its surface. This value actually means that the intensity of the earth's gravitational field is such that it can interact with the standard gravitational field found about a kilogram mass to produce a force of 9.8 N. The standard gravitational field is the field about a kilogram mass. The intensity of interaction of other gravitational fields with this standard gives us a means of rating them. For example, the intensity of the moon's gravitational field is about 1.6 N/kg.

In the same way, the intensities of electric fields are measured in newtons per coulomb. By this we mean that we can rate the intensity of an electric field by placing a standard charge, the coulomb, in the field and measuring the force that acts on it. Once again we are actually measuring the force of interaction between the electric field and the standard electric field about a coulomb of charge.

Magnetic fields result whenever an electric current appears. When a wire one meter long carries a current of one ampere the magnetic field that appears about the wire is the standard magnetic field. Other magnetic fields can be rated by measuring the force of interaction between the field and the standard magnetic field. The result is expressed in newtons per ampere-meter.

Note that in all cases, forces are the result of the interactions of fields. Masses do not interact with masses nor do charges interact with charges. It is the fields about the masses and the fields about the charges that interact. All interactions are field interactions.

**EXAMPLE: Magnetic Induction**

A wire 1.0 m long carries a current of 5.0 A. The wire is at right angles to a uniform magnetic field. The force on the wire is 0.2 N. What is the magnetic induction $B$ of the field?

*Solution:*        $B = \dfrac{F}{IL} = \dfrac{0.2 \text{ N}}{(5.0 \text{ A})(1.0 \text{ m})} = 0.04 \text{ N/A} \cdot \text{m}$

**EXAMPLE:   Force on a Current-Carrying Wire in a Magnetic Field**

A wire 10 cm long is at right angles to a uniform magnetic field. The field has magnetic induction 0.06 N/A·m. The current through the wire is 4.0 A. What force acts on the wire?

*Solution:*     $F = BIL = \left( 0.06 \dfrac{\text{N}}{\text{A} \cdot \text{m}} \right)(4.0 \text{ A})(0.1 \text{ m}) = 0.024 \text{ N}$

## PROBLEMS

1. A wire 0.10 m long carrying a current of 2.0 A is at right angles to a magnetic field. The force on the wire is 0.04 N. What is the magnetic induction of the field?

2. A wire 0.5 m long carrying a current of 8.0 A is at right angles to a field of magnetic induction 0.40 N/A·m. What force acts on the wire?

3. A wire 75 cm long carrying a current of 6.0 A is at right angles to a uniform magnetic field. The force acting on the wire is 0.6 N. What is the magnetic induction of the field?

4. A magnetic field produces a force of 1.0 N on a wire. The wire is 25 cm long and carries a current of 5.0 A. What is the magnetic induction?

5. A copper wire 40 cm long carries a current of 6.0 A and weighs 0.35 N. Placed in a certain magnetic field, the wire remains suspended in the field. What is the magnetic induction of the field?

6. A wire 60 cm long is in a field of magnetic induction 0.4 N/A·m. The force acting on the wire is 1.8 N. What current is in the wire?

7. A wire 0.03 m long carrying a current of 5.0 A is at right angles to a magnetic field. The force acting on the wire is $9.0 \times 10^{-3}$ N. What is the magnetic induction of the field?

1.  0.2 N/A·m

3.  0.13 N/A·m

5.  0.15 N/A·m

7.  $6 \times 10^{-2}$ N/A·m

# 24:8   Force on a Single Charged Particle

The development of efficient air pumps made it possible to manufacture large vacuum tubes. A **vacuum tube** contains a pair of metal electrodes, Figure 24-15. When a high voltage is applied across the electrodes, a stream of electrons moves across the tube from the negative electrode (cathode) to the positive electrode (anode). By applying a magnetic field to the tube, the beam of electrons is deflected.

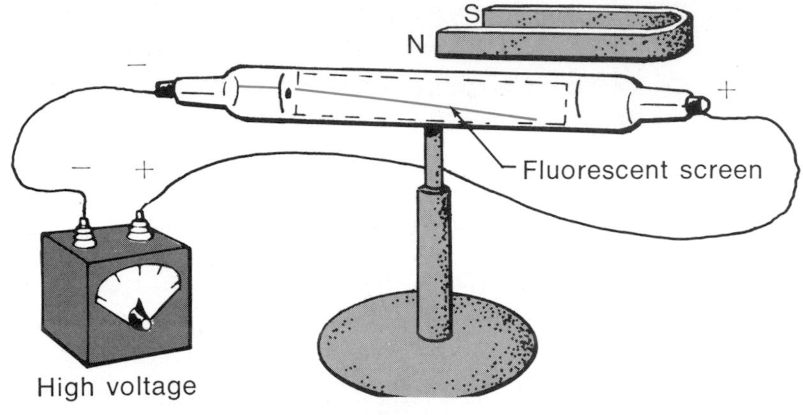

**FIGURE 24-15. This appa-ratus is used to show the effect of a magnetic field on moving electrons.**

To find the force on a single charged particle as it moves through a magnetic field, consider the equation $F = BIL$. The force $BIL$ acts on a short wire at right angles to a magnetic field. $B$ is the induction of the field in newtons per ampere-meter.

$$F = BIL$$

Rewriting $I$ to represent charge per unit time, we get

$$= (B)\frac{(q)}{(t)}(L)$$

Rearranging this expression,

$$= (B)(q)\frac{(L)}{(t)}$$

Since $L/t$ can represent velocity, the expression can be rewritten to read

The force acting on a single charged particle as it moves through a magnetic field is $Bqv$.

$$F = Bqv$$

$B$ is the induction of the magnetic field; $q$ is the charge on the particle; and $v$ is the velocity of the particle. This equation gives the force exerted on a charged particle as it moves through a magnetic field.

**EXAMPLE: Force on a Charged Particle in a Magnetic Field**

A beam of electrons travels at $3.0 \times 10^6$ m/s through a uniform magnetic field. The magnetic induction is $4.0 \times 10^{-2}$ N/A·m. **a.** The beam is at right angles to the magnetic field. What force acts on each electron? **b.** What force acts on a proton moving at the same speed and in the same direction as the electron in Part a?

*Solution:*

**a.** $F = Bqv$

$= (4.0 \times 10^{-2} \text{ N/A·m})(1.6 \times 10^{-19} \text{ C})(3.0 \times 10^6 \text{ m/s})$

$= 1.9 \times 10^{-14} \text{ N}$

**b.** The force is exactly the same on a proton as it is on an electron. The proton and the electron have exactly the same charge. However, because the proton has the opposite sign, it is deflected in the opposite direction.

## PROBLEMS

*Use* $1.6 \times 10^{-19}$ C *as the elementary unit of charge.*

**8.** A beam of electrons moves at right angles to a magnetic field of magnetic induction $6.0 \times 10^{-2}$ N/A·m. The electrons have a velocity of $2.5 \times 10^7$ m/s. What force acts on each electron?

**9.** An electron passes through a magnetic field at right angles to the field at a velocity of $4.0 \times 10^6$ m/s. The strength of the magnetic field is 0.5 N/A·m. What force acts on the electron?

**9.** $3.2 \times 10^{-13}$ N

**10.** A stream of doubly-ionized particles (missing 2 electrons and thus carrying a net charge of 2 elementary charges) moves at a velocity of $3.0 \times 10^4$ m/s perpendicularly to a magnetic field of $9.0 \times 10^{-2}$ N/A·m. What force acts on each ion?

**11.** Triply-ionized particles in a beam carry a net positive charge of three elementary charge units. The beam enters a field of magnetic induction $4.0 \times 10^{-2}$ N/A·m at right angles to the field. The particles have a velocity of $9.0 \times 10^6$ m/s. What force acts on each particle?

**11.** $1.7 \times 10^{-13}$ N

## 24:9   Electric Motors

The current passing through a wire loop in a magnetic field goes in one side of the loop and out the other side. Applying the third left-hand rule to each side of the loop, we find that one side of the loop is forced down while the other side of the loop is forced up. As a result, the loop rotates. An electric motor operates on this principle.

A simple loop of wire in a magnetic field will not rotate more than 180°. In Figure 24-16, the force acting upward on the right side of the loop pushes the loop up. At the same time, the force acting downward on the left side of the loop pushes that side down. The loop turns until it reaches the vertical position. The loop will not continue to turn because the force acting on the right side of the loop is still directed up. It cannot move down through the field. Similarly, the left side of the loop will not move up through the field because the force acting on it is still directed down.

For the loop to rotate 360° in the field, the current running through the loop must reverse direction just as the loop reaches

An electric motor consists of a loop of wire in a magnetic field. When current flows in the loop, the loop rotates.

the vertical position. This reversal causes the loop to rotate, Figure 24-17. To reverse current direction, a split-ring commutator is used. The **split-ring commutator** conducts current into the loop by rubbing against the brushes. The split ring is arranged so that each half of the commutator changes brushes just as the loop reaches the vertical position. Changing brushes reverses the current in the loop. As a result, the direction of the force on each side of the loop is reversed and the loop continues to rotate. This process is repeated each half-turn. Thus, the loop spins in the magnetic field.

A split-ring commutator enables the loop in a motor to rotate 360°.

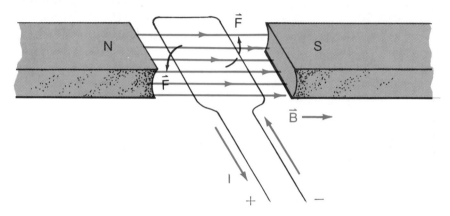

FIGURE 24-16. If a wire loop is placed in a magnetic field, the loop will rotate when current flows.

In practice, electric motors have several rotating loops. Together they make up the **armature** of the motor. The total force acting on the armature is proportional to *BIL*. The force acting on the armature can be varied by changing the magnetic field. The force can also be varied by changing the current or by changing the number of loops in the armature.

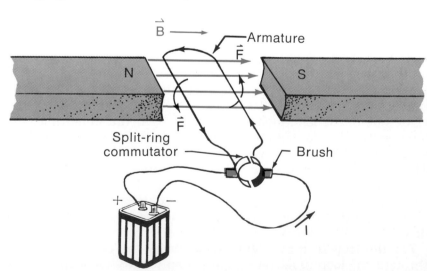

FIGURE 24-17. In an electric motor, split-ring commutators allow the wire loops in the motor to rotate 360°.

## 24:10  Electric Meters

The force acting on a wire loop placed in the field of a permanent magnet depends on the amount of current in the loop. Figure 24-18 shows how the force exerted on a loop of wire in a magnetic field can be used to measure current. A small coil of wire is placed in the strong magnetic field of a permanent magnet. The current to be measured is directed through the coil. The current produces a magnetic field about the coil. The magnetic induction of the field varies with the intensity of the current. Therefore, the force acting on the coil is proportional to the magnitude of the current. The coil turns against the restraining action of a small spring. The meter is calibrated by finding out how much the coil turns when known currents are sent through it. The meter is then used to measure other unknown currents.

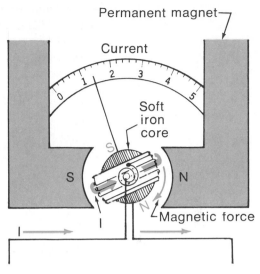

**FIGURE 24-18. The components of an electric meter are shown.**

**Summary**

1. Like magnetic poles repel, unlike magnetic poles attract.  24:1
2. Magnetic fields run from the north pole of a magnet to its south pole.
3. Magnetic field lines always form closed loops.  24:2  } 24:2
4. Whenever an electric current flows in a wire a magnetic field appears about the wire.  24:3
5. A coil of wire (solenoid) through which a current flows also has a magnetic field. The field about the coil will be similar to the field about a permanent magnet.  24:4
6. When a current-bearing wire is placed in a magnetic field, the magnetic field about the wire interacts with the external magnetic field to produce a force.  24:6, 24:7
7. The intensity of a magnetic field is called magnetic induction. Magnetic induction is measured in newtons per ampere-meter.  24:7
8. An electric motor consists of a coil of wire placed in a magnetic field. When a current is introduced into the coil, the coil rotates due to the interaction between the field about the coil and the external field.  24:9

**Questions**

1. State the principle of magnetic attraction and repulsion.
2. Name the three most important magnetic elements.
3. How does a temporary magnet differ from a permanent magnet?

4. Draw a small bar magnet and show the magnetic field lines as they appear about a magnet. Use arrows to show the direction of the field lines.

5. Draw the field between two like magnetic poles and two unlike magnetic poles. Show the directions of the fields.

6. Draw the field around a straight current-bearing wire. Show its direction.

7. Explain the left-hand rule to determine the direction of a magnetic field around a straight current-bearing wire.

8. Explain the left-hand rule to determine the polarity of an electromagnet.

9. Explain the left-hand rule to determine the direction of force on a current-bearing wire placed in a magnetic field.

10. What three factors control the force that acts on a wire carrying a current in a magnetic field?

**Problems**

1. A wire 0.5 m long carrying a current of 8 A is at right angles to a uniform magnetic field. The force on the wire is 0.4 N. What is the strength of the magnetic field?

2. A wire 20 cm long is at right angles to a uniform magnetic field of magnetic induction 0.3 N/A·m. The current through the wire is 6 A. What force acts on the wire?

3. A wire 1.5 m long carrying a current of 10 A is at right angles to a uniform magnetic field. The force acting on the wire is 0.6 N. What is the induction of the magnetic field?

4. The current through a wire 0.8 m long is 5 A. The wire is perpendicular to a magnetic field of induction 0.6 N/A·m. What force acts on the wire?

5. The force on a wire 0.8 m long which is perpendicular to a magnetic field of induction $6.0 \times 10^{-2}$ N/A·m is 0.12 N. What current flows through the wire?

6. The force acting on a wire at right angles to a magnetic field is 3.6 N. The current flowing through the wire is 7.5 A. The magnetic field has an induction of 0.8 N/A·m. How long is the wire?

7. A stream of electrons travels through a magnetic field of induction 0.6 N/A·m at a speed of $4.0 \times 10^6$ m/s. The electrons travel at right angles to the field. What force acts on each of them?

8. Doubly-ionized helium atoms (alpha particles) are traveling at right angles to a magnetic field at a speed of $4.0 \times 10^4$ m/s. The induction of the field is $5.0 \times 10^{-2}$ N/A·m. What force acts on each particle?

**9.** A beta particle (high-speed electron) is traveling at right angles to a magnetic field of induction 0.6 N/A·m. It has a speed of $2.5 \times 10^7$ m/s. What force acts on the particle?

**10.** The mass of an electron is about $9.0 \times 10^{-31}$ kg. What acceleration does the beta particle in Problem 9 undergo in the direction of the force acting on it?

**Applying Physics**

**1.** *Nuclear Research:* In a nuclear research laboratory a proton moves in a particle accelerator through a magnetic field of intensity 0.1 N/A·m at a speed of $3.0 \times 10^7$ m/s.

  **a.** If the proton is moving perpendicular to the field what force acts on it?

  **b.** If the proton continues to move in a direction that is constantly perpendicular to the field what is the radius of curvature of its path?

**2.** *Electric and Magnetic Field Interactions:* An electron is accelerated from rest through a potential difference of 20 000 V which exists between the plates $P_1$ and $P_2$, Figure 24-19. The electron then passes through a small opening into a magnetic field of uniform field strength $B$. As indicated the magnetic field is directed into the page.

**FIGURE 24-19. Use with Applying Physics 2.**

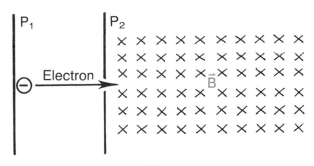

  **a.** State the direction of the electric field between the plates as either $P_1$ to $P_2$ or $P_2$ to $P_1$.

  **b.** In terms of the information given, calculate the electron's speed at plate $P_2$.

  **c.** Describe the motion of the electron through the magnetic field.

  **d.** Since an electron bears an electric charge and magnetic fields can only interact with other magnetic fields, explain how the electron is able to interact with the magnetic field.

**Readings**

Geballe, T. H., "Superconductors in Electric-Power Technology." *Scientific American*, November, 1980.

Keffer, Frederic, "The Magnetic Properties of Materials." *Scientific American*, September, 1967.

Wollman, Phyllis, "Electromagnetic Interference." *Science Digest*, April, 1980.

An electric current can be used to produce a magnetic field. Conversely, a magnetic field can induce an electric current in a wire under certain conditions. This effect is called electromagnetic induction. The principle of electromagnetic induction is used in the design and operation of generators. These generators in the Hoover Dam hydroelectric facility are used to convert mechanical energy to electricity. Not all generators are the size shown here. What devices do you use everyday that contain generators?

# Electromagnetic Induction 25

An electric current flowing through a wire produces a magnetic field. This discovery led scientists to infer that a magnetic field could produce an electric current. In 1831, Joseph Henry of the United States and Michael Faraday of England answered this question. Their experiments revealed that a magnetic field could indeed produce an electric current in a wire. An electric generator operates on this principle.

**GOAL: You will gain knowledge and understanding of the use of magnetic fields in generating electric currents, the design of generators and transformers, and the nature of AC current.**

## 25:1 Faraday's Discovery

Faraday experimented with a moving wire in a magnetic field. He found that when a wire is moved through a magnetic field, an electric current is induced in the wire. Figure 25-1 shows Faraday's experiments. A wire that is part of a closed (complete) circuit is held in a magnetic field. When the wire is moved through the field the meter indicates that an electric current flows in the wire. If the wire moves up through the field, the current flows in one direction in the wire. When the wire moves down through the field, the current flows in the opposite direction. If the wire is held still in the field or is moved parallel to the field, no current flows in the circuit. An electric current is generated in a wire only when the wire cuts through the magnetic field.

For a current to be produced, either the conductor can move through a field or the field can move past a conductor. In both cases, it is the relative motion between the wire and the magnetic field that produces the current. The process of generating a current in this way is **electromagnetic induction.**

When a wire is moved through a magnetic field, a current is generated in the wire.

Electromagnetic induction is the process of generating a current by the relative motion between a wire and a magnetic field.

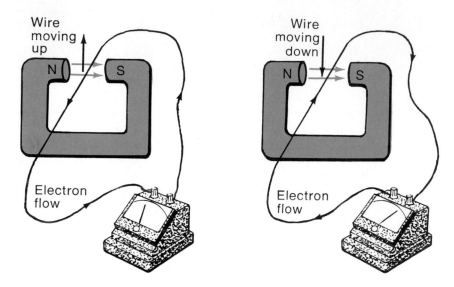

**FIGURE 25-1. When a wire is moved in a magnetic field, an electric current flows in the wire, but only while the wire is moving. The direction of electron current flow depends on the direction the wire is moving through the field.**

If a wire moves through a magnetic field at an angle to the field, only the component of the wire's velocity that is perpendicular to the direction of the field generates a current. The current is proportional to the sine of the angle between the wire and the field.

The force acting on the free electrons in a wire, as the wire moves through a magnetic field, is perpendicular to both the direction in which the wire is moving and the direction of the magnetic field. To find the direction of the electron current that flows in a conductor moving through a magnetic field, use the left-hand rule described in Chapter 24. Hold the left hand such that the thumb points in the direction in which the wire is moving and the fingers point in the direction of the magnetic field. The palm of the hand points in the direction of the force acting on the electrons.

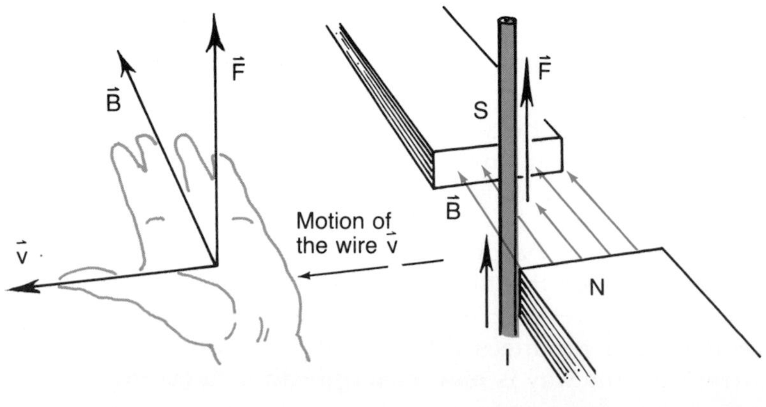

**A left-hand rule indicates the direction of the induced current.**

**FIGURE 25-2. The left-hand rule can be used to find the direction of a current flowing through a conductor that is moving in a magnetic field.**

# 25:2 Induced EMF

When we studied Ohm's law, we learned that a voltage must be present if an electric current is to flow in a wire. This voltage is also called electromotive force, or EMF. **Electromotive force** is the energy given to each electron in the wire. When a wire is moved through a magnetic field, electrons flow in the wire because a voltage appears across the wire. This voltage is referred to as the induced electromotive force. It is equal to the work done on each electron as the wire is moved through the field. The work that must be done to move a wire through a magnetic field depends on the magnetic induction $B$, the length of the wire in the field $L$, and the rate at which the wire is moved in the field $v$. Thus,

$$EMF = BLv$$

EMF is measured in volts. It represents the work done to give energy to the charges that flow in the wire. Note that no current would flow in a simple length of wire moved in a magnetic field. Electricity flows only in complete circuits. If a length of wire is formed into a closed loop and then a part of the loop is moved through a magnetic field, a current flows in the loop.

You should note that the term "electromotive force" is clearly a misnomer since it means energy per unit charge, not force. The term originated before the distinction was fully understood and persists to this day.

EMF is the energy given to electrons in a wire.

Induced EMF is the energy given to electrons when a wire moves through a magnetic field.

EMF is the product of magnetic induction, wire length, and speed of the wire.

**EXAMPLE: Induced EMF**

A wire 0.2 m long moves perpendicularly through a magnetic field of magnetic induction $8.0 \times 10^{-2}$ N/A·m at a speed of 7.0 m/s. **a.** What EMF is induced in the wire? **b.** The wire is a part of a circuit which has a resistance of 0.5 Ω. What current flows in the circuit?

*Solution:* **a.**  $EMF = BLv$

$$= (8.0 \times 10^{-2} \text{ N/A·m})(0.2 \text{ m})(7.0 \text{ m/s})$$

$$= 0.11 \frac{(\text{N})(\text{m})(\cancel{\text{m}})}{\left(\frac{\text{C}·\cancel{\text{m}}}{\cancel{\text{s}}}\right)(\cancel{\text{s}})}$$

$$= 0.11 \frac{\text{N·m}}{\text{C}} = 0.11 \text{ J/C} = 0.11 \text{ V}$$

**b.**  $$I = \frac{V}{R}$$

$$= \frac{0.11 \text{ V}}{0.5 \text{ Ω}} = 0.22 \text{ A}$$

**PROBLEMS**

1. A wire 0.5 m long cuts straight up through a field of magnetic induction 0.4 N/A·m at a speed of 20 m/s.
   a. What EMF is induced in the wire?
   b. The wire is part of a circuit of total resistance 6.0 Ω. What current flows in the circuit?

2. A wire has a total length of 0.6 m perpendicular to a field of magnetic induction 0.5 N/A·m. The wire is moved through the field at a speed of 20 m/s.
   a. What EMF is induced in the wire?
   b. The wire is part of a circuit of total resistance 15.0 Ω. What current flows in the circuit?

3. An instructor connects both ends of a copper wire of total resistance 0.5 Ω to the terminals of a galvanometer. The instructor then holds part of the wire in a field of magnetic induction $2.0 \times 10^{-2}$ N/A·m. The length of the wire between the magnetic poles is 10 cm. If the instructor moves the wire up through the field at 5.0 m/s, what current will the galvanometer indicate?

4. A wire 30 m long moves at 2.0 m/s perpendicularly through a field of magnetic induction 1.0 N/A·m.
   a. What EMF is induced in the wire?
   b. The total resistance of the circuit of which the wire is a part is 15.0 Ω. What current flows?

5. A wire 16.0 m long is perpendicular to a field of magnetic induction 0.5 N/A·m. The wire is moved through the field at 15.0 m/s.
   a. What EMF is induced in the wire?
   b. The wire is part of a circuit with 20 Ω resistance. What current flows?

# 25:3  Electric Generators

The **electric generator** converts mechanical energy to electric energy. The electric generator was invented by Michael Faraday. In essence, an electric generator consists of a number of wire loops placed in a strong magnetic field. All of the loops together form an armature (AR muh chur). The wire loops are mounted so that they rotate freely in the field. As the loops turn, they cut through magnetic field lines. A current is induced. For clarity, Figure 25-3 shows one loop of a generator. Increasing the loops in the armature increases the length of the wire in the field. In accordance with the expression, $EMF = BLv$, the induced EMF also increases.

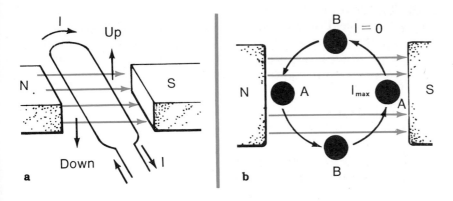

FIGURE 25-3. An electric current is generated in a wire loop as the loop rotates (a). This cross-sectional view (b) shows the position of the loop when maximum current is generated and when no current is generated.

Using Figure 25-3 and the left-hand rule, notice that the current induced in the loop moves in opposite directions in the two sides of the loop. Therefore, a current flows around the entire loop. Only while the loop is in a horizontal position do the two segments cut through the field at a right angle. In this position the current is a maximum. The maximum occurs because the loop cuts through the maximum number of magnetic field lines per unit time in this position. As the loop moves from the horizontal to the vertical position, it cuts through the magnetic field lines at an ever increasing angle. Thus, it cuts through fewer magnetic field lines per unit time and the current decreases. When the loop is in the vertical position, the segments move parallel to the field and the current is zero. As the loop continues to turn, the segment that was moving up begins to move down. The segment that was moving down begins to move up. Thus, the direction of the current in the loop changes. This change in direction takes place each time the loop turns through 180°. The current changes smoothly from zero to some maximum value and back to zero during each half-turn of the loop. Then it reverses direction. The graph of current versus time yields the sine curve of Figure 25-4.

In the previous section we found that the EMF, or voltage, developed in a wire moving through a magnetic field is equal to the product $BLv$. A generator consists of a coil of wire rotating in a strong magnetic field. Thus, the EMF (voltage) developed by the generator depends upon the magnetic induction $B$, the length of wire rotating in the field $L$, and the rate at which the coil (armature) turns in the field $v$.

The current induced in a wire loop changes direction each time the loop rotates 180°.

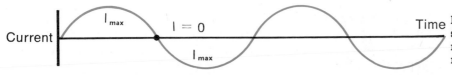

FIGURE 25-4. This graph shows the variation of current with time as a loop rotates.

Maximum current and voltage are produced when the loops move at right angles to the field.

Zero current and voltage are produced when the loops move parallel to the field.

**FIGURE 25-5. This graph shows the variation of voltage with time as a loop rotates.**

As the armature turns in the magnetic field, its loops cut through the field at different angles. Thus, the voltage changes in the same way that the current changes. The voltage is at maximum value when the loops are moving at right angles to the field. The voltage is zero when the loops are moving parallel to the field, Figure 25-5.

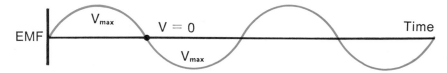

## 25:4   Alternating Current Generator

The armature of a generator is rotated in the magnetic field by the energy source at a set number of turns (revolutions) per second. Commercially, this frequency is usually 60 Hz. The current changes direction after each half-turn. Therefore, the current changes direction, or alternates, 120 times a second.

In Figure 25-6, an alternating current in an armature is transmitted to the rest of the circuit. The brush-slip-ring arrangement permits the armature to turn freely while still allowing the current to pass into the external circuit. As the armature turns, the alternating current varies between some maximum value and zero. The light in the circuit does not appear to dim or brighten because the changes are too fast for the eye to detect.

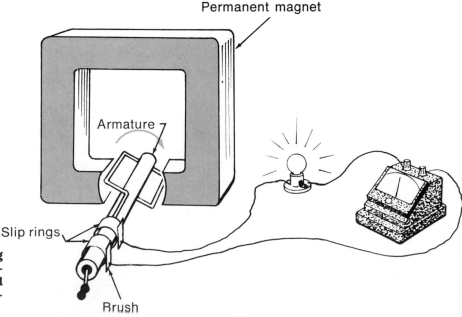

**FIGURE 25-6. Alternating current generators transmit current to an external circuit by way of a brush-slip ring arrangement.**

The effective value of an alternating current is found by comparing it to a direct current. If an alternating current is applied to a heater, the heat the current produces in one minute can be measured. The direct current needed to produce the same amount of heat in the same time is then calculated. The AC current is then compared to the DC current. Such measurements always show that the effective value of an alternating current is equal to its maximum value multiplied by 0.707. Likewise, the effective value of the alternating EMF is 0.707 times the maximum value.

The effective current is 0.707 maximum current.

The effective voltage is 0.707 maximum voltage.

$$I_{eff} = 0.707\,(I_{max})$$
$$V_{eff} = 0.707\,(V_{max})$$

**EXAMPLE:  Effective Voltage and Effective Current**

An AC generator develops a maximum voltage of 100 V and delivers a maximum current of 20 A to a circuit. **a.** What is the effective voltage of the generator? **b.** What effective current is delivered to the circuit? **c.** What is the resistance of the circuit?

*Solution:* **a.**     $V_{eff} = 0.707\,(V_{max})$
$$= 0.707\,(100\ V) = 70.7\ V$$

**b.**     $I_{eff} = 0.707\,(I_{max})$
$$= 0.707\,(20\ A) = 14.1\ A$$

**c.**     $R = \dfrac{V_{eff}}{I_{eff}}$

$$= \frac{70.7\ V}{14.1\ A} = 5.0\ \Omega$$

**PROBLEMS**

**6.** A generator in a power plant develops a maximum voltage of 170 V.
   **a.** What is the effective voltage?
   **b.** A 60-W light bulb is placed across the generator. A maximum current of 0.7 A flows through the bulb. What effective current flows through the bulb?

**7.** The effective voltage of an AC household outlet is 117 V.
   **a.** What is the maximum voltage across a lamp connected to the outlet?
   **b.** The effective current through the lamp is 5.5 A. What maximum current flows in the lamp during a complete cycle?

7. a.  165 V
   b.  7.8 A

8. An AC generator delivers a maximum voltage of 250 V.
   a. What effective voltage is available to a circuit?
   b. An 88-Ω resistor is placed across the generator. What effective current flows through it?
   c. What is the maximum current through the resistor?

9. a. What is the effective EMF across a circuit connected to a generator that delivers a maximum voltage of 310 V?
   b. What effective current does this generator deliver if the resistance of the circuit is 55 Ω?

10. An AC generator delivers a peak voltage of 425 V.
    a. What is the effective voltage in a circuit placed across the generator?
    b. The resistance of the circuit is 500 Ω. What effective current flows in it?

9. a. 220 V
   b. 4.0 A

## 25:5   Generators and Motors

Generators and motors are identical in construction, but they serve opposite purposes. The purpose of a **generator** is to convert mechanical energy to electric energy. The purpose of a **motor** is to convert electric energy to mechanical energy. When an electric current is made to flow through an armature in a magnetic field, the armature turns. This device is a motor.

When an armature is turned in a magnetic field, an electric current is produced. This device is an electric generator. An electric motor can be used as an electric generator. In France, all trains are electric. The same motor that drives a train up a hill

A generator converts mechanical energy to electric energy; a motor converts electric energy to mechanical energy.

**FIGURE 25-7. This experimental electric car runs on electric energy from its batteries rather than fossil fuels.**

*Dave Davidson/Tom Stack & Assoc.*

is used as a generator when the train rolls downhill. A switch is thrown and the motors serve as generators. Thus, the kinetic energy of the train is used to produce electric energy. This electric energy is sent back into the power lines to be used by other trains.

Recently, an increased interest in electric cars and trucks has developed because of fuel shortages. Such vehicles use batteries for power. Their operating range is limited by the batteries in use. To conserve as much energy as possible, the braking system of an electric vehicle is made so that when the driver steps on a brake pedal, contacts are switched to change the motor to a generator. As the electric car slows, it gives its kinetic energy to the generator. The generator produces electric energy to help recharge the batteries. Thus, electric cars can travel a greater distance before their batteries need to be completely recharged.

## 25:6 Lenz's Law

As soon as the armature of a generator starts to turn, current flows in its wires. As a result, a generator must also act like a motor. The motor effect of a generator tries to turn the armature in the opposite direction from which it is turning. If the armature of a hand generator is turned clockwise, the current that flows tries to cause the armature to turn counterclockwise. Therefore, the armature becomes more difficult to turn.

**Lenz's law** states that *an induced current always acts in such a direction that its magnetic properties oppose the change by which the current is induced.*

Lenz's law also applies to motors. As soon as the armature of a motor begins to turn in a magnetic field, it will generate an electric current. The generator effect of a motor attempts to produce current in direct opposition to the current that makes the armature turn. This generator effect of a motor is quite noticeable. It is called the "back-EMF" of the motor. When the armature of the motor is turning, back-EMF opposes the current put into the motor. If a motor is to operate properly, it must have a resistance that accounts for back-EMF. For this reason, a motor's resistance is low. Thus, when a motor is first turned on, it draws a large current. This large current can cause a voltage drop across the entire circuit. Suppose a second device, such as a light bulb, is in the same circuit when the motor is turned on. The voltage across the light decreases for a moment and the light dims. As the motor begins to turn, back-EMF appears. The back-EMF opposes the current flowing into the motor. In effect, it reduces the current flowing in the entire circuit. Thus, the excess voltage drop in the lines is eliminated and the circuit returns to normal.

The current in a generator produces a motor effect. The motor effect opposes the turning of the generator.

A motor produces a back-EMF as it rotates. The generated current opposes the current operating the motor.

As current in a coil
changes, an induced EMF
appears in that same coil.
This effect is called self-
induction.

## 25:7  Self-Induction

Whenever a coil of wire is part of an electric circuit, it produces an effect called **self-induction.** Consider the coil in Figure 25-8. When the switch is closed, a current begins to flow in the circuit. The current causes a magnetic field to appear about the coil. The field does not reach its full magnitude at once. It grows as the current increases toward its maximum value. As it grows, the field moves out and cuts through adjacent loops of the coil. As the field cuts through these loops, an EMF is induced in the coil. By Lenz's law, this induced EMF tends to oppose the current flowing in the loops. The current is prevented from reaching its maximum value for a short time.

In a DC circuit, such as Figure 25-8, the self-inductance of the coil disappears rapidly. It disappears because as soon as the current reaches its maximum value, the field becomes stable and does not change. However, if the source of DC current is replaced with an AC source, the field about the coil constantly changes as the current in the circuit changes. The field constantly moves in and out from the coil cutting through the loops. This movement produces an induced current. By Lenz's law, the induced current always opposes the current in the coil. For this reason, any coil placed in an alternating current circuit presents a strong opposition to the flow of current in that circuit. This opposition (which is not a true resistance) to current flow in an alternating current circuit is called **inductive reactance.**

Inductive reactance
impedes the flow of
current in an AC circuit.

**FIGURE 25-8. Self-inductance of a coil causes opposition to the flow of current in a circuit. In this DC circuit, the opposition to current flow disappears as soon as the current becomes steady.**

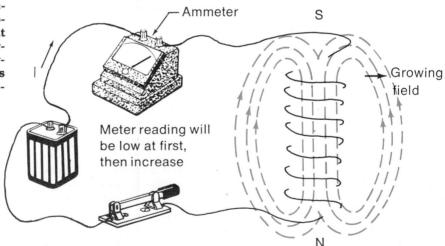

## 25:8  Transformers

A **transformer** has two coils wound around the same core. One coil is called the **primary coil.** The other is called the **secondary**

**coil.** Introducing an alternating current into the primary coil causes the magnetic field about the coil to fluctuate. Because the current changes direction every half cycle, the magnetic field changes direction every half cycle. The varying field cuts through the loops of the secondary coil. Thus, it induces an EMF in the secondary coil.

In a transformer, two coils of different lengths are wound around the same core.

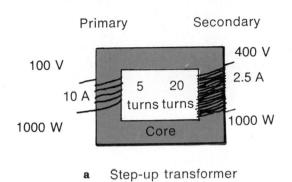

a   Step-up transformer

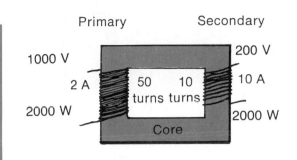

b   Step-down transformer

This induced EMF can be found by using the relationship EMF = *BLv*. The rate of change of magnetic flux is the same about both coils. Thus, *B* is the same around both coils. The velocity *v* is also the same for both coils because the flux passes over both coils in the same time. If the secondary coil has more turns on it than the primary coil, it has a greater length *L* than the primary coil. The lengths are in direct proportion to the number of turns on each coil. Thus, the EMF is greater in the secondary coil. If the secondary coil has fewer turns than the primary coil, its EMF is less. The ratio of the EMF in the primary coil to the EMF in the secondary coil is equal to the ratio of the number of turns on the primary to the number of turns on the secondary.

**FIGURE 25-9. For a transformer, the ratio of input voltage to output voltage depends upon the ratio of the number of turns of the primary to the number of turns of the secondary.**

$$\frac{Primary\ voltage}{Secondary\ voltage} = \frac{Number\ of\ turns\ on\ primary}{Number\ of\ turns\ on\ secondary}$$

$$\frac{V_p}{V_s} = \frac{N_p}{N_s}$$

A transformer may be a step-up or step-down transformer. A **step-up transformer** is used to increase voltage. A **step-down transformer** is used to decrease voltage. In an "ideal" transformer, the power input is equal to the power output. Since electric power is voltage times current ($P = VI$), a transformer that increases voltage must decrease current. A transformer that decreases voltage will increase current. In all cases the power introduced into the primary of a transformer is equal to the power induced in the secondary of the transformer.

A transformer can be used to increase voltage or to decrease voltage.

$$V_p I_p = V_s I_s$$

a

b

**FIGURE 25-10. Transformers are used to increase the voltage of current leaving the power station.**

Transformers make it possible to vary both voltage and current in AC transmission lines. As pointed out in Section 22:11, the equation $\Delta Q = I^2 Rt$ indicates that it is extremely important to keep the current in transmission lines as low as possible to prevent energy loss in the form of heat. Step-up transformers are used at power sources to develop very high voltages and low currents for power transmission to the consumer. Thus, during the transmission, $I^2R$ losses are kept to a minimum. When the power reaches the consumer, step-down transformers are used to provide appropriate low voltages and high currents for use.

There are many other important uses of transformers. X-ray tubes rely on high voltages for their operation. Few devices have contributed as much to medical science as have X-ray tubes. Industrially, high temperatures such as those used during arc welding are obtained by developing high voltages and causing current to arc between electrodes. The temperature of an electric arc exceeds 3000°C. In addition, high voltages are used for many basic research purposes. We shall study some research devices which use high voltage as we progress through the remainder of this text.

**EXAMPLE: Step-up Transformer**

A step-up transformer has 200 turns on its primary coil and 3000 turns on its secondary coil. **a.** The primary coil is supplied with an alternating current at 90 V. What is the voltage in the secondary circuit? **b.** The current in the primary circuit is 30 A.

What current flows in the secondary circuit? **c.** What is the power in the primary? In the secondary?

*Solution:* **a.** $\dfrac{V_p}{V_s} = \dfrac{N_p}{N_s}$ or $V_s = \dfrac{V_p N_s}{N_p}$

$$= \dfrac{(90\text{ V})(3000)}{200} = 1350\text{ V}$$

**b.** $V_p I_p = V_s I_s$ or $I_s = \dfrac{V_p I_p}{V_s}$

$$= \dfrac{(90\cancel{\text{ V}})(30\text{ A})}{1350\cancel{\text{ V}}} = 2\text{ A}$$

**c.** $V_p I_p = (90\text{ V})(30\text{ A}) = 2700\text{ W}$

$V_s I_s = (1350\text{ V})(2\text{ A}) = 2700\text{ W}$

## PROBLEMS

**11.** An ideal step-up transformer's primary has 50 turns. Its secondary has 1500 turns. The primary is connected to an AC generator having an EMF of 120 V.
   **a.** Calculate the EMF of the secondary.
   **b.** Find the current in the secondary circuit if the current in the primary is 90 A.
   **c.** What power develops in the primary? In the secondary?

**11.** a. 3600 V
   b. 3 A
   c. 11 000 W

**12.** The secondary of a step-down transformer has 50 turns. The primary has 1500 turns.
   **a.** The EMF of the primary is 3600 V. What is the EMF of the secondary?
   **b.** The current in the primary is 3.0 A. What current flows in the secondary?

**13.** A step-up transformer has 300 turns on its primary and 90 000 turns on its secondary. The EMF of the generator to which the primary is attached is 60 V.
   **a.** What is the EMF in the secondary?
   **b.** The current flowing in the primary coil is 150 A. What current flows in the secondary?

**13.** a. 18 000 V
   b. 0.5 A

**14.** A step-down transformer has 7500 turns on its primary and 125 turns on its secondary. The voltage across the primary is 7200 V.
   **a.** What voltage is across the secondary?
   **b.** The current in the primary is 0.6 A. What current flows in the secondary?

**15.** A step-up transformer is connected to a generator that delivers 120 V and 100 A. The ratio of the turns on the secondary to the turns on the primary is 1000 to 1.
   **a.** What voltage is in the secondary?
   **b.** What current flows in the secondary?
   **c.** What is the power input?
   **d.** What is the power output?

**15.** a. 120 000 V
   b. 0.1 A
   c. 12 000 W
   d. 12 000 W

**Summary**

1. Michael Faraday discovered that if work is done to move a wire through a magnetic field an electric current will be induced in the wire.   **25:1**

2. The direction taken by the current in a wire moving through a mag- **25:2** netic field depends upon the direction in which the wire is moving.

3. The current produced depends upon the angle between the wire and the magnetic field. Maximum current occurs when the wire is moving at right angles to the field.   **25:2**

4. Electromotive force, EMF, is the energy imparted to each unit of charge by the energy source. EMF is measured in volts.   **25:2**

5. EMF is the product of the magnetic induction $B$, the length of the **25:2** wire in the field $L$, and the speed of the moving wire $v$. EMF $= BLv$.

6. An electric generator consists of a number of wire loops placed in a magnetic field. Since each side of the coil moves alternately up and down through the field, the current alternates direction in the loops. The generator develops alternating current.   **25:3, 25:4**

7. A generator and a motor are the same device. A generator converts an available form of energy to electric energy, while a motor converts electric energy to some other form of energy.   **25:5**

8. Lenz's law states that an induced current always acts in opposition to the change that is causing the current. A motor attempts to act as a generator and a generator attempts to act as a motor.   **25:6**

9. A transformer has two coils wound about the same core. The introduction of an AC current into the primary coil induces an EMF in the secondary coil. The voltages and currents in alternating current circuits may be stepped up or down by the use of transformers. **25:8**

**Questions**

1. Explain how a wire and a strong magnet generate an electric current.

2. What is the difference between the current generated in a wire when the wire is moved up through a magnetic field and when the wire is moved down through the same field?

3. What causes an electron to move in a wire when the wire is moved through a magnetic field?

4. What is EMF?

5. Substitute units to show that $BLv$ = volts.

6. Sketch and describe an AC generator.

7. What is the armature of an electric generator?

8. What is the difference between a generator and a motor?

9. How is the effective value of an AC current determined?

10. What factors determine the EMF of a generator?

11. State Lenz's law.
12. What causes the back-EMF of an electric motor?
13. Why is the self-inductance of a coil an important factor when the coil is in an AC circuit and a minor factor when the coil is in a DC circuit?
14. Upon what does the ratio of the EMF in the primary of a transformer to the EMF in the secondary of the transformer depend?

**Problems**

1. A wire segment 30 cm long moves straight up through a field of magnetic induction $4.0 \times 10^{-2}$ N/A·m at a speed of 15.0 m/s. What EMF is induced in the wire?
2. A wire 0.75 m long cuts straight up through a field of magnetic induction 0.3 N/A·m at a speed of 16 m/s.
   a. What EMF is induced in the wire?
   b. The wire is part of a circuit of total resistance 4.5 Ω. What current flows in the circuit?
3. A wire 20.0 m long moves at 4.0 m/s perpendicularly through a field of magnetic induction 0.5 N/A·m. What EMF is induced in the wire?
4. An AC generator develops a maximum voltage of 150 V. It delivers a maximum current of 30 A to an external circuit.
   a. What is the effective voltage of the generator?
   b. What effective current does it deliver to the external circuit?
5. An electric stove is connected to a 220-V AC source.
   a. What is the maximum voltage across one of the stove's elements when it is operating?
   b. The resistance of the operating element is 11 Ω. What effective current flows through it?
6. An AC generator develops a maximum EMF of 565 V. What effective EMF does the generator deliver to an external circuit?
7. A step-up transformer has 80 turns on its primary coil. It has 1200 turns on its secondary coil. The primary coil is supplied with an alternating current at 120 V.
   a. What voltage is in the secondary coil?
   b. The current in the primary coil is 50 A. What current flows in the secondary circuit?
   c. What is the transformer power input and output?
8. An ideal transformer has 300 turns on its primary coil. It has 9000 turns on its secondary coil. The primary is connected to a 90-V generator.
   a. Calculate the EMF of the secondary.
   b. Calculate the current in the secondary if the current in the primary is 60 A.
   c. Calculate the power developed in the primary and the secondary.

9. The primary of a transformer has 300 turns. It is connected to a 150-V source. Calculate the number of turns on the secondary to supply the following.
   **a.** 900 V     **b.** 270 V     **c.** 12.5 V     **d.** 6 V

10. In a hydroelectric plant, electric energy is generated at 1200 V. It is transmitted at 240 000 V.
    **a.** What is the ratio of the turns on the primary to the turns on the secondary of a transformer connected to one of the generators?
    **b.** One of the plant generators delivers 40 A to the primary of its transformer. What current flows in the secondary?

11. The primary of a transformer has 150 turns. It is connected to a 120-V source. Calculate the number of turns on the secondary needed to supply the following.
    **a.** 600 V     **b.** 300 V     **c.** 6 V

---

**Applying Physics**

1. *Motor Effect of a Generator:* An instructor is moving a loop of copper wire down through a magnetic field $\vec{B}$ as shown in Figure 25-11.
   **a.** Will the induced current move to the right or left in the wire segment shown in the diagram?
   **b.** As soon as the wire is moved in the field, a current appears in it. Thus, the wire segment is a current-bearing wire located in a magnetic field. A force must, therefore, act on the wire. What will be the direction of the force acting on the wire due to the induced current?
   **c.** Suppose your answer to the previous question had been different. Would any physical law be violated? Explain.

**FIGURE 25-11. Use with Applying Physics 1.**

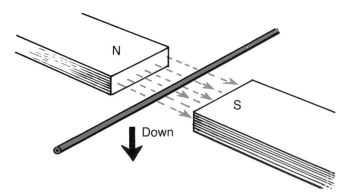

2. *Invention:* An inventor proposes that a considerable amount of gasoline could be conserved each year by mounting antenna like wire segments on the roofs of automobiles. When the autos move perpendicular to or at some angle with the earth's magnetic field a current would be generated in the wires which could be used to charge storage batteries. The batteries could, in turn, power the auto.

**a.** The earth's magnetic field in the United States has an average induction of about $5.0 \times 10^{-5}$ N/A·m. If an auto were moving 72.0 km/h perpendicular to that field (east-west) what would have to be the total length of the wire segments on its roof to develop an EMF of 12 V?

**b.** If, due to its low weight, aluminum wire of resistance $2.6 \times 10^{-4}$ Ω per meter is used for the wire segments what maximum current could be developed?

**c.** Would enough power be developed to move an automobile down a highway?

**d.** Why is the entire scheme impractical under any circumstances?

**Readings**

Carrigan, Richard A., "Quest for the Magnetic Monopole." *The Physics Teacher*, October, 1975.

Overbye, Dennis, "The Sun Turns Savage." *Discover*, November, 1980.

Panofsky, Wolfgang, "Needs Versus Means in High-Energy Physics." *Physics Today*, June, 1980.

Shiers, George, "The Induction Coil." *Scientific American*, May, 1971.

The electromagnetic spectrum includes radiation with wavelengths as short as $10^{-14}$ meters and as long as $10^7$ meters. Very long radio waves originating in outer space are detected using large radio antennas. Scientists are gathering data about events which occurred in space over 300 years ago using radio telescopes. This array consists of twenty-seven individual radio telescopes mounted on a single track. Collectively, they form the largest single radio telescope. The technology associated with using electromagnetic waves has enabled us to learn more about our universe. After studying this chapter, list those devices that you use everyday that operate by using electromagnetic waves.

# Electromagnetic Field Applications 26

We have seen that when a conductor is placed in a changing magnetic field, an induced EMF appears. This EMF indicates that an electric field is present. The electric field pushes electrons through the conductor. A changing magnetic field always generates an electric field.

## 26:1 Generation of Electromagnetic Waves

In 1864, James Clerk Maxwell showed that conductors are not needed to generate magnetic or electric fields. Maxwell predicted that a magnetic field moving in space generates an electric field moving in space. This moving electric field in turn generates a magnetic field moving in space, and so on. The fields pass through space at the speed of light in the form of a wave. Maxwell predicted that the magnetic and electric parts of a wave are always at right angles to each other. Also, they are both at right angles to the direction of propagation of the wave. Experiments confirm this prediction.

To generate an electromagnetic wave, a changing magnetic field or a changing electric field is needed. To produce a changing magnetic field, the current in the wire must be constantly changing. A changing electric current means a changing rate of flow. This changing rate of flow means that charged particles are being accelerated. Accelerated charged particles produce electromagnetic waves which travel off into space.

GOAL: You will gain knowledge and understanding of the generation and transmission of electromagnetic waves and of the behavior of charged particles in electric and magnetic fields.

A changing magnetic field generates a changing electric field.

A changing electric field generates a changing magnetic field.

To produce an electromagnetic wave, a changing field is needed.

Accelerated charges generate electromagnetic waves.

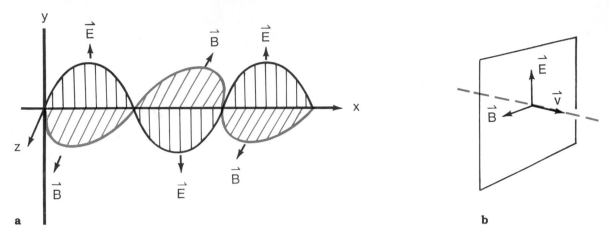

**FIGURE 26-1. A model of an electromagnetic wave (a). Note that the electric and magnetic fields are perpendicular to one another and that they are both perpendicular to the direction in which the wave is traveling (b).**

Light waves are electromagnetic waves generated by the acceleration of electrons within an atom.

Radio waves are generated by accelerating electrons in an antenna.

The relationship between the accelerating charged particles and electromagnetic waves explains several issues. Electromagnetic waves travel at the speed of light as Maxwell predicted. The implication is that light waves are electromagnetic waves. Since electrons are charged particles, the energy transitions of electrons within the atom are thought to be the origin of the characteristic spectra of an atom. This supports the idea that electromagnetic waves are due to the acceleration of charged particles. Electrons accelerate as they move between two different energy levels within an atom. The accelerating electrons produce electromagnetic waves in the visible and ultraviolet regions of the spectrum.

Maxwell's theory has an important implication. If electrons can vibrate in a wire at a constant frequency, an electromagnetic wave of the same frequency should leave the region of the wire. Thus, Maxwell predicted the propagation of radio waves. However, Maxwell did not live to see his prediction confirmed. In 1887, Heinrich Hertz generated and detected the first radio waves.

## 26:2   Discovery of X rays

In 1895 in Germany, Wilhelm Roentgen sent electrons through an evacuated discharge tube. Roentgen used very high voltage across the tube. This voltage accelerated the electrons to very high speeds. The electrons struck the electrode located at the opposite end of the tube. Roentgen noted a glow on a phosphorescent screen a short distance away. He concluded that some kind of highly penetrating rays were coming from the discharge tube. Because of the excitations on the screen, Roentgen recognized that the rays could pass through materials.

Courtesy of Kodansha

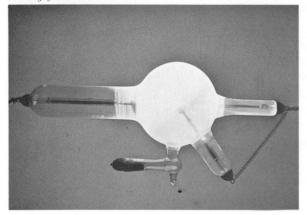

a

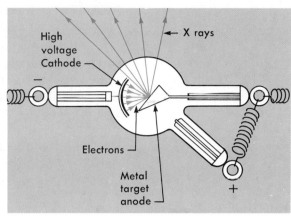

b

Because Roentgen did not know what these strange rays were, he called them X rays. **X rays** are now known to be electromagnetic waves of very high frequency. They are produced by the extremely high rate of deceleration of the electrons as they strike the anode of the tube. The high frequency of X rays indicates the high energy of the electromagnetic wave. The energy of an electromagnetic wave is equal to Planck's constant times the frequency of the wave, $E = hf$. Much of the kinetic energy of the high-speed electrons is converted to the energy of the X rays that result as the particles are decelerated at the anode.

**FIGURE 26-2. This apparatus is used in producing X rays.**

X rays are high-frequency electromagnetic waves generated when electrons strike an anode.

The energy of an X ray is equal to the energy loss of an electron as it strikes the anode.

**EXAMPLE: Accelerating an Electron in a Discharge Tube**

Assume an electron starts from rest at one end of a cathode ray tube where the voltage is $1 \times 10^5$ V. Find the speed of the electron when it reaches the other end of the tube. The mass of an electron is $9.1 \times 10^{-31}$ kg.

*Solution:* From the definition of a volt, we know that 100 000 J of work are done to transfer 1 C of charge across a $1 \times 10^5$ V potential difference. There are $6.25 \times 10^{18}$ electrons in 1 C of charge. Thus, the work done on a single electron to move it through the potential difference is

$$\frac{100\ 000 \text{ J/}\cancel{C}}{6.25 \times 10^{18}\ e^-/\cancel{C}} = 1.6 \times 10^{-14} \text{ J/}e^-$$

The electron converts this energy to kinetic energy as it travels to the anode.

Therefore, at the anode, $\text{KE} = \dfrac{mv^2}{2} = 1.6 \times 10^{-14}$ J

and
$$v = \sqrt{\frac{2(1.6 \times 10^{-14} \text{ J})}{m}} = \sqrt{\frac{3.2 \times 10^{-14} \text{ J}}{9.1 \times 10^{-31} \text{ kg}}}$$

$$= \sqrt{3.6 \times 10^{16} \text{ m}^2/\text{s}^2} = 1.9 \times 10^8 \text{ m/s}$$

**EXAMPLE:  Radiation Produced by Electrons in a Discharge Tube**

Assume the energy found in the preceding example is roughly correct. **a.** Calculate the frequency of the radiation emitted if all the energy of the electron is converted to electromagnetic radiation when the electron strikes the anode. **b.** X rays have frequencies between $10^{16}$ and $10^{21}$ Hz. Is the radiation of Part a of this Example in the X-ray region?

*Solution:* Use Planck's constant ($6.6 \times 10^{-34}$ J/Hz) and the relation $E = hf$.

**a.**
$$f = \frac{E}{h} = \frac{1.6 \times 10^{-14}\,J}{6.6 \times 10^{-34}\,J/Hz} = 2.4 \times 10^{19} \text{ Hz}$$

**b.** Since the frequency is between $10^{16}$ and $10^{21}$ Hz, the rays are X rays.

**PROBLEMS**

1. **a.** $1.3 \times 10^{-14}$ J/$e^-$
   b. $1.3 \times 10^{-14}$ J

**1. a.** Find the energy given to an electron transferred through a potential difference of 80 000 V.
  **b.** What energy does the electron give up as it strikes the anode?

**2.** The electrons in Problem 1 are accelerated across a discharge tube by 80 000 V. Assume the electrons start from rest. What speed do they attain before reaching the anode?

3. $2.0 \times 10^{19}$ Hz

**3.** All the energy given up by each electron in Problem 1 is converted to electromagnetic radiation. What is the frequency of the electromagnetic wave that is produced?

**4.** An electron falls through a potential difference of 10 000 volts.
  **a.** What energy is given up by the electron?
  **b.** The electron passes through a discharge tube while giving up the energy. What speed does it attain?

5. $4.3 \times 10^6$ m/s

**5.** A proton has a mass of $1.7 \times 10^{-27}$ kg. What maximum speed does it attain in falling through a potential difference of 100 000 V?

# 26:3   Transmission and Reception of Electromagnetic Waves

Maxwell showed that accelerated charged particles generate electromagnetic waves. He also predicted that it should be possible to send messages through long distances without the use of wires (wireless). To send such messages, electromagnetic waves of the proper frequency must be generated and detected.

All electromagnetic waves travel through space at the speed of light, $3 \times 10^8$ m/s. They differ from one another only in wavelength and frequency. The frequency of the wave is the same as the frequency of the vibrating charge that produces it.

A typical wavelength of an AM radio is about 300 m. To produce waves of this wavelength, electrons must be made to oscillate about $10^6$ vibrations per second in the broadcast antennas of a radio station. FM radio and TV use wavelengths of only about 3 m. Stations broadcasting these wavelengths must oscillate electrons in their antennas about $10^8$ vibrations per second. This frequency is a hundred times greater than those used by AM stations.

An understanding of radio and TV broadcasting depends on an understanding of resonance. Your first encounter with resonance probably came at a very early age when you first learned to "pump" a swing. At that time, you found that a pendulum (you, ropes, seat) would accept energy only when it is offered at the right frequency. This is the frequency at which the pendulum naturally vibrates. To verify this idea, construct a simple pendulum as shown in Figure 26-3. Strike the bob rapidly. Although you are offering the system a good deal of energy, you will find most of it is rejected. Now try to push the pendulum in time with the natural frequency at which it vibrates. The pendulum will gain energy rapidly.

> AM radio waves have frequencies of about $10^6$ Hz.
>
> FM radio and TV waves have frequencies of about $10^8$ Hz.
>
> Radio and TV transmission and reception depend on resonance.
>
> A system readily accepts energy that is offered at the natural frequency of the system.

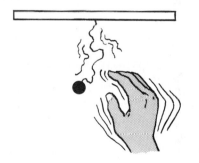 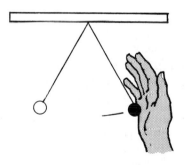

**FIGURE 26-3. Energy can be transferred easily to a pendulum when the frequency of energy input is equal to the natural frequency of the pendulum.**

The presence of waves of a given frequency is detected by applying the principle of resonance. Consider the two tuning forks in Figure 26-4. Both forks vibrate at the same frequency. If one tuning fork is struck by a rubber hammer, it will vibrate and emit a sound wave that has the same frequency as its rate of vibration. The sound wave will travel through the air and cause the second tuning fork to vibrate. The frequency of energy change from the sound wave resonates with the natural frequency of the second tuning fork. Each tuning fork will vibrate in response to a sound wave from the other.

Two objects do not need to be identical in size to vibrate at the same frequency. A picture on a wall can vibrate in response to the sound of a passing truck. The vibrations of a car's engine can explain some noises that occur in other parts of the car. In the same way, the AM radio in your home is not the same size as the radio station that is broadcasting the electromagnetic waves. However, the radio must be able to oscillate charge in its antenna in response to that wave. In effect, your radio is a smaller version of the broadcasting station.

A home radio is a smaller version of a transmitting station.

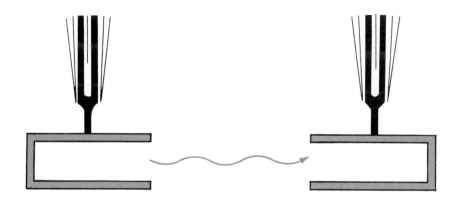

**FIGURE 26-4. A sound wave can cause a tuning fork to vibrate if the frequency of the incoming wave is the same as the frequency at which the fork naturally vibrates.**

Consider the pump-water tank arrangement in Figure 26-5a. Note the tanks are closed on top. Suppose the pump attempts to pump water from one tank to the other. It could only do so for a brief interval. One of the tanks would soon be full and no further water could flow in the pipes. Instead of trying to pump water in just one direction, suppose the pump caused the water to oscillate back and forth. In that event the pump could operate. The pump could operate best at the one frequency that changes the direction of flow precisely when each tank becomes full.

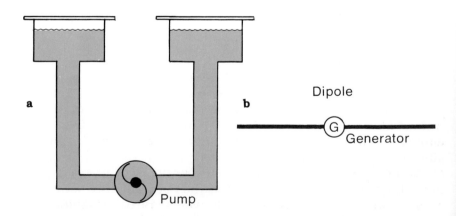

**FIGURE 26-5. A pump-water tank arrangement is shown in (a). The diagram of a dipole antenna is shown in (b).**

The generator-wire arrangement (antenna) shown in Figure 26-5b is called a **dipole.** A direct-current generator cannot cause charge to flow in the dipole for the same reason that the water pump system cannot pump water in only one direction. In the generator, electrons would build up in one of the wires. This buildup would stop all further current in the system. However, an alternating-current generator causes charge to oscillate in the dipole. It does this by sending the current back and forth quickly enough to prevent a strong charge from building up at either end of the dipole. The dipole has a natural frequency of oscillation that depends on its length. Just as a pendulum accepts energy at a particular frequency, a dipole best accepts electric energy at one particular frequency. This frequency is the **natural frequency** of the dipole.

Suppose that a radio or TV station is causing electrons to oscillate in its antenna at the natural frequency of the antenna. If the electrons are oscillating, they are constantly being accelerated. According to Maxwell's prediction, electromagnetic waves will develop about the antenna. As electrons are accelerated in one direction in the dipole, radio waves in the form of closed loops build around the dipole. When the current is accelerated in the opposite direction, new radio waves develop. However, these waves will form loops of opposite direction.

An AC generator causes electrons in a dipole antenna to oscillate.

A dipole operates most efficiently at one particular frequency.

When electrons oscillate in a dipole, electromagnetic waves are generated.

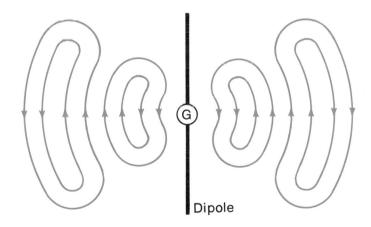

Dipole

**FIGURE 26-6. The diagram shows the electric field lines produced by oscillating charges in a broadcast antenna.**

In Figure 26-6, the electric field lines are shown for one complete cycle of the oscillator. Note that the electric field lines from different half-cycles (loops of opposite direction) next to each other have the same direction. Electric field lines with the same direction repel each other. This repelling force causes each oncoming wave to push the wave before it into space at the speed of light. Only electric field lines are shown in the diagram, but magnetic field lines would also be present. The magnetic field lines would be perpendicular to the electric field lines. They would project into and out of the plane of the page.

Tom Stack/Tom Stack & Assoc.

**FIGURE 26-7. This on-site broadcasting equipment consists of both transmitting and receiving antennas.**

A radio or TV receiver is adjusted to resonate in response to only one station.

Crystals are used to generate high-frequency waves.

The natural frequency of a crystal depends on its size and shape.

Suppose there is another wire antenna some distance from the transmitting antenna. The electric charges in that wire will oscillate in response to the electric and magnetic fields passing over it. Moving magnetic fields cause electrons to flow in a wire.

The antenna of a radio or TV receiver is always exposed to electromagnetic waves that originate from many different radio and TV stations. But the length of an antenna can be adjusted so its natural frequency of electric oscillation matches only one station. Then, the antenna will respond only to that station. In effect, every time you turn a tuning dial on your radio or TV set, you are adjusting the set to respond to one certain station. The radio or TV will exclude all other stations.

In practice, the frequencies of commercial broadcasts range from 500 000 Hz to 1 500 000 Hz. No generator can be built to rotate that rapidly. Therefore, to generate high frequencies, some stations use a small crystal. Small crystals vibrate naturally in this frequency range. The exact frequency of a given crystal depends on its size and shape. Usually these crystals are quartz. Each station must use the proper size crystal. The station uses the crystal to control the frequency at which electrons are sent along its transmitting antenna. Higher frequencies require smaller crystals. The generation of radar waves requires the smallest crystals that can be made.

The crystals needed to generate infrared (heat) waves would be about the size of a molecule. This suggests that heat waves are developed by vibrating molecules and atoms. To generate frequencies in the range of visible light, particles even smaller than molecules or about the size of electrons are needed. This finding agrees with present theory about the origin of light waves. That is, light is a result of the motion of electrons within atoms.

# 26:4 Millikan's Oil-Drop Experiment

Figure 26-8 shows the method used by Robert A. Millikan to measure the charge carried by a single electron. Fine oil drops are sprayed into the air from an atomizer. These drops often have small charges. The charges are a result of the transfer of electrons from the atomizer to the oil drops. These drops then fall through the air. A few enter the hole in the top plate of the apparatus. The two plates are given opposite charges, creating an electric field between the plates. The electric field between the plates and the electric field around a charged particle interact. An oil drop with a negative charge is attracted toward the positive plate. If the top plate is the positive plate, two forces act on the oil drop. The force due to its weight causes it to fall. The other force due to the electric field causes it to rise. The charge on the plates can be adjusted to suspend a charged drop between the plates. Then, the downward force of the weight and the upward force of the electric field are equal.

$$Eq = mg$$

The intensity of the electric field $E$ is found from the voltage across the plates. A second measurement is made to determine the weight of the droplet $mg$. The weight of a tiny oil drop is too small to measure by ordinary methods. To make this measurement, a suspended drop is observed. The rate of its fall is timed when the electric field is shut off. Because of friction, an oil drop quickly reaches a uniform or "terminal" velocity. The velocity is related to the mass of the drop by an equation. This equation is used to calculate the weight of the drop $mg$. Since both $E$ and $mg$ are known, $q$ can be calculated.

From Millikan's oil-drop experiment, the charge of an electron was determined.

When an oil drop is suspended, the electric force and the gravitational force are in balance.

The mass of an oil drop is calculated from its "terminal" velocity.

**FIGURE 26-8.** This apparatus can be used to determine the charge on an oil drop.

a

F. Bernard Daniel

b

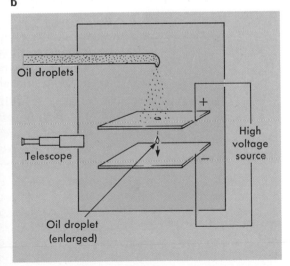

Millikan had no way to know whether a drop of oil carried one or several extra charges. The smallest value obtained for $q$ was $1.6 \times 10^{-19}$ C. All other values were exact multiples of this value. The value $1.6 \times 10^{-19}$ C is now accepted as the magnitude of the charge carried by the electron and the proton.

### EXAMPLE: Finding the Charge on an Oil Drop

An oil drop weighs $1.92 \times 10^{-14}$ N. It is suspended in an electric field of intensity $4.0 \times 10^4$ N/C. **a.** What is the charge on the oil drop? **b.** If the drop behaves as a negative particle in the field, how many excess electrons does the drop have?

*Solution:*

**a.** $mg = Eq$   and   $q = \dfrac{mg}{E} = \dfrac{1.92 \times 10^{-14} \, \text{N}}{4.0 \times 10^4 \, \text{N/C}} = 4.8 \times 10^{-19}$ C

**b.**    $\text{Number of electrons} = \dfrac{\text{Total charge on drop}}{\text{Charge per electron}}$

$$= \dfrac{4.8 \times 10^{-19} \, \text{C}}{1.6 \times 10^{-19} \, \text{C/}e^-} = 3 \, e^-$$

### PROBLEMS

**6.** An oil drop weighs $1.92 \times 10^{-15}$ N. It is suspended in an electric field of intensity $6.0 \times 10^3$ N/C.
  **a.** What is the charge on the oil drop?
  **b.** The particle is negative. How many excess electrons does it carry?

**7. a.** $1.6 \times 10^{-19}$ C
   **b.** one

**7.** A positively-charged oil drop weighs $6.4 \times 10^{-13}$ N. It becomes suspended between two charged plates when the intensity of the electric field is $4.0 \times 10^6$ N/C.
  **a.** What is the charge on the drop?
  **b.** How many electrons is the drop missing?

**8.** A negatively-charged oil drop weighs $8.5 \times 10^{-15}$ N. The drop is suspended between two charged plates that produce an electric field of $5.3 \times 10^{-3}$ N/C.
  **a.** What is the charge on the drop?
  **b.** How many excess electrons does it carry?

**9. a.** student diagram
   **b.** $1.6 \times 10^{-19}$ C
   The slope represents the charge of an electron.

**9.** During a Millikan experiment, a student records the weight of five different oil drops. A record is also made of the field intensity necessary to hold each drop stationary.
  **a.** Plot the readings on a graph of $W$ vs $E$. Plot $W$ vertically.
  **b.** Determine the slope of the line. What does the slope represent?

| $W$ (N) | $E$ (N/C) |
| --- | --- |
| $1.7 \times 10^{-14}$ | $1.06 \times 10^5$ |
| $5.6 \times 10^{-14}$ | $3.5 \times 10^5$ |
| $9.3 \times 10^{-14}$ | $5.8 \times 10^5$ |
| $2.9 \times 10^{-14}$ | $1.8 \times 10^5$ |

# 26:5 Determining the Mass of the Electron

The British scientist Sir J. J. Thomson (1856–1940) constructed a discharge tube similar to the one in Figure 26-9. Electrons that leave the cathode of this tube are accelerated toward
the anode. There is a small hole in the anode. Some of the high-
speed electrons pass through this hole. A second metal plate beyond the anode guarantees that a straight beam of electrons
passes through the remainder of the tube. Only electrons that
align with the holes in both plates can pass on. Farther down
the tube a pair of charged plates is arranged to deflect the negative electrons upward toward the positive plate. The force of the
electric field acting on each electron is *Ee*. Here, *E* represents
the electric field intensity, and *e* the charge on the electron. A
magnetic field is also introduced. It acts at right angles to the
charged plates. The force of the magnetic field on the electrons
*Bev* deflects the electrons downward.

From Thomson's
experiment, the value of
*m/e* was determined.

Thomson observed the
deflection of electrons in
both electric and magnetic
fields.
The electric field, the
magnetic field, and the
electron beam are all
perpendicular to one
another.

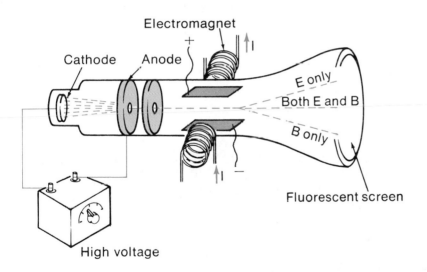

FIGURE 26-9. A cathode-
ray tube similar to the one
shown here was used by
J. J. Thomson to deter-
mine the charge-to-mass
ratio of the electron.

When both the electric and magnetic fields are present, the
fields can be adjusted until the beam of electrons follows a straight
or undeflected path. Then the force on the electrons due to the
electric field is equal to the force due to the magnetic field.

To find the velocity of the
electrons, the fields are
adjusted until electrons
follow an undeflected
path.

$$Bev = Ee$$

Solving this equation for *v*, we obtain the expression

$$v = \frac{Ee}{Be}$$
$$= \frac{E}{B}$$

If the potential difference is removed from the plates, the only force acting on the electrons is due to the magnetic field. This force acts at a 90° angle with the direction of motion of the electrons. Thus, it is a centripetal force and causes the electrons to follow a circular path. When the electric field is absent,

$$Bev = \frac{mv^2}{r}$$

Solving for $Br/v$, we obtain the expression

$$\frac{Br}{v} = \frac{m}{e}$$

Thomson measured the distance between the undeflected spot and the position of the spot when the electrons were subjected only to the magnetic field. He measured the radius $r$ of the circular path given to the electrons by the magnetic field. He also measured the magnetic induction. He found the value of $v$ from $E/B$. Thus, Thomson could calculate $Br/v$. This also gave him the value of $m/e$. Thomson consistently obtained the value $5.68 \times 10^{-12}$ kg/C. Using Millikan's value of $e$, $1.6 \times 10^{-19}$ C, allows the mass of the electron $m$ to be calculated. Since

$$\frac{m}{e} = 5.68 \times 10^{-12} \text{ kg/C}$$

$$m = (5.68 \times 10^{-12} \text{ kg/C})(e)$$
$$= (5.68 \times 10^{-12} \text{ kg/} \cancel{C})(1.6 \times 10^{-19} \, \cancel{C})$$
$$= 9.1 \times 10^{-31} \text{ kg}$$

Thus, the mass of the electron equals $9.1 \times 10^{-31}$ kg.

These equations also apply to a beam of protons sent across a discharge tube in the same way as the electrons. To obtain protons, a small amount of hydrogen gas is placed in the path of high-speed electrons traveling through a discharge tube. The electrons ionize many of the hydrogen atoms. A hydrogen atom consists of a single proton and a single electron. Thus, an ionized hydrogen atom is a proton. The protons are drawn into a tube similar to the one used to measure the mass of the electron. The mass of a proton is $1.7 \times 10^{-27}$ kg.

**EXAMPLE: Straight-Line Motion of an Electron in a Discharge Tube**

A beam of electrons travels an undeflected path in a discharge tube. $E$ is $7.0 \times 10^3$ N/C. $B$ is $3.5 \times 10^{-2}$ N/A·m. What is the speed of the electrons as they travel through the tube?

*Solution:*    $v = \dfrac{E}{B}$

$$= \frac{7.0 \times 10^3 \text{ N/C}}{3.5 \times 10^{-2} \text{ N/A·m}} = 2.0 \times 10^5 \text{ m/s}$$

*When electrons move through a magnetic field, they follow a circular path of radius $r$.*

*The value of $m/e$ can be calculated when $B$, $r$, and $v$ are known.*

*Millikan's value for $e$ allowed the determination of $m$.*

*The mass of a proton can be measured by the same method.*

### EXAMPLE: Path of an Electron in a Magnetic Field

An electron of mass $9.1 \times 10^{-31}$ kg moves with a speed of $2.0 \times 10^5$ m/s across a magnetic field. The magnetic induction is $8.0 \times 10^{-4}$ N/A·m. What is the radius of the circular path followed by the electrons while in the field?

*Solution:*

Since $\quad Bev = \dfrac{mv^2}{r}$

$$r = \frac{mv}{Be} = \frac{(9.1 \times 10^{-31}\text{ kg})(2.0 \times 10^5\text{ m/s})}{(8.0 \times 10^{-4}\text{ N/A·m})(1.6 \times 10^{-19}\text{ C})}$$

$$= 1.4 \times 10^{-3}\text{ m}$$

### PROBLEMS

*Assume the direction of all moving charged particles is perpendicular to any fields.*

**10.** Protons passing through a field of magnetic induction of 0.6 N/A·m are deflected. An electric field of intensity $4.5 \times 10^3$ N/C is introduced. The protons are brought back to their undeflected path. What is the speed of the moving protons?

**11.** A proton moves at a speed of $7.5 \times 10^3$ m/s as it passes through a field of magnetic induction 0.6 N/A·m. Find the radius of the circular path. The mass of a proton is $1.7 \times 10^{-27}$ kg. The charge carried by the proton is equal to that of the electron but is positive.

    **11.** $1.3 \times 10^{-4}$ m

**12.** Electrons move through a field of magnetic induction $6.0 \times 10^{-2}$ N/A·m. An electric field of $3.0 \times 10^3$ N/C prevents the electrons from being deflected. What is the speed of the electrons?

**13.** Calculate the radius of the circular path the electrons in Problem 12 follow in the absence of the electric field. The mass of an electron is $9.0 \times 10^{-31}$ kg.

    **13.** $4.7 \times 10^{-6}$ m

**14.** A proton enters a magnetic field which has a magnetic induction of $6.0 \times 10^{-2}$ N/A·m with a speed of $5.4 \times 10^4$ m/s. What is the radius of the circular path it follows?

**15.** A proton moves across a field of magnetic induction 0.36 N/A·m. It follows a circular path of radius 0.2 m. What is the speed of the proton?

    **15.** $6.8 \times 10^6$ m/s

**16.** Electrons move across a field of magnetic induction $4.0 \times 10^{-3}$ N/A·m. They follow a circular path of radius $2.0 \times 10^{-2}$ m.
   **a.** What is their speed?
   **b.** An electric field is applied perpendicularly to the magnetic field. The electrons then follow a straight-line path. Find the magnitude of the electric field.

## 26:6   Mass Spectrograph

A mass spectrograph is an offspring of the Thomson tube. It is used to measure masses of atoms. A diagram of a mass spectrograph appears in Figure 26-10. In this device, a cathode and an anode are located at one end of the tube. If a high potential difference is placed across these electrodes, electrons are accelerated from the cathode to the anode. When an element in the gas state is placed between the cathode and the anode, its atoms are constantly bombarded by electrons. In this way, many of the atoms of the gas are ionized. These positive ions are then accelerated toward the cathode. Many of the ions pass through the small opening in the cathode and move down the tube at high velocity.

There is no way of knowing how many electrons have been removed from any one atom as a result of collisions between electrons and atoms. The atoms that emerge from the opening in the cathode may have a single, double, or triple positive charge. To be sure all ions in the beam moving through the tube have the same charge, the beam is made to pass between two charged plates. The ions are deflected by the electric field between the plates. The charge on the plates is adjusted so only ions having the same charge can pass through the slit beyond the plates. Ions having too large or too small a charge are deflected so much they miss the slit and strike the metal instead.

**a**

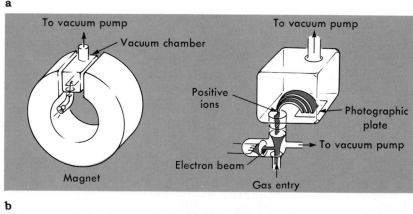

**b**

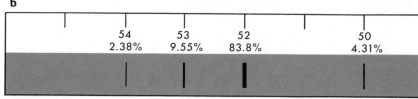

FIGURE 26-10. The diagram of a mass spectrograph (a) shows how the electron beam is deflected. The readout looks similar to that shown for chromium (b). The percentage of each chromium isotope is determined by the intensity of the line.

The beam of uniformly charged particles that passes through the slit is subjected to a strong magnetic field. This field is produced by two electromagnets. In Section 26:5, we found charged particles moving through a magnetic field move in a circular path. The radius of the circular path is found by using the equation $Bev = mv^2/r$.

$$r = \frac{mv}{Be}$$

Hence, the mass of any particle passing through the tube is proportional to its radius of curvature in the magnetic field. Also, because the charged atoms may have more than a single charge, $e$ is expressed as $q$ which is a multiple of $e$. Therefore,

$$m = \frac{Bqr}{v}$$

The radius of curvature of a charged particle in the spectrograph is found by turning the magnetic field off and on. When the field is absent, the ions travel straight down the tube and strike the center of the fluorescent screen. When the field is on, the particles are deflected in proportion to their masses. They will strike the screen above the central position. In a well calibrated spectrograph, the mass of the particle is read directly from the screen.

The first spectrograph was designed by F. W. Aston in England in 1913. When it was put into use, Aston was surprised by the appearance of more than one spot above the center of the screen. This occurred each time he attempted to measure the mass of an atom. It could only mean some elements have atoms with the same chemical properties but with differing masses. Aston had verified the existence of isotopes.

*When the beam of uniformly charged ions passes through a strong magnetic field, it moves in a circular path.*

*Ions are deflected in proportion to their masses.*

**EXAMPLE: The Mass of a Neon Atom**

These measurements were made in a mass spectrograph for a beam of doubly-ionized neon atoms.

$B = 5.0 \times 10^{-2}$ N/A·m       $r = 0.053$ m
$q = 2e = 2 \times 1.6 \times 10^{-19}$ C     $v = 2.5 \times 10^4$ m/s

Calculate the mass of a neon atom.

*Solution:* $m = \dfrac{Bqr}{v}$

$$= \frac{(5.0 \times 10^{-2} \text{ N/A·m})(3.2 \times 10^{-19} \text{ C})(0.053 \text{ m})}{2.5 \times 10^4 \text{ m/s}}$$

$$= 3.4 \times 10^{-26} \text{ kg}$$

# Dimensions in Physics

It is projected that one in five American families will own a personal computer by 1990 as a result of the overwhelming acceptance of computerized toys and games. Computer literacy will become a basic necessity as families move from sophisticated TV games to home information-entertainment centers. Such systems can control the operation of appliances to maintain an energy efficient environment within a house. Personal appointments, household records, stock market reports, and outdoor conditions can be called up in seconds. The computer can scan TV programming and pick those things we may find interesting. Owning a personal computer can allow us to be better informed for making decisions in an age of information.

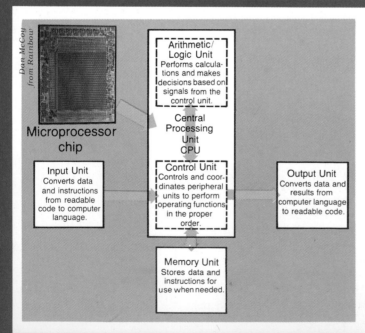

Microprocessor chip

Dan McCoy
from Rainbow

**Arithmetic/Logic Unit**
Performs calculations and makes decisions based on signals from the control unit.

Central Processing Unit
CPU

**Control Unit**
Controls and coordinates peripheral units to perform operating functions in the proper order.

**Input Unit**
Converts data and instructions from readable code to computer language.

**Output Unit**
Converts data and results from computer language to readable code.

**Memory Unit**
Stores data and instructions for use when needed.

Any computer system consists of both hardware and software components. Hardware is the actual mechanical and electronic parts of the computer. Software consists of the programs that tell the hardware how to function. It is the integration of hardware and software that forms an operating computer system.

The computer's brain is called the central processing unit or CPU. The CPU consists of a microprocessor which has the capabilities of performing arithmetic operations and controlling the processing of data. A microprocessing chip is quite small having a thickness of less than 0.15 cm. The design of the chip determines the language that the computer understands. Therefore, software must be compatible with the microprocessor.

Since the microprocessor does not have sufficient room for storing information, an integral part of the on-board system is the memory unit. Memory serves to store data and software programs. Memory capability is measured in kilobytes (K). Each byte of storage will hold one character or word consisting of 8 bits in a computer language.

$$8 \text{ bits} = 1 \text{ byte} = 1 \text{ word}$$

There are two basic types of memory—RAM and ROM. Random access memory (RAM) is used for temporary data storage. RAM is considered volatile memory in that it is erased whenever the power is switched off. Read only memory (ROM) is nonvolatile. Thus, it is used for permanent data storage. ROM contains preprogrammed instructions vital to the total function of the computer. The language used to communicate with the computer is stored on ROM. Generally, language is stored permanently and cannot be reprogrammed. Such permanent information is classified as firmware.

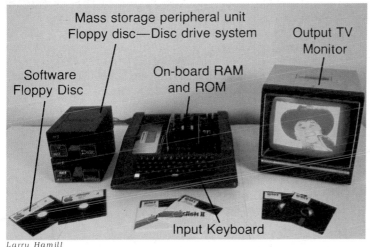

Mass storage peripheral unit
Floppy disc—Disc drive system

Output TV Monitor

Software Floppy Disc

On-board RAM and ROM

Input Keyboard

*Larry Hamill*

A keyboard is a standard means by which you communicate with the central processing unit. A TV screen allows you to see what has been entered and provides the means by which the computer communicates with you.

A printer can be used to produce a hard copy of the output shown on a TV screen. The floppy disc-disc drive assembly and keyboard are input units. The TV screen and printer are output units.

Most personal computers are programmed to respond to commands given in BASIC (Beginner's All Purpose Symbolic Instruction Code). BASIC is a high level language that is easy to learn. An operator merely enters a command statement—PRINT and the computer does the work. A low level assembly language was previously used to program the computer to follow the steps for—PRINT.

ROM firmware also integrates any peripheral devices with the CPU. A peripheral is any input or output device (TV, printer, keyboard, and so on). A personal computer can have up to 16 000 bytes (16 K) ROM and up to 48 000 bytes (48 K) RAM.

The computer's memory capabilities can be expanded by using a mass storage peripheral unit. Floppy discs are now the typical mass storage devices used in home computers. The information on a floppy disc is relayed to the on-board RAM unit via the disc drive assembly. A typical disc can hold 116 K of information, which is 3 times the amount that can be loaded into RAM.

CAN I HELP YOU?

YES, WE'RE INTERESTED IN A PERSONAL COMPUTER SYSTEM. IT SHOULD HAVE AT LEAST 48K OF MEMORY, BE PROGRAMMED IN BASIC...

**Summary**

1. In 1864, James Clerk Maxwell predicted a changing magnetic field would generate a changing electric field which would, in turn, generate a changing magnetic field and so on. In this manner, electromagnetic waves are propagated through space.   26:1

2. In 1887, Hertz verified Maxwell's prediction by causing electrons to oscillate in a wire and detecting the resulting radio waves.   26:1

3. The principle of electrical resonance makes it possible to transmit 26:3 and receive communications by means of electromagnetic waves.

4. When high-speed electrons strike the anode of an evacuated tube their kinetic energies are converted to electromagnetic waves of very high energy called X rays.   26:2

5. Robert Millikan measured the electric charge carried by a single 26:4, 26:5 electron. J. J. Thomson determined the mass of the electron.

6. The mass spectrograph is a device used to measure the masses of atoms and molecules.   26:6

**Questions**

1. Describe the directions of the electric and magnetic field components of an electromagnetic wave in respect to the direction of the wave.

2. Every time a classroom projector is rewound, it begins to vibrate. The vibration occurs for only a short part of the rewinding of the film. How would you explain this vibration?

3. What happens when you turn the tuning dial of a radio?

4. What causes an electron to accelerate as it passes from the cathode to the anode of a discharge tube?

5. What is the function of a mass spectrograph? What principles are involved in its operation?

**Problems**

1. The potential difference between the cathode and anode of a discharge tube is $2.5 \times 10^4$ V. What maximum speed does an electron reach as it travels across the tube? The electron starts from rest.

2. Find the speed an electron reaches in falling through a potential difference of $3.2 \times 10^4$ V. Assume the electron starts from rest.

3. What speed does a proton develop as it falls through a potential difference of $3.4 \times 10^4$ V? The proton starts from rest.

4. The difference in potential between the cathode and anode of a spark plug is 10 000 V.
   a. What energy does an electron give up as it passes between the electrodes?
   b. One fourth of the energy given up by the electron is converted to electromagnetic radiation. What is the frequency of the waves?

**5. a.** What energy is given to an electron to transfer it across a difference in potential of $4.0 \times 10^5$ V?

   **b.** The energy is converted to electromagnetic radiation. What is the frequency of the wave emitted?

**6.** A stream of singly-ionized lithium atoms does not deflect as it passes through a field of magnetic induction $1.5 \times 10^{-3}$ N/A·m perpendicular to an electric field of $6.0 \times 10^2$ N/C.

   **a.** What is the speed of the lithium atoms as they pass through the crossed fields?

   **b.** The lithium atoms move into a field of magnetic induction 0.18 N/A·m. They follow a circular path of radius 0.165 m. What is the mass of a lithium atom?

**7.** An oil drop weighs $9.6 \times 10^{-15}$ N. It is suspended in an electric field of $2 \times 10^4$ N/C.

   **a.** What is the charge on the oil drop?

   **b.** How many excess electrons does it carry?

**8.** A mass spectrograph gives data for a beam of doubly-ionized argon atoms. The values are $B = 5.0 \times 10^{-2}$ N/A·m, $q = 2e = 2(1.6 \times 10^{-19}$ C), $r = 0.106$ m, and $v = 2.5 \times 10^4$ m/s. Find the mass of an argon atom.

**9.** A mass spectrograph gives data for a beam of singly-ionized oxygen atoms. The values are $B = 7.2 \times 10^{-2}$ N/A·m, $q = 1.6 \times 10^{-19}$ C, $r = 0.85$ m, and $v = 3.6 \times 10^5$ m/s. Calculate the mass of an oxygen atom.

**10.** A mass spectrograph yields data for a beam of doubly-ionized sodium atoms. These values are $B = 8.0 \times 10^{-3}$ N/A·m, $q = 2e = 2(1.6 \times 10^{-19}$ C), $r = 0.77$ m, and $v = 5.0 \times 10^4$ m/s. Calculate the mass of a sodium atom.

---

**Applying Physics**

**1.** *Analysis of Nuclear Particles:* An alpha particle has a mass of approximately $6.6 \times 10^{-27}$ kg and bears a double elementary positive charge. Such a particle is observed to move through a magnetic field of induction 2.0 N/A·m along a path of radius 0.5 m.

   **a.** What speed does it have?

   **b.** What is its kinetic energy?

---

**Readings**

Cassill, Kay, "X rays May Soon Result in Much Less Harmful Radiation." *Science Digest*, April, 1980.

Fermi, Laura, *Atoms in the Family: My Life with Enrico Fermi.* Chicago, The University of Chicago Press, 1954.

Nassau, Kurt, "The Causes of Color." *Scientific American*, October, 1980.

A model is a description or analogy used to help visualize something that cannot be directly observed. This galaxy can be considered a good visual model of the atom. However, all models have some limitations. While studying this chapter, refer back to the galaxy model. What aspects of it adequately represent the structure of an atom? What are its limitations?

# Quantum Theory 27

In our study of optics, we examined the wave nature of light. We will now study the particle nature of light. Specifically, we can assume that light consists of discrete bundles of energy. These bundles of energy are called quanta. Quanta of light are also called photons. The **quantum theory** attempts to develop a dual model that fits both the wave nature and the particle nature of electromagnetic radiation.

## 27:1 The Photoelectric Effect

The **photoelectric effect** is the emission of electrons from a metal plate exposed to light of certain frequencies. This effect is studied by the use of a photocell circuit, Figure 27-1. Two metal electrodes are sealed in an evacuated tube made of quartz. One of the electrodes is coated with zinc. A difference in potential is placed across the electrodes. A variable resistor is also included in the circuit. With this resistor, the difference in potential across the electrodes can be varied.

When light is absent, current does not flow in the circuit. However, when light of the proper frequency falls on the zinc electrode, a current does flow in the circuit. Light ejects electrons from the zinc plate. These electrons travel to the positive plate. The circuit is complete. The electrons ejected from the metal plate by the light are called **photoelectrons.** Photoelectrons are the same as any other electrons.

a

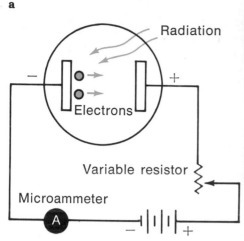

b

**FIGURE 27-1. A diagram of a photocell circuit (a) shows the ejection of electrons from the surface of a metal. Photocells are used in the automatic control of street lighting (b).**

Threshold frequency is the minimum frequency $f_0$ of light needed to eject electrons from a plate.

Light with a frequency higher than $f_0$ imparts KE to the electrons.

Incident light of a certain minimum frequency is needed to eject electrons from the zinc plate. This minimum frequency varies with the metal used. It is called the **threshold frequency,** $f_o$ of that metal. Light of a frequency below $f_o$ does not eject electrons from the metal, no matter how great the intensity of the light. On the other hand, light at or above the threshold frequency causes electrons to leave the metal immediately, even if the light is very faint. The wave theory of light cannot explain this case. More intense light means more energy along the wave fronts and more electrons should leave the plate.

If we think of light as photons, threshold frequency is readily explained. Photons with frequencies below $f_o$ do not have enough energy to give even an easily moved surface electron enough energy to escape the metal.

When light at a frequency higher than $f_o$ strikes a zinc plate in an evacuated tube, electrons travel across the tube with increased kinetic energy. Electrons ejected from the surface of the zinc have the highest energy. Electrons ejected from below the surface have a lower energy. The kinetic energy of electrons having maximum energy can be measured. To do this, a difference in potential is placed across the tube. That is, the zinc plate is made slightly positive and the second metal plate is made slightly negative. The voltage tends to prevent the electrons from leaving the zinc plate. The opposing potential difference is increased until no electrons have enough energy to travel across the tube. This potential difference is the stopping potential. Work is done to stop the electrons having maximum kinetic energy. The work done is equal to the maximum kinetic energy of these electrons and is given by the equation

The KE imparted to electrons by light can be found by calculating the work done to stop these electrons.

$$KE_{max} = V_o e$$

Here, $V_o$ is the stopping potential in volts (J/C), and $e$ is the charge on the electron $(1.6 \times 10^{-19} \text{ C})$. The work done on the electrons having maximum kinetic energy is done at the expense of photons falling on the metal. The sum of the work done to stop the electrons and the work done to free the electrons from the metal surface represents the energy of the photons falling on the metal.

Stopping potential is the opposing potential necessary to stop electrons from traveling across the gap between the electrodes.

### EXAMPLE: Maximum Kinetic Energy of a Photoelectron

The stopping potential to prevent electrons from flowing across a photoelectric cell is 4.0 V. What maximum kinetic energy is given to the electrons by the incident light?

*Solution:*

$$\text{KE}_{max} = V_o e$$
$$= (4.0 \text{ J/C})(1.6 \times 10^{-19} \text{ C}) - 6.4 \times 10^{-19} \text{ J}$$

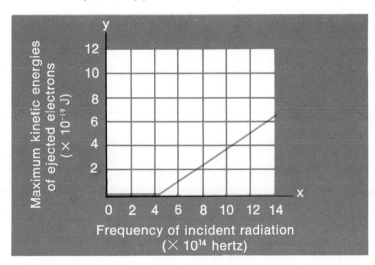

FIGURE 27-2. This graph shows the kinetic energy of ejected electrons versus frequency of incident radiation.

When a plot is made of the maximum kinetic energies of the electrons ejected from a metal versus the frequencies of the incident photons, the resulting graph is a straight line, Figure 27-2. All metals have similar graphs, each with the same slope. The graphs differ only in point of origin. The point of origin varies with the threshold frequency of the metal. The slope of the line is Planck's constant, $h$.

$$h = \frac{\Delta y}{\Delta x} = \frac{\text{Maximum kinetic energies of ejected electrons}}{\text{Frequency of incident photons}}$$
$$= 6.6 \times 10^{-34} \text{ J/Hz}$$

The energy needed to free a surface electron from a metal is called the **work function** of the metal. The work function is the product of the threshold frequency and Planck's constant, $hf_o$.

The work function of a metal is the energy needed to free a surface electron from the metal.

The work function or energy needed to free the surface electrons from a metal is the product of Planck's constant $h$ and threshold frequency $f_0$.

The energy of an incident photon is expressed as $hf$, where $f$ is the frequency of the photon. By subtracting the work function from the energy of the incident photon, the maximum kinetic energy of the emitted electron can be calculated.

$$KE_{max} = hf - hf_o$$

This equation is called the **photoelectric equation.**

### EXAMPLE: Photoelectric Equation

The threshold frequency of sodium is $5.6 \times 10^{14}$ Hz. **a.** What is the work function of sodium? **b.** Sodium is exposed to radiation of frequency $8.6 \times 10^{14}$ Hz. What is the maximum kinetic energy of the ejected electrons?

*Solution:* **a.** Work function = $hf_o$

$$= (6.6 \times 10^{-34} \text{ J/Hz})(5.6 \times 10^{14} \text{ Hz})$$
$$= 3.7 \times 10^{-19} \text{ J}$$

**b.** $KE_{max} = hf - hf_o$

$$= (6.6 \times 10^{-34} \text{ J/Hz})(8.6 \times 10^{14} \text{ Hz}) - 3.7 \times 10^{-19} \text{ J}$$
$$= 2.0 \times 10^{-19} \text{ J}$$

### PROBLEMS

1. $5.1 \times 10^{-19}$ J

**1.** The stopping potential to prevent electron flow through a photocell is 3.2 V. Calculate the maximum kinetic energy of the photoelectrons within the cell.

**2.** The stopping potential to stop electron flow through a photoelectric cell is 5.7 V. Calculate the maximum kinetic energy of the photoelectrons within the cell.

3. a. $6.4 \times 10^{-19}$ J
   b. $2.3 \times 10^{-18}$ J

**3.** The threshold frequency of zinc is $9.7 \times 10^{14}$ Hz.
   **a.** What is the photoelectric work function of zinc?
   **b.** Zinc used in a photoelectric cell is irradiated by radiation of frequency $4.5 \times 10^{15}$ Hz. What is the maximum kinetic energy of the photoelectrons within the cell?

**4.** The threshold frequency of calcium is $6.5 \times 10^{14}$ Hz.
   **a.** What is the photoelectric work function of calcium?
   **b.** An electronvolt, eV, is needed to transfer one electron through a potential difference of one volt. An electronvolt is $1.6 \times 10^{-19}$ J. What is the work function of calcium in electronvolts?

5. $1.1 \times 10^{15}$ Hz

**5.** The work function of chromium is 4.6 eV. What is the threshold frequency of chromium?

**6.** The work function of potassium is 2.2 eV.
   **a.** What is the work function of potassium in joules?
   **b.** What is the threshold frequency of potassium?

# 27:2 Quantum Theory of Light

The photoelectric equation can be rearranged to give the following equation:

$$hf = KE_{max} + hf_o$$

This form of the equation shows that the total energy of photons may be calculated. To do so, the photocell is exposed to photons of known frequency. The stopping potential is found and the maximum kinetic energy of the ejected electrons is calculated, using the equation $KE_{max} = V_0 e$. This energy is then added to the work function to give the total energy of the incident photons. Note that the total energy of a photon is always the product of Planck's constant and the frequency of the photon. All photons have definite frequencies and Planck's constant never changes. Thus, photons must also have definite energy contents. In this way, it was determined that light energy consists of quanta. In other words, light energy is made up of discrete bundles of energy.

In classical physics, a mass is assumed to have a continuous range of potential energies which depends on how far a mass is from the earth's surface. However, even though they have many of the properties of particles, photons have a range of energies that is not continuous. Instead the energies are multiples of Planck's constant.

Consider a ball placed on a step, Figure 27-3. The potential energy of the ball, in this case, can be thought of as quantized. In other words, the ball can have any potential energy which corresponds to a whole number multiple of steps. The ball cannot have a potential energy value between these multiples. In the same way, the energy of photons is quantized. The size of the "step" is Planck's constant.

The total energy of an incident photon can be found by adding the work function and the maximum kinetic energy of the ejected electron.

Planck's constant makes possible the calculation of the energy content of any electromagnetic radiation.

Photons have energies that are multiples of Planck's constant.

The photoelectric effect lends strong support for the quantum theory.

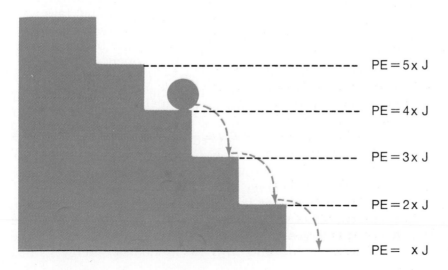

PE = 5 x J

PE = 4 x J

PE = 3 x J

PE = 2 x J

PE = x J

**FIGURE 27-3.** The energies of photons are quantized and can be compared to the potential energies of a ball as it rests on each of these steps.

The photoelectric effect shows energy is quantized. It also indicates Planck's constant contains clues about the structure of the atom. Light is emitted and absorbed in discrete amounts as electrons move between energy levels within an atom. Thus, the atomic energy levels are related by a factor equal to $hf$. The way in which the physicist, Niels Bohr, related atomic structure and Planck's constant will be discussed in the next chapter.

According to the quantum theory, light is made up of a stream of photons.

The highest probability of locating a certain photon in space at a given time is given by its probability wave.

To explain the dual nature of light, the quantum theory of light assumes that light and all other electromagnetic radiation consists of streams of photons. Each photon is characterized in space by a probability wave. The wave determines the position of the photon at any given time. Accordingly, it is more probable for a photon to be located where the amplitude of the probability wave is high. The probability wave also accounts for interference and diffraction phenomena.

Photons escaped notice for many years because of their very small size. Each electromagnetic wave contains a very large number of these tiny particles. Photons acting together make the particle nature of the wave difficult to observe. Photons are noticeable only when they interact with other very small particles such as electrons. The quantum theory is not easy to visualize. However, the fundamental behavior of light and other electromagnetic waves requires this description.

## 27:3   Compton Effect

In 1922, Arthur Compton experimented with X rays aimed at a carbon block. He observed two phenomena. First, he saw the X rays that emerged from the block were often deflected from their original paths. Also, he found when the deflected rays were sent through a grating and their wavelengths were measured, the wavelengths of the emergent rays were longer than the wavelengths of the incident X rays. Thus, the frequency of the emergent X rays was less than the frequency of the incident X rays. The energy content of an electromagnetic wave varies directly with its frequency. A decrease in frequency meant the energy content of the emergent waves was less than the energy of the incident rays. Compton also noticed that electrons were ejected from the carbon block when it was bombarded with X rays. He concluded that X rays were colliding with electrons. In the process, the X rays were losing energy to the electrons.

Compton then measured the kinetic energy of the ejected electrons. The energy of the incident X-ray photons was $hf_1$. The energy of the emergent X rays was $hf_2$. Compton calculated the difference between $hf_1$ and $hf_2$. He found the energy gained

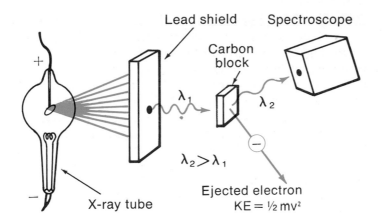

Lead shield   Spectroscope

Carbon block

$\lambda_1$

$\lambda_2$

$\lambda_2 > \lambda_1$

Ejected electron
$KE = \frac{1}{2} mv^2$

X-ray tube

**FIGURE 27-4. Diagram of apparatus used by Compton to study the nature of photons.**

by an ejected electron, $mv^2/2$, was equal to the difference in the energy content of the incident and emergent rays. The laws of conservation of energy and conservation of momentum were upheld. Compton was led to a startling conclusion. Electromagnetic radiation has particle properties and mass!

By observing photon and electron interactions, Compton found that photons have properties of particles.

## 27:4  Heisenberg Uncertainty Principle

The German scientist Werner Heisenberg (1901–1976) stated that *any attempt to study the nature and motion of electrons by bombarding them with photons would change the motion and position of the electron, and thus would lead to uncertainty.* This statement is now known as the **Heisenberg uncertainty principle.** The uncertainty principle applies only to measurements on the subatomic scale. It applies to any attempt to observe electrons closely enough to find out whether they are particles or waves, or both.

The photon is the finest measuring tool a physicist has. To study the nature and motions of an electron, photons are bounced off the electron. For accurate measurements, a photon of very short wavelength must be used. In other words, the photon has a high frequency and also high energy. However, as the Compton effect shows, high energy quanta, like those in the X-ray range, change the motions of electrons. Photons with short wavelengths change the position of the electron too much to be useful in position measurements. If a photon of long wavelength and low energy is used, the interaction between the photon and the electron is smaller. However, inaccurate values result from the long wavelength of the photon. At present, the scientist cannot control a more finite measuring tool than the photon. Thus, a closer look at electron motion is not possible at this time.

The Heisenberg uncertainty principle refers to the inability to measure accurately both the position and momentum of an electron at a given time.

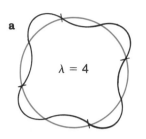

a

$\lambda = 4$

Mismatch—out of phase

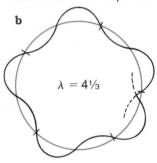

b

$\lambda = 4\frac{1}{3}$

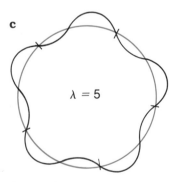

c

$\lambda = 5$

**FIGURE 27-5.** The idea of electron standing waves was first proposed by de Broglie. The circumference of an electron wave must be an integral number of wavelengths. Any circular standing wave pattern that does not meet this requirement will be out of phase.

Recall that the unit J/Hz is equivalent to J·s.

## 27:5 Matter Waves

Compton's studies showed that the momentum $mv$ of a photon is given by the equation

$$mv = \frac{h}{\lambda}$$

Here, $h$ is Planck's constant, and $\lambda$ is the wavelength of the photon. Thus, $\lambda$ would be expressed by the equation

$$\lambda = \frac{h}{mv}$$

The French scientist Louis-Victor de Broglie (1892–    ) reasoned if light has particle properties, then matter must have wave properties. He postulated that particles of matter obey a wave equation just as photons do. He assumed the wavelength of the wave associated with a particle is equal to Planck's constant divided by the momentum of the particle.

$$\lambda = \frac{h}{mv}$$

This is the same equation that describes the wavelength associated with a photon. Thus, de Broglie said that matter and electromagnetic radiation are more closely related than was believed. He also said matter and light display the same wave and particle properties.

The wave properties of matter had never been observed and de Broglie's concept of matter waves was initially met with much doubt. But in 1927, G. P. Thomson, son of J. J. Thomson, succeeded in diffracting electrons by the use of a beam of electrons and a small crystal. The spacing of the atoms in the crystal lattice acted as a diffraction grating for the electrons. Since diffraction is a wave phenomenon, Thomson had shown the wave nature of matter.

de Broglie's equation for the wavelength of matter waves explains why the wave nature of large particles is not observed. Consider the de Broglie wavelength of a baseball with a mass of 0.25 kilograms when it leaves a bat with a speed of 20 meters per second.

$$\lambda = \frac{h}{mv} = \frac{6.6 \times 10^{-34} \text{ J·s}}{(0.25 \text{ kg})(20 \text{ m/s})} = 1.3 \times 10^{-34} \text{ m}$$

This wavelength is far too small to be observed. On the other hand, a calculation of the de Broglie wavelength of one of Thomson's electrons moving with a typical speed of $10^6$ m/s is

$$\lambda = \frac{h}{mv} = \frac{6.6 \times 10^{-34} \text{ J·s}}{(9.1 \times 10^{-31} \text{ kg})(10^6 \text{ m/s})} = 7.3 \times 10^{-10} \text{ m}$$

This wavelength approximates the distance between the atoms in a crystal. The wavelength is suitable for diffraction and interference effects if a crystal is used as a grating. Thus, the wavelengths of very small particles of matter are readily observable.

de Broglie reasoned that if light behaves as particles, particles should behave as waves.

a

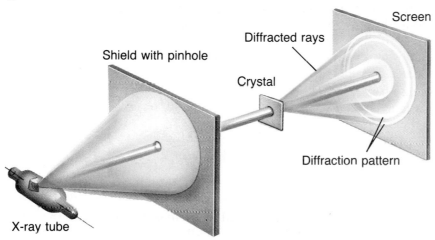

Screen
Diffracted rays
Shield with pinhole
Crystal
Diffraction pattern
X-ray tube

b

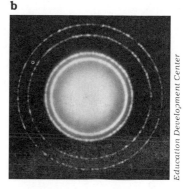

*Education Development Center*

**FIGURE 27-6. A diffraction pattern forms when a narrow beam of electrons passes through thin foil. This pattern is the same as that obtained using an X-ray beam. This technique confirms the wave properties of small particles.**

## PROBLEMS

7. What is the de Broglie wavelength of a proton moving with a speed of $1.0 \times 10^6$ m/s? The mass of a proton is $1.67 \times 10^{-27}$ kg.

8. Calculate the de Broglie wavelength of a Ping-Pong ball of mass 0.015 kg moving at a speed of 3 m/s.

9. What is the de Broglie wavelength of a 75-kg student running at a speed of 10 m/s?

10. Calculate the de Broglie wavelength of a neutron traveling at a speed of $1.0 \times 10^3$ m/s. The mass of a neutron is $1.67 \times 10^{-27}$ kg.

11. Determine the de Broglie wavelength of a ship of mass $2 \times 10^6$ kg moving at a speed of 8 m/s.

12. The earth has a mass of $6.0 \times 10^{24}$ kg. Its average speed is $2.7 \times 10^4$ m/s. Determine the de Broglie wavelength of the earth.

7. $4 \times 10^{-13}$ m

9. $8.8 \times 10^{-37}$ m

11. $4 \times 10^{-41}$ m

**Summary**

1. Light of a minimum frequency, called the threshold frequency, can eject electrons from metals. Each metal has a characteristic threshold frequency. 27:1

2. The photoelectric effect can be accepted only if light is assumed to consist of particles. 27:1, 27:2

3. Photons of frequencies higher than the threshold frequency both eject electrons and give them kinetic energy. **27:2**

4. The quantum theory assumes light and all other electromagnetic radiations consist of streams of particles called quanta or photons. The energy of any quantum (in joules) is equal to Planck's constant multiplied by the frequency of the quantum. **27:2**

5. The Compton effect indicates X rays behave as particles in their abilities to collide with electrons. **27:3**

6. The Heisenberg uncertainty principle recognizes that the interaction between photons and subatomic particles places a limitation on measurements of the position and motion of the particles. **27:4**

7. Louis de Broglie theorized that particles should display wave characteristics just as waves display particle characteristics. This hypothesis was demonstrated experimentally in 1927. **27:5**

## Questions

1. The removal of an electron from nickel requires more energy than the removal of an electron from potassium. Which metal has the higher work function? Which metal has the higher threshold frequency?

2. How does the photoelectric effect show the particle nature of light?

3. What is the constant of proportionality between the energy possessed by a photon and the frequency of the photon?

4. Which has higher energy, photons of long wavelengths or photons of short wavelength?

5. Express $h/mv$ in fundamental units. Prove the expression yields length.

6. Why is it difficult to detect the particle nature of light?

7. Which particle is more likely to have a detectable de Broglie wavelength associated with it, a high-speed electron or a speeding bullet? Use the de Broglie equation to explain your choice.

## Problems

1. The stopping potential to prevent electron flow through a photocell is 5.2 V. What is the maximum kinetic energy of the photoelectrons within the cell?

2. To prevent electron flow in a photocell, a stopping potential of 3.8 V is used. What is the maximum kinetic energy of the photoelectrons within the cell?

3. The threshold frequency of tin is $1.1 \times 10^{15}$ Hz.
   a. What is the work function of tin?
   b. Radiation of frequency $1.8 \times 10^{15}$ Hz falls on tin. What is the maximum kinetic energy of the ejected electrons?

**4.** The work function of iron is $7.5 \times 10^{-19}$ J.
   **a.** What is the threshold frequency of iron?
   **b.** Iron is exposed to radiation of frequency $6.2 \times 10^{15}$ Hz. What is the kinetic energy of the ejected electrons?

**5.** The threshold frequency of magnesium is $9.0 \times 10^{14}$ Hz.
   **a.** What is the work function of magnesium?
   **b.** Radiation of frequency $2.0 \times 10^{15}$ Hz falls on magnesium. What is the kinetic energy of the ejected electrons?

**6.** Find the de Broglie wavelength of a deuteron of mass $3.3 \times 10^{-27}$ kg that moves with a speed of $2.5 \times 10^4$ m/s.

**7.** A spacecraft blasts off and reaches a speed of $1.2 \times 10^3$ m/s. The mass of the spacecraft is $2.0 \times 10^3$ kg. What is the de Broglie wavelength of the spacecraft?

**8.** A proton of mass $1.67 \times 10^{-27}$ kg moves in a particle accelerator at a speed of $2 \times 10^8$ m/s. What is the de Broglie wavelength of the proton?

**1.** *The Mass of a Photon:* Using Compton's expression for the momentum of a photon estimate the mass of an X ray of wavelength $2.5 \times 10^{-11}$ m.

**2.** *The Compton Effect:* During one of Compton's scattering experiments X rays of wavelength $5.0 \times 10^{-11}$ m were used.
   **a.** Determine the momentum of this photon.
   **b.** If one of the photons had collided elastically with an electron as indicated in Figure 27-7, estimate the wavelength of the emergent ray $\lambda'$. Assume the electron to be at rest when the collision occurred.
   **c.** Consult Figure 16-1. Is this new photon of the X ray variety?

**Applying Physics**

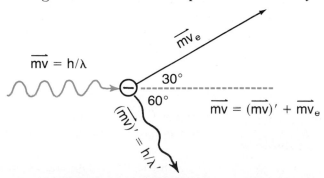

**FIGURE 27-7.** Use with Applying Physics 2.

Ekstrom, P. and Wineland, D., "The Isolated Electron." *Scientific American*, August, 1980.
Overhauser, Albert W., "The Role of Gravity in Quantum Theory." *Scientific American*, May, 1980.

**Readings**

The atom has long been a puzzle. Even now, scientists are not able to see an individual atom. However, using a field ion emission microscope, scientists can study some crystal patterns like that of tungsten shown in this photograph. Theorizing that all substances are made of the same kinds of fundamental particles, how can you explain the great differences in properties such as chemical activity, solubility, crystal structure, color, and conductivity?

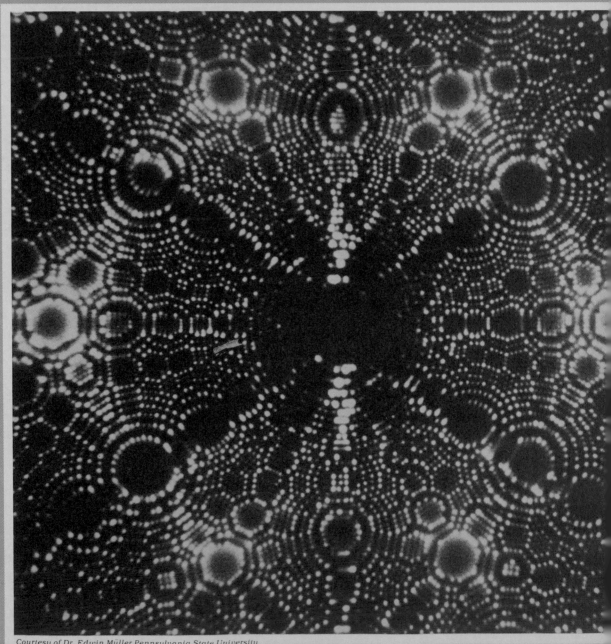

# The Atom 28

Once the electron and the proton were identified, they were thought to be the major particles that make up atoms. Both J. J. Thomson (1856–1940) and Sir Ernest Rutherford (1871–1937) tried to find out how these particles are arranged to form atoms. Their work met with much success.

GOAL: You will gain knowledge and understanding of the basic structure of the atom and of interactions among atoms.

## 28:1  Radioactivity

The experiments Rutherford performed to probe the atom were based on the work of a French physicist, Henri Becquerel (1852-1908). In 1896, Becquerel was working with compounds of the element uranium. To his surprise, he found that even when these uranium compounds were kept some distance from unexposed photographic plates, the plates became fogged or partially exposed. This fogging suggested some kind of ray had passed through the plate coverings. Becquerel also found unexposed plates, even when shielded by several thin sheets of lead, were exposed when placed near the uranium. Only thick layers of lead seemed able to absorb this radiation. At first, he thought he had found some sort of invisible rays similar to X rays. Soon it was revealed that the radiation did not consist of X rays. Several materials other than uranium or its compounds also emitted these rays. Materials which emit this kind of radiation are called **radioactive materials.**

Becquerel discovered that radiation was being emitted from uranium compounds.

**471**

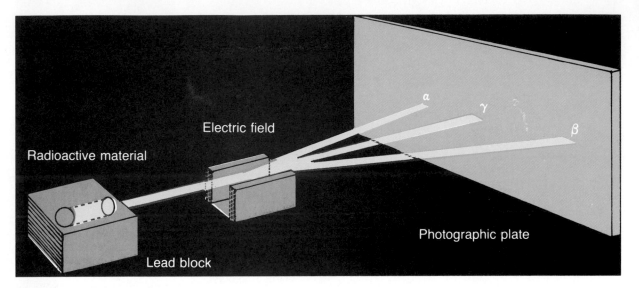

**FIGURE 28-1. Rutherford's apparatus for studying radioactive substances. Note the directions in which the emitted radiations are deflected on passing through an electric field.**

Rutherford found that naturally radioactive materials emit three types of radiation.

Alpha particles are doubly-ionized helium nuclei.

Beta particles are high-speed electrons.

Gamma rays are high-frequency photons.

Figure 28-1 illustrates the method Rutherford used to study radioactive materials. A small amount of radioactive substance was placed at the bottom of a hole drilled in a lead block. The radiation which escaped from the box was limited to a small beam that left the radioactive substance in a direct line with the hole. The rest was absorbed by the lead. The emergent radiation was passed through a strong electric field and fell on a photographic plate. When the plate was developed, three distinct spots were found on the plate. The spots indicated three different types of radiation. They were named alpha ($\alpha$), beta ($\beta$), and gamma ($\gamma$) rays. Alpha, beta, and gamma are the first three letters of the Greek alphabet. A study was made of the behavior of these rays in electric and magnetic fields. **Alpha particles** were found to be doubly-ionized helium atoms (helium nuclei). It was also found that **beta particles** are high-speed electrons, and **gamma rays** are photons of very high frequency.

## 28:2   Discovery of the Nucleus

To explore the structure of atoms, Rutherford's students, Geiger and Marsden, directed alpha rays at very thin sheets of metal which had a thickness of several hundred atoms. They placed a small fluorescent screen in front of a movable telescope. Each time an alpha particle passed through the foil and struck the fluorescent screen in front of the telescope, a small flash of light, or scintillation (sint uhl AY shuhn), was observed. The scintillation was the result of the excitation of the fluorescent material on the screen by the alpha particle.

Rutherford studied atomic structure by bombarding metal foils with alpha particles.

Radiation causes some materials to scintillate, or emit brief flashes of light.

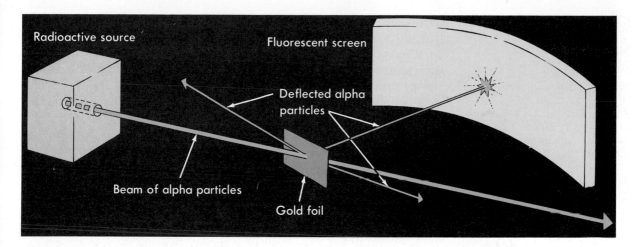

Radioactive source

Fluorescent screen

Deflected alpha particles

Beam of alpha particles

Gold foil

Rutherford's team found that most of the particles passed straight through the foil. Since the foil was at least several hundred atoms thick, it appeared atoms were mostly empty space. A few alpha particles were deflected as they passed through the foil and some even rebounded from the foil.

After observing the angles through which the particles were deflected, Rutherford concluded most of the mass of the atom is located in a very small core or nucleus. Those alpha particles which rebounded from the foil apparently had interacted with nuclei in the foil.

Rutherford's team also measured the velocity of the alpha particles as they approached the foil. Since they knew the charge and the mass of the alpha particles, they could apply Coulomb's law and Newton's laws of motion. In a brilliant series of experiments and analysis of results, they determined the charge carried by the nuclei in the metal foil. Since each proton carries one elementary charge, they determined the number of protons in each nucleus.

The number of protons in the nucleus is the same for every atom of an element. Thus, elements are identified by the number of protons in the nuclei. The number of protons is called the atomic number. For example, the atomic number of oxygen is 8 because oxygen has 8 protons.

**FIGURE 28-2.** After bombarding gold foil with alpha particles, Rutherford's team concluded that most of the mass of the atom was located in the nucleus.

The nature of the deflection of alpha particles by atoms in the metal foil indicates that most of the mass of an atom is located in a central nucleus.

The numbers of protons in several types of atoms was determined through velocity studies of alpha particles during foil bombardments.

## 28:3 The Neutron

As Rutherford's team determined the number of protons in the nucleus, another fact became clear. The mass of the nucleus of a given atom could not be explained in terms of the protons alone. Rutherford postulated the existence of a neutral particle

Atomic mass of an atom
in a.m.u.'s is about
numerically equal to the
number of protons and
neutrons in the nucleus
of the atom.

Electrons located outside
the nucleus have
negligible mass.

within the nucleus. Such a particle could have no net charge. Rutherford called this particle a neutron. In 1932, James Chadwick demonstrated the existence of the neutron. The neutron was found to have a mass approximately equal to the mass of the proton which is about one **atomic mass unit,** a.m.u.* The mass of the protons in an atom plus the mass of the neutrons in the atom account for the mass of the nucleus. Therefore, the number of atomic mass units in a nucleus is roughly the same as the number of protons plus the number of neutrons within that nucleus. Since the electrons outside the nucleus are of negligible mass, the mass of the nucleus is taken to be the mass of the atom.

**EXAMPLE:  Number of Neutrons in a Nucleus**

An atom of iron has an atomic mass of about 56 a.m.u. The atomic number of iron is 26. How many neutrons are in the nucleus of an atom of this isotope?

*Solution:*

Since the mass of the atom is 56 a.m.u., the nucleus must contain a total of 56 protons and neutrons. The atomic number tells us that there are 26 protons in the nucleus. The number of neutrons is the difference between 56 and 26. Thus, this iron nucleus contains 30 neutrons.

## 28:4  Isotopes

For some time, scientists all over the world were puzzled by the fact that the masses of the atoms of most of the elements, measured in atomic mass units, were not exactly whole numbers. If, as was thought, the nucleus is made up of protons and neutrons each with a mass of approximately 1 a.m.u., then the total mass of any atom should be near a whole number. However, most measurements showed that the masses of atoms are not whole numbers. For example, careful measurements of the mass of the boron atom consistently yield 10.8 a.m.u.

The problem presented by decimal values for the mass of the atoms was solved with the mass spectrometer (Chapter 26). The mass spectrometer showed an element has atoms of different masses. For example, neon has atoms of two different masses. Using a pure sample of neon, it was found that not one, but two spots appeared on the screen of the spectrometer. Careful measurements showed the two spots represented neon atoms of different mass. One neon atom has a mass of 20 a.m.u. The second

*The SI unit for atomic mass is the unified atomic mass unit, $u$, and is the same size as an a.m.u. It is equal to $1.66057 \times 10^{-27}$ kg.

neon atom has a mass of 21 a.m.u. All neon atoms have ten protons in their nuclei. In other words, one "kind" of neon has ten neutrons in its nucleus while the other has eleven neutrons in its nucleus. Thus, neon is a mixture of neon atoms which have different numbers of neutrons in their nuclei. When the mass of neon was determined prior to the invention of the mass spectrometer, the result had always given the average mass of 20.183 a.m.u. for the two kinds of neon. Thus, while the mass of any individual atom of neon is close to a whole number, the mass of any given sample of neon is not.

Further study revealed that the situation described for neon was the usual case and not the exception. Chromium, for example, was found to have four kinds of atoms differing only in the number of neutrons contained in their nuclei. These different forms of the element chromium are called the **isotopes** of chromium. Most elements have isotopes. Hydrogen is known to have three isotopes.

Isotopes are atoms which contain the same number of protons but different numbers of neutrons.

The general form for the symbol of an isotope is $^A_Z E$, where $E$ represents the symbol for the element.

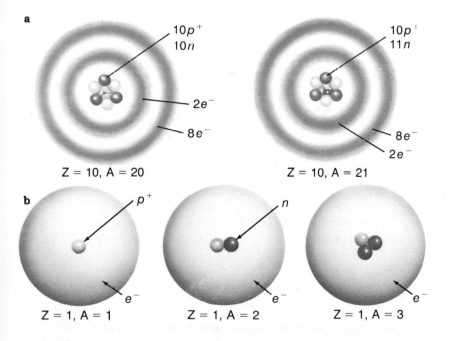

**a**

$10p^+$
$10n$

$2e^-$

$8e^-$

$Z = 10, A = 20$

$10p$
$11n$

$8e^-$
$2e^-$

$Z = 10, A = 21$

**b**

$p^+$

$e^-$

$Z = 1, A = 1$

$n$

$e^-$

$Z = 1, A = 2$

$e^-$

$Z = 1, A = 3$

**FIGURE 28-3. The isotopes of neon (a) and hydrogen (b).**

A special method is used to express the isotopes of the elements. A subscript for the **atomic number** $Z$ is written to the lower left of the symbol of that element. A superscript is written to the upper left of the symbol for the **mass number** $A$. This notation takes the form $^A_Z E$. For example, neon has an atomic number of 10. The isotope with a mass of 20 is written $^{20}_{10}Ne$ and the isotope with a mass of 21 is written $^{21}_{10}Ne$.

The atomic number of an element is represented by the letter $Z$.

The atomic mass of an element is represented by the letter $A$.

### PROBLEMS

1. 7 neutrons

**1.** An isotope of oxygen has a mass number of 15. The atomic number of oxygen is 8. How many neutrons are in the nuclei of this isotope?

**2.** Three isotopes of uranium have mass numbers of 234, 235, and 238 respectively. The atomic number of uranium is 92. How many neutrons are in the nuclei of each of these isotopes?

3. 120 neutrons

**3.** How many neutrons are in an atom of the mercury isotope $^{200}_{80}Hg$?

**4.** Write the symbolic expression for the three isotopes of hydrogen in Figure 28-3b.

5. a. $^{239}_{92}U$
   b. 146 neutrons,
      147 neutrons

**5.** Under certain circumstances, the nucleus of the isotope $^{238}_{92}U$ absorbs another neutron.
  **a.** Write the symbolic expression for this new isotope of uranium.
  **b.** How many neutrons are in the nuclei of each of these isotopes?

**6.** After $^{238}_{92}U$ absorbs the neutron described in Problem 5, a neutron decays forming a proton and ejecting an electron from the nucleus. What new nucleus is formed?

## 28:5   Bohr Model of the Atom

In an atom, the number of electrons is equal to the number of protons.

Most materials have no net charge. This fact led Rutherford to reason that each atom, unless it had been ionized, contains as many electrons as protons. Because electrons are easily removed from the atom, he further postulated the electrons are located outside the nucleus. It had been proposed that electrons orbited the nucleus much like planets orbit the sun. This model, called the **planetary model** of the atom, is shown in Figure 28-4.

**FIGURE 28-4. Bohr's planetary model of the atom showed electrons moving in fixed orbits.**

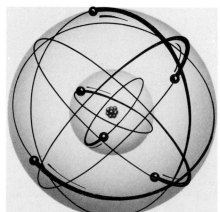

The planetary model of the atom was severely criticized. It has been found that whenever a charged particle is accelerated, energy is emitted in the form of electromagnetic radiation. If an electron follows a circular path, it undergoes continuous acceleration and it should continuously emit radiation. As the electron lost energy, it would spiral down into the nucleus of the atom. In short, on the basis of the planetary model, atoms should not exist.

Another objection to the planetary model was that it failed to account for the quantum nature of electromagnetic radiation. The photoelectric effect clearly showed each photon of light carries a definite quantity of energy.

Also, the spectrum of each element, as seen in a spectroscope, is always the same. In other words, the electromagnetic radiation emitted by any given element is always the same. Maxwell had shown electromagnetic radiation is the result of the accelerations of charged particles. Assuming atoms emit electromagnetic radiation as their electrons are accelerated, the electrons within an atom must undergo some very definite transitions. The planetary model did not provide for transitions. If the electrons could orbit anywhere about the nucleus, then all wavelengths of radiation should be seen for that element within a set range. Thus, the elements emit a continuous spectrum. This does not happen. A new model of the atom was needed.

The Danish physicist Niels Bohr (1885–1962) extended the model of the atom. He presented two bold theories. First, Bohr said electrons can move around the nucleus of an atom without radiating energy. Second, he introduced the idea of the energy states of the atom, suggesting the positive nucleus and the orbiting negative electrons give the atom energy. The energy state of an atom changes when it absorbs or emits radiation. Although orbits are no longer considered to exist, electrons can be imagined as moving around the nucleus of an atom in certain allowed paths called energy levels. Figure 28-5 illustrates the general idea of the Bohr atom. The energy levels represent higher energy as the electron's distance from the nucleus increases. This increase in energy occurs because the force between an electron and the nucleus is one of attraction. Work must be done on the electron to move it farther from the nucleus. The system gains energy when the electron moves from a lower to a higher energy level.

*Rutherford's model did not account for (1) the lack of emission of radiation as electrons move about the nucleus, and (2) the unique spectrum of each element.*

*Bohr suggested that negative electrons could move about the positive nucleus without the emission of radiation.*

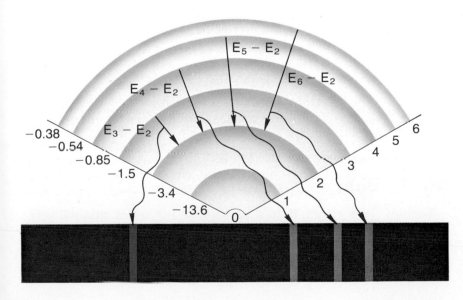

**FIGURE 28-5.** Bohr's model of the hydrogen atom showed that a definite amount of energy is released when an electron moves from a higher to a lower energy level. The energy released in each transition corresponds to a definite line on the hydrogen spectrum.

Thus, the energy content of an electron at $E_2$ is greater than the energy content of an electron at $E_1$. A base level ($PE = 0$) is chosen at an infinite distance from the nucleus. Since an electron loses energy as it approaches the nucleus, the energy states are expressed in negative values.

According to Bohr, the atom emits no radiation as long as the electrons occupy their allowed energy levels. However, if the atom absorbs energy (a photon), an electron can move to a higher energy level. In this way, the potential energy of the atom is increased. Usually, the atom returns immediately to its normal energy state as the electron returns to its normal level. During the down transition, a photon is released. By the law of conservation of energy, the energy content of the photon $hf$ is equal to the energy difference represented by the electron transition, that is

$$hf = E_{initial} - E_{final}$$

Thus, Bohr directly relates the energy changes within the atom to Einstein's photoelectric equation for the energy of a photon, Section 27:1. The photon's energy is the energy released by an atom as its energy content decreases during the transition of an electron from a higher to a lower energy level.

## 28:6    The Electronvolt

One electronvolt (eV) is the energy required to move one electron through one volt.

When dealing with energy exchanges involving subatomic particles, it is customary to use an energy unit called the electronvolt, eV. An **electronvolt** is the energy required to move a single electron through a potential difference of one volt. Since the energy required to move one coulomb of charge ($6.24 \times 10^{18}$ $e^-$) through a potential difference of one volt is one joule, an electron volt is

$$1 \text{ eV} = \frac{1.0 \text{ J}/\mathscr{C}}{6.24 \times 10^{18} \ e^-/\mathscr{C}} = 1.6 \times 10^{-19} \text{ J}$$

Therefore, one electronvolt is equal to $1.6 \times 10^{-19}$ J. A million times the energy of an electronvolt is another useful energy unit, 1 MeV = $1.6 \times 10^{-13}$ J.

## 28:7    Bohr's Equations

Section 28:5 treats Bohr's picture of the atom qualitatively. That is, a description is given of how the atom could be arranged so the discrete spectrum of the atoms and the energy of photons can be explained. If this had been all Bohr had contributed, his concept of the atom might have been ignored. However, Bohr did much more than this. Using Coulomb's law, he defined the force of attraction between the electron and the positive nucleus. Then, he applied Newton's conditions for angular momentum and centripetal force. Adding one or two brilliant hypotheses, he derived several equations. He determined an equation for the radius of the hydrogen energy levels, an equation for the energy content of the allowed levels, and an equation that predicted the frequencies and wavelengths of the hydrogen spectrum in precise agreement with experimental evidence. This type of mathematical evidence lends great strength to theory. Bohr's model of the atom was generally accepted.

Bohr showed mathematically that electron transitions could account for atomic spectra.

The derivations of the Bohr equations are straightforward and easily understood by anyone familiar with simple algebra and Newtonian mechanics. They are, however, lengthy and so are omitted here. However, the equations and their applications are presented. These equations apply only to the hydrogen atom.

The radius of hydrogen energy levels is given by the equation

$$r = \frac{n^2 h^2}{4\pi^2 K m e^2}$$

where $n$ represents whole number values of the levels beginning with 1 for the innermost energy level. $K$ is the constant $9.0 \times 10^9$ N·m²/C² used in Coulomb's law, $h$ is Planck's constant, $m$ is the mass of the electron, and $e$ is the charge in coulombs.

**EXAMPLE:  Radius of a Hydrogen Orbit**

Calculate the radius of the innermost orbital level of the hydrogen atom.

*Solution:*    $n = 1$

$K = 9.0 \times 10^9$ N·m²/C²        $m = 9.1 \times 10^{-31}$ kg

$e = 1.6 \times 10^{-19}$ C

$h = 6.6 \times 10^{-34}$ J·s              $r = \dfrac{n^2 h^2}{4\pi K m e^2}$

$$r = \frac{(1)^2 (6.6 \times 10^{-34} \text{ J·s})^2}{(4)(9.86)\dfrac{9.0 \times 10^9 \cancel{\text{N·m}^2}}{\cancel{C^2}}(9.1 \times 10^{-31}\text{kg})(1.6 \times 10^{-19}\cancel{C})^2}$$

$= 5.3 \times 10^{-11}$ m

The orbital energy of electrons in the hydrogen atom is given by the equation

The orbital energy of electrons in the hydrogen atom can be calculated with the Bohr equation.

$$E = \frac{-2\pi^2 K^2 m e^4}{n^2 h^2}$$

where $K$, $m$, $e$, and $h$ are the same constants used in the equation for the radii of the hydrogen orbits. The constants are combined to give a simplified version of the equation. Hence,

$$E = \frac{-2.17 \times 10^{-18} \text{ J}}{n^2}$$

Since an electronvolt, eV, is equal to $1.60 \times 10^{-19}$ J, the equation may also be written

$$E = \frac{-13.6 \text{ eV}}{n^2}$$

### EXAMPLE: Orbital Energy of Electrons in the Hydrogen Atom

**a.** Determine the energy associated with the innermost energy level of the hydrogen atom ($n = 1$). **b.** Determine the energy associated with the second energy level of the hydrogen atom. **c.** What energy must an incoming photon possess to raise an electron from the first to the second energy level of the hydrogen atom?

*Solution:* **a.**   $E = \dfrac{-13.6 \text{ eV}}{n^2} = \dfrac{-13.6 \text{ eV}}{1^2} = -13.6 \text{ eV}$

**b.**   $E = \dfrac{-13.6 \text{ eV}}{n^2} = \dfrac{-13.6 \text{ eV}}{2^2} = -3.4 \text{ eV}$

**c.**   $hf = E_f - E_i = -3.4 \text{ eV} - (-13.6 \text{ eV}) = 10.2 \text{ eV}$

**Frequency and wavelength of emitted photons can be calculated with the Bohr equation.**

The frequency and wavelength of emitted photons can easily be calculated. Since $hf = E_f - E_i$

$$f = \frac{E_f - E_i}{h}$$

Also, since $c = f\lambda$

$$\lambda = \frac{c}{f}$$

### EXAMPLE: Frequency and Wavelength of Emitted Photons

An electron drops from the second energy level to the first energy level within an excited hydrogen atom. **a.** Determine the energy of the photon emitted. **b.** Calculate the frequency of the photon emitted. **c.** Calculate the wavelength of the photon emitted.

*Solution:* Beginning with the information from the solution to the preceding Example, the energy of the photon equals 10.2 eV.

**a.**   $hf = E_2 - E_1 = -3.4 \text{ eV} - (-13.6 \text{ eV}) = 10.2 \text{ eV}$

**b.** Since   $f = \dfrac{10.2 \text{ eV}}{h}$

$= \dfrac{(10.2 \cancel{\text{ eV}})(1.6 \times 10^{-19} \cancel{\text{ J/eV}})}{6.6 \times 10^{-34} \text{ J/Hz}} = 2.5 \times 10^{15} \text{ Hz}$

**c.**   $\lambda = \dfrac{c}{f} = \dfrac{3.0 \times 10^8 \text{ m/s}}{2.5 \times 10^{15} \text{ Hz}} = 1.2 \times 10^{-7} \text{ m}$

## PROBLEMS

**7.** The Example on page 479 shows how to calculate the radius of the innermost orbit of the hydrogen atom. Note that all factors in the equation are constants with the exception of $n^2$. Use the solution to the Example to find the radius of the second, third, and fourth allowable energy levels in the hydrogen atom.

**8.** Calculate the energy associated with the second, third, and fourth energy levels in the hydrogen atom.

**9.** Calculate the energy difference between $E_3$ and $E_2$ in the hydrogen atom. Do the same between $E_4$ and $E_3$.

**10.** Determine the frequency and wavelength of the photon emitted when an electron drops from
**a.** $E_3$ to $E_2$ in an excited hydrogen atom.
**b.** $E_4$ to $E_3$ in an excited hydrogen atom.

**11.** What is the difference between the energy associated with the energy level $E_4$ and $E_1$ of the hydrogen atom?

**12.** Determine the frequency and wavelength of the photon emitted when an electron drops from $E_4$ to $E_1$ in an excited hydrogen atom.

7. $2.1 \times 10^{-10}$ m, $4.8 \times 10^{-10}$ m, $8.5 \times 10^{-10}$ m

9. 1.9 eV, 0.65 eV

11. 12.8 eV

## 28:8   Success of Bohr's Model of the Atom

The Bohr model of the atom was a major contribution to quantum mechanics. Bohr had shown an orbiting electron radiates energy only when it moves from a higher energy level to a lower energy level, and not when it is accelerating around the nucleus. He had also shown the energy of a photon emitted by the hydrogen atom is equal to the difference in two of its energy levels and obeys the relationship $E = hf$.

Using visible spectra of the elements, Bohr was able to diagram the energy levels of many elements. He was also able to predict several X-ray frequencies by assuming electrons could make transitions to the innermost levels. These X-ray frequencies were later confirmed experimentally. Bohr was also able to calculate the ionization energy of a hydrogen atom. The **ionization energy** of an atom is the energy needed to eject an electron completely from that atom. His calculated values for ionization energy were later confirmed experimentally.

There is one aspect of the Bohr model of the atom that should not be overlooked. It provided an explanation of many of the general chemical properties of the elements. The idea that the atoms of each element have unique electron arrangements is the foundation for much of our knowledge of chemical bonding.

The Bohr model of the atom was a major contribution to quantum mechanics.

Bohr's model of the atom explained many of the chemical properties of elements.

# 28:9    Present Model of the Atom

The present model of the atom is a mathematical model. It gives the probability of the location of an electron at any given time.

Two features of the Bohr model of the atom confused many investigators including Bohr himself. First, it did not explain how electrons, which are negatively charged particles, could accelerate around nuclei and not radiate energy. According to classical physics, the electrons should give up energy and spiral into their nuclei. From the classical viewpoint, the universe should have ended long ago in a brilliant flash of violet light, the so-called "violet death" of the universe. This had obviously not happened. Thus, scientists were left with no other choice than to assume that electrons can orbit the nucleus of an atom and not radiate light. Secondly, the notion that electrons may occupy only certain levels was a further contradiction of accepted physical law. It would seem that electrons should be able to orbit the nucleus at any distance, the distance depending only on the speed of the electron.

The fact that electrons seemed to violate some of the basic principles of classical physics presented a dilemma. This dilemma was solved by Louis de Broglie (1892–    ). He introduced the possibility that particles have wave characteristics just as light waves have particle characteristics. If the electron is considered as a wave rather than a particle, the energy levels proposed by Bohr can be readily understood. In this view, an energy level will exist only when its circumference is a whole number multiple of the wavelength of the orbiting electrons. Thus, the wave can reinforce itself constructively and never lose energy.

de Broglie suggested that particles have wave characteristics.

de Broglie showed that Bohr orbitals exist at levels that are whole number multiples of the wavelength of the electron.

de Broglie showed mathematically that the circumferences of energy levels are exactly equal to whole number multiples of their de Broglie wavelengths. Thus, he provided strong evidence to support both Bohr's model of the atom and his own theory of matter waves.

The present model of the atom is a further modification of de Broglie's version of the Bohr atom. The German physicist, Erwin Schrödinger (1887–1961), expanded de Broglie's matter wave concept to develop a completely mathematical model of the atom. Schrödinger replaced matter waves with "probability" waves which can only give the probable position of an electron at any given instant, not an exact position. The highest probability is that an electron will be at a distance from the nucleus which agrees with one of Bohr's radii. The probability of thousands of points can be calculated. By connecting points of equal probability, a 3-dimensional shape is formed. It is important to note that the atom is 3-dimensional. The high probability volume for an electron is referred to as an **electron cloud.**

**FIGURE 28-6. The modern model of the atom shows regions of high and low probability.**

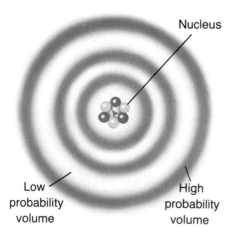

Nucleus

Low probability volume

High probability volume

**Summary**

1. In 1896 Becquerel discovered that uranium compounds emit highly penetrating radiations. **28:1**
2. Rutherford determined the nature of these radiations. He found three types: alpha rays (helium nuclei), beta rays (high-speed electrons), and gamma rays (high-energy photons). **28:1**
3. By directing alpha particles at thin gold sheets, Rutherford found most particles passed right through indicating atoms are mostly empty space. Deflected particles demonstrate the mass of an atom is concentrated in a small region or nucleus. **28:2**
4. The Rutherford model of the atom postulates a nucleus containing protons and neutrons. Electrons are at some distance from the nucleus. **28:3**
5. Niels Bohr revised Rutherford's model of the atom to account for the observed electromagnetic radiations atoms can emit. The Bohr model confines electrons to given energy levels. **28:5**
6. Electrons can make transitions between energy levels. As they do, they emit or absorb electromagnetic radiation. **28:5**
7. The de Broglie model of the atom treats electrons as waves. **28:9**
8. The present model of the atom is a mathematical model. It describes electrons in terms of probability waves. **28:9**

**Questions**

1. Describe Rutherford's methods of analyzing radioactive materials.
2. Name and describe the three types of radiation emitted by naturally occurring radioactive materials.
3. Describe the neutron. How does its mass compare with the mass of a proton?
4. A certain atom has four distinct energy levels as shown in Figure 28-7. If an electron can make transitions between any two levels, how many spectral lines can the atom emit? Which transition emits the photon of highest energy?
5. What two basic assumptions did Bohr make in order to modify Rutherford's model of the atom?
6. How does the Bohr model of the atom account for the emission of radiation by atoms?
7. What two features of the Bohr atom were in direct conflict with classical physics?

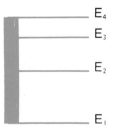

**FIGURE 28-7. Use with Question 4.**

**Problems**

1. An atom of an isotope of magnesium has an atomic mass of about 24 a.m.u. The atomic number of magnesium is 12. How many neutrons are in the nucleus of this atom?

**2.** An atom of an isotope of nitrogen has an atomic mass of about 15 a.m.u. The atomic number of nitrogen is 7. How many neutrons are in the nucleus of this isotope?

**3.** List the number of neutrons in an atom of each of these isotopes.
   **a.** $^{112}_{48}\text{Cd}$      **c.** $^{208}_{83}\text{Bi}$      **e.** $^{1}_{1}\text{H}$      **g.** $^{132}_{54}\text{Xe}$
   **b.** $^{209}_{83}\text{Bi}$      **d.** $^{80}_{35}\text{Br}$      **f.** $^{40}_{18}\text{Ar}$

**4.** Calculate the radius of the allowed energy levels $E_5$ and $E_6$ of the hydrogen atom.

**5.** What energy is associated with the hydrogen atom energy levels $E_2$, $E_3$, $E_4$, $E_5$, and $E_6$?

**6.** Calculate these values for the hydrogen atom.
   **a.** $E_6 - E_5$      **c.** $E_4 - E_2$      **e.** $E_5 - E_3$
   **b.** $E_6 - E_3$      **d.** $E_5 - E_2$

**7.** Use Problem 6 solutions to determine the frequencies of the photons emitted when the hydrogen atom passes through the energy differences.

**8.** Use Problem 7 solutions to determine the wavelengths of the photons having the frequencies listed.

**9.** A photon of energy 16 eV enters a hydrogen atom whose electron is in the ground state. The photon ejects an electron from the atom. What is the kinetic energy of the electron in electronvolts?

*Use Figure 28-8 to solve Problems 10 through 13. The left side of the diagram gives the energy level for mercury in electronvolts. The right side gives the energy required to raise the atom from the ground state to each energy level.*

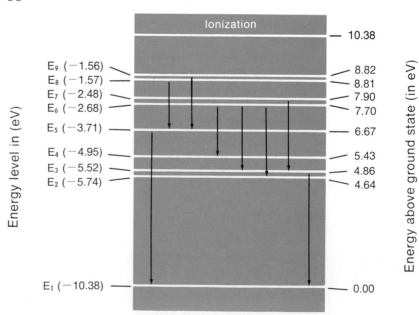

**FIGURE 28-8. Use with Problems 10 and 13.**

**10.** An electron is accelerated by a potential difference of 7.7 V.
   **a.** What energy does the electron possess in electronvolts?
   **b.** The electron strikes a mercury atom in its ground state. The mercury atom is raised to which energy level?

**11.** A mercury atom is in the excited state when its energy level is 6.67 eV above the ground state. A photon of energy 2.15 eV strikes the mercury atom and is absorbed by it. The mercury atom is raised to which energy level?

**12.** A mercury atom drops from 8.81 eV above its ground state to 6.67 eV above its ground state. What is the energy of the photon emitted by the mercury atom?

**13.** In Problem 12, calculate the photon's frequency and wavelength.

---

**Applying Physics**

**1.** *The Bohr Equation:* The Bohr equation for the energy levels of the hydrogen atom can be used as a basis for determining Planck's constant, $h$. To do so, the wavelengths for three of the principal lines of the hydrogen spectrum are used.

   **a.** blue-green: $4.9 \times 10^{-7}$ m
   **b.** blue-violet: $4.3 \times 10^{-7}$ m
   **c.** violet: $4.1 \times 10^{-7}$ m

Remembering that $1$ eV $= 1.6 \times 10^{-19}$ J, use the Bohr equation given below to calculate the value of $h$ as indicated by each of the above wavelengths.

$$h = \frac{(13.6 \text{ eV})(\lambda)}{c}\left(\frac{1}{2^2} - \frac{1}{n^2}\right)$$

Note: For the blue-green line $n = 4$, for the blue-violet line $n = 5$, and for the violet line $n = 6$.

**2.** *Ionization Energy:* In its lowest energy state ($n = 1$), an electron bound to the hydrogen atom has an energy $E_1$ called the ground state. This is $-13.6$ eV. It follows that 13.6 eV of energy added to the electron should remove it completely from the influence of the nucleus. The ionization energy for hydrogen has been measured to be just 13.6 eV. Since photons frequently ionize atoms, calculate the longest wavelength a photon can have and still be capable of ionizing a hydrogen atom in its ground state.

---

**Readings**

Asimov, Isaac, "What's the Universe Made of?" *Science Digest*, April, 1980.
Blanchard, Paul A., *Atoms in Astronomy*, (NASA), Washington, D.C. Superintendent of Documents, 1976.
Trefil, James, "They Just Don't Make Protons Like They Used To." *Science 80*, November, 1980.

The nucleus of an atom is the target of much research today. The atom is a tremendous powerhouse of energy. Scientists feel that nuclear reactions involving hydrogen isotopes may prove to be our greatest energy resource. This fusion reactor is still in experimental stages. Maintaining the conditions necessary for a fusion reaction to occur is the most significant problem to be resolved. Why is fusion research so important? What are the advantages of using fusion as a source of energy?

# The Nucleus 29

The radioactive properties of uranium were discovered by Becquerel. The search for other radioactive elements by Pierre and Marie Curie resulted in the discovery of polonium and radium. Further investigations revealed the radioactive properties of other elements as well as the nature of the radiation. Physicists found that the radiation originated in the nucleus. Today, physicists are investigating not only the structure of the nucleus but the structure of the particles found in the nucleus as well.

GOAL: You will gain knowledge and understanding of the present concepts of the nucleus, nuclear reactions, nuclear accelerators, reactors.

## 29:1 Atomic Number and Mass Number

The nuclei of naturally radioactive elements are unstable. An unstable nucleus undergoes a series of changes until it becomes stable. For example, $^{238}_{92}U$, an unstable isotope of uranium, undergoes fourteen separate transformations before becoming $^{206}_{82}Pb$, a stable lead isotope.

The identity of an element depends only on the number of protons in the nucleus. The number of protons in the nucleus is the atomic number $Z$ of the nucleus.

Nuclei of radioactive elements are unstable.

In Chapter 28, the number of neutrons in the nucleus of an atom was determined by subtracting the number of protons from the atomic mass *A* of the nucleus. This method works only when the atomic mass of the isotope of any given element is stated in terms of a whole number. The standard for the **atomic mass unit** is defined as $\frac{1}{12}$ of the mass of an atom of $^{12}_{6}C$. Precise atomic mass measurements do not yield whole numbers. However, the numbers come close to being whole numbers. These whole numbers are the mass numbers of isotopes. For example, the mass of a helium isotope in atomic mass units is 4.00260 a.m.u. Its mass number is 4. In future sections, we will call the superscript accompanying the symbol of an element the mass number.

The atomic mass unit is defined as 1/12 of the mass of a $^{12}_{6}$ C atom.

The mass number of an isotope is the atomic mass in a.m.u. rounded to the nearest whole number.

## 29:2 Radioactive Transmutation

An unstable nucleus emits radiation in the form of alpha particles, beta particles, and gamma rays. An alpha particle is a helium nucleus. A helium nucleus consists of two protons and two neutrons. If the nucleus of a uranium atom, $^{238}_{92}U$, emits an alpha particle, it loses two protons and two neutrons. Thus, it loses four units of mass from its nucleus. Since the number of protons in the nucleus determines the identity of the element, the atom is no longer uranium. After the loss of two protons, the nucleus has an atomic number $Z = 90$. From Table B-6 of the Appendix, we find that $Z = 90$ is thorium. The mass number of the nucleus is $238 - 4$, or 234. Thus, a thorium isotope, $^{234}_{90}Th$, is formed. The uranium isotope has undergone transmutation. **Transmutation** is the change of one element into another element by a change in the number of protons.

Transmutation is the change of one element into another through a change in proton number.

**FIGURE 29-1. The emission of an alpha particle (a) by uranium-238 results in the formation of thorium-234. The emission of a beta particle (b) by thorium-234 results in the formation of proactinium-234.**

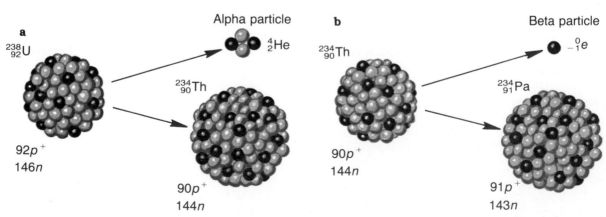

A radioactive atom undergoes beta decay by emitting an electron from the nucleus. Beta decay occurs when a neutron in the nucleus disintegrates forming a proton and an electron. The electron is ejected as a beta particle. The proton remains in the nucleus raising the atomic number of the element by one. The mass of an electron is insignificant. Therefore, the atomic mass of an atom is not changed by the emission of a beta particle. However, increasing the atomic number by one changes the identity of the nucleus. For example, after a uranium atom becomes thorium, the newly formed thorium atom emits a beta particle. In this transmutation, the number of protons in the thorium nucleus increases by one. However, the thorium nucleus undergoes no change in mass. Thus, $^{234}_{90}$Th becomes a protactinium isotope, $^{234}_{91}$Pa.

> A beta particle is an electron which is emitted by an atomic nucleus when a neutron breaks up to form a proton and an electron.

When a gamma ray is emitted by a nucleus, no transmutation takes place. A gamma ray is a quantum of energy that does not have a net charge. By the emission of a gamma ray, excess energy is released from a nucleus as it is rearranged during decay.

> The emission of a gamma ray does not result in a change in the identity of the nucleus.

## 29:3  Nuclear Equations

Nuclear reactions are expressed in equation form. The use of nuclear equations makes the calculation of atomic number and mass numbers in a transformation quite simple. For example, the word equation for the transmutation of uranium to thorium due to the emission of an alpha particle is

$$\text{Uranium 238} \rightarrow \text{Thorium 234} + \text{Alpha particle}$$

The nuclear equation for this reaction is

$$^{238}_{92}\text{U} \rightarrow {}^{234}_{90}\text{Th} + {}^{4}_{2}\text{He}$$

> The symbol for an alpha particle is $^{4}_{2}$He.

No nuclear particles are destroyed during the transmutation process. Thus, the sum of the superscripts on the right side of the equation must equal the sum of the superscripts on the left side of the equation. The sum of the superscripts on both sides of the equation is 238. Electric charge is also conserved. Thus, the sum of the subscripts on the right is equal to the sum of the subscripts on the left.

> In a nuclear equation, the sum of the superscripts on the right side must be equal to the sum of the superscripts on the left side.

> In a nuclear equation, the sum of the subscripts on the right side must be equal to the sum of the subscripts on the left side.

### EXAMPLE:  Nuclear Equation—Alpha Decay

Write the nuclear equation for the transmutation of a radioactive radium isotope $^{226}_{88}$Ra, into a radon isotope, $^{222}_{86}$Rn, by the emission of an alpha particle.

*Solution:*    $$^{226}_{88}\text{Ra} \rightarrow {}^{222}_{86}\text{Rn} + {}^{4}_{2}\text{He}$$

A beta particle is represented by the symbol $_{-1}^{0}e$. This indicates that the electron has one negative charge and an atomic

> The symbol for a beta particle is $_{-1}^{0}e$.

mass number of zero. The equation for the transmutation of a thorium atom by the emission of a beta particle is

$$^{234}_{90}\text{Th} \rightarrow {}^{234}_{91}\text{Pa} + {}^{0}_{-1}e$$

The sum of the superscripts on the right side of the equation equals the sum of the superscripts on the left side of the equation. Also, the sum of the subscripts on the right side of the equation equals the sum of the subscripts on the left side of the equation.

**EXAMPLE: Nuclear Equation—Beta Decay**

Write the nuclear equation for the transmutation of a radioactive lead isotope, $^{209}_{82}\text{Pb}$, into a bismuth isotope, $^{209}_{83}\text{Bi}$, by the emission of a beta particle.

*Solution:* $\qquad {}^{209}_{82}\text{Pb} \rightarrow {}^{209}_{83}\text{Bi} + {}^{0}_{-1}e$

**PROBLEMS**

1. $^{234}_{92}\text{U} \rightarrow {}^{230}_{90}\text{Th} + {}^{4}_{2}\text{He}$

1. Write the nuclear equation for the transmutation of a radioactive uranium isotope, $^{234}_{92}\text{U}$, into a thorium isotope, $^{230}_{90}\text{Th}$, by the emission of an alpha particle.

2. Write the nuclear equation for the transmutation of a radioactive thorium isotope, $^{230}_{90}\text{Th}$, into a radioactive radium isotope, $^{226}_{88}\text{Ra}$, by the emission of an alpha particle.

3. $^{226}_{88}\text{Ra} \rightarrow {}^{222}_{86}\text{Rn} + {}^{4}_{2}\text{He}$

3. Write the nuclear equation for the transmutation of a radioactive radium isotope, $^{226}_{88}\text{Ra}$, into a radon isotope, $^{222}_{86}\text{Rn}$, by the emission of an alpha particle.

4. A radioactive lead isotope, $^{214}_{82}\text{Pb}$, can change to a radioactive bismuth isotope, $^{214}_{83}\text{Bi}$, by the emission of a beta particle. Write the nuclear equation.

5. $^{214}_{83}\text{Bi} \rightarrow {}^{214}_{84}\text{Po} + {}^{0}_{-1}e$

5. A radioactive bismuth isotope, $^{214}_{83}\text{Bi}$, emits a beta particle. Use Table B-6 of the Appendix to determine the element formed. Write the nuclear equation.

6. A radioactive polonium isotope, $^{210}_{84}\text{Po}$, emits an alpha particle. Use Table B-6 of the Appendix to determine the element formed. Write the nuclear equation.

7. $^{56}_{24}\text{Cr} \rightarrow {}^{56}_{25}\text{Mn} + {}^{0}_{-1}e$

7. An unstable chromium isotope, $^{56}_{24}\text{Cr}$, emits a beta particle. Write a complete equation and show the element formed.

# 29:4  Nuclear Bombardment

The nuclei of atoms can be studied by bombarding them with smaller particles such as alpha particles or neutrons. When such particles strike the nucleus of an atom, the nucleus often disintegrates. Much is learned by studying the electromagnetic radiation and particles emitted as the nucleus breaks down.

When a sample of an element emits radiation only after nuclear bombardment, the sample is said to be **artificially radioactive.** Often, nuclear bombardment results in the artificial transmutation of elements. New elements with atomic numbers higher than that of uranium can be created. These elements are called **transuranium elements.**

Some of the more important devices used to bombard the nuclei of atoms will be described in the following sections. These devices accelerate subatomic particles to velocities approaching the speed of light and then direct them at target nuclei. The target nuclei often are broken up as a result. The new particles are then studied to learn more about atomic structure.

Transuranium elements are those elements with atomic numbers above 92.

## 29:5  Cyclotron

In 1930, the cyclotron was developed by E. O. Lawrence. The **cyclotron** is a device which accelerates protons and deuterons ($^2_1$H) to very high velocities. These velocities give them sufficient energy to enter the nuclei of atoms. A cyclotron consists of two hollow half-cylinders. They are called "dees" because of their *D*-shapes. The dees are enclosed in an evacuated chamber and placed between the poles of a powerful electromagnet. The dees are also connected to a source of high frequency ($10^7$ Hz) alternating voltage. The potential difference is at least 50 000 V. With this alternating voltage, the charge on each dee is changed during each half-cycle.

The cyclotron accelerates charged particles to extremely high velocities.

A deuteron is a deuterium nucleus. It consists of one proton and one neutron.

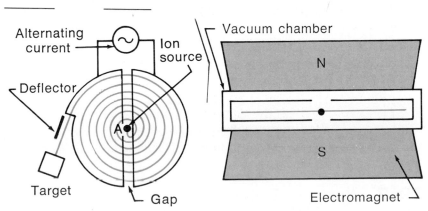

FIGURE 29-2. A cyclotron accelerates particles to very high velocities. The magnetic field causes the particles to follow a circular path.

A diagram of a cyclotron is shown in Figure 29-2. Protons are obtained by stripping electrons from hydrogen atoms at the ion source. They enter the cyclotron at *A*, moving slowly. The strong magnetic field causes them to follow a circular path. When the protons reach the gap between the dees, they are accelerated across the 50 000 volt potential difference. The voltage is synchronized so the dee the protons are leaving is always positive. The opposite dee has a negative charge. Since the magnetic field is constant, the increased velocity results in the protons following a circular path of larger radius. Each time the protons cross the gap, their velocity increases. Therefore, the radius of the path increases. Once the protons are accelerated to a very high velocity, they are aimed at a target. The protons bombard the nuclei of elements in the target. The resulting transformations are then studied.

## 29:6   Linear Accelerators

A **linear accelerator** consists of a long series of hollow evacuated tubes, Figure 29-3. The tubes are connected to a source of high-frequency alternating voltage. As the protons leave each tube, the alternating voltage is synchronized so the tube from which the protons exit has a positive charge. The next tube is given a negative charge. Thus, the proton is accelerated as it leaves one tube and enters another. The total energy given to the proton depends on both the length of the accelerator and the difference in potential placed across the tubes. The largest linear accelerator in the United States is located in Stanford, California. It is about 3.3 km in length.

Linear accelerators use potential differences to accelerate charged particles.

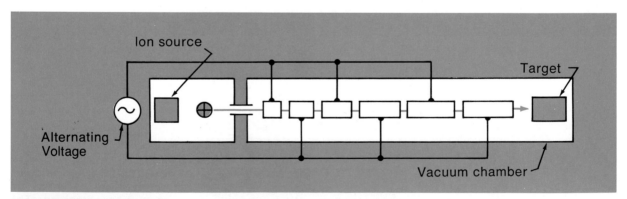

FIGURE 29-3. A proton is accelerated in a linear accelerator by changing the charges on the tubes as the proton moves.

## 29:7   Particle Detectors

Photographic plates become "fogged" or exposed when alpha particles, beta particles, or gamma rays strike them. Thus, photographic plates are used to detect these particles and rays. Many other devices are used to detect charged particles and gamma rays. Most of these devices use the principle that a high-speed particle removes electrons from atoms. The high-speed

Photographic plates can be used to detect radioactive substances.

particles ionize the matter which they bombard. For example, some substances fluoresce when exposed to certain types of radiation. Thus, fluorescent substances can be used in detecting radiation, Section 20:4.

The Geiger-Müller tube employs an avalanche effect, Figure 29-4. The tube contains a gas at low pressure (10 kPa). At one end of the tube is a very thin "window" through which charged particles or gamma rays are allowed to pass. Inside the tube is a copper cylinder with a negative charge. A rigid wire with a positive charge runs down the center of this cylinder. The voltage across the wire and cylinder is kept just below the point where a spontaneous discharge occurs. When a charged particle or gamma ray enters the tube, it ionizes a gas particle located between the copper cylinder and the wire. The ionized gas particle which has a positive charge is accelerated toward the copper cylinder by the potential difference. The electron is accelerated toward the positive wire. As these particles move, they strike other particles forming more ions. These ions, in turn, move toward the negatively-charged cylinder and ionize even more atoms in their path. Thus, an avalanche of charged particles is created and the tube discharges. The discharge can be amplified sufficiently to cause an audible signal such as a click or to operate a counter. To operate the tube continuously, a temporary drop in voltage is placed across the tube to "quench" the discharge. This quenching is done electronically as an automatic reaction to the discharge. Thus, the tube is ready for the beginning of a new avalanche when another particle or gamma ray enters it.

Some fluorescent substances can be used to detect radiation.

A Geiger-Müller tube can be used to detect sensitive radioactive emissions.

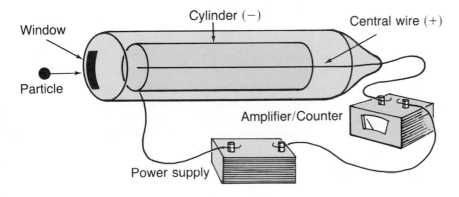

FIGURE 29-4. A Geiger counter can be used to detect gamma rays.

Another device used to detect particles is the Wilson cloud chamber. The chamber creates an area supersaturated with water vapor. When ions travel through the chamber, the water vapor tends to condense on the ions. In this way, visible trails of water particles, or fog, are formed.

A cloud chamber shows the tracks of particles emitted during radioactive decay.

**FIGURE 29-5.** This photograph shows the tracks of a high energy neutrino. Since neutrinos have no charge or mass, they are extremely difficult to detect. Thousands of pictures were taken to record this one event.

The bubble chamber operates on a similar principle. The presence of neutrinos* has been detected indirectly in the bubble chamber. The tracks of other products involved in a reaction with neutrinos confirms their presence.

## 29:8   Artificial Transmutation

**By bombarding an element with alpha particles, a new element can be formed.**

The first deliberate artificial transmutation of an element was achieved by Lord Rutherford. Rutherford bombarded pure nitrogen gas with alpha particles. Oxygen gas appeared in the once pure sample of nitrogen.

Figure 29-6 shows an alpha particle striking the nitrogen nucleus and being absorbed. During the process it ejects a proton from the nitrogen atom. The symbol for a proton is $_1^1$H. This symbol shows that a hydrogen nucleus has an atomic number of one and a mass number of one. By absorbing the alpha particle, the nitrogen nucleus gains one proton to become oxygen. The net addition of one proton and two neutrons increases the mass number to seventeen. This reaction is written

$$\text{Nitrogen} + \text{Alpha particle} \rightarrow \text{Oxygen} + \text{Proton}$$
$$_7^{14}\text{N} \quad + \quad _2^4\text{He} \quad \rightarrow \quad _8^{17}\text{O} \quad + \quad _1^1\text{H}$$

In 1932, James Chadwick confirmed the existence of neutrons. He bombarded beryllium nuclei with alpha particles. Carbon atoms and neutrons were formed according to the equation

$$_4^9\text{Be} + _2^4\text{He} \rightarrow _6^{12}\text{C} + _0^1 n$$

*An uncharged elementary particle, believed to be massless.

The symbol for a neutron is $_0^1n$. This symbol shows that a neutron has an atomic number of zero and a mass number of one. The beryllium nucleus gains two protons. Thus, the atomic number increases from 4 to 6 and a carbon nucleus is formed. The ejected neutrons are excellent particles for bombarding the nuclei of other elements because they have no net charge. Neutrons are not repelled as they approach the positively-charged nucleus of an atom.

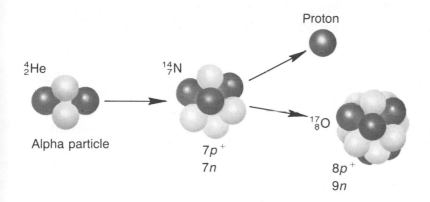

**FIGURE 29-6. The formation of oxygen-17 occurs as the result of the artificial transmutation of nitrogen.**

## 29:9  Artificial Radioactivity

Stable nuclei may become unstable after bombardment with neutrons, alpha particles, beta particles, and accelerated protons. The resulting unstable nuclei emit radiation until they become stable. Artificially radioactive substances, like naturally radioactive substances, can emit alpha and beta particles. Artificially radioactive substances can also emit a particle called a positron. A **positron** is a positive electron. It has the same mass as an electron. Unlike an electron, a positron has a positive charge. Its symbol is $_{+1}^0e$. A positron is produced during the conversion of a proton into a neutron. A neutrino (noo TREE noh) is also formed in the process. A **neutrino** has no charge and has very little mass. Just as a neutron can produce a proton by emitting a negative electron and an antineutrino, a proton can produce a neutron by emitting a positive electron and a neutrino.

When a proton produces a neutron by the emission of a positron, the atomic number $Z$ of the nucleus containing the proton decreases by one. Hence, transmutation takes place. For example, artificially radioactive phosphorus decays by the emission of a positron and forms stable silicon. The equation is

$$_{15}^{30}P \rightarrow _{14}^{30}Si + _{+1}^0e$$

Not only alpha and beta particles but also positrons and neutrinos can be emitted from artificially radioactive substances.

A positron has one positive charge. Like an electron, it has negligible mass.

A neutrino has negligible mass and no charge.

Neutron → Electron + Proton + Antineutrino

Proton → Positron + Neutrino + Neutron

**PROBLEMS**

**8.** Use Table B-6 of the Appendix to complete the following nuclear equations:
**a.** ${}^{14}_{6}C \rightarrow ? + {}^{0}_{-1}e$    **b.** ${}^{55}_{24}Cr \rightarrow ? + {}^{0}_{-1}e$

9. ${}^{238}_{92}U \rightarrow {}^{234}_{90}Th + {}^{4}_{2}He$

**9.** Write the nuclear equation for the transmutation of a uranium isotope, ${}^{238}_{92}U$, into a thorium isotope, ${}^{234}_{90}Th$, by the emission of an alpha particle.

**10.** A radioactive polonium isotope, ${}^{214}_{84}Po$, decays by alpha emission and becomes lead. Write the nuclear equation.

11. **a.** ${}^{210}_{82}Pb \rightarrow {}^{210}_{83}Bi + {}^{0}_{-1}e$
**b.** ${}^{210}_{83}Bi \rightarrow {}^{210}_{84}Po + {}^{0}_{-1}e$
**c.** ${}^{234}_{90}Th \rightarrow {}^{234}_{91}Pa + {}^{0}_{-1}e$
**d.** ${}^{239}_{93}Np \rightarrow {}^{239}_{94}Pu + {}^{0}_{-1}e$

**11.** Write the nuclear equations for the beta decay of these isotopes:
**a.** ${}^{210}_{82}Pb$    **b.** ${}^{210}_{83}Bi$    **c.** ${}^{234}_{90}Th$    **d.** ${}^{239}_{93}Np$

**12.** When bombarded by protons, a lithium isotope, ${}^{7}_{3}Li$, absorbs a proton and then ejects two alpha particles. Write the nuclear equation for this reaction.

13. **a.** ${}^{30}_{15}P \rightarrow {}^{30}_{14}Si + {}^{0}_{+1}e$
**b.** ${}^{205}_{82}Pb \rightarrow {}^{205}_{81}Tl + {}^{0}_{+1}e$

**13.** Complete the nuclear equations for these transmutations:
**a.** ${}^{30}_{15}P \rightarrow ? + {}^{0}_{+1}e$    **b.** ${}^{205}_{82}Pb \rightarrow ? + {}^{0}_{+1}e$

**14.** The radioactive nuclei indicated in each equation disintegrate by emitting a positron. Complete each nuclear equation.
**a.** ${}^{21}_{11}Na \rightarrow ? + {}^{0}_{+1}e$    **b.** ${}^{49}_{24}Cr \rightarrow ? + {}^{0}_{+1}e$

15. **a.** ${}^{14}_{7}N + {}^{4}_{2}He \rightarrow {}^{18}_{9}F$
**b.** ${}^{27}_{13}Al + {}^{4}_{2}He \rightarrow {}^{31}_{15}P$

**15.** Each of the nuclei given below can absorb an alpha particle. Complete the equations. Assume that no secondary particles are emitted by the nucleus that absorbs the alpha particle.
**a.** ${}^{14}_{7}N + {}^{4}_{2}He \rightarrow ?$    **b.** ${}^{27}_{13}Al + {}^{4}_{2}He \rightarrow ?$

**16.** In each of these reactions, a neutron is absorbed by a nucleus. The nucleus then emits a proton. Complete the equations.
**a.** ${}^{65}_{29}Cu + {}^{1}_{0}n \rightarrow ? + {}^{1}_{1}H$    **b.** ${}^{14}_{7}N + {}^{1}_{0}n \rightarrow ? + {}^{1}_{1}H$

17. **a.** lithium
**b.** ${}^{10}_{5}B + {}^{1}_{0}n \rightarrow {}^{7}_{3}Li + {}^{4}_{2}He$

**17.** When a boron isotope, ${}^{10}_{5}B$, is bombarded with neutrons, it absorbs a neutron and then emits an alpha particle.
**a.** What element is also formed?
**b.** Write the nuclear equation for this reaction.

# 29:10  Half-Life

The half-life of an element is the time required for half of the quantity of the radioactive element to decay.

The time required for half of the atoms in any given quantity of a radioactive element to disintegrate is the **half-life** of that element. The half-life of a pure radioactive isotope is unique to that particular isotope. For example, the half-life of radium isotope, ${}^{226}_{88}Ra$, is 1600 years. In other words, in 1600 years, half of a given quantity of the sample of ${}^{226}_{88}Ra$ will disintegrate and form another element. In another 1600 years, half of the remaining sample will have disintegrated. Only one fourth of the original amount will remain at that time.

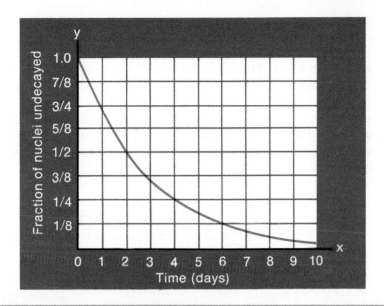

Figure 29-7. Half-life graph for $^{238}_{93}$Np. The half-life of this isotope is 2 days. What does the shape of the graph indicate?

**TABLE 29-1**

**Half-Life of Selected Isotopes**

The half-lives of radio-active isotopes differ widely.

| Element | Isotope | Half-Life | Radiation Produced |
|---|---|---|---|
| hydrogen (tritium) | $^{3}_{1}H$ | 12.3 years | beta |
| carbon | $^{14}_{6}C$ | 5730 years | beta |
| iodine | $^{131}_{53}I$ | 8.07 days | beta and gamma |
| lead | $^{212}_{82}Pb$ | 10.6 hours | beta and gamma |
| polonium | $^{194}_{84}Po$ | 0.5 seconds | alpha |
| polonium | $^{210}_{84}Po$ | 138 days | alpha |
| uranium | $^{227}_{92}U$ | 1.3 minutes | alpha |
| uranium | $^{235}_{92}U$ | $7.1 \times 10^8$ years | alpha and gamma |
| uranium | $^{238}_{92}U$ | $4.51 \times 10^9$ years | alpha and gamma |
| plutonium | $^{236}_{94}Pu$ | 2.85 years | alpha and gamma |
| plutonium | $^{242}_{94}Pu$ | $3.79 \times 10^5$ years | alpha |

## 29:11  Binding Force within the Nucleus

The electrons that surround the positively-charged nucleus of an atom are held in place by a force of electric attraction. The nucleus consists of positively-charged protons and neutral neutrons. The protons are very close together. Normally, the strong electric repulsive force between the protons would cause them to fly apart. This does not happen because an even stronger

Nuclear binding force
holds the nucleus
together.

Nucleons are the particles
that make up the nucleus.

Nuclear binding force
results from the
conversion of mass into
energy.

The mass defect of the
nucleus is the amount of
the atomic mass that has
been converted into
nuclear binding energy
($E = mc^2$).

force exists within the nucleus to hold it together. This force is called the **nuclear binding force.** The nuclear binding force exists only when particles are very close together as in the nucleus of an atom. The particles that make up the nucleus are called **nucleons.** To develop the binding force, mass is converted into energy. The lost mass equals the binding energy. For example, the helium nucleus, $^4_2$He, consists of 2 protons and 2 neutrons. The mass of a proton is 1.007825 a.m.u. The mass of a neutron is 1.008665 a.m.u. Thus, the mass of a helium nucleus should be equal to the sum of the masses of 2 protons and 2 neutrons, or 4.032980 a.m.u. Careful measurement shows the mass of a helium nucleus to be only 4.00260 a.m.u. Thus, when a helium atom is formed, 0.03038 a.m.u. is missing. Hence, the mass of the helium nucleus is less than the mass of its constituent parts. This difference is called the **mass defect** of the nucleus.

The mass represented by the mass defect of a nucleus is changed into energy in the form of radiation. It is in keeping with the equation $E = mc^2$. Before a nucleus can be separated into its parts, the same amount of energy must be restored to it. For example, before a helium nucleus can be split into 2 protons and 2 neutrons, energy in the amount of $(0.03038$ a.m.u.$)c^2$ must be added.

## 29:12  Calculating Binding Energy

The mass defect of a nucleus provides its binding energy. It follows that the binding energy of any nucleus can be calculated if its mass and number of protons and neutrons are known. First, find the mass defect. Then, use $E = mc^2$ to determine the energy equivalent of the mass defect.

Mass defects are determined in atomic mass units. If the energy equivalent of 1 a.m.u. is found, this quantity can be multiplied by any mass defect. Thus, we have a way to convert mass defects to binding energies. An atomic mass unit is equivalent to $1.66 \times 10^{-27}$ kg. The energy equivalent of 1 a.m.u. is

$$E = mc^2$$
$$= (1.66 \times 10^{-27}\text{kg})(3.0 \times 10^8\text{m/s})^2$$
$$= 14.9 \times 10^{-11} \text{ J}$$

Recall that an electronvolt is $1.6 \times 10^{-19}$ J. The electronvolt energy equivalent of 1 a.m.u. can be calculated.

$$\text{Energy equivalent for 1 a.m.u.} = \frac{14.9 \times 10^{-11} \text{ J}}{1.6 \times 10^{-19} \text{ J/eV}}$$
$$= 9.31 \times 10^8 \text{ eV}$$

It is customary to express mass-energy equivalents as millions of electronvolts, MeV.

$$1 \text{ a.m.u.} = 931 \text{ MeV}$$

### EXAMPLE: Mass Defect and Nuclear Binding Energy

The mass of a proton is 1.007825 a.m.u. The mass of a neutron is 1.008665 a.m.u. The mass of the nucleus of a helium isotope, $^4_2$He, is 4.00260 a.m.u. **a.** What is the nuclear mass defect of this helium nucleus? **b.** What is the binding energy of this helium nucleus?

*Solution:* **a.** As indicated by the superscript and subscript in the symbol for helium, its nucleus contains 2 protons and 2 neutrons. Its mass defect can be found as follows:

Mass of 2 protons = (2)(1.007825 a.m.u.) = 2.015650 a.m.u.
Mass of 2 neutrons = (2)(1.008665 a.m.u.) = 2.017330 a.m.u.

$$\text{Total} = 4.032980 \text{ a.m.u.}$$
$$\text{Mass of helium nucleus} = 4.00260 \text{ a.m.u.}$$

$$\text{Mass defect} = 0.03038 \text{ a.m.u.}$$

**b.** Since 1 a.m.u. is equivalent to 931 MeV, the binding energy of the helium nucleus can be calculated.

Binding energy of $^4_2$He nucleus = (0.03038 a̶.̶m̶.̶u̶.̶)(931 MeV/a̶.̶m̶.̶u̶.̶)
$$= 28.3 \text{ MeV}$$

### PROBLEMS

*Use these values in the following problems: mass of a proton = 1.007825 a.m.u., mass of a neutron = 1.008665 a.m.u., and 1 a.m.u. = 931 MeV.*

**18.** A carbon isotope, $^{12}_6$C, has a nuclear mass of 12.0000 a.m.u.
   **a.** Calculate its mass defect.
   **b.** Calculate its binding energy in MeV.

**19.** The isotope of hydrogen that contains 1 proton and 1 neutron is called deuterium. The mass of its nucleus is 2.0140 a.m.u.
   **a.** What is its mass defect?
   **b.** What is the binding energy of deuterium in MeV?

**19. a. 0.0025 a.m.u.**
     **b. 2 MeV**

**20.** A nitrogen isotope, $^{15}_7$N, has 7 protons and 8 neutrons. Its nucleus has a mass of 15.00011 a.m.u.
   **a.** Calculate the mass defect of this nucleus.
   **b.** Calculate the binding energy of the nucleus.

**21.** An oxygen isotope, $^{16}_8$O, has a nuclear mass of about 15.99491 a.m.u.
   **a.** What is the mass defect of this isotope?
   **b.** What is the binding energy of its nucleus?

**21. a. 0.137 01 a.m.u.**
     **b. 128 MeV**

## 29:13   Nuclear Particles

When the nucleus is bombarded, many types of particles may be emitted.

Neutrons and protons are the major nuclear particles. In addiition, many other particles can be produced from the nucleus. Many of these particles have been discovered as a result of bombardment and detection techniques. Some of the particles appear to be constituent parts of protons and neutrons. Other particles seem to be formed at the moment the bombarding particle strikes the nucleus.

The discovery and identification of the neutron as the second major nuclear particle led the Japanese physicist Hideki Yukawa (1907–      ) to theorize about the force needed to hold the nucleus together. Yukawa thought this force resulted from particles of "middle mass," or **mesons.** The mesons could pass back and forth between the neutrons and the protons. Yukawa predicted the mass of the meson to be about 300 times the mass of the electron. Eventually, different types of mesons were discovered. There were pi mesons (pions) and K mesons (kaons).

Mesons pass back and forth between neutrons and protons. This exchange holds the nucleus together.

Pi mesons have a mass of about 273 times the mass of the electron. There are three types of pi mesons. One has a single positive charge, $\pi^+$, one has a single negative charge, $\pi^-$, and the other is a neutral meson, $\pi^0$. When a proton emits a $\pi^+$ meson, it becomes a neutron. When a neutron absorbs a $\pi^+$ meson, it becomes a proton. Similarly, when a neutron emits a $\pi^-$ meson, the neutron becomes a proton. If a proton absorbs the $\pi^-$ meson, the proton becomes a neutron. The passing of mesons back and forth between neutrons and protons holds the nucleus together.

The discovery of mesons explained nuclear binding forces. However, the origin of the beta particles was still in question. The beta particle is an electron which is emitted from the nucleus. For some time, physicists thought the nucleus contained individual electrons. The nuclear electrons seemed to explain how the nucleus is held together. However, physicists found free electrons do not exist in the nucleus. First, mesons alone satisfactorily explained the nuclear binding force. Second, matter waves associated with electrons did not fit the diameter of the nucleus. Studies finally showed that beta particles are formed in the transformation of a nuclear neutron into a nuclear proton. During the transformation, beta particles receive energy and leave the nucleus at high speed.

One fact still puzzled physicists. All the beta particles did not leave their respective nuclei with the same amount of energy. This observation did not agree with the law of conservation of energy. The contradiction led to the prediction of yet another particle to share energy with the beta particle during the transformation of a neutron into a proton. The new particle would have almost zero mass and no charge. The predicted particle was the neutrino, or little neutron. The small mass and absence of charge made the neutrino a very difficult particle to detect. Finally, experiments showed that neutrinos do exist.

The bombardment of nuclei with protons and electrons led to the identification of many other particles. Additionally, every particle has an antiparticle. The proton has the antiproton; the neutron has the antineutron; the electron has the positron, and so on. A particle and an antiparticle undergo annihilation (uh ny uh LAY shuhn) when they meet. In this process, the particles destroy each other. The annihilation is accompanied by the emission of gamma radiation. The radiation carries away the momentum and energy of the particles.

There appears to be an antiparticle for every particle.

Annihilation occurs when a particle meets an antiparticle.

Nuclear physicists have been searching for yet more fundamental particles in the hope that the complex array of known particles can be better understood. High energy devices such as the particle accelerator at Fermilab, in Illinois, can smash matter into smaller and smaller pieces. One result of recent research activities indicates the proton, long considered to be an elementary particle, consists of yet smaller particles called **quarks.**

Rather than making the structure of matter less confusing to us, the discovery of quarks seems only to complicate matters more. There is evidence for at least five types (flavors) of quarks; they are $u$ (for up), $d$ (for down), $s$ (for strange), $c$ (for charm) and $b$ (for bottom). Further, each of these comes in three types (colors), labeled "red," "white," and "blue." Neither the term flavor nor the term color, as used with respect to quarks, bears any relation to the normal meaning of these words. They are merely another way of saying "kinds of."

If you find the particle nature of matter confusing, it is to be expected. Nuclear physicists also find the field very complex and very confusing.

# 29:14  Nuclear Fission

During **fission,** a nucleus is split into two or more nearly equal fragments. When fission occurs, the mass of the fragments is less than the mass of the original nucleus. The mass difference is converted into energy in the form of radiation. The observed value for this energy agrees with the value given by the equation $E = mc^2$. The best known example of nuclear fission is the fission of the uranium isotope $^{235}_{92}\text{U}$. The $^{235}_{92}\text{U}$ nucleus splits when struck by a neutron of proper speed. The split sometimes forms the elements barium and krypton. The reaction is

Fission is the splitting of a nucleus into two or more fragments of almost equal size. Fission is accompanied by the release of large amounts of energy.

$$^{235}_{92}\text{U} + {}^{1}_{0}n \rightarrow {}^{92}_{36}\text{Kr} + {}^{141}_{56}\text{Ba} + 3\,{}^{1}_{0}n + 200 \text{ MeV}$$

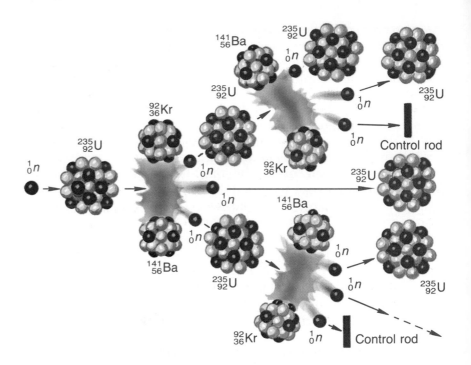

**FIGURE 29-8. A model of a nuclear fission chain reaction of uranium-235 in a nuclear reactor.**

The splitting of a $^{235}_{92}$U nucleus is accompanied by the liberation of free neutrons. These neutrons can cause other $^{235}_{92}$U nuclei to split. If the sample of $^{235}_{92}$U is large enough, the neutrons freed in the splitting of these atoms have a high probability of striking the nuclei of other $^{235}_{92}$U atoms. A chain reaction occurs. If the sample is too small, the free neutrons have a high probability of escaping the sample without hitting other nuclei. Then a chain reaction is highly improbable.

Fermi, Bohr, Teller, and other scientists who helped to produce the first chain reaction had one major problem. Uranium samples consist mainly of the isotope $^{238}_{92}$U. Only a tiny quantity of $^{235}_{92}$U is found in any sample of uranium. However, only $^{235}_{92}$U could sustain the chain reaction. Thus, the isotopes had to be separated. Separation of these isotopes was a problem because their mass difference is extremely small and their chemical properties are identical.

## 29:15 Nuclear Reactors

A chain reaction cannot take place in an ordinary sample of uranium even when the sample is large. Ordinary uranium contains many more atoms of $^{238}_{92}$U than $^{235}_{92}$U. Neutrons released by fissioning atoms of $^{238}_{92}$U are fast neutrons. Fast neutrons are easily absorbed by $^{238}_{92}$U nuclei. When an atom of $^{238}_{92}$U absorbs a

**Fast neutrons are neutrons released by fissioning atoms.**

neutron, it does not undergo fission. It only increases its atomic mass number by 1 a.m.u. and becomes a new uranium isotope, $^{239}_{92}U$. The tendency of $^{238}_{92}U$ to absorb neutrons keeps most of the neutrons in the sample from reaching the fissionable $^{235}_{92}U$ atoms. Thus, a chain reaction cannot take place in the sample.

Enrico Fermi suggested that a chain reaction might be possible in an ordinary sample of uranium if the sample is broken into small pieces and placed among rods of graphite. Graphite is a form of carbon. Carbon atoms are small enough to recoil when struck by a neutron. Thus, a carbon atom absorbs some of a neutron's momentum. In this way, the neutron loses speed or becomes a slow neutron. The graphite creates many slow neutrons in the system. A substance which slows but does not stop particles in a reactor is called a **nuclear moderator.**

Slow neutrons are more likely to be absorbed by $^{235}_{92}U$ than by $^{238}_{92}U$. Accordingly, the abundance of slow neutrons in the system greatly increases the possibility that a neutron released by a $^{235}_{92}U$ atom will cause some other $^{235}_{92}U$ atom to undergo fission. If there is enough uranium in the pile, a **chain reaction** can occur.

A **nuclear reactor** consists of many metric tons of graphite or another moderator surrounding rods of uranium. Between the uranium rods are cadmium rods. Cadmium absorbs neutrons easily. The cadmium rods are lifted in and out of the reactor to control the rate of energy release. These rods are called **control rods.** When the control rods are placed completely in the pile, they absorb enough neutrons to stop the reaction. As they are lifted out of the pile, the rate of energy release increases.

The energy released by the fission of uranium inside the reactor can be converted to electric energy, Figure 29-10. The reactor is surrounded by water. Energy from the nuclear reaction heats the water, forming steam. The steam is used to operate turbines which generate electricity.

When the $^{235}_{92}U$ atoms in a nuclear reactor split, they release other elements with less mass as well as energy. These other elements must eventually be removed from the reactor. Another important product of a reactor is the new element plutonium. Plutonium fissions in much the same way as $^{235}_{92}U$.

The production of plutonium in reactors is the result of the absorption of neutrons by $^{238}_{92}U$. An atom of $^{238}_{92}U$ does not fission when a neutron enters its nucleus. Instead, it becomes the uranium isotope $^{239}_{92}U$.

$$^{238}_{92}U + ^{1}_{0}n \rightarrow ^{239}_{92}U$$

The isotope $^{239}_{92}U$ is unstable. It has a half-life of 23.5 minutes. When $^{239}_{92}U$ decays, it emits a beta particle. When a beta particle is emitted by the breakup of a neutron, a proton is also formed.

A slow neutron is a more effective bombarding particle than a fast neutron.

**FIGURE 29-9. Diagram of a nuclear pile reactor indicating graphite block moderators, the cadmium control rods, and the uranium-235 fuel cylinders (a). The blue glow surrounding the reactor core is called the Cerenkov effect (b).**

a

Uranium fuel rods

Cadmium control rods

Carbon (graphite) blocks

b

Dave Spier/Tom Stack & Assoc.

When U-235 undergoes fission, elements with less mass are produced. Vast quantities of energy are also released.

Thus, the atomic number of the atom increases by one. Neptunium is formed in this reaction.

$$^{239}_{92}\text{U} \rightarrow \,^{239}_{93}\text{Np} + \,^{0}_{-1}e$$

Neptunium is also unstable. It has a half-life of only 2.35 days. Neptunium also decays by the emission of a beta particle. Plutonium is formed.

$$^{239}_{93}\text{Np} \rightarrow \,^{239}_{94}\text{Pu} + \,^{0}_{-1}e$$

**FIGURE 29-10. Diagram of a nuclear power plant in which heat energy released in nuclear reactions is converted to electric energy.**

Plutonium is relatively stable and has a half-life of 24 400 years. Plutonium can be produced in quantity in the nuclear reactor. It can then be removed from the reactor and used to fuel other reactors.

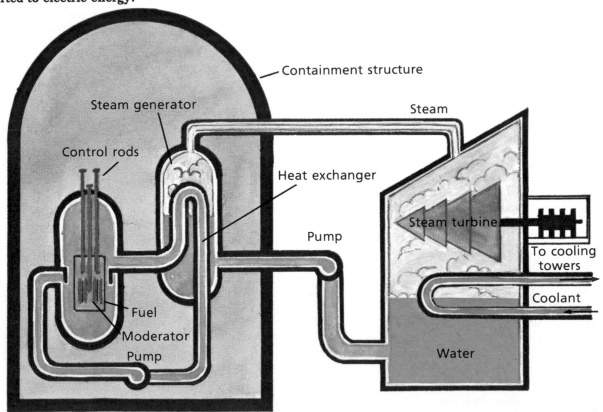

Nuclear reactors are an important source of electric power.

Nuclear reactors can be important sources of electric power. The operation of nuclear reactors results in much less environmental pollution than the operation of fossil-fueled power plants. By the year 2000, nuclear reactors are expected to be supplying a significant percentage of the world's electricity requirements.

## 29:16   Breeder Reactors

A **breeder reactor** can actually produce more fissionable fuel than it uses. If plutonium and $^{238}_{92}U$ are both present in the reactor, the plutonium will undergo fission in the manner of $^{235}_{92}U$. During the process, many of the free neutrons from the fission of plutonium are absorbed by the $^{238}_{92}U$. In this reaction, $^{239}_{92}U$ is formed. As described earlier, this isotope soon becomes plutonium by beta emission. For every two plutonium atoms that undergo fission, three new ones are formed. Soon, more fissionable fuel can be recovered from this reactor than was originally present.

A breeder reactor produces more atoms of fissionable material than it originally contained.

## 29:17   Nuclear Fusion

During **fusion,** the nuclei of elements with small masses combine to form nuclei with larger masses. In this process, huge amounts of energy are released. A typical example of fusion is the process which occurs in the sun. Four hydrogen nuclei fuse in several steps to form one helium nucleus. The mass of four separate hydrogen nuclei is greater than the mass of one helium nucleus. The mass lost during the reaction is converted to energy in accordance with the relationship

Fusion is the union of small nuclei to form larger nuclei.

During fusion, mass is converted to energy.

$$E = mc^2$$

The mass difference is the result of the work that must be done to separate the particles. To separate the particles of a helium nucleus, a great deal of work must be done on the particles. A cyclotron

Fusion reactions release even larger quantities of energy than fission reactions.

Dan McCoy from Rainbow

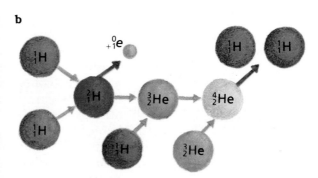

FIGURE 29-11. Laser fusion implosion pellets are shown greatly magnified (a). The hydrogen fusion reaction is a stepwise process (b).

or other high-energy device is needed. This work, or energy input, does not appear in the form of kinetic energy. It appears as an increase in the mass of the particles, in keeping with $E = mc^2$. If the particles recombine, they must release the amount of energy that was needed to separate them. The recombination results in a corresponding decrease in mass. This mass decrease in the case of helium produces about 27 000 000 eV of energy. In comparison, the explosion of a dynamite molecule releases about 20 eV of energy.

Nuclear fusion takes place only when temperatures are extremely high, about $2 \times 10^7$ K. Fusion reactions are called thermonuclear reactions. Temperatures in the interior of the sun are suitable for the fusion of hydrogen. This reaction is responsible for the sun's radiant energy.

*Fusion reactions are also called thermonuclear reactions because they take place at extremely high temperatures, such as those of the sun's interior.*

## 29:18   Controlled Fusion

Scientists are investigating methods for producing controlled fusion reactions. Controlled fusion would give the world an almost limitless source of energy. In order to control fusion, some very difficult problems must be solved.

To start fusion, the temperature of hydrogen isotopes must be raised to millions of degrees Celsius. Initially, hydrogen gas is passed through an electric arc. In this arc, the temperature of the gas is raised and atoms are stripped of their electrons. The gas then consists of high-temperature, charged particles and is called a plasma. The temperature of the plasma can be greatly increased by compressing it.

*The pinch effect refers to the compression of plasma rotating in the changing magnetic field.*

One major problem is finding a container that can withstand the high temperatures without melting or allowing the plasma to cool. The temperature of the plasma must be raised to millions of degrees. However, all known materials melt at less than 5000°C. Magnetic fields can be used to contain a plasma. A magnetic field is not a material and therefore is not affected in the same way as a material container. A plasma can be kept rotating in a magnetic bottle. When the plasma is rotating, quick changes in field strength compress the plasma by "pinching" it. Fusion has been achieved in such magnetic bottles. So far, instabilities in the plasma flow have prevented the achievement of a sustained reaction. Methods of controlling plasma flow are currently being researched.

*The Tokamak reactor is a research device for studying the control of fusion reactions.*

One of the most promising fusion reactors under development is the Tokamak reactor (see page 486). Essentially, the Tokamak provides a doughnut-shaped field in which the plasma rotates. Currently the Tokamak is used in plasma-flow research. This research should lead to future sustained fusion reactors.

A second and totally new approach to controlled fusion is the multiple-laser, pellet-implosion program. In this process, liquid pellets of the hydrogen isotopes deuterium, $^2_1$H, and tritium, $^3_1$H, are subjected to intense radiation from multiple laser beams. The radiation causes the pellet to implode, or burst inward, violently. In this process, the temperature of the hydrogen isotopes can be raised to fusion levels.

Implosion is being studied as a means of raising the temperature of hydrogen isotopes to fusion temperatures.

## 29:19  Pair Production

During the course of this chapter you have studied several examples of how matter can be converted directly into energy. Also, throughout the text we have noted the importance of the symmetry found in nature. Faraday reasoned if electric currents can develop magnetic fields then magnetic fields should bring about electric currents. Faraday eventually discovered the principle of generating electric currents by means of magnetic fields. In a similar fashion, de Broglie reasoned that if waves display particle aspects then particles should display wave characteristics and indeed they do. From the evident symmetry of nature, we can expect that since matter can be converted into energy, then energy should be capable of forming matter. After a long search, the transition of energy to matter was observed in several laboratories. This transition takes the form of a process called pair production. Pair production follows energy-matter exchange in exactly the way we expect.

The transition of matter to energy has been observed in the laboratory.

Einstein's equation tells us that energy is equivalent to mass.

$$E = mc^2$$

Let us use this equation to calculate the energy equivalence of the mass of the electron which is $9.1 \times 10^{-31}$ kg.

$$E = mc^2$$
$$= (9.1 \times 10^{-31}\,\text{kg})(3.0 \times 10^8\,\text{m/s})^2$$
$$= 8.2 \times 10^{-14}\,\text{J}$$

An electronvolt is the energy an electron gives up as it falls through a potential difference (an electric field) of 1 V. This is a very, very minute amount of energy, $1.6 \times 10^{-19}$ J. Still, in terms of the size of electrons it is not so small. The mass of an electron is equal to

$$\frac{8.2 \times 10^{-14}\,\text{J}}{1.6 \times 10^{-19}\,\text{J/eV}} = 510\,000\,\text{eV}$$

Thus, according to Einstein's equation we would expect that this amount of energy, 0.51 MeV, could be converted into an electron. For example, there are many photons which have at least 0.51 MeV of energy.

a

b

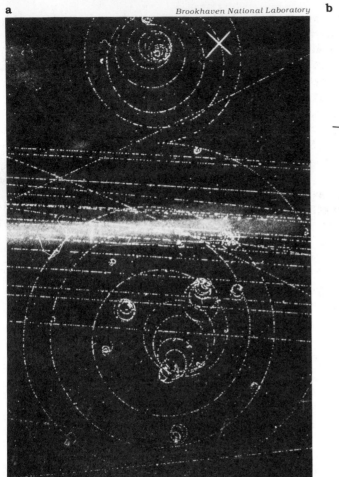

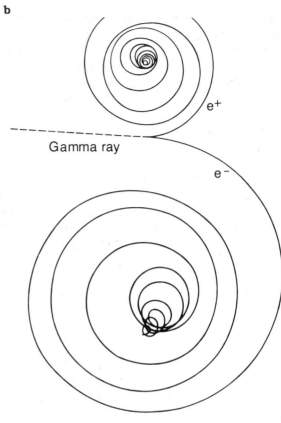

**FIGURE 29-12. The production of a positron-electron pair in a bubble chamber is shown in (a). A diagram of the conversion process is shown in (b).**

The production of pairs of particles having opposite charges does not violate the law of conservation of charge.

Actually, a photon containing 0.51 MeV of energy could not create an electron because the electron bears a single elementary unit of charge. To create an electron would mean that a unit of charge would also be created which would be a direct violation of the law of conservation of charge. (Charge can neither be created nor destroyed.) Thus, conservation of charge prohibits the production of a single electron. However, interestingly enough, it does not prohibit the production of an electron and a positron at the same time. The sum of a single negative charge and a single positive charge is zero, and so the production of both at the same time does not violate the conservation law.

A positron has the same mass as an electron. Therefore, we might expect that a gamma ray ($\gamma$) of energy equal to twice 0.51 MeV or 1.02 MeV would, under proper circumstances, cause the creation of a pair of electron-positron antiparticles. This is exactly what we find happens and the process is called **pair production.**

Direct evidence for pair production is illustrated in Figure 29-12. Here, gamma rays are showered upon a bubble chamber. The rays enter from the left leaving no tracks, since they are without charge and produce no ions for the vapor to condense upon. The tip of the arrow indicates the tracks left by a newly created electron-positron pair. The cloud chamber is in a magnetic field causing the oppositely charged particles to curve in opposite directions. The photon, of course, disappears.

Photons with energies in excess of 1.02 MeV are capable of causing pair production. The excess energy appears in the form of kinetic energy given to the two particles.

A positron does not travel far before it comes in contact with an electron. The electron and positron annihilate one another. Usually, two $\gamma$ rays each with an energy of 0.51 MeV are the result.

Protons have considerably more mass than electrons. Therefore, the production of a proton-antiproton pair requires a comparably large amount of energy. Particle accelerators are able to develop the required energy. The proton-antiproton pair was first produced and observed in 1955 at Berkeley, California.

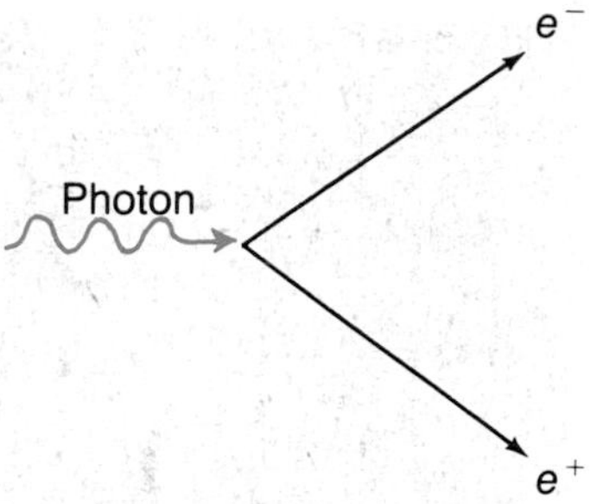

**FIGURE 29-13. In pair production, a photon produces an electron and positron.**

Photons with energies in excess of 1.02 MeV are capable of causing pair production.

## PROBLEM

**22.** The mass of a proton is about $1.7 \times 10^{-27}$ kg.
   **a.** Using Einstein's equation determine the energy equivalence of the proton's mass in joules.
   **b.** Convert this value to eV.

**Summary**

1. The identity of an element depends on the number of protons in its nuclei. **29:1**

2. Nuclear transmutation is a change in the identity of a radioactive element. **29:2**

3. An alpha particle is a helium nucleus. It consists of 2 protons and 2 neutrons. When a nucleus emits an alpha particle, the atomic number of the nucleus decreases by two and the mass number by four. **29:2, 29:3**

4. A beta particle (electron) is the result of the decay of a neutron into a proton which causes an increase in atomic number of one. **29:2, 29:3**

5. The emission of a gamma ray brings about no change in a nucleus. **29:2**

6. Cyclotrons and linear accelerators are used to bombard nuclei. **29:5, 29:6**

7. Artificially radioactive substances often emit positive electrons called positrons. If a proton emits a positron, a neutron is formed. The atomic number decreases by one. **29:9**

8. The half-life of a radioactive substance is the time required for half its atoms to decay. Half-lives are unique for particular isotopes. **29:10**

29:11  **9.** Nuclear binding force is the force that holds the nucleus together.

29:19 **10.** Just as matter can be destroyed to form energy, energy, too, can be destroyed to form matter. The process is called pair production.

**Questions**

**1.** What is meant by the term transmutation as used in nuclear physics?

**2.** What happens to the atomic number and atomic mass of an atom that ejects an alpha particle?

**3.** What happens to the atomic number and atomic mass of an atom that ejects a beta particle?

**4.** Distinguish between natural and artificial radioactivity.

**5.** Describe the changes that take place within a nucleus when it emits a positron.

**6.** What changes take place in a nucleus when it emits a gamma ray?

**7.** Write the symbol of the following particles:
   **a.** proton    **c.** positron    **e.** alpha particle
   **b.** electron    **d.** neutron

**8.** Explain what is meant by the half-life of a radioactive element.

**9.** What is the mass defect of a nucleus? What does it account for?

**10.** Explain how it is possible for a modern fission reactor to produce more fissionable fuel than it uses. What are such reactors called?

**11.** Of what advantage would it be to control the fusion process? What two different processes are presently being studied in hopes of controlling fusion?

**12.** The creation of electron-positron pairs and proton-antiproton pairs has been observed many times in the laboratory. Since positrons and antiprotons are relatively easy to produce, why are they not normally found in nature?

**13.** Could a positron replace an electron in a hydrogen atom or would the positron require an antiproton (negative proton) to circle about?

**Problems**

**1.** An aluminum isotope, $_{13}^{25}$Al, when bombarded by alpha particles absorbs an alpha particle and then emits a neutron. Write a nuclear equation for this transmutation.

**2.** The first fusion reaction produced artificially involved the use of deuterons, or heavy hydrogen nuclei. The symbol for a deuteron is $_1^2$H. During this reaction, two deuterons combine to form a helium isotope, $_2^3$He. What other particle is produced?

**3.** On the sun, the nuclei of four ordinary hydrogen atoms combine to form a helium isotope, $_2^4$He. What type of particle is missing from the following equation for this reaction?

$$4_1^1\text{H} \rightarrow \,_2^4\text{He} + 2(?)$$

4. A mercury isotope, $^{200}_{80}$Hg, is bombarded with deuterons ($^2_1$H). The mercury nucleus absorbs the deuteron and then emits an alpha particle.
   a. What element is formed by this reaction?
   b. Write the nuclear equation for the reaction.

5. A nitrogen isotope, $^{14}_7$N, has 7 protons and 7 neutrons in its nucleus. Its nuclear mass is approximately 14.00307 a.m.u.
   a. Calculate the mass defect of the nucleus.
   b. What is the binding energy of this nucleus?

6. Assume that each nucleon shares equally in the binding energy of the nucleus. Calculate the energy needed to eject a neutron from the nucleus of a nitrogen isotope, $^{14}_7$N.

7. A carbon isotope, $^{13}_6$C, has a nuclear mass of 13.00335 a.m.u.
   a. What is the mass defect of this isotope?
   b. What is the binding energy of its nucleus?

1. *Conservation:* Rubbish can be successfully treated and used as a fuel. Generally it has a fuel value of about $1.5 \times 10^7$ J/kg.
   a. If a large city collects $3.0 \times 10^9$ kg of rubbish each year and uses it in a power plant that operates at 45% efficiency, what amount of energy in kilowatt hours does it realize each year?
   b. At a value of $0.08 per kWh what is the gross value of the electricity thus generated?
   c. The fuel value of uranium is about $5.0 \times 10^{11}$ J/kg. What quantity of uranium could a power company save each year by using rubbish as a fuel rather than uranium?

2. *Energy through Nuclear Fusion:* During the fusion process 0.07 percent of the mass of deuterium atoms is converted to energy.
   a. Deuterium, $^2_1$H, makes up about 0.00015% of ordinary water. Determine the amount of energy in joules that could be obtained by the fusion of the deuterium atoms in 10.00 kg of water.
   b. How many liters of fuel oil of energy content $3.00 \times 10^7$ J/L would be required to produce the same energy as the 10 kg of water?

**Applying Physics**

March, Robert, "Protons Are Not Forever." *Omni*, November, 1980.
Marshall, Eliot, "Matching Wits With a Nuclear Reactor." *Smithsonian*, June, 1980.
Simmons, Henry T., "The Moment of Truth Nears for Fusion Power." *SciQuest*, September, 1980.
Weaver, Kenneth F., "The Promise and Peril of Nuclear Energy." *National Geographic*, April, 1979.

**Readings**

# APPENDIX A
# Relativity

Up to this point a discussion of the relationship between relativity and many aspects of physics has been neglected. The reasons for this neglect are twofold. First, it is our belief that all beginning physics students should be thoroughly grounded in Newtonian mechanics before considering relativity. Secondly, the study of relativity should be an uninterrupted process. It is deemed preferable to include a short discussion here, rather than introduce relativistic effects in a disjointed manner. Careful, thoughtful consideration of the following should allow the reader to gain a basic insight into Albert Einstein's outstanding contributions to our knowledge of the universe.

## A:1  Special Theory of Relativity

In 1905 Albert Einstein published three papers. The first dealt with the quantum theory of light and the photoelectric effect; the second was on Brownian motion as a proof for the existence of atoms; the third was on special relativity. Although Doctor Einstein is best known for his relativity theories, he was awarded the Nobel prize in physics in 1921 for his quantum description of the photoelectric effect which, by then, had been experimentally confirmed. He never received an award for his relativity theories. These theories were viewed with a good deal of skepticism by many physicists for a long time. However, as time has shown, the skeptics were wrong and Einstein was right. Every experiment designed by scientists to test the relativity theories has invariably confirmed these theories. Today relativity is basic to modern physics.

The Special Theory of Relativity deals with space-time relationships and with the physics of frames of reference moving with *different uniform* velocities with respect to one another. The more comprehensive General Theory of Relativity includes an analysis of accelerated frames of references, curved motion, and the concepts of gravity, acceleration, space and time. In this treatment of relativity we will concentrate on the Special Theory.

## A:2  All Motion Is Relative

Imagine two people traveling on a train. The train is moving along a track at a constant 80 kilometers an hour. One of the two people is seated while the other is walking toward the front of the train at 4 km an hour. How can we describe the motions of the two people? The seated passenger's motion could be described in one of two ways, each of which would be correct. We could say that the passenger is moving at 80 km/h or we could say, just as correctly, that the passenger is at rest. The answer depends upon the frame of reference we use. Relative to the floor of the train, the passenger is at rest. Relative to the earth the passenger is moving at 80 km/h. Likewise, the motion of the passenger walking forward through the train could be described as either 4 km/h or 84 km/h depending on the frame of reference we use.

At this point you may say that the motion of the train's passengers should be stated with respect to the earth since the earth is the "natural" frame of reference. This way of thinking is by no means true. The earth is *not* the natural frame of reference for all the motions of the universe. In fact the earth itself is undergoing some quite complex motions. In reference to a point at the center of the earth, the passengers may be moving as fast as 1500 km/h depending on how close the train is to the equator. If the passengers on the train used the sun as their frame of reference, their speed would be somewhere in the region of 110 000 km/h along the earth's orbital path. The entire solar system orbits the center of the Milky Way Galaxy which is itself moving. A good question to ask at this point would be the same one that scientists asked for a good many years. "What then is the true or real motion of the earth?" In the next section it will be shown that experimental evidence indicates that motion is not as simple as it seems. Despite the fact that we all have a strong inner feeling that there must be an absolute speed of the earth and all other astronomical bodies, such is not the case. *There is no real or absolute motion for any object simply because there is no absolute frame of reference.* The only motion that can be measured, or that means anything is the relative speeds between objects.

## A:3  Michelson-Morley Experiment

Until the year 1887, physicists were convinced that an absolute frame of reference existed. It had been shown that light is a form of wave motion. Thus, they felt that space must have some universal medium that vibrates in response to the frequencies of the light waves passing through it. They referred to this medium as the "ether." Scientists believed that the ether was at rest, pervaded all of space, and would serve as an absolute frame of reference by which all the absolute motions of all objects could be measured.

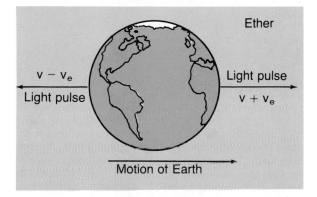

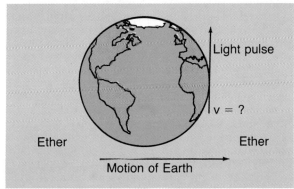

**FIGURE A-1. Light sent in different directions from a moving object would have different velocities through the ether.**

In 1887, two American physicists, A. A. Michelson and E. W. Morley conducted an experiment designed to confirm the existence of the ether. Essentially, the experiment was based upon the assumption that light travels through the ether at the same speed in all directions. It was also assumed that if light is sent through the ether from a moving body such as the earth its speed should depend upon the direction in which the beam is projected. According to this assumption, if the beam is sent forth in the same direction in which the earth is moving, its speed should be the normal speed of light in the ether plus the speed of the earth. Conversely if the beam were sent in the direction just opposite to the earth's motion its speed should be its normal speed in the ether *minus* the earth's speed. By comparing the speeds of light

sent in various directions with the earth's motion, the two scientists expected to be able to calculate the earth's absolute speed through space.

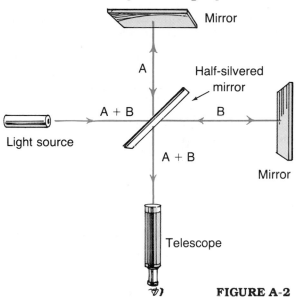

**FIGURE A-2**

The apparatus used during the experiment is called an interferometer and is diagrammed in Figure A-2. When the interferometer is in operation the light is sent from the source to a half-silvered mirror. A half-silvered mirror is sometimes called a partially transmitting-partially reflecting mirror for it transmits and reflects the light that falls on it. As shown in the diagram, the half-silvered mirror splits the initial light beam into two beams which we may label A and B. Beam A is reflected at right angles to a second fully-silvered mirror where it is again reflected back through the half-silvered mirror and falls upon the observer's telescope. Beam B passes through the half-silvered mirror, travels to another fully-silvered mirror, is reflected back to the half-silvered mirror where it is once again reflected. It then joins beam A and travels to the observer's telescope. Great care is taken to ensure that the path length of the two beams is exactly equal.

If this interferometer could be placed in space and brought to complete rest with respect to the ether, the expected result would be that the two light beams falling on the observer's telescope would produce no interference pattern. The two beams would travel equal distances in equal times because the speed of light in the ether is the same in all directions. Therefore the two beams should arrive at the telescope in phase (crest on crest and trough on trough) and no interference pattern could be observed. Since the apparatus was on the earth and the earth supposedly travels through a stationary ether, the expected result was an interference pattern. The two beams would have to travel in different directions with respect to the earth's motion and would have to travel the equal distances at slightly different speeds. Therefore, the two beams had to arrive at the observer's telescope slightly out of phase and would yield an interference pattern. Michelson and Morley expected an interference pattern to form and a shift in the interference fringes as the apparatus was rotated. However, when the two scientists attempted the experiment they were amazed to find that there was no interference pattern whatever. No matter how they rotated the apparatus, they were not able to produce such a pattern.

The scientific world was stunned by the results of the Michelson-Morley experiment for it indicated two startling conclusions. First, *there is evidently no such thing as an ether* and secondly, *the motion of a light source has no affect on the velocity of the light beam.* For example, you and a friend are standing at opposite ends of a flatcar attached to a train moving at 70 km/h. You are throwing a ball back and forth. The ball would travel at different speeds if the earth is used as the frame of reference. If you and your friend throw the ball back and forth at 20 km/h relative to the flatcar, a stationary observer on the ground would perceive its speed to be either 90 km/h or 50 km/h depending upon the direction the ball is traveling. The results of the Michelson-Morley experiment clearly indicate that light does not behave this way at all. Instead, the experiment demonstrated that any measurement of the velocity of light in space must always give the same value ($3 \times 10^8$ m/s) whether the light source, the observer, or both should be moving. That is, if you and your friend were sending light pulses back and forth on the flatcar rather than throwing a ball, a stationary observer standing next to the track would measure the speed of light pulses to be $3 \times 10^8$ m/s regardless of which

way the pulses were moving and regardless of the speed of the train. Even if the train were moving at half the speed of light, the observer would still obtain the same value every time the speed of the light pulses was measured. Also, if you and your friend measured the speed of the pulses you send to each other you would both arrive at the same speed, $3 \times 10^8$ m/s.

## A:4  Einstein's Postulates

For some time scientists were bewildered by their new knowledge of the behavior of light. Several theories were proposed which attempted to explain away the fact that light does not behave like ordinary projectiles. None of these theories was taken seriously, however, because none of them was accompanied by a shred of supporting evidence.

Einstein's approach to the speed of light dilemma was quite different. He did not try to explain away the behavior of light but, instead, he simply accepted the results of the Michelson-Morley experiment. *There is no ether, there is no absolute frame of reference*, the only motion that can be dealt with is the relative motion between two objects. For instance, suppose you were on a space journey. After some months, you find yourself far out in space where there are no planets or other objects about you. If you were to put on your space suit and step outside your rocket, you may be surprised to find that your rocket would seem to have stopped moving. By all appearances, it would have no motion because you cannot measure its speed against empty space. You must have some other object as a reference point if motion is to mean anything. Even then, the results of your motion measurement depends not just upon the motion of your rocket or the motion of the other object, but upon the relative motion between the two objects. If,

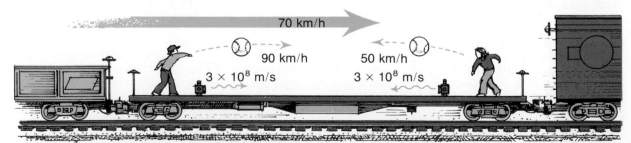

**FIGURE A-3. The relative speeds of light pulses are not affected by the motion of the source. However, the relative speeds of the ball are affected by the motion of the source.**

while you are outside your rocket, you should observe a second rocket going by, you would be completely unable to tell which rocket is moving, or if both are moving. Both you and your counterpart on the other rocket could simultaneously say "look at that rocket going by." The only motion that either of you could measure would be the relative motion between your rocket and the other rocket. Einstein stated this idea as his first postulate for his special theory of relativity.

*All physical laws are exactly the same in all frames of references moving with uniform velocity.*

By this postulate, Einstein points out that because physical laws are exactly the same in every frame of reference moving with uniform velocity there is no way that the magnitude of that velocity can be measured. If physical laws changed with different uniform velocities, then absolute speed could easily be detected. You would know what your speed is every second of your space journey. You would also be able to determine the speed of the passing rocket. However, absolute speeds can never be detected. Tea can be poured on a high speed airplane just as in your kitchen. You can bounce a ball on a train in exactly the same way as you might on a sidewalk. In fact, if you lived in a completely sealed boxcar traveling through empty space, you would not be able to determine whether the boxcar was moving or at rest. (Acceleration would easily be detected since you would feel the force causing the acceleration.)

*Measurements of the velocity of light in space will always give the same value regardless of the motion of the light source or the motion of the observer.*

To illustrate the major implications of the second postulate we may use Figure A-4. Here an observer on Earth is watching a person on Planet X read a book. (Planet X has suddenly appeared from outer space and appears to be zooming past the earth at very high speed.) Both the person on Planet X and the observer on Earth decide to measure the velocity of the light coming from the lamp directly above the reader's book. Since the person on Planet X is moving along with the book in the same frame of reference, that person sees the distance from the lamp to the book as $S_y$. The Planet X person finds the time for the light to travel this distance as $t_o$. Dividing the distance by the time, the velocity of light $c$ turns out to be $3.0 \times 10^8$ m/s. Meanwhile the observer on Earth naturally takes the distance traveled by the light to be $S_e$. To the earth observer, the light is not moving straight down but also has a horizontal velocity $v$ as it moves along with the planet. The time required for the light to travel the distance $S_e$ as measured by the earth observer is $t$. Dividing the distance $S_e$ by the time $t$, the earth observer obtains a value for the velocity of light of $3.0 \times 10^8$ m/s.

The person on Planet X and the observer on the earth have measured the velocity of the same light pulse and arrived at the same value. How can that be, when each of them measured different path lengths for the light pulse between the same two points? We must closely examine our notions about space and time.

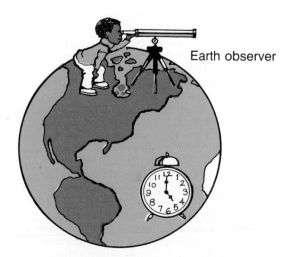

Earth observer

**FIGURE A-4.**

## A:5 Time Dilation

There is only one way that the two observers could have obtained the same value for the velocity of light over different distances. The observer who measured the longer distance must also have measured a longer time. To the earth observer, events on Planet $X$ must occur more slowly than they do on Earth. Thus, when our observer on Earth measured the speed of light not only did the distance turn out to be longer, but time also was longer. If the earth observer were to compare a clock on Earth with an identical clock on Planet $X$, the observer would find that the clock on Planet $X$ is running slower than the clock on Earth. However, the person on Planet $X$ sees the clock as operating quite normally with all events taking place at their normal rates. It is only the earth observer who notices anything odd about what is happening on Planet $X$. To that observer everything on Planet $X$ occurs more slowly than normal. This apparent difference in time due to the relative motion between two frames of reference is known as time dilation.

The relationship between time intervals in the two frames of reference (Earth and Planet $X$) can be derived from the geometry of the situation in a simple manner. This is done in Figure A-5. The final expression is known as the Lorentz transformation. It relates time in the observer's frame of reference to the relative time $t$ in any other frame of reference moving relative to the observer's frame of reference.

$$c^2 t^2 = (c^2 t_o^2) + (v^2 t^2)$$
$$c^2 t^2 - (v^2 t^2) = (c^2 t_o^2)$$
$$t^2 (1 - v^2/c^2) = t_o^2$$
$$t^2 = \frac{t_o^2}{(1 - v^2/c^2)}$$
$$t = \frac{t_o}{\sqrt{1 - (v^2/c^2)}}$$

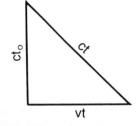

**FIGURE A-5. The Lorentz transformation shows the lengths of the sides of the triangle are given as the velocity of light multiplied by the time. The distance measured by the observer on Planet $X$ is $ct_o$. The distance measured by the observer on Earth is $ct$. The distance the light travels due to the motion of Planet $X$ is $vt$.**

It is important to understand that $v$ in this expression refers to the relative speed between the two reference frames. As has already been pointed out, there is no such thing as an absolute velocity.

The symbol $c$ refers to the velocity of light which never varies in space under any circumstances.

An inspection of the equation makes one point clear immediately. If there is any relative velocity whatever between the two frames of references, then $t$ must be greater than $t_o$, since the expression $1 - (v^2/c^2)$ will necessarily be less than one. If there is no relative motion between two reference frames, there is no time dilation since $1 - (v^2/c^2)$ equals one and $t_o$ must equal $t$. It is only when $v$ becomes very high that a noticeable difference between time in the two frames of reference becomes evident. Should $v$ be as high as 87% of the speed of light, two hours would pass on the earth for every hour recorded on Planet $X$. In the event that $v$ approches the velocity of light the expression $1 - (v^2/c^2)$ approaches zero (an infinitely small number), and $t$ becomes infinitely large. This statement means that, in the impossible situation where Planet $X$ is moving by the earth at the speed of light, the earth observer would find that the clock on Planet $X$ has stopped. Time would be standing still on Planet $X$. However, the residents of that planet would not be aware of this. They would still see all events around them taking place quite naturally. In the more realistic sense, if Planet $X$ were moving at 90 percent the speed of light relative to the earth, only 25 minutes would pass on their clocks while 60 minutes passed on ours. At about 99% the speed of light, ten hours would pass on Earth for every hour recorded on Planet $X$.

We should now wonder what an observer on Planet $X$ would see if the situation were reversed and the observer watched events taking place on the earth. At first it might seem logical to assume that to the Planet $X$ observer, events on the earth would take place much faster than they do on Planet $X$. However, relativity says this will not be the case. Remember that the motion between the two planets is relative, not absolute. Neither observer can tell which planet is moving or, if both are moving. As far as the observer on Planet $X$ is concerned, the earth is passing Planet $X$ and the clocks on the earth are running slowly. The Planet $X$ observer would see exactly the same slowing of events on Earth as the earth observer sees on Planet $X$.

One of the more interesting predictions relating to time dilation is the difference in aging that would result from space travel. If astronauts left the earth on a space journey and traveled to a distant star at sufficiently high speeds relative to the earth, it is entirely conceivable that while 50 years elapsed on Earth a mere 6 or 7 years would pass on the spaceship. Upon their return, the astronauts would find themselves only 6 or 7 years older while their associates on the earth had aged 50 years or more. In fact, they could be chronologically younger than their own children. Should the astronauts depart on a trip of some 30 years at speeds close to the speed of light in space, they would return to find an Earth that had aged thousands of years during their absence. However, despite popular rumor, the astronauts could never return prior to their departure. It is not considered possible to travel backward in time.

Such space trips are technologically impossible at this time. To accelerate a spaceship to speeds approaching the velocity of light would require billions of kilograms of fuel. The mass of the spaceship would increase tremendously as it accelerates to such speeds. Another prohibitive effect would result from the collisions that would take place between interstellar particles (mostly hydrogen atoms) and the spaceship. At such speeds, radiation resulting from these collisions would be fatal to the astronauts in a very short time.

## A:6    Length Contraction

Time is not the only quantity that an observer will detect changes in by looking into another frame of reference. Space, as well as time, will undergo changes. The length of an object in motion relative to an observer will appear shorter than if it were at rest with respect to the observer. For example, a meter stick on Planet $X$ will not appear to be one meter long to our Earth observer. Instead, it will appear somewhat shorter than a meter depending again upon the relative velocity between the two frames of reference. This contraction is in accordance with an expression first developed by Fitzgerald to account for the null result of the Michelson-Morley experiment. It is known as the Lorentz-Fitzgerald contraction.

$$L = L_o \sqrt{1 - (v^2/c^2)}$$

Here, $v$ represents the relative velocity between any two frames of references. The length $L$ is the length of an object noted by an observer looking into the frame of reference in which the object is located. The length $L_o$ is the length of the same object when it is at rest relative to the observer. If you were to measure the length of a rocket $L_o$ while it was at rest on its launching pad you would find this length to be longer than the length of the rocket $L$ after it has been launched. The rocket would contract as it increases its velocity relative

to the earth. However, an astronaut inside the rocket would detect no change in its length at any time.

Does the rocket really contract at high relativistic speeds? To be sure you would have to travel along with the rocket and measure its length as it gains speed. However, the meter stick that you use to measure the length of the rocket would also contract and you would be unable to detect any change in the length of the rocket. Both time and length contraction are only noticeable when one looks from one frame of reference into another frame of reference. Time and length are relativistic contractions.

Just as time dilation is only significant at very high speeds, so too, length contraction is only significant at high speeds. As a result, we don't see automobiles shrinking as they speed past us on highways. Even those objects we consider to be moving very fast will display no obvious shrinking. A rocket circling the earth at orbital velocity (about 29 000 km/h) has 99.999% the length it had when it was on the launching pad. There is no significant change in its length. However, if the rocket were to be moving at nine-tenths the speed of light, $L$ would appear to be less than half its launching pad length $L_o$. At 99.5% the speed of light, the rocket would look like a pancake to an observer on a relatively at-rest Earth. Length contraction takes place only in the direction of motion. Thus, if the rocket is moving horizontally with respect to the observer, there would be no vertical contraction and the rocket would appear to be flattened.

## A:7    Relativity of Mass

As seen from the earth a rocket in flight is shorter than it was on the ground, its clocks tick more slowly than they did on the ground and, in addition, its mass is greater than it was on the ground. If the rest mass $m_o$ of the rocket is the mass as measured by someone at rest with respect to the rocket (such as one of the astronauts in the rocket) the mass $m$ that will be measured by an observer on Earth will be

$$m = \frac{m_o}{\sqrt{1 - (v^2/c^2)}}$$

Thus, an Earth observer would notice an increase in the mass of the rocket as it accelerates away from the earth. However, an astronaut looking at the earth would notice an increase in the mass of the earth, while the mass of the rocket remains unchanged.

Atomic scientists working with particle accelerators have observed an increase in the masses of the particles being accelerated. In this way, relativistic mass increase has been verified so many times that it must be accepted as fact.

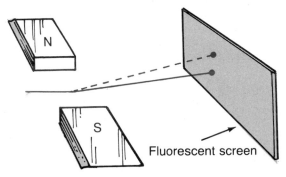

**FIGURE A-6. An atomic particle follows the path shown by the solid line as it passes through a magnetic field. If relativistic mass were not considered, the particle would follow the dotted line.**

## A:8 Mu-Mesons

Good experimental evidence for the existence of both time dilation and length contraction is provided by the behavior of the highly unstable particles called mu-mesons. Mu-mesons are created roughly 6000 to 8000 m above the earth's surface as high energy cosmic rays bombard the nuclei of atoms in the air. The mu-meson is a particle somewhat similar to an electron, but with a larger mass than an electron. Being highly unstable, the mu-meson has an average lifetime of $2.0 \times 10^{-6}$ s and then decays into an electron. The speeds of the mu-mesons as they head toward the surface of the earth have been measured and found to be about $2.994 \times 10^8$ m/s or very nearly the speed of light.

Under ordinary circumstances a moving object is governed by the equation $s = vt$. Using this equation, a mu-meson could travel

$$(2.994 \times 10^8 \text{ m/s})(2.0 \times 10^{-6} \text{ s}) = 600 \text{ m}$$

before it decays into an electron. Thus, the mu-mesons created more than 6000 m above the earth should not reach the surface of the earth at all. Yet, they do reach sea level in great numbers.

To understand how the mu-mesons can travel more than 8000 m rather than 600 m before they decay we must apply the results of the Special Theory of Relativity. Using the Lorentz transformation, the lifetime of the particle appears lengthened by the following factor.

$$t = \frac{t_o}{\sqrt{1 - (v^2/c^2)}}$$
$$= \frac{2 \times 10^{-6}}{\sqrt{1 - (2.994 \times 10^8)^2/(3.0 \times 10^8)^2}}$$
$$= 4.0 \times 10^{-5} \text{ s}$$

From this aspect, the distance the mu-meson can travel toward the earth is $(2.994 \times 10^8 \text{ m/s})$ $(4.0 \times 10^{-5})$, or nearly 12 000 meters. This distance is more than enough to allow the particles to reach the earth before decay takes place.

We can look at the flight of the particle from the aspect of distance alone. The value $2.994 \times 10^8$ m/s is equivalent to $0.998c$. Applying the Lorentz-Fitzgerald contraction we find that from the mu-meson's view what we call 9500 m is no more than 600 m.

$$L = L_o \sqrt{1 - (v^2/c^2)}$$
$$= L_o \sqrt{1 - (0.998c)^2/(c)^2}$$
$$= 9500 \text{ m} \times 0.063$$
$$= 600 \text{ m}$$

Thus, the Special Theory of Relativity predicts that the mu-mesons can easily reach the surface of the earth. The fact that they do serves to verify the theory.

## A:9 Mass-Energy Equivalence

The most remarkable achievement of Einstein's Special Theory of Relativity is the revelation of the equivalence of mass and energy. Newtonian physics predicts that a constant force causes a constant acceleration which, for all purposes, is correct at low speeds. However, as speeds attain a significant percentage of the velocity of light the mass of an object being accelerated increases causing a corresponding decrease in acceleration. The work done on an object (the energy input) not only increases its kinetic energy, but its mass as well. Thus, energy is converted to mass, and mass and energy are equivalent. The total energy of a moving object is $mc^2$ which is the product of its relativistic mass and the speed of light squared. The rest energy of an object is $m_0c^2$ or the product of its mass when at rest and the speed of light squared. The difference between any object's total energy and its rest energy is just the kinetic energy of the object.

The mass-energy relationship is one of the more famous physics equations.

$$E = mc^2$$

Because $c^2$ is very large it can be recognized that even a small amount of mass corresponds to a large amount of energy. Nuclear reactions release significant amounts of energy due to sizeable mass variations. This fact explains how energy is generated on the sun and during nuclear reactions.

## A:10  On Understanding Relativity

You may have found the Special Theory of Relativity somewhat confusing. This is to be expected. Relativistic effects are not ordinarily observed and most people live their entire lives completely unaware of time dilations, length contractions and mass increases. Still, these phenomena exist whether they fit into our personal scheme of how the universe should behave or not.

If you do not understand relativity you are not alone. Consider carefully just what you mean when you talk about understanding something. Most people believe they understand something when they have either directly observed the phenomenon in question and are accustomed to it, or when they can readily compare the phenomenon to something with which they are familiar. However, you cannot make these statements with relativity. Nobody observes relativistic effects directly, nor are there analogous phenomenon with which relativity can be compared. So we don't understand relativity, instead we accept it as fact. You know about gravity. You expect a ball you throw into the air to fall back to Earth. However, observing the ball does not mean that you understand gravity. In fact, you know as little about gravity as you do about relativity. Yet, you probably think that you understand gravity quite well—which you don't.

Einstein's relativity does not contradict Newton's physics. Instead it modifies the work of Newton and extends the entire scope of physics. It allows us to consider ourselves to be more familiar with the universe and after all, that is the purpose of science.

## Questions

1. A hostess on a jet passenger plane traveling at 200 m/s pours a cup of coffee for a passenger.
   a. What is the horizontal velocity of the coffee as observed by the hostess?
   b. What is the horizontal velocity of the coffee as observed by a stationary observer on the earth?
2. Two children are throwing a ball back and forth inside a passenger car that is part of a train moving at 30 m/s. If they throw the ball at 4.0 m/s,

a. what is the velocity of the ball as observed by a passenger in the same car?
b. what are the velocities of the ball as measured by a stationary observer standing on a platform next to the track?

3. In Question 2, which observer is measuring the correct velocity of the ball? Explain.

4. After traveling for six earth-months on a spacecraft at high speeds, you step outside the ship. Describe the motion of the spacecraft.

5. If you could build a rocket that would attain speeds close to the speed of light, why could you not safely launch it into space with astronauts aboard?

6. What would be the velocity of light as measured by an observer traveling in the same direction as a pulse of light at nine-tenths the speed of light?

7. If you were on a spacecraft traveling away from Cape Kennedy at nearly the speed of light, what changes would you observe in your wristwatch, in your mass, in your volume?

8. What changes would Space Control Headquarters in Houston detect in your wristwatch, your mass, and your volume while you are on the ship of Question 7? What changes might you detect in Space Control Headquarters?

9. How do physical laws vary from one frame of reference to another?

10. The National Aeronautics and Space Administration has requested Congress to fund a program that would send a group of astronauts on a 30-year journey at speeds close to the speed of light. (Thirty years astronaut's time.) As a member of Congress, how would you vote on the request and why?

11. A spaceship passes the earth traveling at about 87% the speed of light relative to the earth. An Earth observer notes that at this speed, the clocks on the spaceship appear to be running half as fast as those on earth. For each hour on the ship, two hours pass on Earth.
    a. Verify the observation by calculation.
    b. What observation would an astronaut on the spaceship make about the clocks on Earth?

12. If a spaceship passes the earth traveling at 97% the speed of light, how many hours would pass on the spaceship for each hour that passes on the earth in the view of an observer located on the earth?

## TABLE B-1    Trigonometric Functions

| Angle | sin | cos | tan | Angle | sin | cos | tan |
|-------|------|--------|--------|-------|--------|--------|----------|
| 0°  | .0000 | 1.0000 | .0000 | 45° | .7071 | .7071 | 1.0000 |
| 1°  | .0175 | .9998 | .0175 | 46° | .7193 | .6947 | 1.0355 |
| 2°  | .0349 | .9994 | .0349 | 47° | .7314 | .6820 | 1.0724 |
| 3°  | .0523 | .9986 | .0524 | 48° | .7431 | .6691 | 1.1106 |
| 4°  | .0698 | .9976 | .0699 | 49° | .7547 | .6561 | 1.1504 |
| 5°  | .0872 | .9962 | .0875 | 50° | .7660 | .6428 | 1.1918 |
| 6°  | .1045 | .9945 | .1051 | 51° | .7771 | .6293 | 1.2349 |
| 7°  | .1219 | .9925 | .1228 | 52° | .7880 | .6157 | 1.2799 |
| 8°  | .1392 | .9903 | .1405 | 53° | .7986 | .6018 | 1.3270 |
| 9°  | .1564 | .9877 | .1584 | 54° | .8090 | .5878 | 1.3764 |
| 10° | .1736 | .9848 | .1763 | 55° | .8192 | .5736 | 1.4281 |
| 11° | .1908 | .9816 | .1944 | 56° | .8290 | .5592 | 1.4826 |
| 12° | .2079 | .9781 | .2126 | 57° | .8387 | .5446 | 1.5399 |
| 13° | .2250 | .9744 | .2309 | 58° | .8480 | .5299 | 1.6003 |
| 14° | .2419 | .9703 | .2493 | 59° | .8572 | .5150 | 1.6643 |
| 15° | .2588 | .9659 | .2679 | 60° | .8660 | .5000 | 1.7321 |
| 16° | .2756 | .9613 | .2867 | 61° | .8746 | .4848 | 1.8040 |
| 17° | .2924 | .9563 | .3057 | 62° | .8829 | .4695 | 1.8807 |
| 18° | .3090 | .9511 | .3249 | 63° | .8910 | .4540 | 1.9626 |
| 19° | .3256 | .9455 | .3443 | 64° | .8988 | .4384 | 2.0503 |
| 20° | .3420 | .9397 | .3640 | 65° | .9063 | .4226 | 2.1445 |
| 21° | .3584 | .9336 | .3839 | 66° | .9135 | .4067 | 2.2460 |
| 22° | .3746 | .9272 | .4040 | 67° | .9205 | .3907 | 2.3559 |
| 23° | .3907 | .9205 | .4245 | 68° | .9272 | .3746 | 2.4751 |
| 24° | .4067 | .9135 | .4452 | 69° | .9336 | .3584 | 2.6051 |
| 25° | .4226 | .9063 | .4663 | 70° | .9397 | .3420 | 2.7475 |
| 26° | .4384 | .8988 | .4877 | 71° | .9455 | .3256 | 2.9042 |
| 27° | .4540 | .8910 | .5095 | 72° | .9511 | .3090 | 3.0777 |
| 28° | .4695 | .8829 | .5317 | 73° | .9563 | .2924 | 3.2709 |
| 29° | .4848 | .8746 | .5543 | 74° | .9613 | .2756 | 3.4874 |
| 30° | .5000 | .8660 | .5774 | 75° | .9659 | .2588 | 3.7321 |
| 31° | .5150 | .8572 | .6009 | 76° | .9703 | .2419 | 4.0108 |
| 32° | .5299 | .8480 | .6249 | 77° | .9744 | .2250 | 4.3315 |
| 33° | .5446 | .8387 | .6494 | 78° | .9781 | .2079 | 4.7046 |
| 34° | .5592 | .8290 | .6745 | 79° | .9816 | .1908 | 5.1446 |
| 35° | .5736 | .8192 | .7002 | 80° | .9848 | .1736 | 5.6713 |
| 36° | .5878 | .8090 | .7265 | 81° | .9877 | .1564 | 6.3138 |
| 37° | .6018 | .7986 | .7536 | 82° | .9903 | .1392 | 7.1154 |
| 38° | .6157 | .7880 | .7813 | 83° | .9925 | .1219 | 8.1443 |
| 39° | .6293 | .7771 | .8098 | 84° | .9945 | .1045 | 9.5144 |
| 40° | .6428 | .7660 | .8391 | 85° | .9962 | .0872 | 11.4301 |
| 41° | .6561 | .7547 | .8693 | 86° | .9976 | .0698 | 14.3007 |
| 42° | .6691 | .7431 | .9004 | 87° | .9986 | .0523 | 19.0811 |
| 43° | .6820 | .7314 | .9325 | 88° | .9994 | .0349 | 28.6363 |
| 44° | .6947 | .7193 | .9657 | 89° | .9998 | .0175 | 57.2900 |
| 45° | .7071 | .7071 | 1.0000 | 90° | 1.0000 | .0000 | $\infty$ |

**TABLE B-2**

**SI Base Units**

| Measurement | Unit | Symbol |
|---|---|---|
| length | meter | m |
| mass | kilogram | kg |
| time | second | s |
| electric current | ampere | A |
| temperature | kelvin | K |
| amount of substance | mole | mol |
| intensity of light | candela | cd |

**TABLE B-3**

**SI Prefixes**

| Prefix | | Multiplication Factor | Prefix | | Multiplication Factor |
|---|---|---|---|---|---|
| exa | E | $1\ 000\ 000\ 000\ 000\ 000\ 000 = 10^{18}$ | deci | d | $0.1 = 10^{-1}$ |
| peta | P | $1\ 000\ 000\ 000\ 000\ 000 = 10^{15}$ | centi | c | $0.01 = 10^{-2}$ |
| tera | T | $1\ 000\ 000\ 000\ 000 = 10^{12}$ | milli | m | $0.001 = 10^{-3}$ |
| giga | G | $1\ 000\ 000\ 000 = 10^{9}$ | micro | $\mu$ | $0.000\ 001 = 10^{-6}$ |
| mega | M | $1\ 000\ 000 = 10^{6}$ | nano | n | $0.000\ 000\ 001 = 10^{-9}$ |
| kilo | k | $1\ 000 = 10^{3}$ | pico | p | $0.000\ 000\ 000\ 001 = 10^{-12}$ |
| hecto | h | $100 = 10^{2}$ | femto | f | $0.000\ 000\ 000\ 000\ 001 = 10^{-15}$ |
| deka | da | $10 = 10^{1}$ | atto | a | $0.000\ 000\ 000\ 000\ 000\ 001 = 10^{-18}$ |

**TABLE B-4**

**Units with Special Names Derived from SI Base Units**

| Measurement | Unit | Symbol | Expressed in Base Units |
|---|---|---|---|
| energy, work | joule | J | $kg \cdot m^2/s^2$ |
| force | newton | N | $kg \cdot m/s^2$ |
| frequency | hertz | Hz | $1/s$ |
| illuminance | lux | lx | $cd \cdot sr/m^2\ (lm/m^2)$ |
| luminous flux | lumen | lm | $cd \cdot sr$ |
| potential difference | volt | V | $kg \cdot m^2/A \cdot s^3 (W/A)$ |
| power | watt | W | $kg \cdot m^2/s^3 (J/s)$ |
| pressure | pascal | Pa | $kg/m \cdot s^2 (N/m^2)$ |
| quantity of electric charge | coulomb | C | $A \cdot s$ |
| resistance | ohm | $\Omega$ | $m^2 \cdot kg/s^3 \cdot A^2 (V/A)$ |

## TABLE B-5
### Reference Data: Physical Constants, Conversion Factors, Useful Equations

### Physical Constants

Absolute zero temperature: $0 \text{ K} = -273°C$

Acceleration due to gravity at sea level, lat. $45°$: $g = 9.806 \text{ m/s}^2$

Avogadro's number: $N_o = 6.02 \times 10^{23}$

Charge of an electron: $e = -1.602 \times 10^{-19} \text{ C}$

Constant in Coulomb's law: $K = 8.988 \times 10^9 \text{ N·m/C}^2$

Gravitational constant: $G = 6.670 \times 10^{-11} \text{ N·m}^2/\text{kg}^2$

Mass of an electron: $m_e = 9.109 \times 10^{-31} \text{ kg}$

Mass of a proton: $m_p = 1.672 \times 10^{-27} \text{ kg}$

Mean wavelength of sodium light: $5.893 \times 10^{-7} \text{ m}$

Planck's constant: $h = 6.626 \times 10^{-34} \text{ J/Hz} = 4.136 \times 10^{-15} \text{ eV·s}$

Speed of light in a vacuum: $c = 2.997\ 93 \times 10^8 \text{ m/s}$

### Conversion Factors

1 atomic mass unit $= 1.66 \times 10^{-27} \text{ kg}$

1 electronvolt $= 1.602 \times 10^{-19} \text{ J}$

1 joule $= 1 \text{ N·m}$

1 joule $= 1 \text{ V·C}$

1 coulomb $= 6.242 \times 10^{18}$ elementary charge units

### Useful Equations

Quadratic equation: A quadratic equation may be reduced to the form

$$ax^2 + bx + c = 0$$

then
$$x = \frac{-b \pm \sqrt{b^2 - 4ac}}{2a}$$

Remember that the sign immediately preceding the coefficient is carried with the coefficient in solving for the two values of $x$.

Circumference of a circle: $C = 2\pi r$ or $C = \pi d$

Area of a circle: $A = \pi r^2$

Volume of a cylinder: $V = \pi r^2 h$

Surface area of a sphere: $A = 4\pi r^2$

Volume of a sphere: $V = \dfrac{4\pi r^3}{3}$

# TABLE B-6
## International Atomic Masses

| Element | Symbol | Atomic number | Atomic mass | Element | Symbol | Atomic number | Atomic mass |
|---|---|---|---|---|---|---|---|
| Actinium | Ac | 89 | 227.02777* | Mercury | Hg | 80 | 200.59 |
| Aluminum | Al | 13 | 26.98154 | Molybdenum | Mo | 42 | 95.94 |
| Americium | Am | 95 | 243.06139* | Neodymium | Nd | 60 | 144.24 |
| Antimony | Sb | 51 | 121.75 | Neon | Ne | 10 | 20.179 |
| Argon | Ar | 18 | 39.948 | Neptunium | Np | 93 | 237.04819 |
| Arsenic | As | 33 | 74.9216 | Nickel | Ni | 28 | 58.70 |
| Astatine | At | 85 | 209.98704* | Niobium | Nb | 41 | 92.9064 |
| Barium | Ba | 56 | 137.33 | Nitrogen | N | 7 | 14.0067 |
| Berkelium | Bk | 97 | 247.07032* | Nobelium | No | 102 | 255.093* |
| Beryllium | Be | 4 | 9.01218 | Osmium | Os | 76 | 190.2 |
| Bismuth | Bi | 83 | 208.9804 | Oxygen | O | 8 | 15.9994 |
| Boron | B | 5 | 10.81 | Palladium | Pd | 46 | 106.4 |
| Bromine | Br | 35 | 79.904 | Phosphorus | P | 15 | 30.97376 |
| Cadmium | Cd | 48 | 112.41 | Platinum | Pt | 78 | 195.09 |
| Calcium | Ca | 20 | 40.08 | Plutonium | Pu | 94 | 244.06424* |
| Californium | Cf | 98 | 251.07961* | Polonium | Po | 84 | 208.98244* |
| Carbon | C | 6 | 12.011 | Potassium | K | 19 | 39.0983 |
| Cerium | Ce | 58 | 140.12 | Praseodymium | Pr | 59 | 140.9077 |
| Cesium | Cs | 55 | 132.9054 | Promethium | Pm | 61 | 144.91279* |
| Chlorine | Cl | 17 | 35.453 | Protactinium | Pa | 91 | 231.03590* |
| Chromium | Cr | 24 | 51.996 | Radium | Ra | 88 | 226.0254 |
| Cobalt | Co | 27 | 58.9332 | Radon | Rn | 86 | 222* |
| Copper | Cu | 29 | 63.546 | Rhenium | Re | 75 | 186.207 |
| Curium | Cm | 96 | 247.07038* | Rhodium | Rh | 45 | 102.9055 |
| Dysprosium | Dy | 66 | 162.50 | Rubidium | Rb | 37 | 85.4678 |
| Einsteinium | Es | 99 | 254.08805* | Ruthenium | Ru | 44 | 101.07 |
| Erbium | Er | 68 | 167.26 | Samarium | Sm | 62 | 150.4 |
| Europium | Eu | 63 | 151.96 | Scandium | Sc | 21 | 44.9559 |
| Fermium | Fm | 100 | 257.09515* | Selenium | Se | 34 | 78.96 |
| Fluorine | F | 9 | 18.998403 | Silicon | Si | 14 | 28.0855 |
| Francium | Fr | 87 | 223.01976* | Silver | Ag | 47 | 107.868 |
| Gadolinium | Gd | 64 | 157.25 | Sodium | Na | 11 | 22.98977 |
| Gallium | Ga | 31 | 69.72 | Strontium | Sr | 38 | 87.62 |
| Germanium | Ge | 32 | 72.59 | Sulfur | S | 16 | 32.06 |
| Gold | Au | 79 | 196.9665 | Tantalum | Ta | 73 | 180.9479 |
| Hafnium | Hf | 72 | 178.49 | Technetium | Tc | 43 | 96.90639* |
| Helium | He | 2 | 4.00260 | Tellurium | Te | 52 | 127.60 |
| Holmium | Ho | 67 | 164.9304 | Terbium | Tb | 65 | 158.9254 |
| Hydrogen | H | 1 | 1.0079 | Thallium | Tl | 81 | 204.37 |
| Indium | In | 49 | 114.82 | Thorium | Th | 90 | 232.0381 |
| Iodine | I | 53 | 126.9045 | Thulium | Tm | 69 | 168.9342 |
| Iridium | Ir | 77 | 192.22 | Tin | Sn | 50 | 118.69 |
| Iron | Fe | 26 | 55.847 | Titanium | Ti | 22 | 47.90 |
| Krypton | Kr | 36 | 83.80 | Tungsten | W | 74 | 183.85 |
| Lanthanum | La | 57 | 138.9055 | Uranium | U | 92 | 238.029 |
| Lawrencium | Lr | 103 | 256.099* | Vanadium | V | 23 | 50.9414 |
| Lead | Pb | 82 | 207.2 | Xenon | Xe | 54 | 131.30 |
| Lithium | Li | 3 | 6.941 | Ytterbium | Yb | 70 | 173.04 |
| Lutetium | Lu | 71 | 174.97 | Yttrium | Y | 39 | 88.9059 |
| Magnesium | Mg | 12 | 24.305 | Zinc | Zn | 30 | 65.38 |
| Manganese | Mn | 25 | 54.9380 | Zirconium | Zr | 40 | 91.22 |
| Mendelevium | Md | 101 | 258* | Element 104† | | 104 | 257* |
| | | | | Element 105† | | 105 | 260* |

*The mass of the isotope with the longest known half-life.

†Names for elements 104 and 105 have not yet been approved by the IUPAC. The USSR has proposed Kurchatovium (Ku) for element 104 and Bohrium (Bh) for element 105. The United States has proposed Rutherfordium (Rf) for element 104 and Hahnium (Ha) for element 105.

# Physics-Related Careers

Careers in physics-related fields are many and varied. Requirements for some jobs in these fields may consist only of on-the-job training. Others may consist of seven or eight years of formal college training plus experience through on-the-job programs.

Below is a list of just a few of the jobs open in physics-related fields. This list includes brief job descriptions and minimum training requirements. These may vary somewhat from place to place or job to job. You will want to check with local companies, schools, and professional groups for details.

### Training and Education Key

| | | | |
|---|---|---|---|
| Job | = On-the-job training | BS | = Bachelor of Science degree |
| VoTech | = Vocational or technical school | MS | = Master of Science degree |
| JC | = Junior college (2 yr) | PhD | = Doctor of Philosophy degree (science) |

## PHYSICIST

Physicists attempt to discover the basic interactions between matter and energy. Some physicists perform research to learn facts. Others (theoretical physicists) analyze data and invent theoretical models. Many theoretical and research physicists are also involved in teaching.

| Career | Training | Job Description |
|---|---|---|
| Acoustical scientist | BS, MS | does research in the control of sound; develops acoustical systems |
| Astrophysicist | BS, MS, PhD | studies the structure and motion of the universe and all its bodies |
| Biophysicist | BS, MS, PhD | applies physics to biology, medical fields, and related areas |
| Elementary-particle physicist | BS, MS, PhD | studies properties of the electron, the proton, and the many other particles produced in high-energy collisions |
| Geophysicist | BS, MS, PhD | studies the composition and physical features of the earth |
| Low-temperature physicist | BS, MS | studies the behavior of materials at extremely low temperatures |
| Nuclear physicist | BS, MS, PhD | studies the structure of atomic nuclei and their interactions with each other |
| Optical scientist | BS, MS | develops optical systems; does laser research |
| Plasma physicist | BS, MS, PhD | studies matter in the plasma state; does research directed toward the control of fusion |
| Radiological physicist | BS | detects radiation and plans health and safety programs at nuclear power plants |
| Teacher (High school) | BS | instructs students about general areas of physics |
| Teacher (College) | BS, MS, PhD | instructs students about general and specific areas of physics |

## ENGINEER

It is often difficult to distinguish between the duties of a physicist and an engineer. It is not unusual to find an engineer engaged in pure research or a physicist designing a specialized piece of equipment. Generally, engineers apply scientific principles to practical problems. They design equipment, develop new materials, and find methods for making raw materials and power sources into useful products. Engineers are also frequently involved in sales.

| Career | Training | Job Description |
|---|---|---|
| Aerospace engineer | BS | designs and develops flight systems, aircraft, and spacecraft |
| Biomedical engineer | BS | develops instruments and systems to improve medical procedures; studies the engineering aspects of the biological systems of humans and animals |
| Ceramic engineer | BS | develops methods for processing clay and other nonmetallic minerals into a variety of products, such as glass and heat-resistant materials |

| | | |
|---|---|---|
| Chemical engineer | BS | plans, designs, and constructs chemical plants; develops processes |
| Civil engineer | BS | designs bridges, buildings, dams, and many other types of structures |
| Electrical engineer | BS | designs electric equipment and systems for the generation and distribution of power |
| Electronics engineer | BS | designs TV, radio, stereo systems; often works in the computer field |
| Mechanical engineer | BS | designs and develops machines that produce power, such as engines and nuclear reactors |
| Metallurgical engineer | BS | develops methods to process metals and convert them into useful products |

## COMPUTER-RELATED

Careers in the field of computers exist at all levels. People using computers for scientific or engineering applications will need training in the physical sciences as well as computer science.

| Career | Training | Job Description |
|---|---|---|
| Computer programmer | BS | develops the detailed instructions followed by a computer in processing information. |
| Systems analyst | BS,MS | analyzes data flows in an organization and designs more useful and efficient data processing systems to handle these flows |
| Computer technician | VoTech, JC | operates and services sophisticated computers |

## TECHNICIAN

Technicians work directly with physicists and engineers. They are specially trained in certain aspects of science, math, and technology. They help in developing and testing laboratory and industrial equipment and processes, and are frequently involved in sales. Many opportunities exist for technicians in a variety of fields of specialization.

| Career | Training | Job Description |
|---|---|---|
| Aeronautical technician | VoTech, JC | works with engineers and scientists to develop aircraft; works in field service |
| Chemical technician | JC | helps to develop, sell, distribute chemical products and equipment; conducts routine tests |
| Civil engineering technician | JC, Job | assists civil engineers in planning, designing and constructing bridges, dams, and other structures |
| Electronics technician | VoTech, Job | develops, constructs, and services a wide range of electronic equipment |
| Mechanical technician | VoTech, Job | helps to develop and construct automotive tools and machines |
| Nuclear technician | Job, JC | operates monitoring systems; supports and assists nuclear engineers |

## Additional Information

Following is a list of addresses for a few sources of additional information. Further information about physics-related careers and a more complete listing of additional sources can be found in the *Occupational Outlook Handbook* and *Keys to Careers in Science and Technology*. Check also with your school guidance counselors for any information they may be able to supply.

American Institute of Physics
335 East 45th Street
New York, New York 10017

*Encyclopedia of Careers and Vocational Guidance*
Doubleday and Co., Inc.
501 Franklin Avenue
Garden City, New York 11530

*Keys to Careers in Science and Technology*
National Science Teachers Association
1742 Connecticut Avenue, N.W.
Washington, D.C. 20009

*Occupations*
Armed Forces Vocational Testing Group
Universal City, Texas 78148

*Occupational Outlook Handbook*
U.S. Department of Labor
Bureau of Labor Statistics
Washington, D.C. 20212

U.S. Civil Service Commission
Washington, D.C. 20415

# Glossary

**absolute zero:** Temperature at which an ideal gas would have zero volume.

**absorption spectrum:** Spectrum of energy absorbed by the gaseous atoms of an element when white light is passed through the gas.

**acceleration:** The rate of change of velocity.

**acceleration of gravity:** Rate of change of velocity due to gravitational attraction of the earth.

**accuracy:** The closeness of a measurement to the actual value of a quantity.

**adhesion:** Attraction between unlike particles.

**allowed transitions:** Change of an electron from one specific energy level to another by the absorption or emission of a quantum of energy of exactly the correct amount.

**alpha particles:** Helium nuclei consisting of two protons and two neutrons.

**ammeter:** Electric device used to measure current.

**ampere:** Unit for the rate of flow of charged particles. One ampere equals a flow of one coulomb of charge per second.

**amplitude:** The maximum displacement from zero of any periodic phenomenon.

**aneroid barometer:** Barometer using an evacuated disc instead of liquid mercury to measure atmospheric pressure.

**angle of incidence:** Angle between a light ray and a line perpendicular to the surface which the ray is striking.

**angle of refraction:** Angle between a refracted ray and a line perpendicular to the surface which the ray is leaving.

**antinodal line:** Line connecting points at which two waves interfere constructively at their maximum amplitudes.

**antiparticle:** Mirror image of a particle having the same mass and spin but opposite charge and magnetic moment.

**armature:** Coil of wire which produces current in a generator and torque in an electric motor.

**atomic number:** Number of protons in the nucleus of an atom.

**back-EMF:** The potential difference created by the generator action of a running motor.

**barometer:** Device for measuring the pressure of the atmosphere.

**beta particles:** High speed electrons.

**bimetallic strip:** Two dissimilar metals welded together so that thermal expansion causes the strip to bend.

**binding energy:** Energy equivalent of the mass defect, which represents the amount of energy required to separate the nucleus into individual nucleons.

**black hole:** A collapsed astronomical object of sufficient density to prevent the escape of light.

**Boyle's law:** The volume of a fixed mass of gas at a constant temperature varies inversely as the pressure.

**breeder reactor:** A nuclear reactor which converts non-fissionable material to fissionable material with the production of energy.

**Brownian motion:** Motion of very small particles due to their bombardment by molecules of a fluid.

**candela:** Unit of luminous intensity.

**capillary action:** Rise of a liquid in a narrow tube due to surface tension.

**Celsius temperature scale:** Scale with 0° equal to the freezing point of air-saturated water and 100° equal to the boiling point of water.

**center of curvature:** Center of the sphere from which a spherical mirror is taken.

**centripetal acceleration:** The acceleration produced by a centripetal force.

**centripetal force:** A force, directed toward the center of a circle, which keeps particles moving in uniform circular motion.

**Charles' law:** The volume of a fixed mass of gas at constant pressure varies directly with the absolute temperature.

**chromatic aberration:** Failure of a lens to bring all wavelengths of light to focus at the same point.

**coherent light:** Light in which all waves leaving the source are in phase.

**cohesive force:** Attraction between like particles.

**components of a vector:** Two or more vectors (usually perpendicular) which, when added together, produce the original vector.

**Compton effect:** Interaction of X rays and electrons as the X rays traverse matter resulting in a lengthening of the X-ray wavelength.

**concurrent forces:** Forces acting on the same point.

**condensation:** Change of a gas to a liquid.

**conductor:** Material through which charged particles move readily.

**control rods:** Devices in a nuclear reactor used to regulate the rate of the nuclear reaction.

**convection current:** Current caused by motion of a body of fluid due to differences in density resulting from thermal expansion.

**converging lens:** A lens, thick in the middle and thin at the edge, which causes parallel rays to converge.

**converging mirror:** Concave mirror capable of causing parallel rays to converge.

**coulomb:** Unit of quantity of electric charge equal to the charge found on $6.25 \times 10^{18}$ electrons.

**Coulomb's law:** The force between two charged objects varies directly as the product of the charges on the two objects and inversely as the square of the distance between them; $F \propto QQ'/r^2$.

**cyclotron:** Device used to accelerate subatomic particles in a spiral path.

**de Broglie principle:** Material particles have wavelike characteristics, e.g., wavelength when in motion.

**deceleration:** Negative acceleration.

**derived unit:** Unit of measurement defined in terms of other units.

**deuteron:** Nucleus of the hydrogen isotope, deuterium, consisting of one proton and one neutron.

**diffraction:** Bending of light waves around an object in its path.

**diffuse reflection:** Reflected light scattered in many directions.

**dimensional quantities:** Physical measurements expressed in defined units.

**dipole:** A type of antenna used for the detection and broadcast of radio and television waves.

**direct variation:** an increase (or decrease) in one variable causes a proportional increase (or decrease) in another variable.

**dispersion:** The refraction of light into a spectrum of the wavelengths composing the light.

**displacement:** A vector quantity. The linear change in position of a moving object.

**distance:** A scalar quantity. The sum of an object's displacements.

**diverging lens:** A lens, thin in the middle and thick at the edge, which causes parallel rays to diverge.

**diverging mirror:** A convex mirror capable of causing parallel light rays to diverge.

**domain:** Region of a metal in which atoms are aligned in a common direction.

**Doppler effect:** Apparent increase (decrease) in frequency as the source and detector of waves move toward (away from) each other.

**dynamics:** The study of the motion of particles acted upon by forces.

**echo:** Rebound of a pulse from an impenetrable surface.

**elastic collision:** Total kinetic energy of two objects is the same after their collision as before.

**electric circuit:** Continuous path which can be followed by charged particles.

**electric current:** Flow of charged particles.

**electric field:** The space around a charged object in which the charged object has an effect on a second charged object.

**electric field intensity:** The ratio between the force exerted by a field on a charged particle and the charge on the particle.

**electric force:** A force between two objects due to their like (or opposite) charges.

**electromagnet:** A device in which a magnetic field is generated by an electric current.

**electromagnetic induction:** Generation of an electric current by having a wire cut (or cut by) magnetic flux lines.

**electromagnetic wave:** A wave consisting of alternate electric and magnetic fields which move at the speed of light in space.

**electromagnetism:** The interrelationship of magnetic fields and electric currents.

**electromotive force:** Potential difference generated by electromagnetic induction.

**electron:** Subatomic particle of negligible mass and negative charge.

**electron collision excitation:** Collision between an electron and an atom resulting in an excited atom.

**electron gas:** The free electrons present in a metallic conductor.

**emission spectrum:** Spectrum produced by the excited gaseous atoms of an element.

**energy:** The capacity to do work.

**equilibrant:** A force equal in magnitude to a resultant, but opposite in direction.

**equilibrium:** The condition in which the net force on an object is zero.

**excited atom:** An atom with one or more electrons in a higher than normal energy level.

**eyepiece:** The magnifying lens of a telescope or microscope.

**fast neutron:** Neutron with a kinetic energy greater than some arbitrary limit.

**fiber optics:** Light transmitting plastic fibers which make use of the principle of total internal reflection to transmit light along irregular paths.

**first law of thermodynamics:** see *law of conservation of energy*.

**fluid:** A material that flows, e.g., liquids and gases.

**fluorescence:** Phenomenon in which atoms emit light when excited by an outside source, and the light emission ceases as soon as the exciting source is removed.

**focal length:** Distance from the focal point to the vertex of a mirror or lens.

**focal point:** Point of convergence, real or apparent, of rays reflected by a mirror or refracted by a lens.

**force:** An effect of an object which results in accelerating or deforming an object.

**Fraunhofer lines:** Absorption lines in the sun's spectrum, due to gases in the solar atmosphere.

**frequency:** Number of occurrences in a unit of time.

**fundamental units:** Units of measurement defined in terms of a physical standard, not in terms of other units.

**gamma rays:** Quanta of extremely high frequency.

**gas:** State of matter in which particles follow random paths and in which the space between particles is large compared to the size of the particles themselves.

**Geiger-Müller tube:** Device used to detect radiation by using the ionizing property of radiation.

**generator:** Device using available energy to produce an electric potential difference.

**graph:** Plot of ordered pairs on rectangular coordinates.

**gravitational field:** The distortion of space due to the presence of a mass.

**gravitational force:** Attraction between objects due to their gravitational fields.

**grounding:** Connecting a charged object to the earth to remove the object's charge.

**half-life:** Length of time for one-half a sample of a radioactive material to decay.

**heat:** The quantity of thermal energy transferred from one object to another object.

**hertz:** Unit of frequency equal to one event (cycle) per second.

**hyperons:** Heavy subatomic particles.

**illuminance:** Rate at which light energy falls on a surface.

**illuminated body:** Object on which light is falling.

**implode:** Opposite of the explosion process in which forces are directed inward.

**impulse:** Product of a force and the time during which it acts.

**inclined plane:** A flat surface at an angle to the horizontal and vertical directions.

**index of refraction:** $n = (\sin i/\sin r)$, where $n$ = index of refraction, $i$ = angle of incidence, and $r$ = angle of refraction.

**inductive reactance:** The opposition to electric current flow due to self-induction.

**inelastic collision:** Collision in which some of the kinetic energy of colliding objects is changed to another form of energy.

**inertia:** Resistance of an object to a change in its motion.

**instantaneous quantity:** The value at a given instant for a quantity which is changing.

**insulator:** Material through which the flow of charged particles is greatly restricted.

**interference:** The combining of two waves (disturbances) arriving at the same point at the same time.

**internal energy:** The sum of the kinetic and potential energies of the constituent particles of an object.

**International System of Units (SI):** A system of measurement based on the following fundamental units: mass (kilogram), length (meter), time (second), temperature (kelvin), amount of substance (mole), electric current (ampere), luminous intensity (candela).

**inverse variation:** An increase in one variable causes a proportional decrease in another variable.

**isolated system:** System not being acted upon by outside forces.

**isotopes:** Two or more atoms of the same element, differing in masses due to different numbers of neutrons.

**joule:** Unit of work or energy equal to a newton-meter.

**kelvin temperature:** Temperature of an object based on the kelvin, or absolute, temperature scale.

**kelvin temperature scale:** Scale with 0 = absolute zero and 273.16 = triple point of water.

**Kepler's laws:** 1. Orbits of planets are ellipses with the sun at one focus. 2. Line connecting planets and sun sweeps out equal areas in equal times. 3. The ratio of the squares of the periods of revolution of two planets is the same as the ratio of the cubes of their average distances from the sun.

**kinematics:** The study of the motion of particles.

**kinetic energy:** Energy of an object due to its motion.

**kinetic theory:** Concept that all matter is made of small particles which are in constant motion.

**laser:** An optical device for producing coherent light.

**latent heat of fusion:** Energy required to change 1 gram of a substance from solid to liquid at the melting point.

**latent heat of vaporization:** Energy required to change 1 gram of a substance from liquid to vapor (gas) at the boiling point.

**law of conservation of charge:** Electric charge can be neither created nor destroyed.

**law of conservation of energy:** In nonnuclear changes, energy can be neither created nor destroyed.

**law of conservation of mass-energy:** The sum of matter and energy in the universe is a constant.

**law of conservation of momentum:** If two or more particles interact without the application of external force, the total momentum after the interaction must be equal to the total momentum before the interaction.

**law of cosines:** $c^2 = a^2 + b^2 - 2ab \cos C$.

**law of reflection:** The angle of incidence is equal to the angle of reflection when a light ray strikes a surface.

**law of sines:** $a/\sin A = b/\sin B = c/\sin C$.

**law of universal gravitation:** $F = Gm_1 m_2/r^2$, where $G$ is a constant, $m_1$ and $m_2$ are the masses of two objects, and $r$ is the distance between them.

**left-hand rule:** 1. If a wire is grasped in the left hand with the extended thumb pointing in the direction of electron flow, the fingers circle the wire in the direction of the magnetic field. 2. If a coil of wire is grasped in the left hand with the fingers curved in the direction of the electron flow, the extended thumb points to the north seeking pole. 3. If a current-carrying wire is moving relative to a magnetic field, extend the thumb, index finger, and middle finger in mutually perpendicular directions with the thumb pointing in the direction of current flow and the index finger in the direction of the magnetic field, then the middle finger gives the direction of the force on the wire.

**length:** Distance between two points.

**Lenz's law:** The magnetic field generated by an induced current always opposes the field generating the current.

**leptons:** Light subatomic particles.

**light:** Electromagnetic radiation of $4 \times 10^{-7}$ to $7 \times 10^{-7}$ meter wavelength.

**linear accelerator:** Device for accelerating charged particles in a straight line path.

**liquid:** State of matter in which particles are in close proximity but may readily change their relative positions.

**longitudinal wave:** Wave in which the disturbance is in the same direction as the direction of travel of the wave.

**lumen:** Unit of luminous flux.

**luminous body:** An object emitting light.

**luminous flux:** Flow of light from a source.

**luminous intensity:** Measure of light emitted by a source.

**magnetic field:** The space around a magnet in which another magnet will be affected by the original magnet.

**magnetic flux:** All the magnetic flux lines associated with a magnet.

**magnetic flux density:** The number of magnetic flux lines per unit area.

**magnetic flux lines:** Imaginary lines indicating the magnitude and direction of a magnetic field.

**magnetic force:** A force between two objects due to their magnetic fields repelling (or attracting) each other.

**magnetic induction:** Strength of a magnetic field.

**maser:** Device for producing coherent microwaves.

**mass:** The quantity of matter in an object measured by its resistance to a change in its motion.

**mass defect:** Difference in mass between the actual atomic nucleus and the sum of the particles from which the nucleus was made.

**mass number:** Number of protons and neutrons (nucleons) in an atom.

**mass spectrograph:** Device used to measure the mass of atoms and molecules.

**mechanical equivalent of heat:** When work is done to produce only heat, the energy lost by the object doing the work is exactly equal to the heat energy produced.

**mechanical wave:** A disturbance traveling through a medium.

**mesons:** Medium mass subatomic particles.

**momentum:** Product of an object's mass and velocity.

**monochromatic light:** Light of a single wavelength.

**neutrino:** A chargeless, massless particle emitted along with beta particles.

**neutron:** Subatomic particle of approximate mass 1 a.m.u. and no charge.

**neutron star:** A collapsed star in which gravitational force has caused the combination of electrons and protons to form neutrons.

**newton:** SI unit of force.

**Newton's laws of motion:** 1. Unless acted upon by an outside force, an object at rest will remain at rest and an object in motion will remain in motion at the same speed and in the same direction. 2. A change in motion of an object acted upon by an outside force will vary directly as the force and inversely as the mass of the object. 3. For every action there is a reaction equal in magnitude and opposite in direction.

**nodal line:** Line connecting points at which two waves interfere totally destructively (crest meets trough).

**node:** A point in a medium or field which remains unchanged when acted upon by more than one disturbance simultaneously.

**normal force:** A force perpendicular to a surface.

**nova:** A collapsed star which flares occasionally as it pulls material from its companion in a binary star system.

**nuclear binding force:** Very short range force holding protons and neutrons together in the atomic nucleus.

**nuclear equation:** Equation representing a nuclear reaction.

**nuclear fission:** Splitting a large atomic nucleus into two approximately equal parts.

**nuclear force:** see *nuclear binding force.*

**nuclear fusion:** The combining of very small nuclei into a larger nucleus.

**nuclear moderator:** Substance used to slow neutrons in a nuclear reactor.

**nuclear reactor:** Device for obtaining energy from a controlled fission reaction.

**nucleon:** Proton or neutron.

**nucleus:** Core of an atom containing the protons and neutrons.

**objective lens:** The light-gathering and image-forming lens of a microscope or telescope.

**ohm:** Unit of electric resistance.

**Ohm's law:** Current flowing in a wire varies directly with the potential difference and inversely with the resistance.

**oil-drop experiment:** Experiment, performed by Robert Millikan, designed to measure the charge on the electron.

**opaque material:** Material which does not transmit light.

**optical density:** Property determining the speed of light in a medium.

**pair production:** The creation of an electron-positron pair (matter) from energy.

**parallax:** Change in relative position of objects with change in viewing angle.

**parallel circuit:** Circuit in which there are two or more paths for the charged particles to follow as they complete the circuit.

**pascal:** Unit of pressure equal to a newton per square meter.

**period:** The time duration of a phenomenon or event.

**phosphorescence:** Emission of light by atoms excited by an outside source. The emission persists for a time after the outside source is removed.

**photoelectric effect:** Ejection of electrons from the surface of a metal exposed to visible light.

**photoelectron:** Electrons ejected by the photoelectric effect.

**photon:** Quantum of visible light.

**photon collision excitation:** A collision between a photon and an atom resulting in an excited atom.

**pinch effect:** Squeezing of a plasma in a magnetic field.

**planetary model:** Model of an atom in which the electron(s) orbit(s) the nucleus much as planets orbit the sun.

**plasma:** High temperature state of matter in which collisions are so violent that atoms are disrupted into electrons and positive ions or nuclei.

**polarized light:** Light in which all disturbances occur in the same plane.

**positron:** Positively charged electron.

**potential difference:** Difference in electric potential energy at two points.

**potential energy:** Energy of an object due to its position.

**power:** Rate of doing work.

**precision:** The degree of relative error in a measurement.

**pressure:** Force per unit area.

**principal axis:** Radius connecting the center of curvature of a spherical mirror with its geometric vertex.

**projectile motion:** Motion of objects moving in two dimensions under the influence of gravity.

**proton:** Subatomic particle of mass approximately 1 a.m.u. and a positive charge.

**pulsar:** A rotating neutron star which emits a beam of radiation periodically.

**pulse:** A single disturbance in a medium or field.

**pumping:** Exciting a very large number of atoms in a laser or maser.

**Pythagorean theorem:** $a^2 + b^2 = c^2$.

**quantum:** A discrete quantity of energy.

**quantum theory of light:** Light is emitted and absorbed in small packets called quanta and the energy in each quantum can be expressed as $E = hf$, where $E$ = energy, $h$ = Planck's constant, and $f$ = frequency.

**quark:** Basic "building block" of subatomic particles.

**radioactive materials:** Materials which exhibit the phenomenon of radioactivity.

**radioactivity:** Spontaneous nuclear decay.

**ray:** A line drawn to represent the path traveled by a wave front.

**real image:** An image formed by rays which actually recombine to form the image.

**refraction:** Change in direction of a wave front as it passes from one medium to another.

**resistance:** Opposition to flow of electric current.

**resolving power:** Ability of an optical device to produce separate images of two closely-spaced objects.

**resonance:** The simultaneous in phase vibration of two linked systems.

**resultant:** A single force which has the same effect on an object.

**satellite:** An object in orbit around a planet.

**scalar quantity:** A quantity having magnitude (size) only.

**scientific notation:** Expressing numbers in the form: $M \times 10^n$ where $1 \le M \le 10$ and $n$ is an integer.

**scintillation:** Flash of light emitted when a substance is struck by radiation.

**second law of thermodynamics:** Heat can only flow from an area of high concentration (high temperature) to an area of low concentration (lower temperature).

**self induction:** The induced EMF in a coil creates a magnetic field which opposes the field originally inducing the EMF.

**series circuit:** Circuit in which the charged particles must flow through each component of the circuit, one after the other.

**significant digits:** The number which represents reliable digits in a measurement.

**simple harmonic motion:** Motion in which a particle repeats the same path periodically.

**SI:** An internationally agreed upon consistent method of using the metric system of measurement.

**slow neutron:** Neutron with a kinetic energy less than some arbitrary limit.

**Snell's law:** The ratio of the sine of the angle of incidence to the sine of the angle of refraction is a constant for two specific substances in contact where a light ray passes.

**solid:** State of matter in which particles are close together and in fixed positions relative to each other.

**sonic boom:** Shock wave associated with an object moving through a fluid at a speed greater than that of sound.

**sound wave:** Audible longitudinal disturbance in matter.

**specific heat capacity:** Energy required to change the temperature of 1 gram of a substance 1 Celsius degree.

**spectrum:** An array of the various wavelengths composing a beam of light.

**speed:** The rate of change of position.

**speed of light:** $3.00 \times 10^8$ m/s.

**spherical aberration:** Failure of a spherical mirror to bring all rays parallel to the principal axis to focus at the same point.

**spherical concave mirror:** A converging mirror which is formed of a spherical segment of one base.

**standard pressure:** $1.013\ 25 \times 10^5$ Pa = 101.325 kPa = 1 atm = 760 mm Hg = 760 torr.

**standing wave:** A wave whose nodes are stationary.

**stopping potential:** Potential difference needed to prevent the photoelectric effect for a specific metal and light of a specific frequency.

**superconductivity:** A state of some materials at very low temperatures, in which state a material exhibits zero electric resistance.

**surface tension:** Strong attraction of surface particles for each other due to unbalanced forces.

**symmetry:** A property which is unchanged by altering operations or reference frames.

**temperature:** The average kinetic energy of molecules.

**terminal velocity:** The velocity of a falling object when the air resistance is equal to the gravitational attraction.

**thermal excitation:** Exciting an atom by heating it.

**thermal expansion:** The moving apart of particles as their temperature rises and they collide more violently.

**thermometer:** Device used to measure temperature.

**thermonuclear reaction:** A nuclear fusion reaction.

**threshold frequency:** Lowest frequency of light which will cause the photoelectric effect with a specific substance.

**time:** The interval between two events.

**total internal reflection:** Refraction of a light ray at such a severe angle that the ray remains in the original medium.

**transformer:** Device used to transfer energy from one circuit to another circuit by mutual inductance across two coils.

**translucent material:** Material transmitting light but distorting it during passage.

**transmutation:** Nuclear change of one element into another.

**transparent material:** Material transmitting light undistorted.

**transuranium element:** Element with an atomic number greater than 92.

**transverse wave:** Wave in which the disturbance is perpendicular to the direction of travel of the wave.

**trigonometry:** The study of triangles and the relationships of their parts.

**uncertainty principle:** The more accurately one determines the position of a particle, the less accurately the momentum is known, and vice versa.

**uniform quantity:** A quantity of constant value, e.g., acceleration of speed.

**uniform circular motion:** Particles moving in a circular path at a constant speed.

**van der Waals forces:** Attraction between particles due to the unequal distribution of charge.

**vaporization:** Change of a liquid to a gas.

**vector quantity:** A quantity having both magnitude (size) and direction.

**velocity:** The direction and rate of change of position.

**virtual image:** Image whose rays appear to emanate from a point without actually doing so.

**volatile:** Easily evaporated.

**volt:** Unit of potential difference.

**voltmeter:** Electric device used to measure potential difference.

**watt:** Unit of power.

**wave:** A traveling disturbance in a field or medium.

**wavelength:** Distance between corresponding points on two successive pulses in a wave.

**weak force:** A force involved in the decay of atomic nuclei and nuclear particles.

**weight:** Gravitational attraction of the earth for an object.

**work:** Force acting through a distance.

**work function:** Energy needed to produce the photoelectric effect for a specific substance.

**X rays:** Electromagnetic waves of very short wavelength.

# Index